Atlas of Invertebrate Macrofossils

Atlas of Invertebrate Macrofossils

Edited by
John W. Murray

Longman
The Palaeontological Association

Longman Group Limited
Longman House, Burnt Mill, Harlow
Essex CM20 2JE, England
Associated companies throughout the world

Published in the United States of America
by Halsted Press, a Division of John Wiley & Sons, Inc.

Published in collaboration with the Palaeontological Association

First published 1985

British Library Cataloguing in Publication Data
Atlas of invertebrate macrofossils.
1. Invertebrates, Fossil—Atlases
I. Murray, John W.
562'.022'2 QE770

ISBN 0-582-30099-1

Typeset in 9/11pt Old Style, by CCC, printed and bound in Great Britain by William Clowes Limited, Beccles and London

Contents

List of Contributors

Dr D. E. G. Briggs,
Goldsmiths' College, London
Chapter 9, sections 9.1–9.4

Dr L. R. M. Cocks,
British Museum (Natural History), London
Chapter 5

Dr R. A. Fortey,
British Museum (Natural History), London
Chapter 9, section 9.5 (joint author)

Professor M. R. House,
University of Hull
Chapter 6, section 6.7

Professor J. W. Murray,
University of Exeter
Chapter 1. Chapter 7, section 7.9

Dr J. S. Peel,
The Geological Survey of Greenland, Copenhagen
Chapter 6, sections 6.1–6.3, 6.6

Dr R. B. Rickards,
University of Cambridge
Chapter 8

Dr J. K. Rigby,
Brigham Young University, Provo, Utah
Chapter 2, section 2.1

Dr B. R. Rosen,
British Museum (Natural History), London
Chapter 3, section 3.3 (part)

Dr C. T. Scrutton,
University of Newcastle
Chapter 2, section 2.2. Chapter 3, sections 3.1, 3.2, 3.3 (part), 3.4

Dr P. W. Skelton,
The Open University, Milton Keynes
Chapter 6, sections 6.4, 6.5

Dr A. B. Smith,
British Museum (Natural History), London
Chapter 7, sections 7.1–7.8

Dr P. D. Taylor,
British Museum (Natural History), London
Chapter 4

Dr A. T. Thomas,
University of Aston, Birmingham
Chapter 9, section 9.5 (joint author)

Preface

The first three volumes in this series concern rock-forming minerals in thin section (MacKenzie and Guilford: *Atlas of Rock-forming Minerals in Thin Section*; MacKenzie, Donaldson and Guilford: *Atlas of Igneous Rocks and their Textures*; Adams, MacKenzie and Guilford: *Atlas of Sedimentary Rocks under the Microscope*). The ability to recognize a hundred or so rock-forming minerals provides a firm basis for the identification of most rock-types.

Whereas there are probably no more than 3000 named minerals, there are tens of thousands of genera and hundreds of thousands of species of macrofossils. Thus, the student of palaeontology faces a daunting task. Most undergraduate courses deal with the morphology of fossils and the principles involved in using fossils in the broader context of geology. The application of palaeontology to geological problems has as its starting-point the identification of specimens. The purpose of this book is to provide an illustrated classification of the major macrofossil groups. In most cases identification to generic level will be possible. For further detail the user will need to refer to source-books such as monographs and treatises, details of which are given in the references to each section. The large number of references entailed precludes a complete list and only the more important are given in the selected list of references.

The editor is grateful to a great many people for their help in producing this volume. First, to the Council of the Palaeontological Association and to Dr Iain Stevenson of Longman for their encouragement to proceed. Second, to all the authors for the enthusiasm and dedication with which they have tackled the task of writing and illustration, and last, but not least, to Professor A. Hallam who read the entire work and offered much helpful and constructive comment.

J. W. Murray
May 1984

Acknowledgements

The production of this volume involved the help and co-operation of a large number of people whom we gratefully thank.

Chapter 1. Introduction: J. W. Murray
Dr E. B. Selwood for comments and Mrs G. C. Wright for typing (both of University of Exeter).

Chapter 2. Porifera: Sclerospongidea: C. T. Scrutton

Chapter 3. Cnidaria: C. T. Scrutton
For providing specimens or sections figured here: Dr J. H. Bennett (University of Newcastle), Dr M. Coen-Aubert (Institut royal des Sciences naturelles, Brussels), Ms J. Darrell (British Museum(Nat. Hist.)), Mr K. B. Goodger (University of Newcastle), Dr J. S. Jell (University of Queensland), Dr R. J. F. Jenkins (University of Adelaide), Dr M. Kato (University of Hokkaido), Mr M. Mitchell (British Geological Survey, Leeds), Dr B. Neuman (University of Bergen), Dr W. A. Oliver, Jr (United States Geological Survey, Washington), Ms S. M. Parfrey (Geological Survey of Queensland), Dr Y. Plusquellec (University of Brest), Dr D. Price (University of Cambridge), Dr B. R. Rosen (British Museum (Nat. Hist.)), Dr P. Semenoff-Tian-Chansky (Centre National de la Recherche Scientifique, Paris) and Dr D. E. White (British Geological Survey, London).

A grant from the University of Newcastle Research Fund helped finance visits to museums in connection with this project. Mr B. Richardson prepared a number of thin sections and Ms Christian Cochrane drafted Figs 2.2.1, 2.2.2 and 3.3.1.

Section 3.3. Zoantharia: B. R. Rosen
H. Taylor and P. Crabb for photography, and J. Darrell for SEM and general assistance (all of British Museum (Nat. Hist.)). J. P. Cuif provided Pl. 3.3.108(A) and 3.3.109(B). J. P. Cuif (Université de Paris Sud), A. Russo (Università di Modeno), and J. W. Wells (Cornell University) kindly gave comments on the manuscript.

Chapter 4. Bryozoa: P. D. Taylor
Miss P. L. Cook (British Museum (Nat. Hist.)).

Chapter 5. Brachiopoda: L. R. M. Cocks
M. G. Bassett, C. H. C. Brunton, E. F. Owen and A. D. Wright for supplying some photographs, and to the Photographic Unit at the British Museum (Natural History), particularly H. Taylor, for taking new pictures, and to C. H. C. Brunton for comments on the original typescript.

Chapter 6. Mollusca
Sections 6.4, 6.5. Bivalvia, Rostroconchia: P. W. Skelton
The preparation of sections 6.4 and 6.5 has benefited enormously from the generously given advice and constructive criticism of Noel Morris at the British Museum (Natural History). Valuable comments and assistance were also given by Pat Nuttall, Ron Cleevely, Solene Morris and John Taylor, also at the British Museum (Natural History), as well as by Tom Waller of the Smithsonian Institution, Washington, DC, and Peter Ellis of the Open University. Any remaining errors or ambiguities are entirely the author's responsibility. John Projeta, Jr, and the US Geological Survey are thanked for Pl. 6.4.12. I would also like to thank Janet Dryden (Open University) for carrying out the laborious task of typing the complicated manuscript.

Section 6.7. Cephalopoda: M. R. House
Advice and help given by specialists in the preparation of this chapter, particularly J. H. Callomon, D. T. Donovan, M. K. Howarth, W. J. Kennedy, H. D. Powell, J. D. Price, W. H. C.

Ramsbottom, P. F. Rawson, N. J. Riley, H. S. Torrens, J. R. Senior and E. T. Tozer. J. D. Price has kindly read and commented on the typescript and given help with photography. J. Garner, M. Lawson and I. M. Young, all of the University of Hull, have done the photographic printing and typing respectively.

Chapter 7. Echinodermata

Sections 7.1–7.8. Echinodermata: A. B. Smith
Help and encouragement received from Dr C. H. C. Paul. Over the past few years we have had many discussions about the phylogeny and classification of echinoderms which have been invaluable in broadening my understanding of the group. He was also kind enough to read a first draft of the typescript for this section and suggest a number of improvements. Also, Harry Taylor of the British Museum (Natural History) who took some of the photographs.

Section 7.9. Echinoidea: J. W. Murray
The Royal Albert Memorial Museum, Exeter, for the loan of specimens from the Sladen Collection, Mr J. Jones for photography, Mrs G. Wright for typing and Dr A. B. Smith for valuable comment on the manuscript, and for providing the artificial key.

Chapter 9. Arthropods

Sections 9.1–9.4. Arthropods: D. E. G. Briggs
For photography, T. Easter, for specific photographs, H. B. Whittington, Pl. 9.1.1 and 9.1.2, E. N. K. Clarkson, Pl. 9.2.5, W. D. I. Rolfe, Pl. 9.4.3, for access to/loan of material, S. F. Morris, for comments on typescript, E. A. Jarzembowski, S. F. Morris, P. A. Selden, P. Whalley.

We are indebted to the following for permission to reproduce illustrative copyright material:

Akademia Nauk U.S.S.R. for Pls. 6.7.44, 6.7.46, 6.7.84, 6.7.85, 6.7.106 from Figs. 111, 119 13d, g Vol. 5, Pl. 31 Figs. 1a, b Vol. 6 *Osnovi Paleontologi*; The British Museum (Natural History) for Pls. 6.7.65 from Pl. 11, Figs. 7a-b *Catalogue of Ammonites* – Spath, 6.7.63 from Pl. 67, Figs. 3a+b BM(NH) *Bull. Geology* Vol. 4, 6.7.93 from Pl. 27, Fig. 1 *IDEM* Vol 15; the Author, Dr. R. Casey for Pls. 6.7.96, 6.7.97 from Pl. 2, Figs. 3a-b, Pl. 7 Figs. 1, 3 *The Boreal Lower Cretaceous* by Casey & Lawson, pub. Seal House Press; Ferdinand Enke Verlag & the author, Prof Dr U. Lehmann for Pl. 6.7.107 from Fig. 4 *Ammoniten, Ihr Leben und ihre Umwelt*, Stuttgart 1976; the authors, Dr A. G. Fischer & Dr Curt Teichert for Pl. 6.7.2 from Pl. 1, Fig. 3a, b, Pl. 4, Fig. 4 *Univ. Kansas Paleontological Contributions* paper 37; The Geological Society of America & the University of Kansas Publishers for Pls. 6.7.5 from Figs. 3.11, 3a-b, 3.12a-c, 271.2a, 6.7.7 from Fig. 330. 1a-b, 6.7.9 from Fig. 134 in (Teichert *et al* 1964); Gustav Fisher Verlag & the author, R. Schlegelmilch for Pl. 6.7.62 from Fig. 1, Pl. 14 *Die Ammoniton des suddeutschen Lias* 1976; Museum National d'Histoire & the author, J. P. Cuif for Pls. 3.3.108, 3.3.109 from Fig. 35(a), Pl. 17 pp 324, 118 *Bulletin du Museum National d'Histoire Naturelle*, No's 275, 310 Nov-Dec '74, May-June '75 *Sciences de la Terre* 40, 44; The Secretary, Paleontological Society for Pl. 6.7.115 from text-fig. 3b by Seilacher *Jl of Paleontology* Vol 34, Pt. 1; The Secretary, Paleontological Society & the author, Dr R. Casey for Pls. 6.7.119, 6.7.121 from text-fig 93, pl-xivii, Fig. 2a, b *The Ammonoidea of the Lower Greensand*; the Editor, Trans. Leicester Lit. & Phil. Soc. & the author, Prof J. M. Callomon for Pls. 6.7.103, 6.7.105 from Figs. 7, 8 *Trans. Leicester Lit. & Phil. Soc.* Vol 57; the US Geological Survey & the photographers, R. H. McKinney & H. E. Mochizuki for Pl. 6.4.12 from Pl. 7, Fig. 10 'Review Ordovicion Pelecypods' by J. Pojeta Jr in *US Geol. Survey* Prof. Paper 695 (1971) IV; the author, M. Wimbledon & The Geological Society, London for Pl. 6.7.95 from Pl. 3, Figs. 1, 2 *Jl. Geol. Soc.* Vol 135.

Generalized time scale for the Phanerozoic
(alternative spellings in brackets)

Era	Period/subperiod		Epoch	Age	Alternative terms
Cenozoic (Cainozoic)	Quaternary		Holocene		
			Pleistocene		
	Tertiary	Neogene	Pliocene	Piacenzian	
				Zanclian	
			Miocene	Messinian	
				Tortonian	
				Serravalian	
				Langhian	
				Burdigalian	
				Aquitanian	
		Palaeogene (Paleogene)	Oligocene	Chattian	
				Rupelian	
			Eocene	Priabonian	
				Bartonian	
				Lutetian	
				Ypresian	
			Palaeocene (Paleocene)	Thanetian	
				Danian	
Mesozoic	Cretaceous		Upper	Maastrichtian	Senonian
				Campanian	
				Santonian	
				Coniacian	
				Turonian	
				Cenomanian	
			Lower	Albian	
				Aptian	
				Barremian	Neocomian
				Hauterivian	
				Valanginian	
				Ryazanian	Berriasian
	Jurassic		Upper	Tithonian	Portlandian/Volgian
				Kimmeridgian	
				Oxfordian	
			Middle	Callovian	
				Bathonian	
				Bajocian	
				Aalenian	
			Lower	Toarcian	
				Pliensbachian	
				Sinemurian	
				Hettangian	
	Triassic		Upper	Rhaetian	
				Norian	
				Carnian	
			Middle	Ladinian	
				Anisian	
			Lower	Scythian	

Era	Period/subperiod		Epoch		Age	Alternative terms
Palaeozoic (Paleozoic)	Permian			Upper	Tartarian	
					Kazanian	
					Ufimian	
				Lower	Kungurian	
					Artinskian	
					Sakmarian	
					Asselian	
	Carboniferous	Pennsylvanian	Silesian	Upper	Stephanian	
					Westphalian	
					Namurian	Yeadonian
						Marsdenian
						Kinderscoutian
		Mississippian				Alportian
						Chokierian
						Arnsbergian
						Pendleian
			Dinantian	Lower	Visean	Brigantian
						Asbian
						Holkerian
						Arundian
						Chadian
					Tournaisian	Courceyian
	Devonian			Upper	Famennian	
					Frasnian	
				Middle	Givetian	
					Eifelian	
				Lower	Emsian	
					Siegenian	
					Gedinnian	
	Silurian		Pridoli	Upper		
			Ludlow			
			Wenlock			
			Llandovery	Lower		
	Ordovician		Ashgill	Upper		
			Caradoc			
			Llandeilo	Middle		
			Llanvirn			
			Arenig	Lower		
			Tremadoc			
	Cambrian		Merioneth	Upper		
			St Davids	Middle		
			Comley	Lower		

CHAPTER 1

Introduction

by J. W. Murray

Fossils are important to geologists for three reasons: they provide the most accurate means of *age determination* of rocks in which they occur; they provide a major means of establishing the *environment* of formation of the sediments of the past in which they occur and hence the key to palaeoecological and palaeogeographical reconstructions; and they provide the raw data for determining the *evolution* of past organisms. The principles of these applications and the details of the morphology of the major groups of invertebrate macrofossils are discussed in a number of student textbooks and are not repeated here. However, the undergraduate trying to identify a fossil will find little to help in a standard textbook and will be frustrated by the overpowering wealth of detail in treatises and monographs. This book aims to bridge the gap and to make identification simpler and thereby less onerous. Each chapter provides an illustrated classification of the main groups of invertebrate macrofossils. Where possible a key or guide to the basis of classification has been included. Many of the commonly occurring genera are described and illustrated. Details are also given of their stratigraphic range, geographical distribution and palaeoecology, where appropriate. The name of the illustrated specimen is given at the end of each generic entry. The choice of genera is aimed at world-wide rather than regional coverage.

Taxonomy, systematics, classification

These three terms are given to the study of the diversity of modern and fossil organisms and to their arrangement into an ordered system. *Classification* refers to the division of organisms into an hierarchical series of groups. *Taxonomy* is the science of identification and classification of organisms. Traditionally, taxonomy and classification are based on morphological similarities and differences and this is the approach used here. Some specialists use *numerical taxonomy* in which mathematical techniques aid objective assessment. *Systematics* is a term commonly used as a synonym of taxonomy.

The philosophical basis for the subdivision and grouping of organisms is controversial and more than one scheme is used. *Natural* classifications are based on morphological resemblances without implying any evolutionary relationships, but where these are implied, the classification is *phylogenetic*. A particular form of phylogenetic classification involving recognition of common ancestry is *cladistic classification*.

Contrary to what might be expected, the classification of organisms is not static. As new fossils are found, more knowledge is built up, and new ideas of relationships are introduced, so too are classification schemes changed. However, for simplicity, in this book no discussion is given of either alternative classification schemes or their historical development. The one used for each taxonomic group is that deemed to be the most satisfactory at the present state of knowledge.

Any ordered and natural group of organisms is known as a *taxon* (plural taxa). Classification schemes make use of an hierarchy of taxa the commonest of which are given below:

Singular	Plural	Example
Phylum	Phyla	Brachiopoda
Class	Classes	Articulata
Order	Orders	Orthida
Superfamily	Superfamilies	Orthacea
Family	Families	Orthidae
Genus	Genera	*Orthis*
Species	Species	*collactis*

Division of any of these taxa into two or more units can be identified by the prefix 'sub', e.g. subphylum, suborder. In the example above, the superfamily Orthacea is in the suborder Orthidina.

The smallest taxonomic unit normally recognized is the *species*. Individuals of one living species are able to interbreed successfully, but species of fossil organisms are defined on common morphological characters. A group of species which shows some degree of morphological similarity, and therefore probably some common evolutionary relationship, is termed a *genus*.

The taxonomy of organisms must be carried out in accordance with an internationally accepted set of rules, the *International Code of Zoological Nomenclature* (Stoll *et al.* 1964). The basic rules are:

1. The name must be binominal, i.e. consist of one generic and one specific name. The author and date of publication are also normally given.

   Example: *Anarcestes* *praecursor* French, 1897
   genus species author date

2. To be valid a new species and a new genus must be described and illustrated in a formal publication such as a scientific journal or a book. The descriptions are based on *type specimens* which should illustrate the average form (holotype) and the variability (paratypes); type material should be available for study in a museum.
3. Sometimes two different authors independently give a name to the same new taxon. In this case the '*Law of Priority*' normally applies whereby the first published name is the one that is valid. All other names are *synonyms*.

Other rules relate to the latinization of names, the need for generic and species names to agree in gender and case, and to the avoidance of offensive names.

A new species may be erected even if there is uncertainty about the genus to which it belongs. However, each genus must be based on a *type species*, that is, one species which exemplifies the morphological characteristics of the genus. A genus may be *monospecific* if it comprises only one species or it may be *polyspecific* if there are several species. Reassignment of a species from one genus to another is permissible. However, if the type species of a given genus is reassigned to another genus, by definition the two genera must be considered synonymous and the one that was named first is the valid one. When a species is assigned to a genus different from that used in the original name, the author's name is placed in parentheses. Thus *Manticoceras simulator* (Hall) was originally named *Goniatites simulator* Hall, 1874. Subsequently Hyatt (in 1884) defined the new genus *Manticoceras* with *Goniatites simulator* Hall as the type species.

The importance of correctly identifying fossils cannot be overstressed. The names of fossils provide an international language for communication between palaeontologists. All other facets and applications of palaeontology depend on a sound taxonomic basis. Interpretations based on incorrectly identified material are likely to be worthless. Yet, having said that, it must also be emphasized that taxonomy is not the main aim of palaeontology. It is the application of correctly identified fossils to the problems of biostratigraphy and palaeoecology which makes palaeontology a major part of geology.

Identification

The main taxonomic unit considered in this book is the genus because this is the one most commonly used by undergraduates.

Brief notes on morphological terms are given in each chapter, but for further details a basic textbook such as Tasch (1973) or Clarkson (1979) should be consulted. It is assumed that the reader will have sufficient knowledge to be able to assign an unnamed specimen to one phylum or even a class.

For each major taxonomic group there are details of the relative importance of the main morphological features used in classification. In some cases there is a key or table of criteria to narrow down the possibilities to an order or superfamily. Thereafter, it will be necessary to compare the illustrations and descriptions of individual genera. It should be possible to assign a specimen with some certainty to a given genus or group of genera. For those interested in further detail, it will be necessary to consult the appropriate treatise volume. These list monographs and other papers which will help with identification to species level. In some cases it will not be possible to effect an identification because:

1. The scope of the Atlas is limited to common genera.
2. The preservation of the specimen may be poor so that essential morphological features are missing.
3. There may be problems due to parallel evolution, convergence or homoeomorphy.

Palaeontologists who are unable to make a precise identification are able to express degress of uncertainty in the following way:

1. Informal use of group names, e.g. orthacean for the brachiopod probably of the superfamily Orthacea but which cannot be identified to generic level.
2. The term 'cf.', meaning 'compare with' for a specimen which is similar to, but not identical with a given genus or species, e.g. cf. *Anarcestes*.
3. The term 'aff.', meaning 'affinity with' e.g. aff. *Anarcestes*. This represents a greater degree of certainty than cf. *Anarcestes*.

CHAPTER 2

Sponges, chaetetids and stromatoporoids

2.1 PORIFERA: DEMOSPONGEA, HEXACTINELLIDA, CALCAREA

The Porifera, the sponges, are relatively unspecialized organisms. Modern sponges are of essentially cellular grade, and lack muscles or circulatory, digestive and nervous systems. They are unique among animals; their largest openings are excurrent (osculum, Fig. 2.1.1). They are filter-feeders, extracting minute organisms and other food particles out of water pumped through the innumerable canals in the wall.

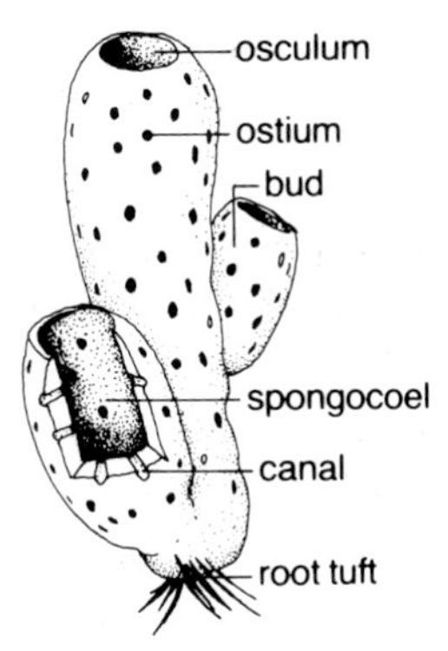

Fig. 2.1.1. Morphological terms applied to sponges.

Sponges indicate aqueous environments. Most fossil sponges were marine, although both marine and freshwater forms abound today. They range from arctic to tropical realms.

Most living sponges have skeletons of organic fibres (spongin) or of organic fibres stiffened with mineralized spicules (Fig. 2.1.2). It is principally the spicules and their relationships that are used to classify fossil examples. Taxonomy is based on chemical composition and shapes of main body spicules, canal patterns and general shapes of the sponges.

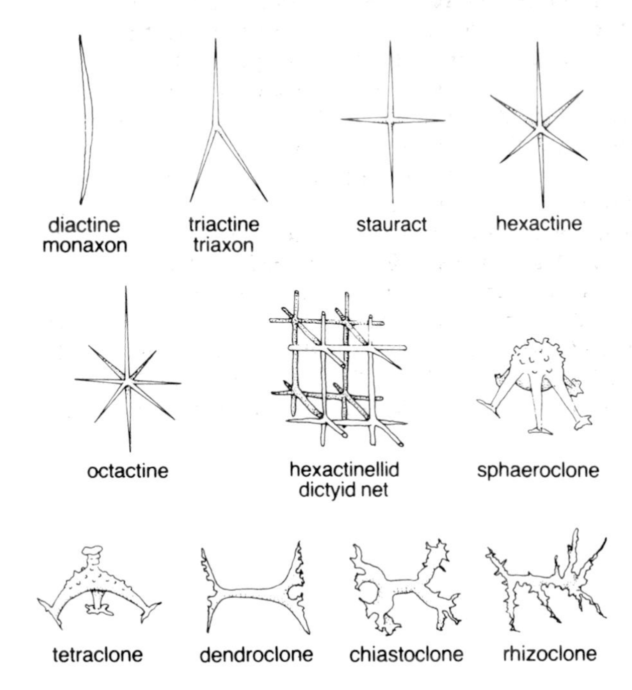

Fig. 2.1.2. Morphological terms applied to sponge spicules.

Sponges of the class **Demospongea** have skeletons of spongin or of spongin and siliceous spicules. These spicules are generally monaxons or tetraxons, which may be simple tetracts or modified spicules whose rays are not at right angles (Fig. 2.1.2). Sponges in the **Hexactinellida** are characterized by siliceous stauracts or hexactines (Fig. 2.1.2), spicules in which the basic rays meet at 90° to each other (Pl. 2.1.6–2.1.9). Sponges included in the **Calcarea** have triactine spicules whose rays meet at approximately 120° (Pl. 2.1.15, 16), or octactine spicules (Fig. 2.1.2, Pl. 2.1.11), or may totally lack spicules but have bead-like skeletons made of calcium carbonate (Pl. 2.1.3, 2.1.14). The **Sclerospongidea**, a fourth group treated in section 2.2 as a subclass of the Demospongea, have massive calcareous basal skeletons but with siliceous spicules.

Class Demospongea

Pl. 2.1.1. *Choia* Walcott, 1920
Cap-shaped monaxonid; central disc densely thatched; large coronal oxeas extend as a fringe; diameter 1 to 150 cm.
Cambrian, coronal spicules suspended disc above bottom.
Choia carteri Walcott: M. Cambrian, British Columbia, Canada.

Pl. 2.1.2. *Archaeoscyphia* Hinde, 1889
Tubular, annulate lithistid, with stacked horizontal radiating canals. Skeleton of ladder-like trabs with 'rungs' of dendroclones; ranges up to 30 cm high.
Ordovician, grew upright, possibly partially submerged in matrix or cemented to a solid substrate.
Archaeoscyphia minganensis (Billings): Mingan Islands, Quebec, Canada.

Pl. 2.1.3. *Haplistion* Young & Young, 1877
Globular lithistid, composed of gridwork of radiating, concentric and horizontal tracts, up to 2 mm in diameter, of clustered rhizoclones. Average diameter 10 cm, but may be much larger.
Silurian–Permian, may be pioneer organism in muddy environments or cemented in reef environments.
Haplistion sphaericum Finks: U. Carboniferous, Utah, USA.

Pl. 2.1.4. *Astylospongia* Romer, 1860
Spheroidal to shallow bowl-shaped lithistid; stacked excurrent canals concentric parallel to exterior. Minor canals radiating from centre of the sponge. Spicules sphaeroclones. Average diameter 2 to 3 cm.
Ordovician–Devonian, may have lived free.
Astylospongia praemorsa (Goldfuss): M. Silurian, Tennessee, USA.

Pl. 2.1.5. *Attungaia* Pickett, 1969
Smooth conical–cylindrical lithistid, with thin walls; skeleton of sphaeroclones; up to 15 cm tall.
U. Devonian, lived upright in reef-associated environments.
Attungaia wellingtonensis Pickett: U. Devonian, Western Australia.

Class Hexactinellida

Pl. 2.1.6. *Protospongia* Salter, 1869
Thin-walled, conical to cup-shaped; skeleton of ranked stauracts with rays oriented vertically and horizontally; 1 to 20 cm high.
Cambrian–Ordovician, root tufts may have attached the sponge to the substrate.
Protospongia hicksi Hinde: M. Cambrian, Utah, USA.

Pl. 2.1.7. *Diagoniella* Rauff, 1894
Thin-walled conical to goblet-shaped; skeleton of ranked stauracts arranged diagonally; 1 to 6 cm high.
Cambrian–Ordovician, quiet water, attached by tufts.
Diagoniella robisoni Rigby: M. Cambrian, Utah, USA.

Pl. 2.1.8. *Hydnoceras* Conrad, 1842
Thin-walled conical, distinguished by knobs in annular swellings; skeleton of vertical and horizontal straps of monaxial and hexactine-based spicules; may be 20 cm or more tall.
U. Devonian–Carboniferous, lived in muddy environments.
Hydnoceras tuberosum Conrad: Devonian, New York, USA.

Pl. 2.1.9. *Coeloptychium* Goldfuss, 1833
Stalked platter-like, surface marked with radiating branching ridges with numerous ostia. Skeleton hexactine-based, fused three-dimensional gridwork. Average diameter 5 cm.
U. Cretaceous, shallow marine, base cemented to solid substrates.
Coeloptychium agricoides Goldfuss: Cretaceous, France.

Pl. 2.1.10. *Root tufts*
Fibrous masses of subparallel spicules of various sizes.
Cambrian–Recent, may be detached from sponge, commonly preserved as intact spicule clusters in fine-grained matrix.
Root tuft: Tertiary, N. Carolina, USA.

Class Calcarea

Pl. 2.1.11. *Astraeospongium* Romer, 1854
Bowl-shaped heteractinid, up to 10 cm in diameter; skeleton of ranked large calcareous octactines in felted mass lacking canals.
Silurian–Devonian, benthic, shallow marine, may have lived free.
Astraeospongium meniscus (Romer): M. Silurian, Tennessee, USA.

Pl. 2.1.12. *Regispongia* Rigby, 1978
Cylindrical to thick-walled heteractinid, skeleton grossly 'vermiculate' of encrusted polyactine spicules, average height of sponge 8 to 10 cm.
Carboniferous, a common sponge in argillaceous rocks.
Regispongia contorta (King): U. Carboniferous, Oklahoma, USA.

Pl. 2.1.13. *Girtyocoelia* Cossmann, 1909
Sphinctozoan of spherical bead-like chambers with tubular incurrent openings, 'strung' on tubular central canal; chambers 1 cm in diameter.
U. Carboniferous–Permian, reef-former, may form clumps.
Girtyocoelia dunbari King: Permian, Texas, USA.

Pl. 2.1.14. *Cystothalamia* Girty, 1908
Tubular sphinctozoan of stacked, porous, bubble-like chambers lacking filling structures. Tubes 3 to 10 cm long.
Permian, common reef-dweller.
Cystothalamia nodulifera Girty: Permian, Tunisia.

Pl. 2.1.15. *Peronidella* Hinde, 1893
Branching pharetrone in bush-like clumps, stems 6 to 10 mm diameter, with central spongocoel, skeletal fibres of triactines in calcareous cement.
Triassic–Cretaceous, shallow marine attached.
Peronidella prolifera (Hinde): L. Cretaceous, England.

Pl. 2.1.16. *Raphidonema* Hinde, 1884
Open vase- to funnel-shaped with small canals in thick wall. Skeleton pharetronid of cemented triactines and monaxons in secondary overgrowth. Average height 4 to 5 cm.
Triassic–Cretaceous, attached, shallow-water form.
Raphidonema farringdonense (Sharpe): L. Cretaceous, England.

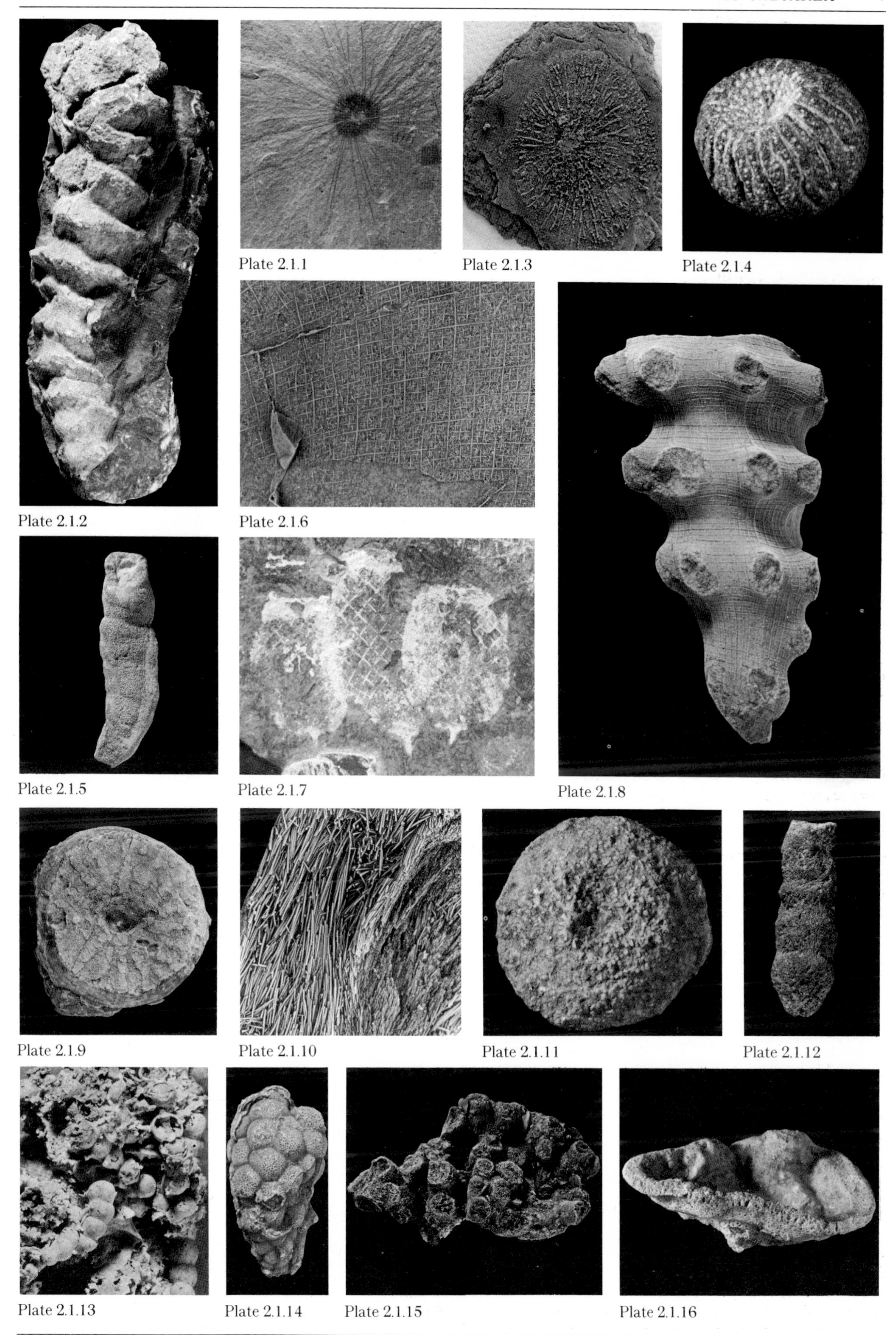

Plate 2.1.1

Plate 2.1.3

Plate 2.1.4

Plate 2.1.2

Plate 2.1.6

Plate 2.1.5

Plate 2.1.7

Plate 2.1.8

Plate 2.1.9

Plate 2.1.10

Plate 2.1.11

Plate 2.1.12

Plate 2.1.13

Plate 2.1.14

Plate 2.1.15

Plate 2.1.16

2.2 PORIFERA: SCLEROSPONGIDEA, STROMATOPOROIDEA

Class Demospongea

SUBCLASS SCLEROSPONGIDEA

Sponges with a basal calcareous skeleton containing proteinaceous fibres, which may entrap siliceous spicules. Calcareous skeleton composed of more or less well-defined, long, slender calicles less than 1 mm diameter, and either solidly infilled or partitioned by horizontal plates. ?Cambrian, Ordovician–Recent.

(Note: The Sclerospongidea was proposed for rediscovered living coralline sponges of cryptic habitat. Three orders of sclerosponges are now recognized, all of which have fossil representatives. The orders Ceratoporellida Hartman & Goreau, 1972 and Tabulospongida Hartman & Goreau, 1975 have few Mesozoic species, but the similarity of these and living forms to the fossil chaetetids, long considered to be tabulate corals or hydrozoans, led Hartman and Goreau (1972) to transfer them, as an order, to the sclerosponges. Furthermore, monaxonid spicules have since been described in association with one Mesozoic and one Palaeozoic chaetetid species. This assignment of the chaetetids (essentially the Chaetetidea of Hill, 1981) is accepted here although they may prove to be a polyphyletic grouping.)

Order Chaetetida

Sclerosponges with a cerioid or meandroid basal skeleton (see Fig. 2.2.1). Walls fibrous, tufted, calcitic or aragonitic. Calicles slender, normally less than 1 mm diameter, of polygonal to meandrine cross-section, aporose. Scattered spines may project into the lumen from the walls. Monaxonid spicules preserved in some. Simple horizontal partitions usually present. Increase by pseudoseptal longitudinal fission or basal fission. ?Cambrian, Ordovician–Cretaceous. Each genus is illustrated by a transverse section (A) and a longitudinal section (B).

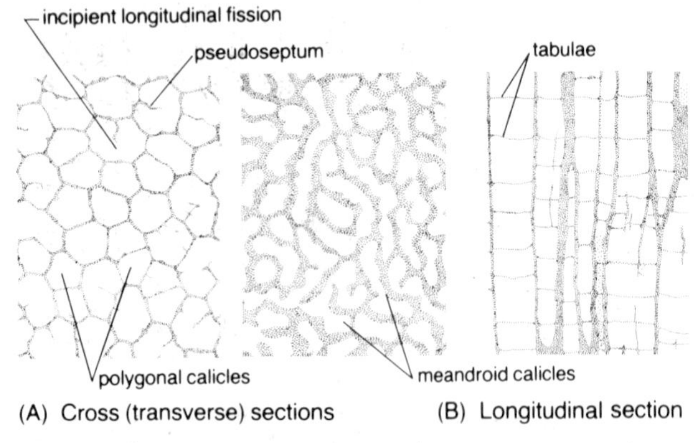

Fig. 2.2.1. Morphological terms applied to chaetetids (redrawn from various sources).

FAMILY CHAETETIDAE

Pl. 2.2.1. *Chaetetes* Fischer von Waldheim in Eichwald, 1829
Massive, hemispherical or subglobular, commonly showing zoned growth so that skeleton readily splits into sheets. Calicles long, slender, prismatic to weakly meandroid. Walls of varying thickness. Pseudoseptal spines and ridges may be present. Calicles partitioned by horizontal plates. Increase by bipartite longitudinal fission and basal fission.
?Silurian, M. Devonian–Permian, shallow-water limestones and calcareous shales. Europe–Asia–N. America.
Chaetetes (Boswellia) mortoni Gray: Viséan, Llangollen, N. Wales, × 4.

Pl. 2.2.2. *Chaetetella* Sokolov, 1962
Corallum tabular, in thin sheets due to zoned growth, each sheet with a basal plate. Increase dominantly basal. Calicles long, slender, prismatic to weakly meandroid. Walls, generally thin. Horizontal partitions thin, of similar height in adjacent calicles.
U. Ordovician–Carboniferous, shallow-water limestones (biostromes) and calcareous shales. Europe–Asia–N. America.
Chaetetella septosa (Fleming): Carboniferous, Bryn Gwyn Caerwys, Wales, × 4.

Pl. 2.2.3. *Blastochaetetes* Dietrich, 1919
Massive, commonly showing zoned growth. Long, slender calicles, irregularly prismatic and with discontinuous walls. Horizontal partitions thin. Increase by longitudinal fission and intraparietal addition.
Triassic–U. Cretaceous, shallow-water limestones. Europe–Asia.
Blastochaetetes bathonicus Fischer: Bathonian, Gloucestershire, England, × 4.

Class Stromatoporoidea

?Sponges with a basal calcareous skeleton (coenosteum) variously laminar, domal, columnar or digitate in form (see Fig. 2.2.2). Skeleton finely reticulate in structure, usually composed of distinct horizontal laminae and vertical pillars but sometimes with structural elements undifferentiated. Some with systems of stellate, branching, tabulated canals in the horizontal plane linked by discontinuous vertical tubes (astrorhizae).
?Cambrian, Ordovician–Cretaceous, ?Oligocene.
Most genera are illustrated with a transverse section (A) and a longitudinal section (B).

(Note: The stromatoporoids were long considered to be extinct hydrozoans (Lecompte 1956), but similarities with some living sclerosponges have led several specialists to refer them to the Porifera (e.g. Stearn 1972, 1975). The classification of Stearn (1980) is followed here, but the group is still of uncertain affinities and others favour a status distinct from both Cnidaria and Porifera. Stromatoporoids are well distributed in the Ordovician to Devonian but become extremely rare thereafter. Similar organisms, distinguished as Sphaeractinoidea, are treated separately by some but included with the stromatoporoids by others (Stearn 1972). They are moderately common in Jurassic and Cretaceous limestones. These Mesozoic forms are considered stromatoporoids here, but their classification is in need of revision.)

Order Labechiida

Stromatoporoids in which the primary horizontal structures are dissepiments. Ordovician–Carboniferous.

FAMILY LABECHIIDAE

Pl. 2.2.4. *Labechia* Edwards & Haime, 1851
Coenosteum composed of strong, vertically continuous pillars which form tubercles on the coenosteal surface. Horizontal tissue of thin dissepiments. No astrorhizae.
Ordovician–Carboniferous, shallow-water limestones (bioherms and biostromes) and calcareous shales. Europe–Asia–N. America.
Labechia conferta (Lonsdale): Wenlock, Dudley, England, × 5.

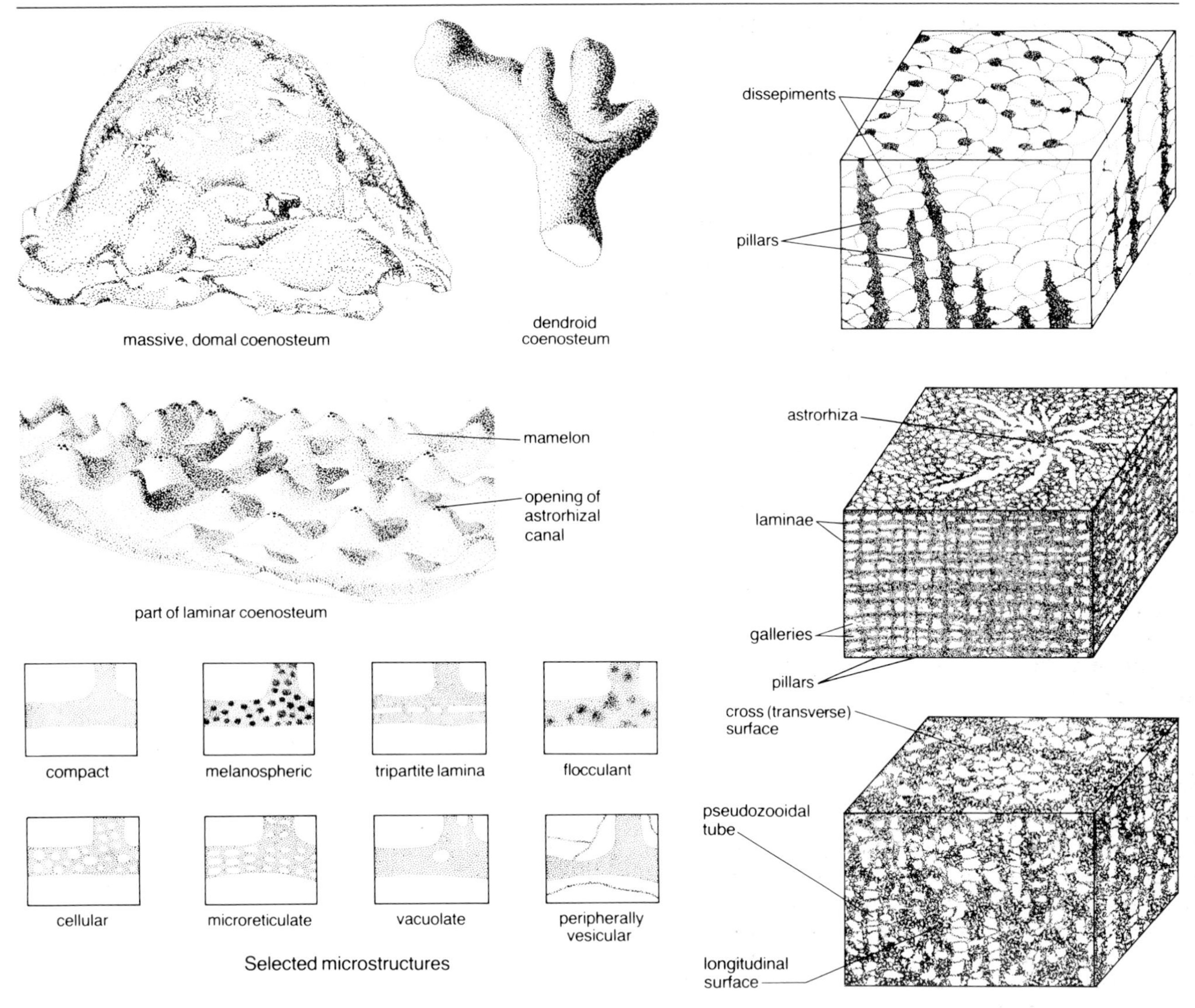

Fig. 2.2.2. Morphological, structural and microstructural terms applied to stromatoporoids (redrawn from various sources).

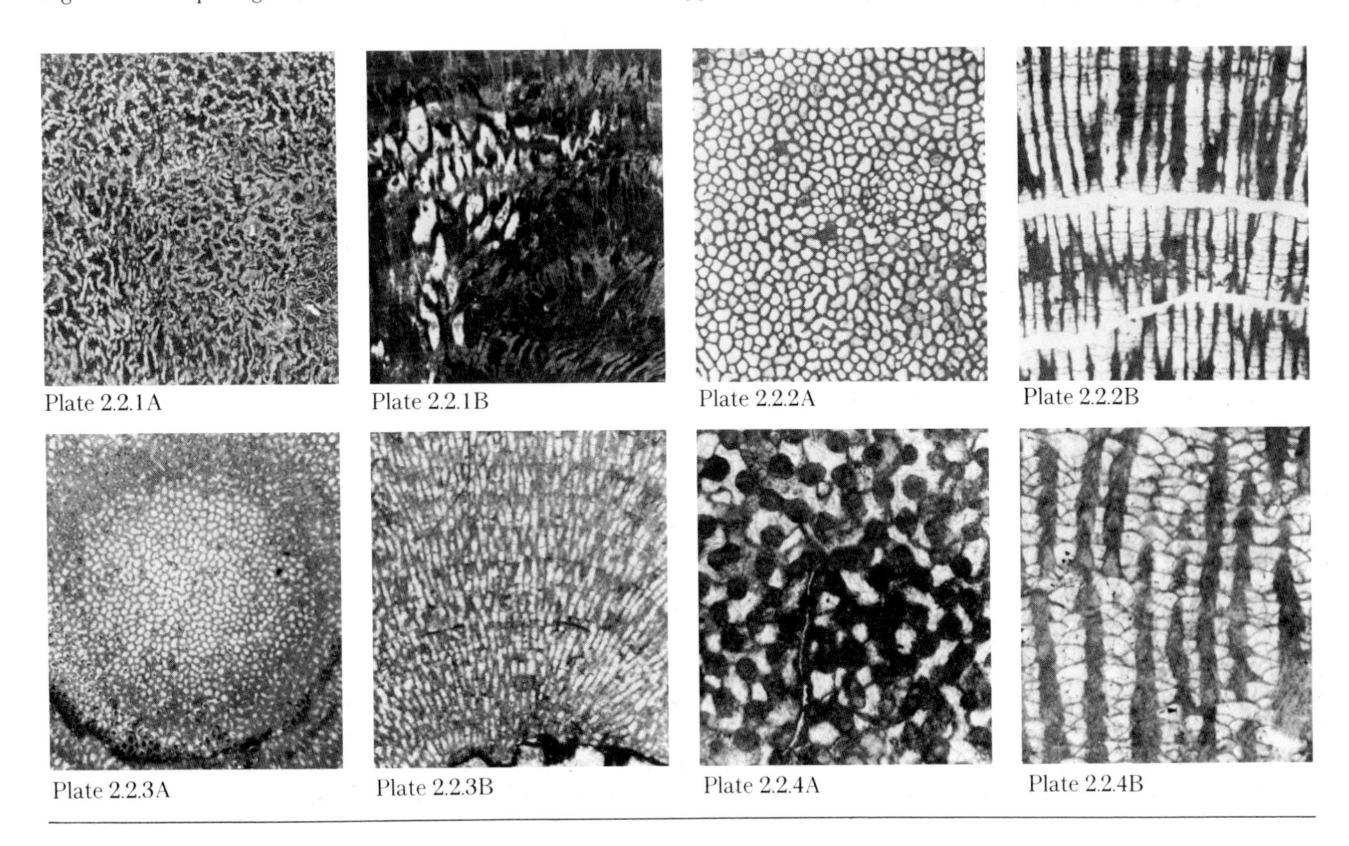

Plate 2.2.1A Plate 2.2.1B Plate 2.2.2A Plate 2.2.2B

Plate 2.2.3A Plate 2.2.3B Plate 2.2.4A Plate 2.2.4B

FAMILY ROSENELLIDAE

Pl. 2.2.5. *Rosenella* Nicholson, 1886
Coenosteum composed of large dissepimental plates which bear small vertical denticles not extending to next highest dissepiment.
Silurian–L. Carboniferous, shallow-water limestones. Europe–Asia–N. America.
Rosenella dentata (Rosen): Llandovery, Estonia, × 4.

FAMILY AULACERIDAE

Pl. 2.2.6. *Aulacera* Plummer, 1843
Coenosteum cylindrical, with axial row of coarse cysts enveloped by steeply inclined rows of dissepimental tissue.
Ordovician–Silurian, shallow-water limestones. Cosmopolitan.
Aulacera nodulosa (Billings): Cincinnatian, Kentucky, USA, × 1.5.

Order Actinostromatida

Stromatoporoids with long, continuous pillars and single-layer, commonly discontinuous laminae formed of processes given off from the pillars. ?Cambrian, Ordovician–L. Carboniferous.

FAMILY ACTINOSTROMATIDAE

Pl. 2.2.7. *Actinostroma* Nicholson, 1886
Coenosteum composed of long, slender pillars which at regular intervals give off horizontal, rod-like radial processes, usually 6 in number. Processes join neighbouring pillars to form net-like laminae. Astrorhizae may be present. Tissue compact.
?Cambrian, Ordovician–L. Carboniferous, limestones including reef and reef-associated facies. Cosmopolitan.
Actinostroma clathratum Nicholson: Devonian, Australia, × 5.

Order Clathrodictyida

Stromatoporoids in which laminar structures predominate. Pillars are normally confined to an interlaminar space but may be superimposed. ?Cambrian, Ordovician–L. Carboniferous, ?Permian.

FAMILY CLATHRODICTYIDAE

Pl. 2.2.8. *Clathrodictyon* Nicholson & Murie, 1878
Coenosteum composed of continuous, imperforate laminae, commonly undulose and funnelled downwards to form solid pillars. Pillars confined to 1 interlaminar space. Tissue of laminae and pillars continuous; texture compact commonly speckled.
?Cambrian, Ordovician–Devonian, ?Permian, limestones, including reefs and bioherms. Cosmopolitan.
Clathrodictyon vesiculosum Nicholson & Murie: Wenlock, Shropshire, England, × 5.

FAMILY AMPHIPORIDAE

Pl. 2.2.9. *Amphipora* Schulz, 1883
Coenosteum narrowly cylindrical, rarely branching, with or without an axial canal and a peripheral ring of larger, vesicular spaces. Internal elements thick, forming a porous, crudely reticulate mass in which laminae and pillars are not distinguished.
Silurian–Devonian, limestones, characteristically back-reef or restricted environments. Europe–N. Africa–Asia–Australia–N. America.
Amphipora ramosa (Phillips): Givetian, S. Devon, England, × 4.

Pl. 2.2.10. *Dendrostroma* Lecompte, 1952
Coenosteum dendroid, typically with an axial, tabulated canal. Other canals of similar size radiate from the axial canal. Laminae thick; parabolic about axial canal. Pillars confined to an interlaminar space, not superimposed. Microstructure compact.
Devonian, shallow-water limestones. Europe.
Dendrostroma occulatum (Nicholson): Devonian, Büchel, W. Germany, × 4.

Order Stromatoporellida

Stromatoporoids with prominent, consistent laminae with a persistent, distinct axial zone (i.e. tripartite) and short, commonly spool-shaped pillars. Silurian–L. Carboniferous.

FAMILY HERMATOSTROMATIDAE

Pl. 2.2.11. *Hermatostroma* Nicholson, 1886
Coenosteum composed of thin, continuous, tripartite laminae and thick, spool-shaped pillars that are interrupted by the laminae but are accurately superposed. Pillars and laminae enclosed in thin membrane supported by small processes, or a series of marginal vesicles lining the galleries.
Silurian–Devonian, shallow-water limestones. Cosmopolitan.
Hermatostroma schlueteri Nicholson: Devonian, Hebborn, W. Germany, × 5.

FAMILY STACHYODITIDAE

Pl. 2.2.12. *Stachyodes* Bargatsky, 1881
Coenosteum dendroid, rarely submassive. Each cylinder with an axial canal or canals with radial branches of narrower diameter arranged conformably or normal to lamination of tissue. Tissue dense, with parabolic laminae defined as thin layers of granules, and thick pillars normal to the laminae, both best defined peripherally where small galleries may be open.
Devonian, limestones including reef associated facies. Europe–Asia–Australia.
Stachyodes verticillata (M'Coy): Devonian, Hebborn, W. Germany, × 3.5.

Order Stromatoporida

Stromatoporoids with coenosteum composed of an amalgamated network of thickened tissue in which laminae are sometimes poorly defined and discrete pillars are generally not distinguished. Galleries vermiform in section, some with vertical pseudozooidal tubes. Ordovician–L. Carboniferous, Permian.

FAMILY STROMATOPORIDAE

Pl. 2.2.13. *Stromatopora* Goldfuss, 1826
Coenosteum an amalgamated network of thickened tissue in which neither laminae nor pillars can be distinguished. Galleries more extensive in concentric rather than radial directions and thin concentric microlaminae may be present.
Ordovician–L. Carboniferous, Permian, limestones, mainly reef associated facies. Cosmopolitan.
Stromatopora concentrica Goldfuss: Devonian, Gerolstein, W. Germany, × 5.

FAMILY SYRINGOSTROMELLIDAE

Pl. 2.2.14. *Parallelopora* Bargatsky, 1881
Coenosteum an amalgamated network of thick, continuous pillars and thick, discontinuous laminae. Galleries predominantly long, tabulated, pseudozooidal tubes. Microstructure cellular with large, distinctive, vertically elongate cellules.
Devonian, limestones, mainly reef associated facies. Cosmopolitan.
Parallelopora goldfussi Bargatsky: Devonian, Steinbrecke, E. Germany, × 5.

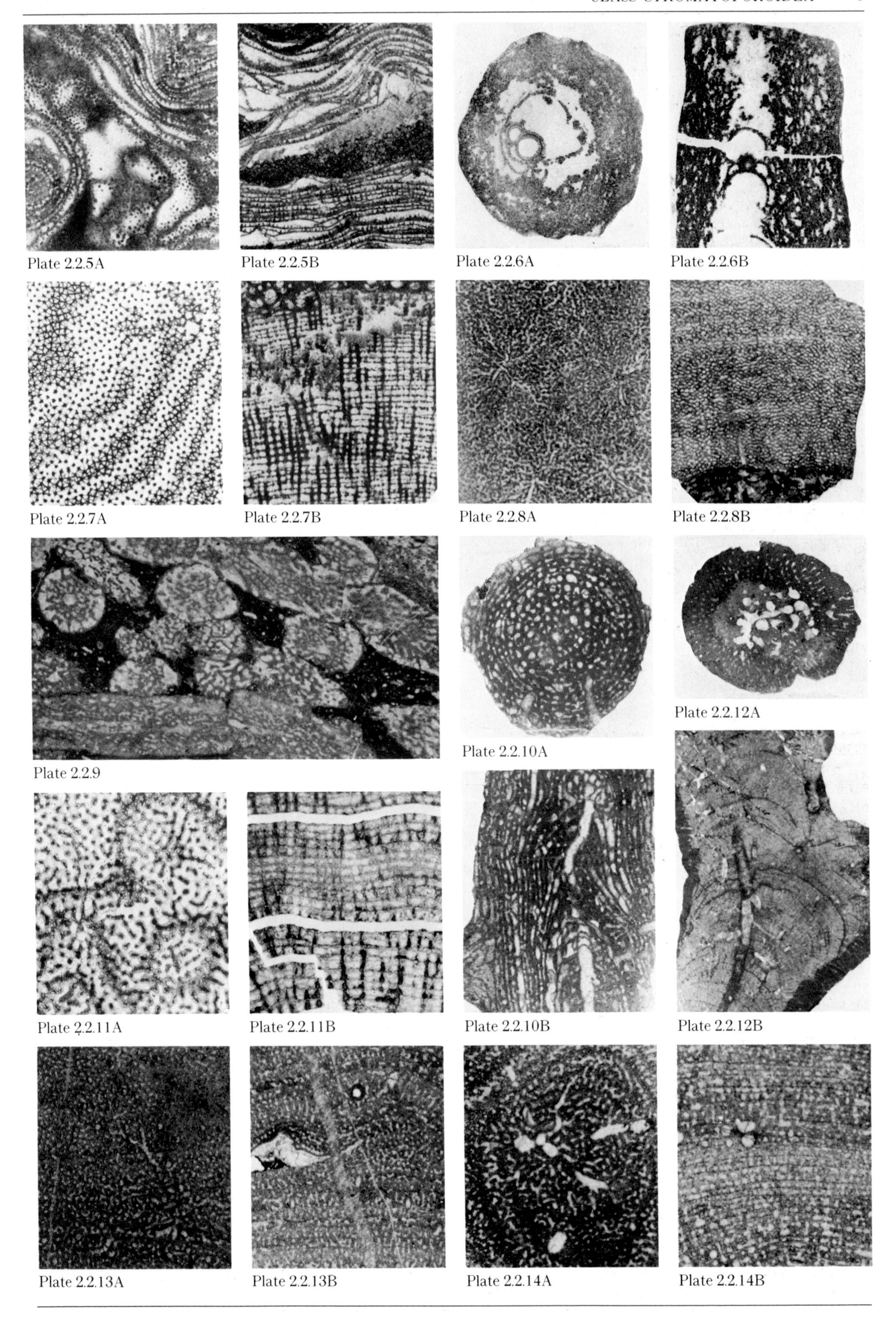

Plate 2.2.5A Plate 2.2.5B Plate 2.2.6A Plate 2.2.6B

Plate 2.2.7A Plate 2.2.7B Plate 2.2.8A Plate 2.2.8B

Plate 2.2.9 Plate 2.2.10A Plate 2.2.12A

Plate 2.2.11A Plate 2.2.11B Plate 2.2.10B Plate 2.2.12B

Plate 2.2.13A Plate 2.2.13B Plate 2.2.14A Plate 2.2.14B

FAMILY SYRINGOSTROMATIDAE

Pl. 2.2.15. *Syringostroma* Nicholson, 1875

Coenosteum an amalgamated network of thick, continuous pillars and persistent microlaminae, intermittently thickened. Pseudozooidal tubes short. Microstructure cellular or microreticulate.

Silurian–Devonian, limestones, mainly reef associated facies. Europe–Asia–Australia–N. America.

Syringostroma densum Nicholson: Devonian, Ohio, USA, × 5.

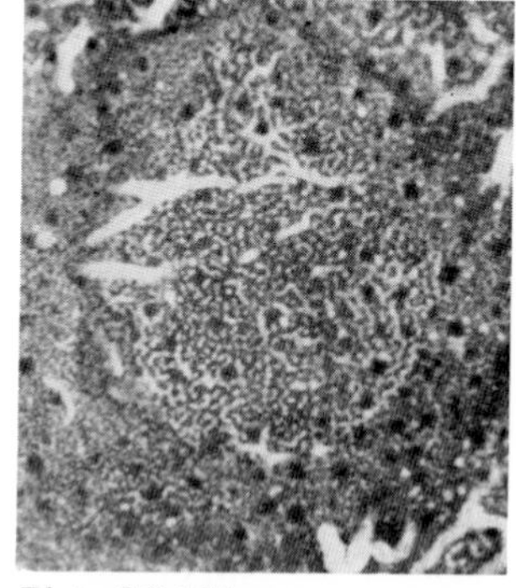

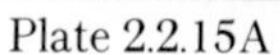

Plate 2.2.15A

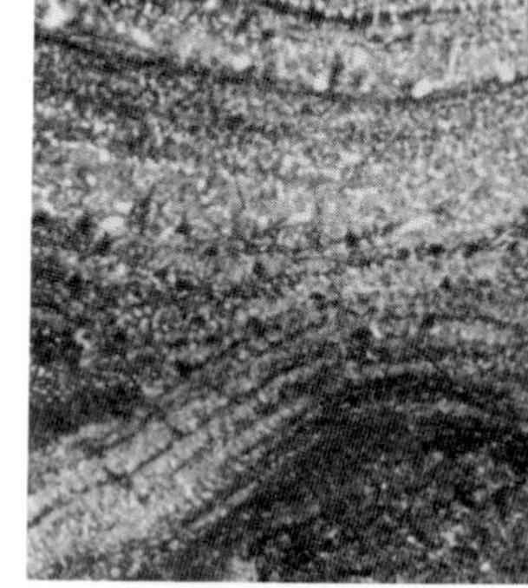

Plate 2.2.15B

Order Milleporellida

Stromatoporoids with coenosteum composed of amalgamated pillars, usually of vermiform cross-section, and lacking laminae. Vertically continuous galleries with thin tabulae. Microstructure fibrous. Jurassic–Cretaceous.

FAMILY PARASTROMATOPORIDAE

Pl. 2.2.16. *Dehornella* Lecompte, 1952

Coenosteum nodular or encrusting, a reticulum of pillars, both discrete and linked by thinner, narrow vertical laminar sheets. Galleries tabulated, with tabulae sometimes aligned to form continuous concentric plates. Astrorhizae usually common.

U. Jurassic, shallow-water limestones. Europe–Asia.

Dehornella omanensis Hudson: Jurassic, Oman, × 5.

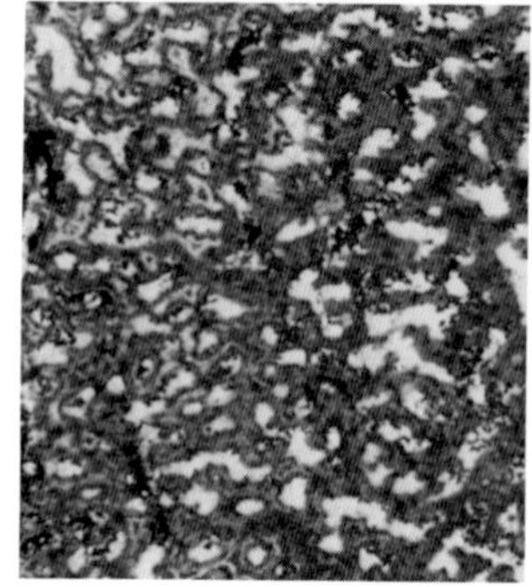

Plate 2.2.16A

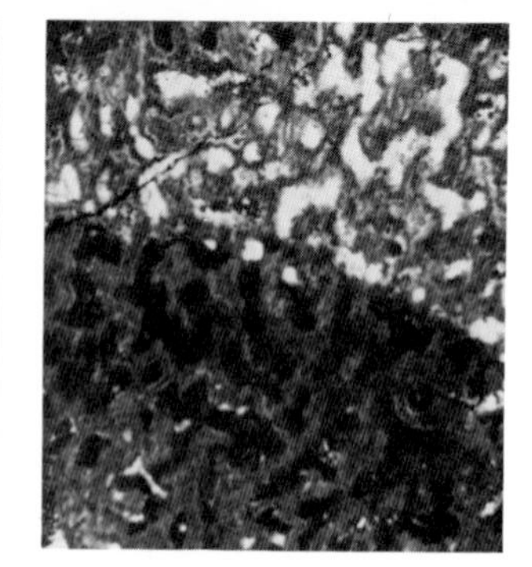

Plate 2.2.16B

CHAPTER 3

Cnidaria

The Cnidaria include the hydrozoans and scyphozoans as well as the various groups of corals belonging to the class Anthozoa and representing the bulk of the Cnidarian fossil record.

Members of the classes Hydrozoa and Scyphozoa are relatively rare as fossils, despite their long geological record. The first hydrozoans are late Precambrian (Vendian) chondrophores. Possible hydrozoan medusae appear in the Cambrian, although some of the unassigned Precambrian medusae may be hydrozoan. The first thecate hydrozoans are Ordovician. These groups have a scattered fossil record thereafter and are joined by the orders Milleporida and Stylasterida, both with calcareous basal skeletons, in the U. Cretaceous.

The Scyphozoa also have a sparse record of medusan fossils stretching back to the Precambrian. In addition rare chitinous tubular fossils first appearing in the U. Cambrian are interpreted as scyphopolyps. An extinct group of rather more common chitinophosphatic fossils, the Conulata, are of uncertain affinity but have been assigned to the Scyphozoa. They are treated as a separate class here. They first appear in the late Precambrian and become extinct in the Triassic.

The Anthozoa have possible Precambrian fossils in the supposed pennatulaceans (sea-pens) which belong to the subclass Octocorallia. Otherwise octocorals are extremely rare fossils, even in the Mesozoic when some forms with massive calcareous basal skeletons and others with calcified axes appear in the record. Octocoral spicules are also seldom recognized as fossils. Members of the subclass Ceriantipatharia are even more rare with a single Miocene record. On the other hand, the subclass Zoantharia includes the scleractinian corals which appear in the M. Triassic and have a rich fossil record culminating in their present-day prominence in coral reefs. Other groups of corals were earlier also assigned to the Zoantharia but now, more conservatively, have been made subclasses of the Anthozoa in their own right (Hill 1981). These are the Rugosa, Tabulata and Heterocorallia, all of the Palaeozoic. The first undisputed corals occur in the Ordovician, but there are also a few scattered Cambrian fossils which may be anthozoans (Scrutton 1979). Various authors have suggested that the Scleractinia might be direct descendants of the Rugosa but recent opinion refutes this (Oliver 1980), as is explicit in this classification.

3.1 Class Hydrozoa

Cnidarians with tetrameral or polymeral radial symmetry. Polymorphic with both polypoid and medusoid forms or exclusively medusoid. The enteron lacks a stomodaeum and is undivided by ridges or partitions. Oral end of polyps elongated into a hydranth. Medusae almost exclusively with a muscular shelf on the inner rim of the umbrella (velum). Exoskeleton, if present, generally chitinous, rarely calcareous. U. Precambrian–Recent.

(Note: Not all subdivisions are defined here as fossils are relatively rare. Two examples are given, one a Precambrian chondrophore (related to the living *Velella*), the other a polypoid hydrozoan colony that lived commensally with Mesozoic and Tertiary Annelida with calcareous tubes.)

Subclass Hydroidea

Order Chondrophora

Polymorphic, free-swimming or floating hydrozoan colonies. Float with air chambers, with large, central gastrozooid on

Plate 3.1.1

Plate 3.1.2A

Plate 3.3.1

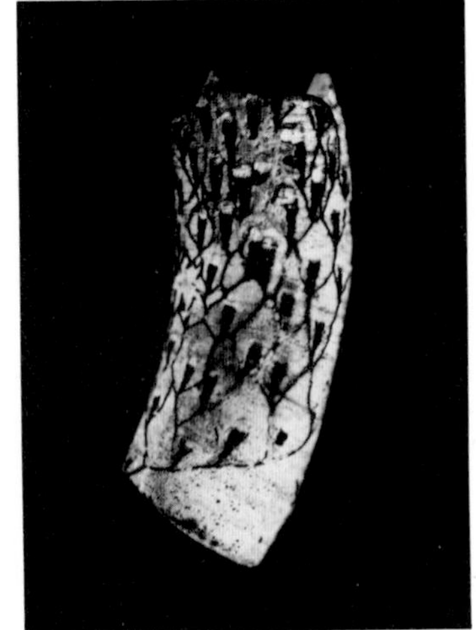

Plate 3.1.2B

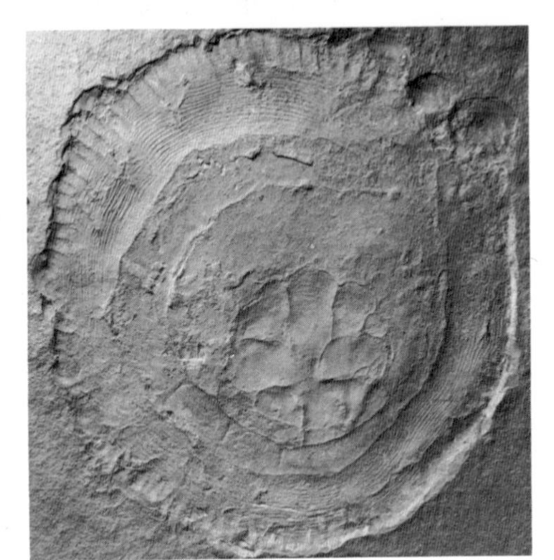

Plate 3.2.1

underside encircled by gonozooids with mouth, medusiform gonophores and marginal, tentacle-like dactylozooids. Gonophores freed as medusae. U. Precambrian–Recent.

Pl. 3.1.1. *Chondroplon* Wade, 1971
Chondrophore with a float bilaterally symmetrical about a narrow axis. Initial chamber of float ovate, at proximal end of axis. Later chambers at first annular about the initial chamber but becoming progressively less encircling, narrower and laterally more extensive. Towards distal end of axis, chambers continue to narrow but are progressively shorter. Both a proximal and a distal notch are formed, respectively early and late in growth.
U. Precambrian, pelagic. Australia.
Chondroplon bilobatum Wade: U. Precambrian, Flinders Range, Australia. Plate with axis horizontal near upper margin, proximal end to right, × $\frac{3}{8}$.

Order Hydroida

Hydroids with polypoid generation dominant. Few, naked, solitary species. Colonial forms with exoskeleton generally chitinous or occasionally weakly calcareous. Free medusae budded off, or structures present resembling abortive medusae. Medusae velate. ?Precambrian, Cambrian–Recent.

Pl. 3.1.2. *Protulophila* Rovereto, 1901
Hydroid with a stolonal network diamond to hexagonal shaped or less well ordered, growing at the lip of a serpulid tube and thereby incorporated into the calcareous tube. Polyps arise at or close to stolonal junctions, distally free through apertures in the serpulid tube wall. Polymorphism not apparent.
M. Jurassic–Pliocene, commensal on usually epifaunal serpulids in shallow-water muds. Europe–?Asia.
Protulophila gestroi Rovereto: commensal on *Parsimonia* sp., Albian, Kent, England, external surface (A), × 4; with outer layer of serpulid tube removed (B), × 5.

3.2 Class Scyphozoa

Cnidarians with tetrameral radial symmetry. Polymorphic with both polypoid and medusoid forms but the latter overwhelmingly dominant. The enteron lacks a stomodaeum but is extended into 4 gastric pockets separated by 4 septa. Hard parts usually lacking but some with a thin, chitinous periderm. U. Precambrian–Recent.

(Note: Not all subdivisions are defined here as fossils are so rare. A single example is given, a Mesozoic jellyfish.)

Order Lithorhizostomatida

Scyphozoans with dome-shaped bell with 16 lappets, each with 8 cluster lappets and with tentacles in 8 clusters. Mouth cruciform, functional, with non-functional secondary branches. No oral arms. Four gonad sacs, reniform to subtriangular in shape. U. Jurassic.

Pl. 3.2.1. *Rhizostomites* Haeckel, 1866
Large medusae with cruciform mouth. Each branch of mouth bifurcating to form a pair of non-functional adradial grooves defining insert inter-radial lobes. No oral arms. Mouth area encircled by rugose ring bearing 4 reniform ?gonad sacs. Outer annular zone with concentrically striated ring muscle. Margin with 128 short, round lappets.
U. Jurassic, pelagic, Europe.
Rhizostomites admirandus Haeckel: U. Jurassic, Eichstätt, W. Germany, × ¼.

3.3 Class Anthozoa

Exclusively polypoid cnidarians, solitary or colonial. Oral end expanded to form oral disc. Enteron with stomodaeum, subdivided radiobilaterally or biradially by paired or unpaired, complete or incomplete mesenteries. Some groups with horny or calcareous spicular endoskeleton or calcareous exoskeleton. ?U. Precambrian, ?Cambrian, Ordovician–Recent.

Subclass Octocorallia

Sedentary, colonial anthozoans. Polyps with 8 tentacles and enteron with 8 complete mesenteries. Some with horny or calcareous spicular skeleton, rarely a massive calcareous skeleton. ?U. Precambrian, ?Silurian, L. Jurassic–Recent.

Order Pennatulacea

Unbranched colony with a primary polyp producing a barren, proximal stalk to anchor colony in substrate, and a polypiferous distal rachis from which secondary polyps arise either directly or from lateral ridge- or blade-like polyp leaves. ?U. Precambrian, ?Silurian, Recent.

Pl. 3.3.1. *Charniodiscus* Ford, 1958
?Pennatulacean with large, leaf-like frond. Rachis extended proximally as a stalk which is attached to the centre of a disc with a central circular boss on the undersurface. Frond with 30–50 side branches, opposite or alternating, diverging from rachis at 45°–90°. Each branch linked to immediate neighbour by a foliate base and supporting a transversely grooved polyp leaf.
U. Precambrian, disc buried in fine-grained sandstones. Europe–Australia.
Charniodiscus arboreus (Glaessner): U. Precambrian, Flinders Range, Australia, × ¼.

Subclass Rugosa

Solitary or colonial corals with septa inserted in 4 loci in the corallite. Major and minor septa of contrasting length usually developed, and occasionally higher orders of septa are present. Epitheca, or holotheca, almost always present. A marginarium of dissepiments or thickened and contiguous septal ends may develop peripherally in the zone of the minor septa. The tabularium is occupied by complete or incomplete, variously shaped and disposed tabulae. An axial structure may be present. M. Ordovician–U. Permian.

Glossary of Selected Terms

These definitions of morphological terms applied to rugose (R), heterocoral (H) and tabulate (T) corals are keyed into the illustrations of genera as far as possible. Only the more important terms are defined. Those not covered here will be found in Hill (1981). Some terms apply also to scleractinian corals (S), but other specifically scleractinian terms are listed separately.

Alar fossula Interseptal space at the locus of insertion of septa on the counter side of the alar septum (Pl. 3.3.55) (R).

Alar septum One of a pair of protosepta located approximately midway between the cardinal and counter septa (Pl. 3.3.55) (R).

Alveolitoid Inclined corallites in a colony in which the upper wall is vaulted and the lower wall reflects the form of the surface on which it grows (Pl. 3.3.95) (T).

Aphroid Massive corallum in which the corallites are not individually bounded by an epitheca and the septa are withdrawn from peripheral areas so that corallites are united by dissepiments only (Pl. 3.3.34) (R).

Astraeoid Massive corallum in which the corallites are not individually bounded by an epitheca and the septa from adjacent corallites intermingle to form a weak pseudotheca (Pl. 3.3.49) (R).

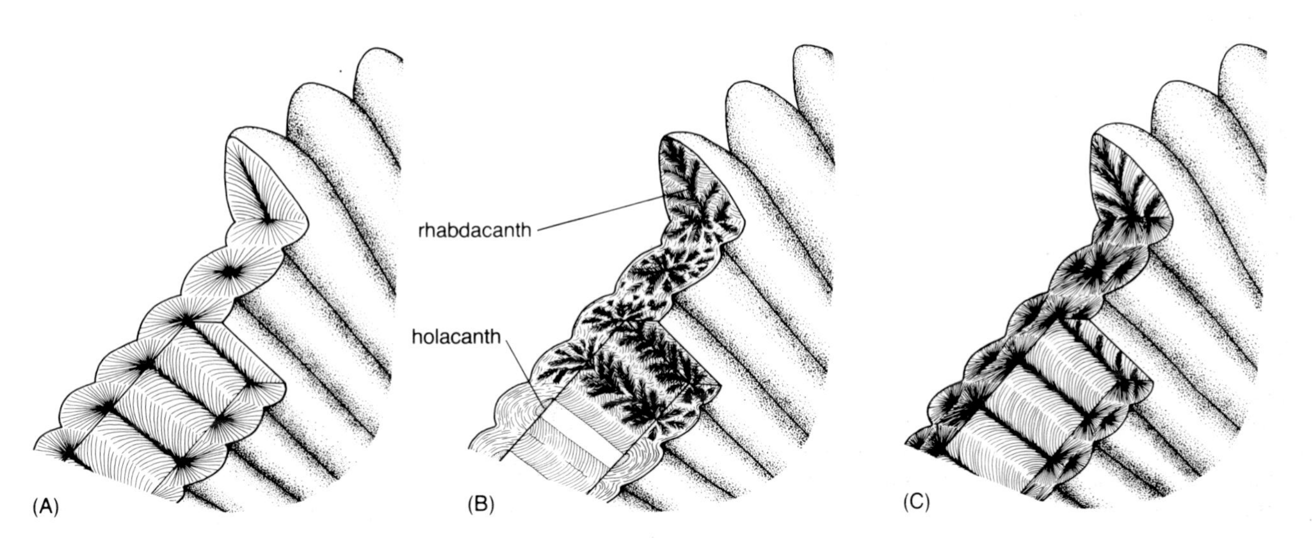

Fig. 3.3.1. Diagrammatic septal microstructure. (A) monacanthine trabeculae; (B) rhabdacanthine and holacanthine trabeculae; (C) rhipidacanthine trabeculae. Holacanths are thought to be mainly recrystallized rhabdacanths but some may be recrystallized monacanths (based on Hill 1981: Fig. 7).

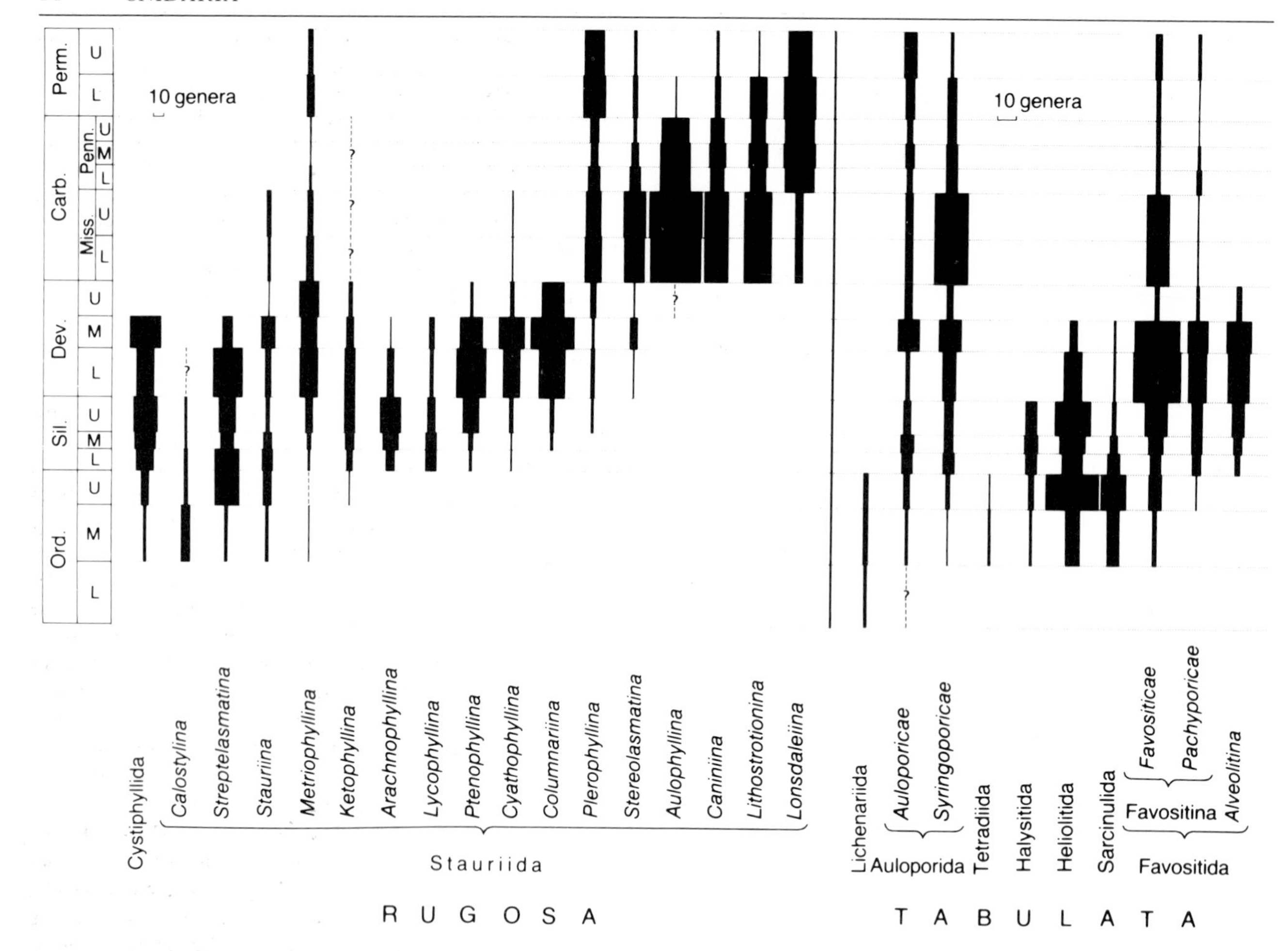

Fig. 3.3.2. Ranges and diversity in numbers of genera of orders and selected suborders and superfamilies of rugose and tabulate corals. Note scale difference between the two subclasses. Stratigraphic scale approximately proportional to time. No partial ranges distinguished within subdivisions shown. Data from Hill (1981).

Aulos Tubular structure in the centre of the tabularium aligned along the axis of growth (Pl. 3.3.71) (R).

Axial increase Formation of offsets by the growth of new dividing walls in the axial area of a corallite. The process is always parricidal (Pl. 3.3.14, 46, 51) (R, T).

Axial structure Collective term for various longitudinal structures occupying the axial zone of a corallite, either solid or composed of various modified structural elements (Pl. 3.3.65, 66) (R, T).

Calice Distal surface of a corallite, often bowl-shaped, occupied by the polyp in life (Pl. 3.3.2) (R, H, T, S).

Cardinal fossula Interseptal space in the region of the cardinal septum, which may be shortened, usually coincident with a depression of the tabularial floor. Represents the combined sites of septal insertion on either side of the cardinal septum (Pl. 3.3.56) (R).

Cardinal septum A protoseptum in the plane of bilateral symmetry of the corallite with loci of septal insertion immediately on either side of it (Pl. 3.3.56) (R).

Carina Flange on the septal face, parallel with the axis of a septal trabecula. Yard-arm carinae have flanges coincident on opposite faces of septa, zigzag carinae have flanges slightly offset on opposite faces of septa (Pl. 3.3.52) (R).

Catenoid (cateniform) Colonial corals in which corallites are united laterally like the posts in a palisade fence, appearing chain-like in cross-section. The palisades are usually linked in a network (Pl. 3.3.101–103) (R, T).

Ceratoid Slender, horn-shaped solitary coral in which the apical angle of the horn is about 20° (Pl. 3.3.60) (R).

Cerioid Massive corallum in which the walls of adjacent polygonal corallites are closely united back to back (Pl. 3.3.14, 69) (R, T).

Coenenchymal increase Type of increase in which new tabularia arise in the coenenchymal tissue (Pl. 3.3.98) (T).

Coenenchyme Common skeletal tissue uniting tabularia in colonial corals. May be most frequently tubular or vesicular (Pl. 3.3.97–99) (T).

Columella Usually solid axial rod in a corallite formed by the modified end of a septum, frequently the counter septum or the ends of several septa and projecting into the calice as a boss or spine (Pl. 3.3.28, 60) (R).

Contratingent Minor septum that rests against the adjacent major septum on the counter side (Pl. 3.3.28) (R).

Corallum The exoskeleton of a solitary or colonial coral (R, H, T, S).

Counter septum One of the protosepta in the plane of symmetry opposite the cardinal septum (Pl. 3.3.60) (R).

Counter-lateral septum One of a pair of major septa (possibly protosepta) that flank the counter septum on either side (R).

Cylindrical Solitary coral of nearly uniform diameter, except for the proximal tip (Pl. 3.3.19, 80) (R, H, S).

Dendroid Fasciculate corallum in which the corallites branch irregularly and diverge (R, T, S).

Discoid Solitary corallite with flat base and reflexed calice (Pl. 3.3.32) (R, S).

Dissepiment Small, usually vesicular plate in the peripheral area of many corallites (Pl. 3.3.67) (R, S).

Dissepimentarium Zone of corallite occupied by dissepiments (Pl. 3.3.67) (R).

Epitheca Thin external sheath surrounding an individual corallite, either solitary or within a colony (R, T, S).

Fossula Interseptal space of unusual shape and size (R).

Holacanth Thin, clear, rod-like structure in a septum, presumed to be a diagenetically modified trabecula (Fig. 3.3.1B) (R, T).

Holotheca Thin, continuous epithecal sheath surrounding many massive colonial corals (R, T).

Horseshoe dissepiment Highly inflated saddle-shaped dissepiment, horseshoe-shaped in longitudinal section (Pl. 3.3.51) (R).
Increase Addition of a new corallite to a colony (R, T).
Lateral increase Formation of offsets by lateral growth away from the parent corallite so that the latter's cross-sectional area and appearance are virtually unaffected (Pl. 3.3.16) (R, T).
Lonsdaleoid Condition in which large peripheral dissepiments interrupt septa which fail to extend to the outer wall of the corallite or do so only as crests on the dissepiments (Pl. 3.3.74) (R).
Major septum One of the protosepta or metasepta (Pl. 3.3.22) (R, H, T).
Marginarial increase Alternative term for lateral and peripheral increase (R, T).
Marginarium Peripheral area of the corallite, outside the tabularium, usually occupied by dissepiments or deposits of skeletal tissue forming a stereozone (R, T).
Massive Colonial corallum in which the constituent corallites are closely united (R, T, S).
Metaseptum One of the main septa of a corallite other than the protosepta, usually distinguished by greater length from the minor septa (R).
Minor septum One of the shorter septa that alternate between the major septa (may be confined to the peripheral wall or suppressed in some corals) (Pl. 3.3.22) (R).
Monacanth Trabecula in which fibres are related to an axis resulting from a migrating single centre of calcification (Fig. 3.3.1A) (R, T).
Mural pore Small circular or oval hole in the wall separating adjacent corallites (Pl. 3.3.88, 94) (T).
Offset New corallite formed by increase (R, T).
Parricidal Increase which results in the cessation of growth of the parent corallite (Pl. 3.3.51) (R, T).
Patellate Solitary corallite with a basal angle about 120° (Pl 3.3.3) (R).
Peripheral increase Formation of offsets in peripheral zone of corallite so that the cross-sectional area of the parent is reduced. May be parricidal in some cases (Pl. 3.3.77) (R, T).
Phaceloid Fasciculate corallum in which the corallites are subparallel (Pl. 3.3.106) (R, T, S).
Protoseptum One of the first-formed four (excluding counter-lateral septa) or six septa of a corallite (R).
Ramose Branching form of a corallum in which each branch is composed of few to many closely united corallites (Pl. 3.3.96) (R, T, S).
Rhabdacanth Compound trabecula with second-order trabeculae grouped around its primary axis of growth (Fig. 3.3.1B) (R, T).
Rhipidacanth Compound trabecula with second-order trabeculae diverging from the median septal plane (Fig. 3.3.1C) (R).
Rhopaloid septum Septum in which the axial edge is thickened to appear club-shaped in cross-section (Pl. 3.3.59) (R, S).
Sclerenchyme Calcareous tissue of a corallite (R, H, T).
Sclerocone Zone of skeletal thickening on successive, more or less widely spaced calicular floors of a corallite (Pl. 3.3.11) (R).
(Septal) lamella Radially disposed longitudinal plate in the axis of a corallite aligned with a septum but discontinuous from it (Pl. 3.3.73) (R, S).
Septal spine (spinule) Discrete trabecular spine, usually one of a longitudinal series, projecting from the wall or a dissepiment or tabula (Pl. 3.3.6) (R, T, S).
Septum Radially disposed longitudinal partition of a corallite (Pl. 3.3.22) (R, H, T, S).
Stereozone Area of dense skeletal deposits in a corallite, generally marginarial in position (Pl. 3.3.25) (R, T).
Tabella Small subglobose plate in the axial part of a corallite not extending across the full width of the tabularium (Pl. 3.3.73) (R, T).
Tabula Transverse partition extending across the tabularium, planar, domed or dished in form (Pl. 3.3.4) (R, H, T).
Tabularial increase Alternative term for axial increase, and peripheral increase extending into the tabularium of the parent corallite. Always parricidal (R, T).
Tabularium Axial part of a corallite surrounded by the marginarium, or whole internal area when marginarium absent, in which tabulae or tabellae are developed (Pl. 3.3.67) (R, H, T).
Thamnasterioid Massive corallum with no internal walls in which the septa of adjacent corallites are confluent (Pl. 3.3.70, 71) (R, S).
Trabecula Pillar of radiating calcareous fibres forming a constituent element of septa and related structures (Fig. 3.3.1) (R, H, T).
Trochoid Solitary coral with a basal angle of about 40° (Pl. 3.3.22) (R).
Tubule, coenenchymal Small, tabulated, longitudinal chamber with rounded or polygonal cross-section individually or severally constituting coenenchyme between tabularia (Pl. 3.3.97) (T).
Tubule, connecting Small, horizontal open tubular passageway between adjacent corallites in some fasciculate coralla (Pl. 3.3.106) (T).
Turbinate Solitary coral with a basal angle of about 70° (Pl. 3.3.53) (R).
Wall Outer wall of a corallite, usually consisting of the epitheca thickened internally by fibrous sclerenchyme (R, H, T).

Classification of corals, which show great variation in the plasticity of their constituent skeletal elements, is not amenable to representation by key above the generic level. The scheme followed here takes into account degrees of relationship as well as degrees of morphological similarity. For example, lonsdaleoid dissepiments, which may be characteristic of some groups of corals (e.g. family Axophyllidae), occur widely and sporadically in many other groups also. Important structural features used in classification are the nature of septa, laminar or spinose, continuous or discontinuous, their length, presence or absence of carinae and the development of minor septa; the form of tabulae, complete, incomplete, the presence of subsidiary plates and the form of the tabularial surface; presence or absence of dissepiments, their shape, size and distribution; presence and thickness of marginarial deposits; axial structures; to some extent growth form, solitary or colonial, and type of increase. About 35% of rugose coral genera are colonial.
Illustrations: Rugose and tabulate corals are usually illustrated by both cross-section and longitudinal section to show internal structures. In the Rugosa, the cardinal septum, if distinguishable, is orientated top centre. In some cases, only a cross-section is included, in others a hand specimen is illustrated, either in addition to, or instead of sections, as appropriate. In most cases the nature of the illustrations is obvious and no further comments are made on those for individual species.

Order Cystiphyllida

Mainly solitary but some fasciculate and massive corals; some solitary forms with opercula. Septa mainly spinose, well developed to almost absent; occasionally laminar. Horizontal elements may be absent, or tabulae only when commonly complete, or tabulae and dissepiments, vesicular and not sharply differentiated forming bowl-shaped calicular floors. M. Ordovician–M. Devonian, ?U. Devonian.

FAMILY PALAEOCYCLIDAE

Pl. 3.3.2. *Palaeocyclus* Edwards & Haime, 1849
Small, solitary, discoid with tip of corallum central on undersurface. Major and minor septa of laterally contiguous monacanthine trabeculae, with dentate distal edges in calice. No tabulae, dissepiments or axial structure.
L. Silurian (upper Llandovery)–?M. Silurian (basal Wenlock), quiet-water calcareous shales to silt-grade sediments. Europe–N. America.
Palaeocyclus porpita (Linné): Silurian, Gotland, Sweden, × 1¼.

Pl. 3.3.3. *Rhabdocyclus* Lang & Smith, 1939
Small, solitary, discoid or patellate with tip of corallum eccentric on undersurface. Major and minor septa rhabdacanthine or dimorphacanthine, laminar with spinose distal edges in calice. No tabulae, dissepiments or axial structure.
L. Silurian–L. Devonian, quiet-water calcareous shales to silt-grade sediments. Europe–Asia–N. America.

Rhabdocyclus porpitoides (Lang & Smith): Wenlock, Dudley, England, × 1½.

FAMILY TRYPLASMATIDAE
Subfamily Tryplasmatinae

Pl. 3.3.4. *Tryplasma* Lonsdale, 1845
Solitary, commonly ceratoid-cylindrical; rarely with parricidal offsets but not forming colony. Septa rhabdacanthine, holacanthine or dimorphacanthine, forming narrow peripheral stereozone of contiguous laminar plates, extended axially as short to long free trabeculae. Tabulae complete, usually flat, sometimes with median notch. No dissepiments.
U. Ordovician–L. Devonian, quiet-water limestones and calcareous shales. Cosmopolitan.
Tryplasma loveni (Edwards & Haime): Wenlock, Presthope, England, × 2.

?FAMILY FLETCHERIIDAE (possibly tabulate corals)

Pl. 3.3.5. *Fletcheria* Edwards & Haime, 1851
Small ramose colonies with cylindrical corallites that may become prismatic where closely packed. Thin peripheral stereozone, septa not obvious. Tabulae mostly complete, horizontal. No dissepiments. Increase calicular, parricidal.
M. Silurian, limestones including bioherms and calcareous shales. Europe.
Fletcheria sp.: Wenlock, Benthall Edge, England, × 4.

FAMILY HOLMOPHYLLIDAE

Pl. 3.3.6. *Holmophyllum* Wedekind, 1927
Solitary, occasionally with a few offsets. Major and minor septa composed of long, discrete rhabdacanths or tufted monacanths, subequal in length. Dissepimentarium wide, of numerous, small inclined dissepiments. Tabulae clearly distinguished, flat to slightly sagging, mainly complete.
L. Silurian–M. Devonian, shallow-water calcareous shales and limestones. Europe–Asia–Australia.
Holmophyllum holmi Wedekind: Ludlow, Gotland, Sweden, × 3.

FAMILY GONIOPHYLLIDAE

Pl. 3.3.7. *Goniophyllum* Edwards & Haime, 1850
Solitary, square in section (pyramidal); calice with operculum of 4 triangular plates (usually missing). Septa short, thick, mostly laminar and contiguous. Dissepiments and tabulae not strongly distinguished, vesicular, thickened in zones.
L.–M. Silurian, shallow-water calcareous shales and limestones. Europe–N. America.
Goniophyllum pyramidale (Hisinger): Wenlock; (A) Dudley, England, × 1½; (B), (C) Gotland, Sweden, × 2.

Pl. 3.3.8. *Calceola* Lamarck, 1799
Solitary, semicircular in section, flat face convexly curved (calceoloid). Calice with operculum (often missing). Interior more or less filled with solid sclerenchyme, laminated parallel to corallite walls and calicular floor, and almost wholly burying septa. Usually counter septum can be seen as ridge in centre of flat side.
L.–M. Devonian, shallow-water calcareous shales and limestones. Europe–Africa–Asia–Australia.
Calceola sandalina (Linné): M. Devonian, Eifel district, Germany; (A) with, (B) without operculum, × 1.

Pl. 3.3.9. *Rhizophyllum* Lindström, 1866
Solitary, sometimes with few offsets, calceoloid. Calice with operculum (often missing). Septa fine, short, spinose, also sporadically developed on dissepiments; may thicken to form peripheral stereozone. Tabulae not distinguished from dissepiments, vesicular, seldom thickened.
L. Silurian–L. Devonian, shallow-water calcareous shales and limestones. Europe–Asia–N. America.
Rhizophyllum tennesseensis (Roemer): Niagaran, Tennessee, USA; (A) × 1, (B), (C) × 1¾.

FAMILY CYSTIPHYLLIDAE

Pl. 3.3.10. *Cystiphyllum* Lonsdale, 1839
Solitary, turbinate to cylindrical. Septa spinose, developed on upper surface of dissepiments and outer wall. Sclerocones variably developed; thickening light and usually stronger, or only present, peripherally. Dissepiments and tabulae vesicular, not strongly differentiated.
Silurian, shallow-water limestones and calcareous shales. Cosmopolitan.
Cystiphyllum siluriense Lonsdale: Wenlock, Wenlock Edge, England, × 2¼.

Pl. 3.3.11. *Cystiphylloides* Chapman, 1893
Solitary, rarely colonial (phaceloid or subcerioid). Septa spinose, scattered or in septal combs. Sclerocones usually developed particularly in early stages; thickening usually pronounced and strongest axially. Dissepiments and tabulae vesicular, not strongly differentiated.
L.–M. Devonian, shallow-water limestones and calcareous shales. Cosmopolitan.
Cystiphylloides secundum (Goldfuss): M. Devonian, Eifel district, W. Germany, × 1¼.

Pl. 3.3.12. *Microplasma* Dybowski, 1873
Colonial, phaceloid with peripheral increase. Narrow peripheral stereozone with short, thorn-like septa in wall and developed on surfaces of dissepiments and tabulae. Dissepiments steeply inclined; tabulae flat-lying, weakly arched to globose.
L. Silurian–M. Devonian, shallow-water limestones and calcareous shales. Europe–Asia–Australia–N. America.
Microplasma lovenianum Dybowski: Wenlock, Usk, S. Wales, × 2.

FAMILY DIGONOPHYLLIDAE

Pl. 3.3.13. *Mesophyllum* Schlüter, 1889
Solitary or phaceloid. Septa thin, laminar or partly laminar, slightly withdrawn from axis and discontinuous peripherally where they may be represented by crossbar carinae only. Minor septa weak, but those flanking counter septum developed like major septa. Bowl of calice deep, weakly keyhole-shaped. Dissepiments and tabulae vesicular; tabulae larger, flatter, less inflated. Sclerocones weak. Solitary forms may reach 10 cm + in diameter.
M. Devonian, shallow-water limestones and calcareous shales. Europe–Asia–Australia.
Mesophyllum maximum (Schlüter): M. Devonian, Eifel district, Germany, × ¾.

Order Stauriida

Solitary and colonial. Septa laminar, composed of contiguous trabeculae in all but one suborder. Septa usually well developed, but may be withdrawn from the periphery (lonsdaleoid) or the tabularium, or only well developed axially immediately above tabulae (amplexoid). Dissepiments may be absent when marginarium is a stereozone. Tabulae complete or incomplete. M. Ordovician–U. Permian.

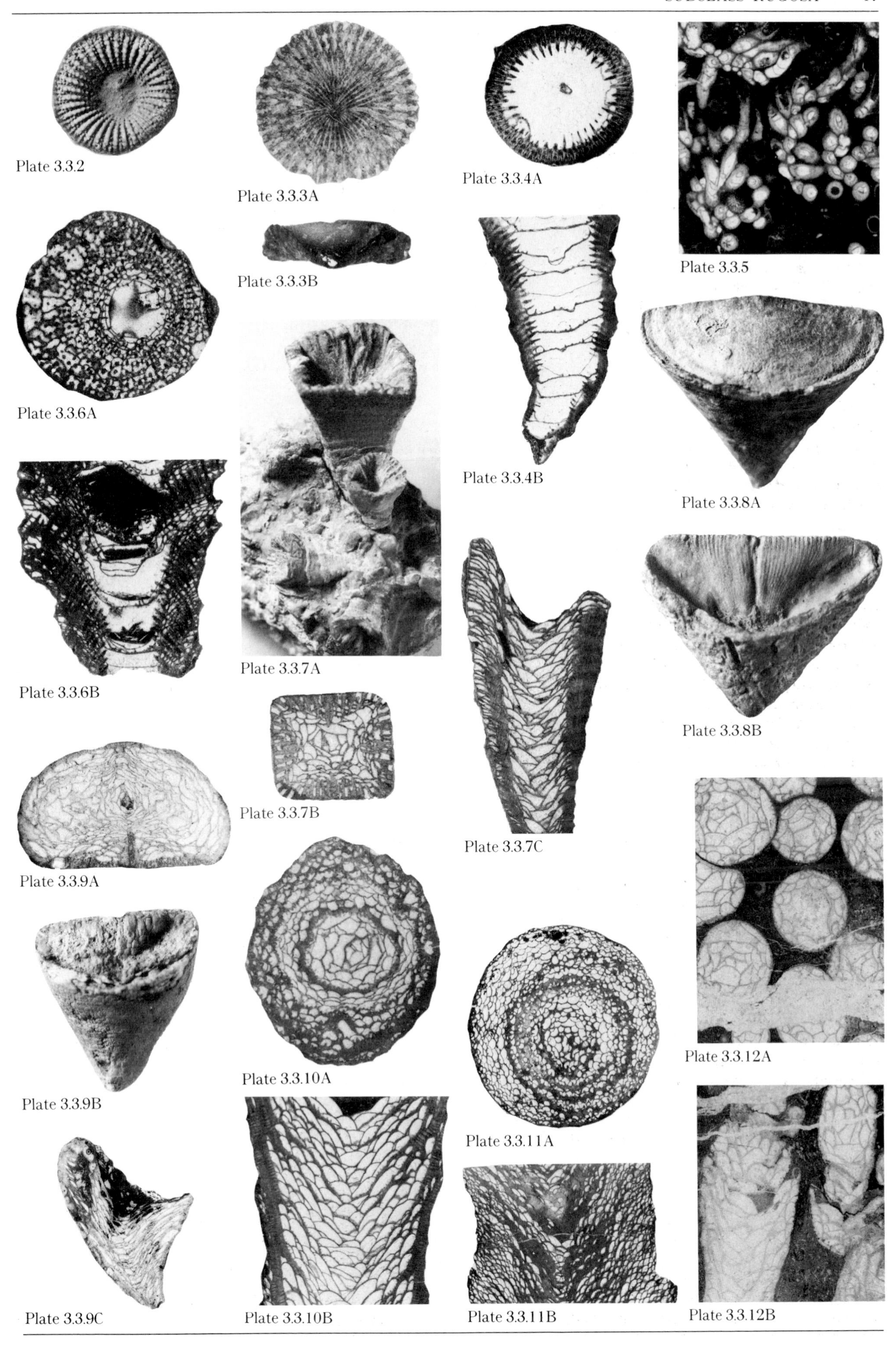

Plate 3.3.2

Plate 3.3.3A

Plate 3.3.4A

Plate 3.3.5

Plate 3.3.3B

Plate 3.3.6A

Plate 3.3.4B

Plate 3.3.8A

Plate 3.3.7A

Plate 3.3.6B

Plate 3.3.8B

Plate 3.3.7B

Plate 3.3.9A

Plate 3.3.7C

Plate 3.3.12A

Plate 3.3.10A

Plate 3.3.9B

Plate 3.3.11A

Plate 3.3.9C

Plate 3.3.10B

Plate 3.3.11B

Plate 3.3.12B

Plate 3.3.13A

Plate 3.3.13B

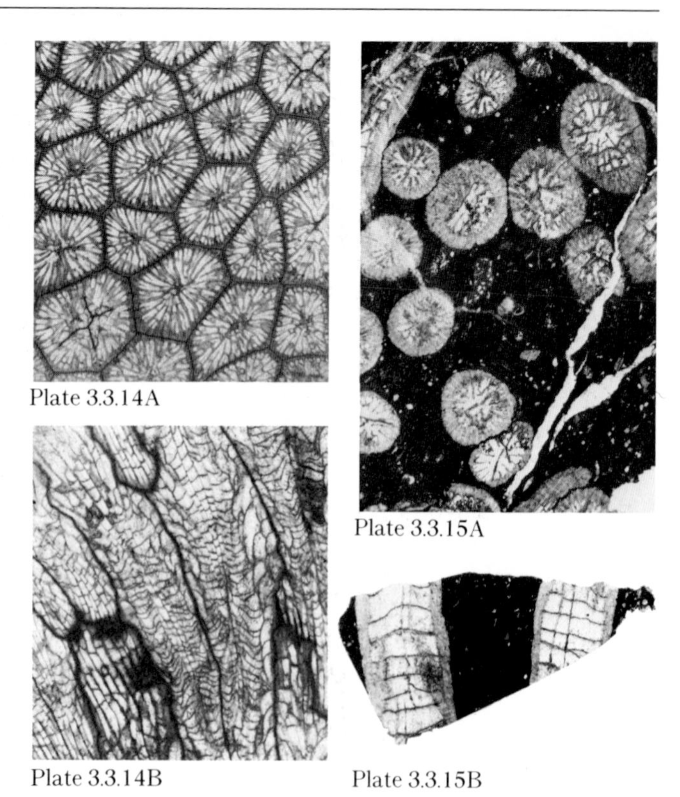

Plate 3.3.14A

Plate 3.3.14B

Plate 3.3.15A

Plate 3.3.15B

Suborder Stauriina

Colonial, fasciculate or cerioid. Marginarium a stereozone or with sporadic elongate dissepiments. Septa without axial lobes or acanthine inner margins, rarely lonsdaleoid. Tabulae usually complete. M. Ordovician–Carboniferous.

FAMILY STAURIIDAE

Pl. 3.3.14. *Stauria* Edwards & Haime, 1850
Cerioid, less commonly partly phaceloid. Increase axial, parricidal; usually 4, occasionally 3, offsets. Major septa long, close to or reaching axis; minor septa short. Dissepiments from sparse and isolated to up to 2 series; may interrupt minor septa. Tabulae mainly complete, subhorizontal to weakly arched, with few tabellae.
L.–M. Silurian, shallow-water limestones and calcareous shales. Europe–Asia.
Stauria favosa (Linné): Wenlock, Gotland, Sweden, × 2.

Pl. 3.3.15. *Dendrostella* Glinski, 1957
Dendroid or phaceloid with non-parricidal, peripheral increase. Stereozone moderately thick. Major septa long, almost reaching axis; minor septa short. No dissepiments. Tabulae complete, flat to slightly arched.
L.–M. Devonian, shallow-water limestones. Europe–Asia–Australia–Canada.
Dendrostella trigemme (Quenstedt): Givetian, S. Devon, England, × 1½.

Pl. 3.3.16. *Favistina* Flower, 1961
Cerioid, with non-parricidal lateral increase. Major septa thin, long, almost reaching axis; minor septa short ridges on wall. No dissepiments. Tabulae complete, flat, usually with downturned edges and sometimes an axial depression.
M.–U. Ordovician, shallow-water limestones. Europe–Asia–Australia–N. America.
Favistina stellata (Hall): Cincinnatian, Kentucky, USA, × 3.

Pl. 3.3.17. *Palaeophyllum* Billings, 1858
Phaceloid, phacelocerioid or phacelocateniform with non-parricidal lateral increase. Thin peripheral stereozone. Major septa thin, usually long, reaching or almost reaching the axis; minor septa short. No dissepiments. Tabulae complete, flat usually with slightly downturned edges and sometimes an axial depression.
M. Ordovician–M. Silurian, shallow-water limestones. Europe–Asia–Australia–N. America.
Palaeophyllum thomi (Hall): Cincinnatian, Texas, USA, × 2½.

FAMILY PYCNOSTYLIDAE

Pl. 3.3.18. *Depasophyllum* Grabau, 1936
Fasciculate, with non-parricidal, lateral increase. Major septa thin, extending to prominent but imperfect inner wall (aulos); minor septa rudimentary. No dissepiments. Tabulae domed to mesa-shaped, irregularly stacked to form imperfect aulos.
M. Devonian, shallow-water limestones. N. America.
Depasophyllum adnetum Grabau: Givetian, Michigan, USA, × 2.

FAMILY AMPLEXIDAE

Pl. 3.3.19. *Amplexus* Sowerby, 1814
Solitary, cylindrical, scolecoid to geniculate coralla. Wall very thin. Major septa thin, continuous vertical laminae only at wall, but extend axially for about half the corallite radius as low ridges on the upper surfaces of tabulae (amplexoid). Minor septa usually absent. No dissepiments. Tabulae complete, flat with downturned margins and cardinal fossula depression.
L. Carboniferous, shallow-water limestones, lime–mud bioherms. Europe–Asia–N. America.
Amplexus coralloides Sowerby: Carboniferous, England, × 1¾.

Pl. 3.3.20. *Heterophrentis* Billings, 1875
Solitary, ceratoid to trochoid with prominent cardinal fossula on convex side of corallum. Major septa thick peripherally, amplexoid, thinning axially. Cardinal septum very short; minor septa short. No dissepiments. Tabulae mainly complete with

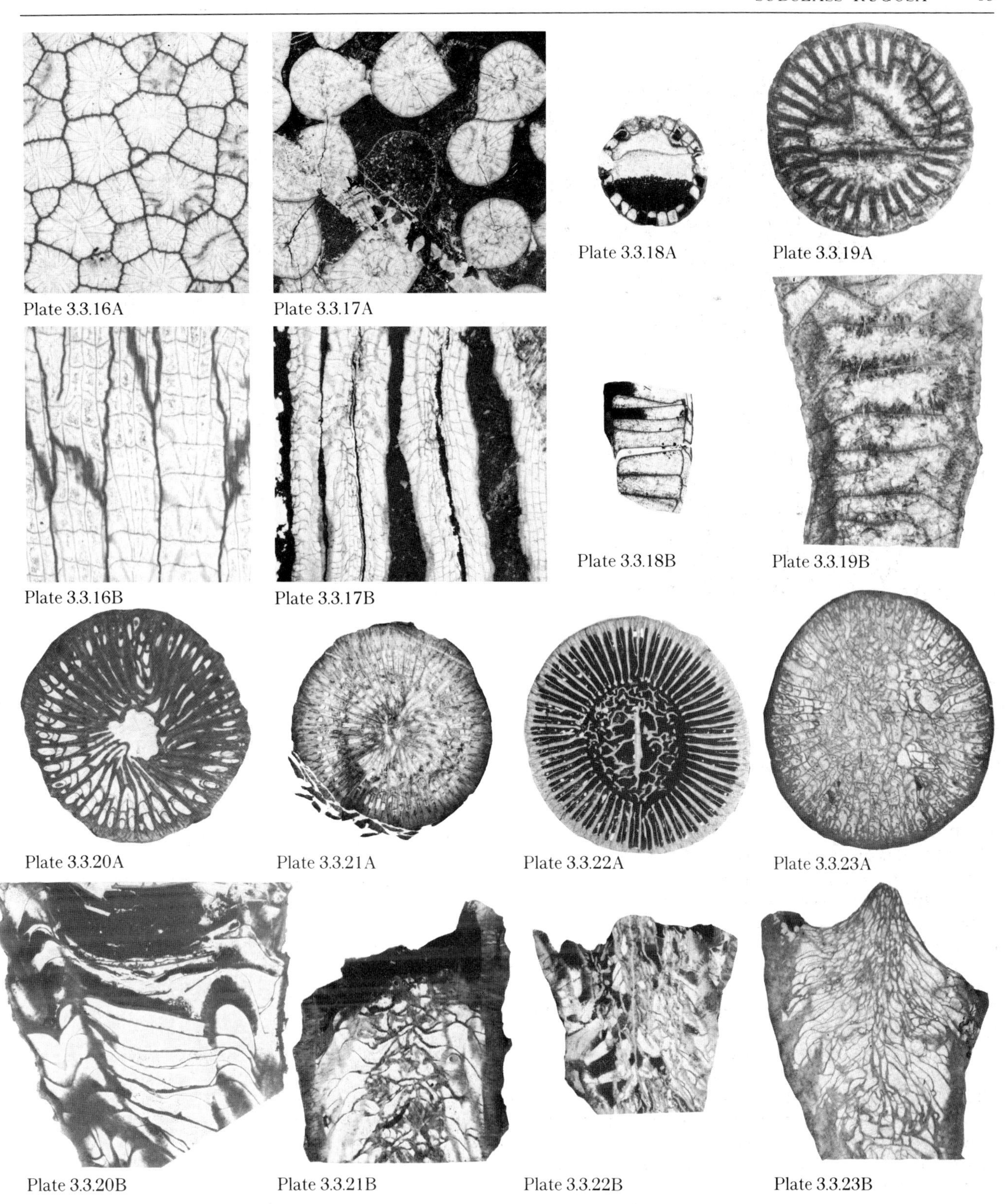

Plate 3.3.16A Plate 3.3.17A Plate 3.3.18A Plate 3.3.19A

Plate 3.3.16B Plate 3.3.17B Plate 3.3.18B Plate 3.3.19B

Plate 3.3.20A Plate 3.3.21A Plate 3.3.22A Plate 3.3.23A

Plate 3.3.20B Plate 3.3.21B Plate 3.3.22B Plate 3.3.23B

wide, flat axial area, peripheral ridge and sharply downturned margins.
M. Devonian, shallow-water calcareous shales and limestones. Europe (Spain)–N. America–S. America.
Heterophrentis simplex (Hall): Givetian, New York, USA, × 2.

Suborder Streptelasmatina

Predominantly solitary with peripheral stereozone and no dissepiments. Septa laminar, of coarse contiguous trabeculae. Major septa usually with vermiform lobes at axial edges which may form a distinct axial structure; minor septa usually short. Fossula inconspicuous. Tabulae complete, less commonly incomplete, domed. M. Ordovician—M. Devonian.

FAMILY STREPTELASMATIDAE

Subfamily Streptelasmatinae

Pl. 3.3.21. *Streptelasma* Hall, 1847
Solitary, trochoid, ceratoid to cylindrical. Peripheral stereozone. Major septa long in early stages with lobate axial edges forming loose axial structure; withdrawn from axis and thinner in later

stages. Minor septa short or missing. No dissepiments. Tabulae mainly complete, domed, with wide axial depression.
M. Ordovician–L. Silurian, shallow-water calcareous shales and limestones. Europe–Asia–N. America–S. America.
Streptelasma craigense M'Coy: Caradoc, Girvan, Scotland, × 2.

Pl. 3.3.22. *Grewingkia* Dybowski, 1873
Solitary, trochoid, ceratoid to cylindrical. Peripheral stereozone. Major septa long, initially rather dilated and forming loose axial structure; in later stages thin with wide, pronounced, spongy axial structure which may or may not have a strong median plate. Minor septa variably developed. No dissepiments. Tabulae mainly complete, domed.
U. Ordovician, shallow-water calcareous shales and limestones. Europe–?Asia–N. America.
Grewingkia contexta Neuman: U. Ordovician, Dalarna, Sweden, × 2.

Subfamily Dinophyllinae
Pl. 3.3.23. *Dinophyllum* Lindström, 1882
Solitary, curved trochoid, ceratoid to cylindrical corals. Major septa long, thin, reaching axis where they form an axial structure and calicular boss with or without a pronounced vortex. Minor septa very short. No dissepiments. Tabulae mostly complete, steeply conical.
L.–?M. Silurian, shallow-water calcareous shales and limestones. Europe–Asia–Australia–N. America (Greenland).
Dinophyllum involutum Lindström: Wenlock, Gotland, Sweden, × 1¼.

Subfamily Dalmanophyllinae
Pl. 3.3.24. *Dalmanophyllum* Lang & Smith, 1939
Solitary, ceratoid. Narrow peripheral stereozone. Major septa thick, long, with axial lobes joining prominent counter-cardinal columella. Short cardinal septum in fossula. Minor septa very short. No dissepiments. Tabulae steeply conical.
L.–M. Silurian, shallow-water calcareous shales and limestones. Europe–N. America.
Dalmanophyllum dalmani (Edwards & Haime): Wenlock, Gotland, Sweden, × 2.

FAMILY KODONOPHYLLIDAE
Pl. 3.3.25. *Kodonophyllum* Wedekind, 1927
Solitary or weakly fasciculate. Marginarium a distinctive, wide peripheral stereozone. Major septa thin, almost reaching axis; minor septa confined to stereozone. No dissepiments. Tabulae incomplete, broadly arched. Increase peripheral, parricidal.
?U. Ordovician–Silurian–?L. Devonian, shallow-water limestones and calcareous shales. Europe–Asia–N. America.
Kodonophyllum truncatum (Linné): Wenlock, Much Wenlock, England, × 1½.

Suborder Calostylina

Solitary or colonial. Septa of two orders, perforate, sometimes with lateral connecting bars. Horizontal plates very thin. M. Ordovician–U. Silurian or L. Devonian.

FAMILY CALOSTYLIDAE
Pl. 3.3.26. *Calostylis* Lindström, 1868
Solitary; distal region without epitheca. Major and minor septa slightly perforate and connected by lateral bars. Axial ends of major septa form spongy axial structure. Tabulae very thin, domed, complete and widely separated.
M. Ordovician–U. Silurian or L. Devonian, shallow-water calcareous shales and limestones. Europe–Asia–Australia–N. America.
Calostylis cribraria Lindström: Wenlock, Gotland, Sweden, × 2.

FAMILY LAMBELASMATIDAE
Subfamily Lambelasmatinae
Pl. 3.3.27. *Lambeophyllum* Okulitch, 1938
Solitary, conical, small, corallite mainly occupied by deep calice. Major septa reach axis in floor of calice, but short and denticulate in mature stages. Minor septa short spines. Long, narrow, cardinal fossula. Tabulae not known.
M. Ordovician, shallow-water calcareous shales and limestones. N. America.
Lambeophyllum profundum (Conrad): M. Ordovician, Kentucky, USA, × 2.

Suborder Metriophyllina

Small, solitary corals, with narrow peripheral stereozone usually lacking dissepiments. Septa, laminar, commonly with fine trabeculae. Minor septa may be contratingent. May be a columella or aulos. Tabulae commonly complete, tent-shaped. M. Ordovician–U. Permian.

FAMILY CYATHAXONIIDAE
Pl. 3.3.28. *Cyathaxonia* Michelin, 1847
Ceratoid-cylindrical with prominent columella, developed independently of the septa but in contact with them, forming calicular boss. Long and contratingent minor septa. Tabulae tent-shaped; no dissepiments.
U. Devonian–U. Permian, shallow to deeper water calcareous shales. Europe–Asia–Australia–N. America–N. Africa.
Cyathaxonia cornu Michelin: Viséan, Derbyshire, England, × 3½.

FAMILY METRIOPHYLLIDAE
Pl. 3.3.29. *Metriophyllum* Edwards & Haime, 1850
Turbinate to ceratoid, erect or slightly curved. Major septa with horizontal flanges with upturned lateral edges alternating on adjacent septa. Major septa meet in axis. Minor septa not contratingent. No dissepiments. Tabulae thin, sloping downwards and away from the axis.
M. Silurian–U. Devonian, ?L. Carboniferous, L. Permian, shallow to deeper water calcareous shales. Europe–Asia–Australia–N. America.
Metriophyllum bouchardi Edwards & Haime: Frasnian, Ferques, France, × 3.

FAMILY LACCOPHYLLIDAE
Subfamily Laccophyllinae
Pl. 3.3.30. *Syringaxon* Lindström, 1882
Ceratoid. Axial ends of major septa slightly withdrawn from axis and thickened to contiguity forming an aulos. Minor septa contratingent. Tabulae flat in aulos, declined adaxially between major septa but abaxially between major and contratingent minor septa.
Silurian–Devonian, shallow- to deeper-water calcareous shales and dark limestones. Europe–Asia–Australia–N. and S. America.
Syringaxon siluriensis (M'Coy): Silurian, Dudley, England, × 3½.

Subfamily Amplexocariniinae
Pl. 3.3.31. *Amplexocarinia* Soshkina, 1928
Cylindrical. Major septa withdrawn from axis to abut relatively wide aulos. Minor septa very short. Tabulae flat-topped domes, stacked vertically to form aulos. Sporadic dissepiments in some.
M. Devonian–U. Permian, shallow-water calcareous shales and

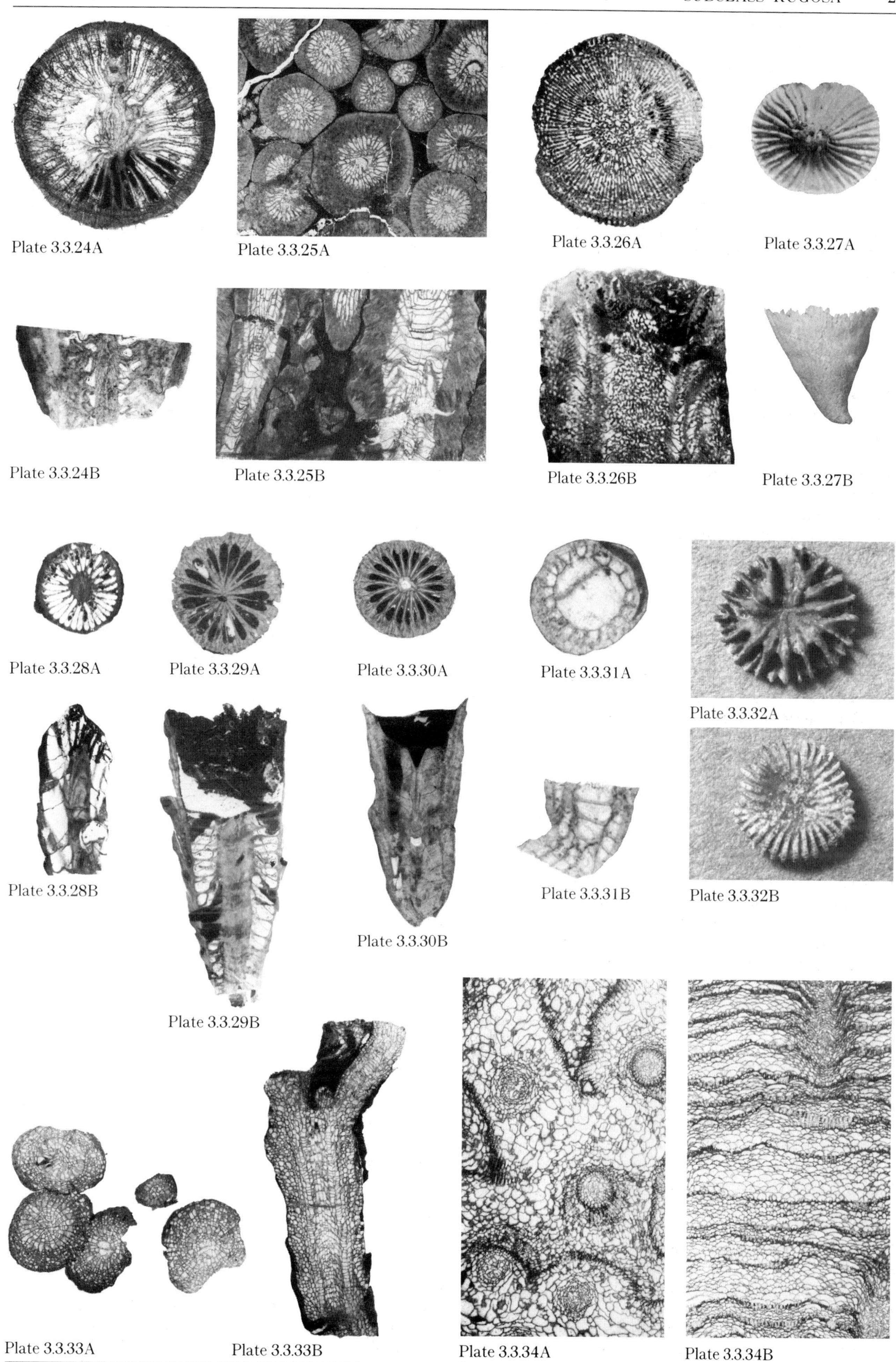
Plate 3.3.24A
Plate 3.3.25A
Plate 3.3.26A
Plate 3.3.27A
Plate 3.3.24B
Plate 3.3.25B
Plate 3.3.26B
Plate 3.3.27B
Plate 3.3.28A
Plate 3.3.29A
Plate 3.3.30A
Plate 3.3.31A
Plate 3.3.32A
Plate 3.3.28B
Plate 3.3.31B
Plate 3.3.32B
Plate 3.3.30B
Plate 3.3.29B
Plate 3.3.33A
Plate 3.3.33B
Plate 3.3.34A
Plate 3.3.34B

dark limestones. Europe–Asia–N. America.
Amplexocarinia tortuosa (Philips): Givetian, S. Devon, England, × 4.

FAMILY COMBOPHYLLIDAE

Pl. 3.3.32. *Combophyllum* Edwards & Haime, 1850
Discoid and lacking an epitheca. Septal trabeculae coarse. Major and minor septa denticulate and carinate. Prominent, parallel-sided cardinal fossula. No dissepiments or tabulae.
L. Devonian, shallow-water calcareous shales. Europe–N. Africa.
Combophyllum osismorum Edwards & Haime: M. Devonian, Brest, France, × 4.

Suborder Arachnophyllina

Solitary and colonial corals with predominantly long septa which may be carinate or variously modified in the dissepimentarium. Numerous small globose dissepiments, some with lonsdaleoid dissepiments. Tabulae usually incomplete, somewhat arched, often with an axial depression. L. Silurian–M. Devonian.

FAMILY ENTELOPHYLLIDAE

Pl. 3.3.33. *Entelophyllum* Wedekind, 1927
Solitary or fasciculate. Septa long, smooth or carinate. Major septa slightly withdrawn from axis. Fossula indistinct. Dissepiments small, globose, numerous. Tabularium with axial plateau and periaxial trough formed of small tabellae. Increase in fasciculate forms peripheral parricidal (tabularial).
Silurian, shallow-water calcareous shales and limestones, sometimes biohermal. Europe–Asia–Australia–N. America.
Entelophyllum articulatum (Wahlenberg): Ludlow, Gotland, Sweden, × 1¾.

FAMILY ARACHNOPHYLLIDAE

Pl. 3.3.34. *Arachnophyllum* Dana, 1846
Astraeoid or aphroid. Tabularium narrow with incomplete steeply domed tabulae. Very wide dissepimentarium of numerous small dissepiments. Septa develop as crests on dissepiments, thickened and contiguous in zones and may extend into tabularium as more complete laminae.
Silurian, shallow-water limestones, often biohermal. Europe–N. America.
Arachnophyllum diffluense (Edwards & Haime): Wenlock, Much Wenlock, England, × 2.

Suborder Ketophyllina

Solitary and colonial corals. Dissepimentarium wide, lonsdaleoid with septal crests commonly thickened. Tabularium flat or mesa-shaped, composed of complete or incomplete tabulae. U. Ordovician–U. Devonian, ?Carboniferous.

FAMILY KETOPHYLLIDAE

Pl. 3.3.35. *Dokophyllum* Wedekind, 1927
Solitary, often large. Septa long, becoming discontinuous at higher levels as ridges, thickened on lonsdaleoid dissepiments, thin on tabulae. Fossula often marked. Dissepiments very variable in size. Tabulae flat, mainly complete, with edges up- or downturned.
M. Silurian–U. Silurian, shallow-water calcareous shales and limestones. Europe–Asia–N. America.
Dokophyllum turbinatum (Linné): Wenlock, Dudley, England, × 1.

FAMILY KYPHOPHYLLIDAE

Pl. 3.3.36. *Donacophyllum* Dybowski, 1873
Solitary or phaceloid. Septa thin, long, major nearly reaching axis, discontinuous peripherally in dissepimentarium. Fossula indistinct. Dissepimentarium with longer lonsdaleoid dissepiments and smaller interseptal dissepiments. Tabularium domed with axial depression, composed of large tabellae.
U. Ordovician–U. Silurian, shallow-water calcareous shales and limestones. Europe–Asia–Australia.
Donacophyllum lindstroemi (Wedekind): Wenlock, Gotland, Sweden, × 1¼.

FAMILY ENDOPHYLLIDAE

Pl. 3.3.37. *Endophyllum* Edwards & Haime, 1851
Subcerioid, cerioid or thamnasterioid. Corallites large with peripheral septal stereozone, lonsdaleoid dissepiments and inner normal dissepiments. Septa long, major almost reach axis, often convolute. Tabulae closely spaced flat-topped domes. Increase peripheral, parricidal.
?L. Devonian, M. Devonian–U. Devonian, shallow-water limestones, sometimes biohermal. Europe–Asia–Australia.
Endophyllum abditum Edwards & Haime: Givetian, N. Devon, England; (A) × 1¾; (B) × 1.

Pl. 3.3.38. *Tabulophyllum* Fenton & Fenton, 1924
Solitary. Major septa long but withdrawn from axis and discontinuous in lonsdaleoid dissepimentarium of variable width. Fossula not apparent. Dissepiments large. Tabulae wide, close-spaced flat-topped domes and largely complete.
?L. Devonian, M. Devonian–U. Devonian, shallow-water calcareous shales and limestones. Europe–Asia–Australia–N. America.
Tabulophyllum sp.: Frasnian, S. Devon, England, × 2.

Suborder Ptenophyllina

Solitary or compound with wide dissepimentarium, usually of small globose dissepiments but with lonsdaleoid dissepiments in some. Major and minor septa usually well developed. Tabularium characteristically bowl-shaped, commonly with an axial notch. Tabulae complete or incomplete. L. Silurian–U. Devonian.

FAMILY SPONGOPHYLLIDAE

Pl. 3.3.39. *Spongophyllum* Edwards & Haime, 1851
Cerioid with slightly thickened corallite walls. Major septa reach axis, narrowly tapering. Minor septa short, discontinuous. Dissepimentarium a single row of large steeply inclined dissepiments. Tabulae complete, flat or sagging, wide spaced.
?M. Silurian, U. Silurian–M. Devonian, shallow-water limestones. Europe–Asia–Australia–N. America.
Spongophyllum sedgwicki Edwards & Haime: Eifelian, S. Devon, England, × 3.

FAMILY PTENOPHYLLIDAE

Subfamily Ptenophyllinae

Pl. 3.3.40. *Acanthophyllum* Dybowski, 1873
Solitary with long fusiform septa. Major septa have variably thickened axial ends which are usually twisted in a weak vortex. Minor septa long. Septa may degenerate peripherally to isolated trabeculae. Dissepimentarium wide with numerous small globose dissepiments. Tabulae small, complete, forming concave tabularial floors with a median notch.
?L. Devonian, M. Devonian, shallow-water calcareous shales and limestones. Europe–N. Africa–Asia–Australia.
Acanthophyllum heterophyllum Edwards & Haime: M. Devonian, Eifel district, W. Germany, × 1¼.

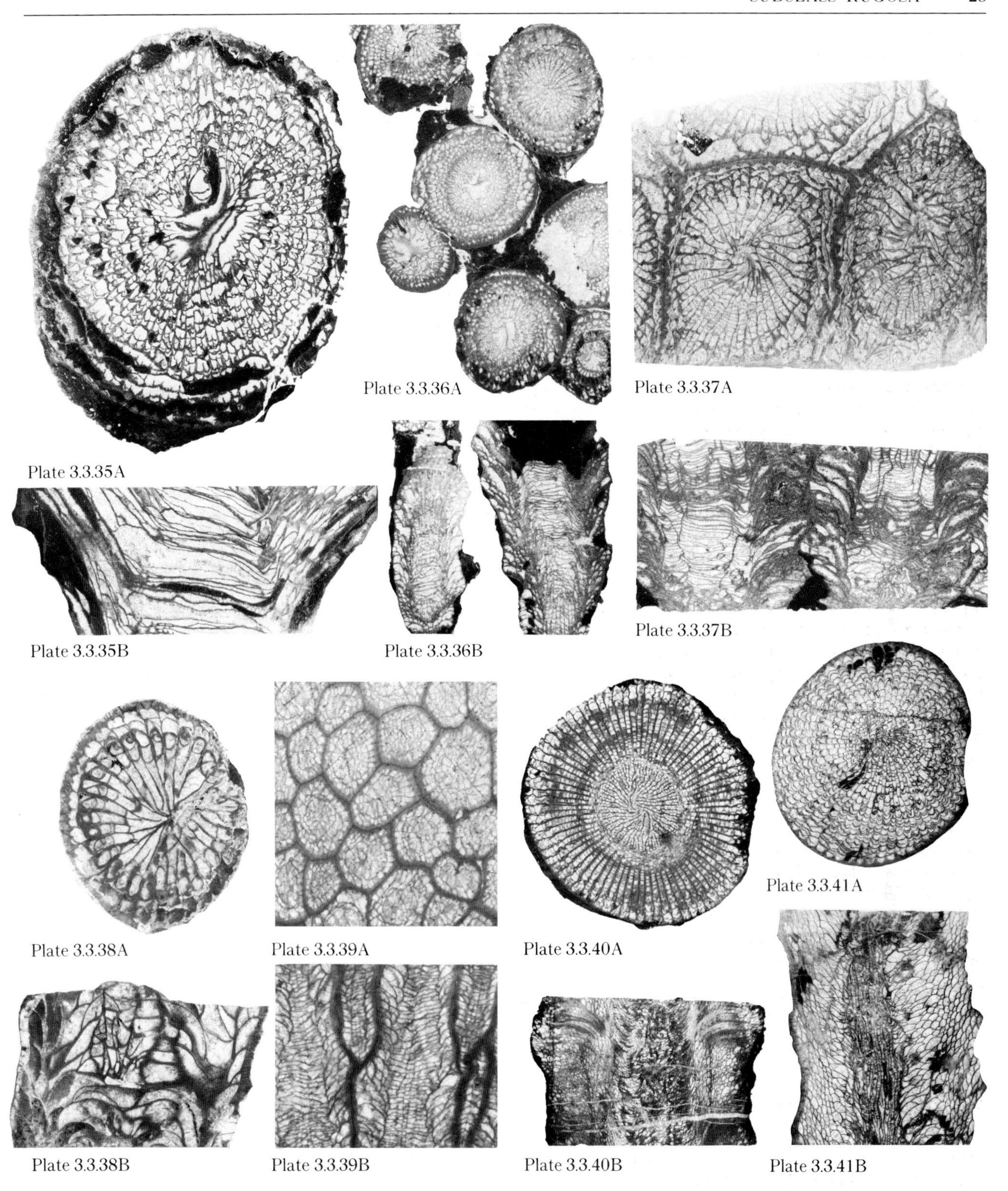

Pl. 3.3.41. *Grypophyllum* Wedekind, 1922

Solitary, usually subcylindrical with numerous thin septa. Major reach close to axis, but without thickening and with little twisting. Minor septa long, sometimes discontinuous peripherally. Wide dissepimentarium with numerous small dissepiments, rarely lonsdaleoid. Tabularium narrow, flat with central notch; tabulae mainly incomplete.

M. Devonian–basal U. Devonian, shallow-water calcareous shales and limestones. Europe–Asia–N. America.

Grypophyllum convolutum (Wedekind): Givetian, S. Devon, England, × 1¼.

Pl. 3.3.42. *Xystriphyllum* Hill, 1939

Cerioid with long major septa, sometimes convolute in tabularium. Minor septa thin, locally absent. Dissepimentarium wide, composed of small globose dissepiments which may be sparsely lonsdaleoid. Tabularium narrow, slightly concave, composed of thin, close-spaced incomplete tabulae. Increase peripheral, non-parricidal (marginarial).

U. Silurian–M. Devonian; shallow-water limestones. Europe–Asia–Australia–N. America.

Xystriphyllum dunstani (Etheridge): M. Devonian, Queensland, Australia, × 1¼.

Subfamily Actinocystinae

Pl. 3.3.43. *Spongophylloides* Meyer, 1881
Solitary, subturbinate or trochoid. Major septa nearly reach axis but largely confined to tabularium. Septa zigzag, flanged or crenulate parallel to their distal edge. Wide dissepimentarium of small, globose lonsdaleoid dissepiments. Tabularium shallowly conical with small elongate tabellae inclined towards median pit.
M. Silurian, shallow-water calcareous shales and limestones. Europe–Australia–N. America.
Spongophylloides grayi (Edwards & Haime): Wenlock, Dudley, England, × 1¼.

FAMILY STRINGOPHYLLIDAE

Pl. 3.3.44. *Stringophyllum* Wedekind, 1922
Solitary, with septa tapering axially composed of coarse, discrete or contiguous monacanthine trabeculae. Major septa long, arranged bilaterally about counter-cardinal plane in axis. Dissepiments of variable size with few or many lonsdaleoid dissepiments. Tabularium dished with axial notch, composed of complete and incomplete tabulae.
L.–M. Devonian, shallow-water calcareous shales and limestones. Europe–N. Africa–Asia–Australia.
Stringophyllum buechelense (Schlüter): Givetian, Eifel district, W. Germany, × 1¾.

Suborder Lycophyllina

Solitary, rarely fasciculate with numerous long septa which may be thickened in the tabularium. Fossula usually clear. Dissepiments small, globose, numerous. Tabularium flat to dished, composed usually of close-spaced, incomplete tabulae. Silurian–M. Devonian.

FAMILY LYKOPHYLLIDAE

Pl. 3.3.45. *Phaulactis* Ryder, 1926
Solitary, ceratoid, with long septa thickened to contiguity in early stages, but very thin except possibly for local thickening around cardinal fossula in adult stages. Minor septa long. Septa may have distinct bilateral distribution. Dissepiments small, numerous, globose, steeply sloping. Tabularium surface flat to slightly convex or concave, composed of tabellae.
L.–U. Silurian, shallow-water calcareous shales and limestones. Europe–Asia–Australia–N. America.
Phaulactis tabulatum (Wedekind): Wenlock, Gotland, Sweden, × 1¾.

Suborder Columnariina

Solitary or colonial, usually with well-developed septa. Dissepiments small, globose, sometimes including specially modified forms such as horseshoe and flat dissepiments. Tabulae usually incomplete, tabularium of variable form. M. Silurian–U. Devonian.

FAMILY ACERVULARIIDAE

Pl. 3.3.46. *Acervularia* Schweigger, 1819
Cerioid or phacelocerioid with quadripartite parricidal increase. Major and minor septa long, thickened within dissepimentarium to form sharply defined inner wall. Dissepiments in 3 zones, globular peripherally, flat plates just outside septal wall, globose and steeply dipping within wall, merging with tabellae. Tabularial surface arched.
M.–U. Silurian, shallow-water calcareous shales, limestones sometimes biohermal. Europe–N. America.
Acervularia ananas (Linné): Wenlock, Much Wenlock, England, × 2½.

FAMILY DISPHYLLIDAE

Subfamily Disphyllinae

Pl. 3.3.47. *Disphyllum* de Fromentel, 1861
Phaceloid to subcerioid with long septa which may be dilated and are sometimes weakly carinate. Trabeculae monacanths, in half-fans. Dissepiments globose, in several rows, little modified. Tabulae flat-topped domes with peripheral, inclined globose plates.
L.–U. Devonian, shallow-water calcareous shales, limestones sometimes reefal. Europe–N. Africa–Asia–Australia–N. America.
Disphyllum caespitosum (Goldfuss): Frasnian, S. Devon, England, × 1¼.

Subfamily Hexagonariinae

Pl. 3.3.48. *Hexagonaria* Gürich, 1896
Cerioid with fusiform septa bearing close-spaced yard-arm carinae. Monacanthine trabeculae arranged in broad fan. Dissepiments small, globose, horizontal or abaxially sloping at the periphery, steeply sloping adaxially towards tabularium. Tabulae incomplete, horizontal or slightly concave.
M.–U. Devonian, shallow-water calcareous shales, limestones sometimes reefal. Europe–Asia–Australia–N. America.
Hexagonaria hexagona (Goldfuss): Frasnian, Ferques, France, × 1½.

FAMILY PHILLIPSASTRAEIDAE

Pl. 3.3.49. *Phillipsastrea* d'Orbigny, 1849
Astraeoid, thamnasterioid or aphroid with fusiform septa. Trabeculae rhipidacanthine, arranged in fan diverging from pipe of horseshoe dissepiments surrounding tabularium. Outer dissepiments globose. Tabulae complete and incomplete with axial flat-topped domes.
L.–U. Devonian, shallow-water calcareous shales, limestones sometimes reefal. Europe–N. Africa–Asia–Australia–N. America.
Phillipsastrea hennahi (Lonsdale): Givetian/Frasnian, Torquay, England, × 2.

Pl. 3.3.50. *Frechastraea* Scrutton, 1968
Astraeoid to thamnasterioid with septa uniformly thick in dissepimentarium, thickened at junction with tabularium and majors usually extending uniformly attenuate into tabularium. Trabeculae in tight fans diverging from imperfect pipe of horseshoe dissepiments; outer dissepiments vesicular. Tabulae complete or incomplete, flat to slightly dished or arched.
U. Devonian, shallow-water calcareous shales, limestones often biohermal. Europe–Asia–N. America.
Frechastraea goldfussi (de Verneuil & Haime): Frasnian, S. Devon, England, × 3½.

Pl. 3.3.51. *Thamnophyllum* Penecke, 1894
Dendroid or phaceloid, septa fusiform, of variable length in tabularium. Trabeculae in fan, diverging from pipe of horseshoe dissepiments. Dissepimentarium biserial with row of flat dissepiments outside horseshoes. Tabulae complete or incomplete, flat to gently arched, generally with more steeply inclined peripheral plates.
L.–U. Devonian, shallow-water calcareous shales and limestones. Europe–N. Africa–Asia–Australia.
Thamnophyllum germanicum Scrutton: Eifelian, S. Devon, England, × 3.

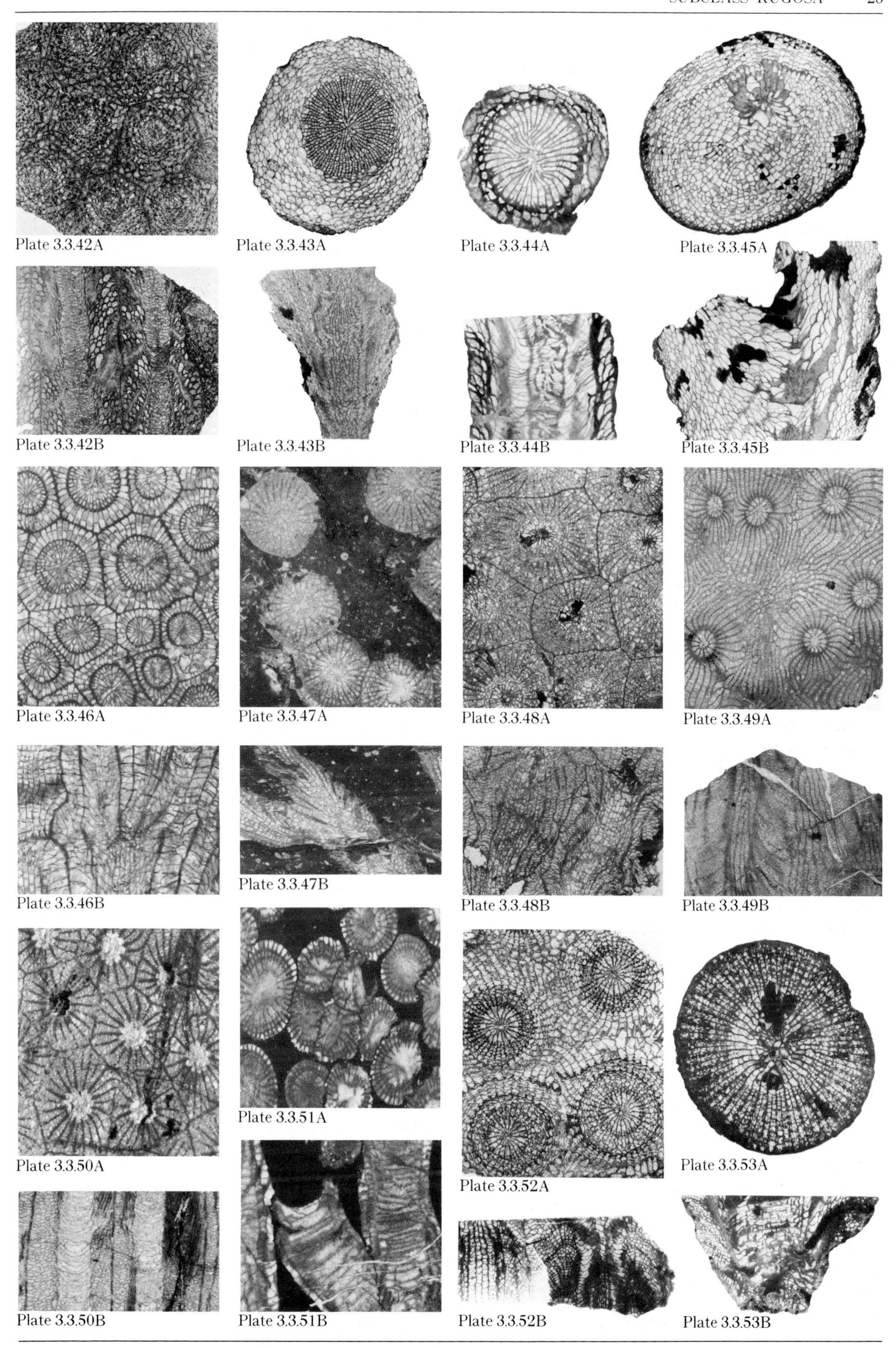
Plate 3.3.42A
Plate 3.3.43A
Plate 3.3.44A
Plate 3.3.45A
Plate 3.3.42B
Plate 3.3.43B
Plate 3.3.44B
Plate 3.3.45B
Plate 3.3.46A
Plate 3.3.47A
Plate 3.3.48A
Plate 3.3.49A
Plate 3.3.46B
Plate 3.3.47B
Plate 3.3.48B
Plate 3.3.49B
Plate 3.3.50A
Plate 3.3.51A
Plate 3.3.52A
Plate 3.3.53A
Plate 3.3.50B
Plate 3.3.51B
Plate 3.3.52B
Plate 3.3.53B

Suborder Cyathophyllina

Solitary or colonial with long alternate septa, usually carinate or otherwise modified in dissepimentarium. Dissepiments small, globose. Tabulae complete or incomplete, variable in arrangement. L. Silurian–L. Carboniferous.

FAMILY ERIDOPHYLLIDAE

Subfamily Cylindrophyllinae

Pl. 3.3.52. *Asterobillingsa* Oliver, 1974
Astraeoid to thamnasterioid with long, carinate, uniformly attenuate septa. Major septa nearly reach axis; minor septa long. Dissepiments small, globose, flat lying peripherally and gently arched adjacent to the tabularium. Tabulae mainly incomplete, gently domed.
L.–M. Devonian, shallow-water calcareous shales and limestones sometimes biohermal. N. America.
Asterobillingsa magdisa steorra Oliver: Eifelian, Ontario, Canada, × 1¾.

FAMILY ZAPHRENTIDAE

Pl. 3.3.53. *Heliophyllum* Hall in Dana, 1846
Solitary or weakly colonial with long septa, attenuate except for thickening around cardinal fossula in some. Well-developed yard-arm carinae on septa in dissepimentarium. Dissepiments numerous globose to subglobose. Tabulae mainly incomplete, tabularial surface weakly domed to concave.
L. Devonian–M. Devonian, shallow-water calcareous shales and limestones. Europe–N. Africa–Australia–N. and S. America.
Heliophyllum halli Edwards & Haime: Givetian, New York, USA, × 1¼.

FAMILY CYATHOPHYLLIDAE

Pl. 3.3.54. *Cyathophyllum* Goldfuss, 1826
Solitary, fasciculate or massive with numerous long, thin septa which are smooth or carinate and may become spongy in appearance peripherally. Major septa may almost reach axis or be slightly withdrawn. Cardinal fossula indistinct. Dissepiments numerous, globose. Tabularium surface flat or sagging, composed of complete and incomplete tabulae.
?L. Devonian, M. Devonian, shallow-water calcareous shales and limestones. Europe–?Asia–?Australia–?N. America.
Cyathophyllum spongiosum (Schulz): Eifelian, Eifel district, W. Germany, × 1.

Suborder Stereolasmatina

Small, solitary corals lacking a dissepimentarium. Major septa long, composed of fine trabeculae, sometimes forming solid axial structure. Cardinal fossula usually, and alar fossulae sometimes, distinct. Minor septa, except those flanking the counter septum, short. Tabulae declined abaxially. L. Devonian–U. Permian.

FAMILY HAPSIPHYLLIDAE

Subfamily Hapsiphyllinae

Pl. 3.3.55. *Amplexizaphrentis* Vaughan, 1906
Solitary, trochoid to ceratoid, curved with prominent cardinal fossula on concave side. Major septa long, uniting around fossulae, but withdrawing in deep calice. Alar fossulae clear in earlier stages. Tabulae mainly complete domes flattened or depressed axially.
L. Carboniferous, shallow- to deeper-water calcareous shales and dark limestones. Europe–N. Africa–Asia–N. and S. America.
Amplexizaphrentis enniskilleni (Edwards & Haime): Viséan, Dublin, Ireland, × 3.

Pl. 3.3.56. *Zaphrentites* Hudson, 1941
Conical, slightly curved with cardinal fossula on concave side. Major septa long and unite around fossula. Cardinal septum long but shortening before other septa. Alar fossulae not so strongly marked. Septa withdraw from axis and become radially arranged in calice. Tabulae incomplete, tabularium surface conical.
M. Devonian–U. Carboniferous, shallow- to deeper-water calcareous shales and dark limestones. Europe–Asia–N. America.
Zaphrentites parallelus (Carruthers): (A) Tournaisian, Liddesdale, Scotland, × 3; (B), (C), *Z. carruthersi* Hudson, Namurian, Yorkshire, England, × 3.

Suborder Plerophyllina

Predominantly solitary with 1 or more protosepta longer than other septa and often rhopaloid or more rhopaloid. Minor septa commonly not extending beyond wall. Tabulae commonly complete, flat to arched to steeply declined abaxially. Some with dissepimentarium and longer minor septa. U. Silurian–U. Permian.

FAMILY POLYCOELIIDAE

Subfamily Polycoeliinae

Pl. 3.3.57. *Calophyllum* Dana, 1846
Small solitary with cardinal, counter and 2 alar septa longer and thicker than other major septa. All major septa equally short in upper part of calice. No dissepiments. Tabulae complete, flat axially with downturned margins.
?L. Carboniferous, Permian, shallow-water, sometimes reef, limestones. Europe–Asia.
Calophyllum donatianum (King): U. Permian, Sunderland, England, × 4.

FAMILY PLEROPHYLLIDAE

Subfamily Plerophyllinae

Pl. 3.3.58. *Plerophyllum* Hinde, 1890
Solitary, ceratoid with 5 septa, the cardinal, counter-lateral and alar septa more prominent and rhopaloid than other major septa. Septa thickened to infill lumen in early stages. Minor septa very short. No dissepiments. Tubulae gently declined from axis.
Permian, shallow-water calcareous shales and limestones. Europe–Asia–Australia.
Plerophyllum australe Hinde: Permian, Irwin River, Western Australia, × 2½.

FAMILY PENTAPHYLLIDAE

Subfamily Pentaphyllinae

Pl. 3.3.59. *Tachyelasma* Grabau, 1922
Solitary, small, with short cardinal septum, long thin counter septum, but alar and counter-lateral septa thicker and more rhopaloid than other major septa. Minor septa very short. Tabulae sparse.
Permian, shallow-water calcareous shales and limestones. Asia.
Tachyelasma timorense (Gerth): U. Permian, Basleo, Timor, × 2½.

FAMILY LOPHOPHYLLIDAE

Pl. 3.3.60. *Lophophyllidium* Grabau, 1928
Solitary with long, usually rhopaloid major septa. Cardinal septum short, in distinct fossula. Counter septum long, its axial end, with or without contiguous septal lamellae, forming a strong, dense styliform columella. No dissepiments. Tabulae complete, more or less flat axially and steeply declined peripherally.
U. Carboniferous–Permian, shallow-water calcareous shales and

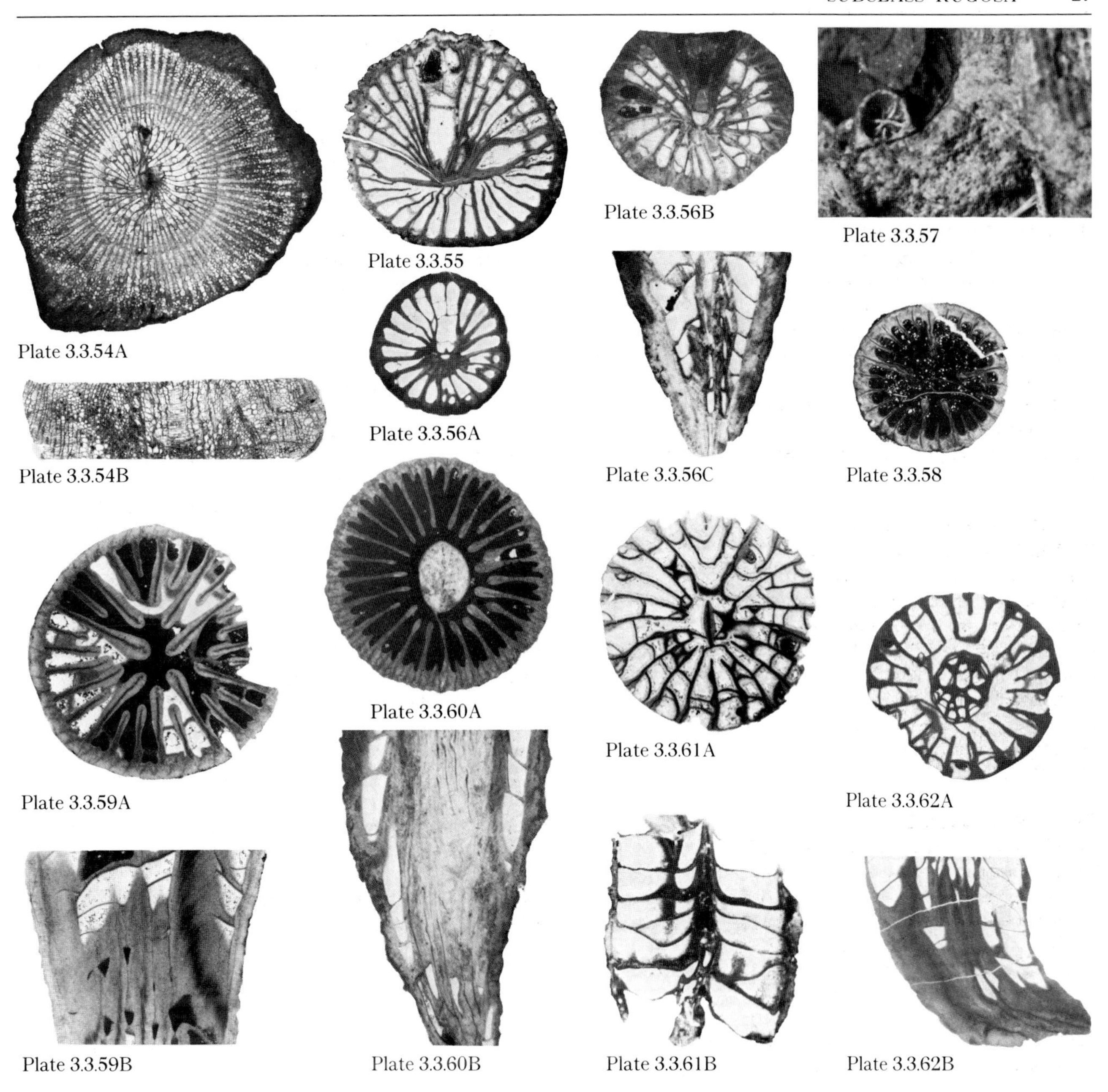

Plate 3.3.54A
Plate 3.3.54B
Plate 3.3.55
Plate 3.3.56A
Plate 3.3.56B
Plate 3.3.56C
Plate 3.3.57
Plate 3.3.58
Plate 3.3.59A
Plate 3.3.59B
Plate 3.3.60A
Plate 3.3.60B
Plate 3.3.61A
Plate 3.3.61B
Plate 3.3.62A
Plate 3.3.62B

limestones. Europe–Asia–Australia–N. and S. America.
Lophophyllidium profundum (Edwards & Haime): U. Carboniferous, Texas, USA, × 3.

FAMILY TIMORPHYLLIDAE

Pl. 3.3.61. *Timorphyllum* Gerth, 1921
Solitary, subcylindrical with short cardinal septum and subequal, rhopaloid major septa. Prominent lath-like columella buttressed by upturned axial edges of flat, complete tabulae. No dissepiments.
U. Permian, shallow-water calcareous shales and limestones. Asia–N. America.
Timorphyllum wanneri Gerth: U. Permian, Basleo, Timor, × 2.

FAMILY VERBEEKIELLIDAE

Pl. 3.3.62. *Verbeekiella* Penecke, 1908
Solitary with subequal major septa and short cardinal septum. Prominent axial structure of septal lamellae and tabellae. No dissepiments. Axial tabellae domed or conical, peripheral part of tabularium with weak to moderately globose, abaxially declined tabellae.
Permian, shallow-water calcareous shales and limestones. Asia–Australia–?N. America.
Verbeekiella australis (Beyrich): Permian, Soompak, Timor, × $2\frac{1}{2}$.

Suborder Caniniina

Predominantly solitary, frequently large corals. Dissepimentarium intermittent to more commonly wide, often lonsdaleoid. Cardinal fossula usually distinct. Septa thickened and long in early stages, amplexoid in tabularium in adult stages. Tabularium usually flat with downturned margins; tabulae usually complete. L. Carboniferous–U. Permian.

FAMILY CYATHOPSIDAE

Pl. 3.3.63. *Caninia* Michelin, 1840
Solitary, curved conical to cylindrical. Major septa long and thickened in early stages, shortening in later stages to leave wide, open axial area. Cardinal fossula with short cardinal septum. Minor septa very short, may be discontinuous. Dissepi-

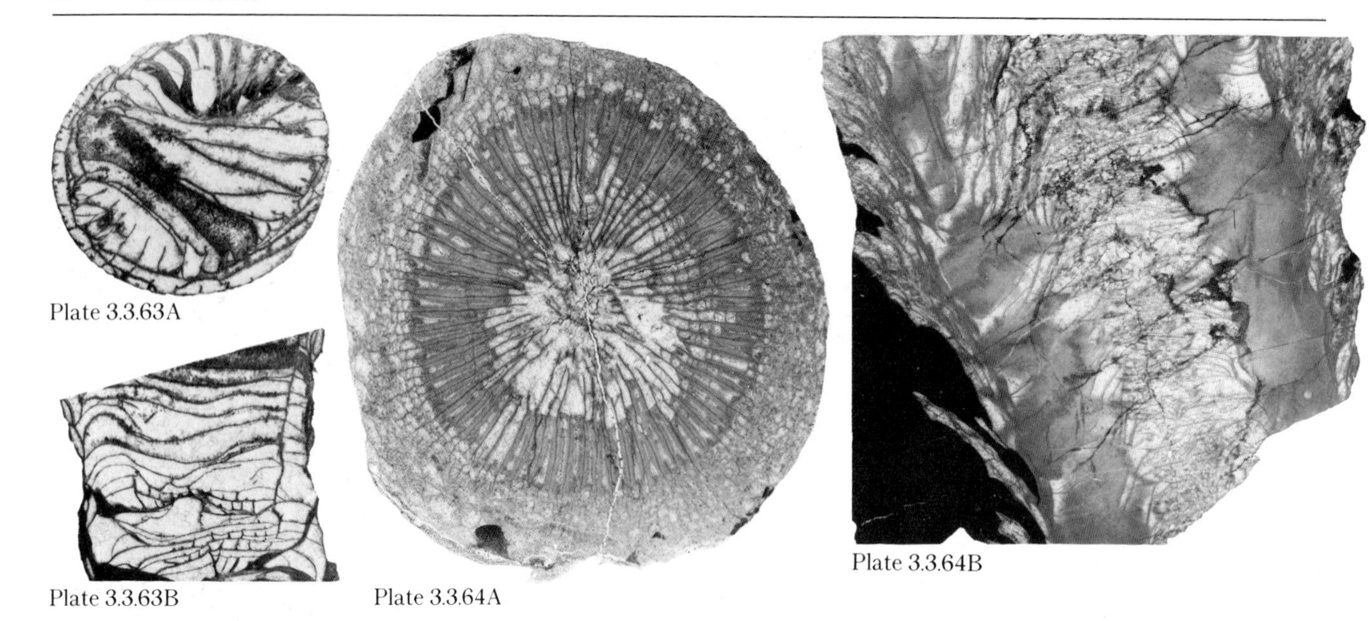
Plate 3.3.63A
Plate 3.3.63B
Plate 3.3.64A
Plate 3.3.64B

mentarium intermittently developed, narrow, may be lonsdaleoid in part. Tabulae mainly complete, flat to low, wide mesa-shaped.
L.–U. Carboniferous, shallow-water calcareous shales and limestones. Europe–North Africa–Asia–N. America.
Caninia cornucopiae Michelin: Viséan, Dublin, Ireland, × 2.

Pl. 3.3.64. *Siphonophyllia* Scouler MS in M'Coy, 1844
Large, solitary, conico-cylindrical. Septa numerous, major septa withdrawn from axis and thickened in peripheral zone of tabularium. Cardinal fossula with short cardinal septum. Minor septa short. Dissepimentarium lonsdaleoid. Dissepiments steeply inclined. Tabularium surface wide flat-topped domes; tabulae mainly complete, close spaced.
L. Carboniferous, shallow-water calcareous shales and limestones. Europe–N. Africa–Asia.
Siphonophyllia cylindrica Scouler: L. Carboniferous, Weston-super-Mare, England, × 1.

Suborder Aulophyllina

Predominantly solitary with a wide, normal dissepimentarium. Septa long, numerous, may retain thickening in tabularium, particularly in cardinal quadrants in later stages. Commonly with an axial structure, usually complex and prominent. Tabulae declined abaxially except when axial structure weak or absent when they may be flat or sagging. ?U. Devonian–L. Permian.

FAMILY AULOPHYLLIDAE
Subfamily Aulophyllinae

Pl. 3.3.65. *Aulophyllum* Edwards & Haime, 1850
Solitary with numerous septa and well-defined axial structure composed of close-packed lamellae and tabellae lacking a median plate. Major septa dilated in tabularium, particularly around narrow cardinal fossula into which the axial structure projects. Minor septa moderately long. Dissepiments small, normal. Tabularium wide, domed with axial depression in axial structure, flat to slightly sagging peripherally where the plates are much more widely spaced and largely complete.
L. Carboniferous–U. Carboniferous, shallow-water limestones and calcareous shales. Europe–N. Africa–Asia.
Aulophyllum fungites (Fleming): Namurian, Weardale, England, × 1.

Subfamily Dibunophyllinae

Pl. 3.3.66. *Dibunophyllum* Thompson & Nicholson, 1876
Solitary with axial structure typically one-third as wide as corallum, usually with a strong median plate, few radiating septal lamellae and numerous axial tabellae, moderately to steeply declined abaxially. Major septa almost reach axial structure, thickened in tabularium. Minor septa discontinuous. Dissepiments small, numerous. Periaxial tabellae small, gently declined abaxially.
L.–U. Carboniferous, shallow-water limestones and calcareous shales. Europe–N. Africa–Asia–N. America.
Dibunophyllum bipartitum (M'Coy): Namurian, Weardale, England, × $1\frac{3}{4}$.

Pl. 3.3.67. *Koninckophyllum* Thompson & Nicholson, 1876
Solitary or weakly dendroid. Septa numerous, long but amplexoid in tabularium where they may be thickened. Minor septa long and discontinuous. Axial structure reduced to lath-like columella or absent in later stages. Dissepimentarium wide, of numerous small dissepiments. Tabularium broad flat-topped domes or conical with columella; tabellae elongate, close-spaced.
L.–U. Carboniferous, shallow-water limestones and calcareous shales. Europe–N. Africa–Asia–N. America.
Koninckophyllum magnificum Thompson & Nicholson: Viséan, Pen-y-Ghent, England, × $1\frac{1}{4}$.

FAMILY PALAEOSMILIDAE

Pl. 3.3.68. *Palaeosmilia* Edwards & Haime, 1848
Solitary, ?fasciculate, with very numerous, long, radially arranged septa and long, narrow cardinal fossula. Dissepimentarium wide with small, numerous dissepiments. Tabularium flat-topped domes with upturned margins; tabulae incomplete. (*Note*: Cerioid, astraeoid or aphroid '*Palaeosmilia*' referred to *Palastraea* M'Coy, 1851.)
?U. Devonian, L.–U. Carboniferous, shallow-water limestones and calcareous shales. Europe–N. Africa–Asia.
Palaeosmilia murchisoni Edwards & Haime: Viséan, Arnside, England, × 1.

Suborder Lithostrotionina

Colonial, commonly with an axial lath-like columella continuous initially with cardinal and counter septa, but in adult stages

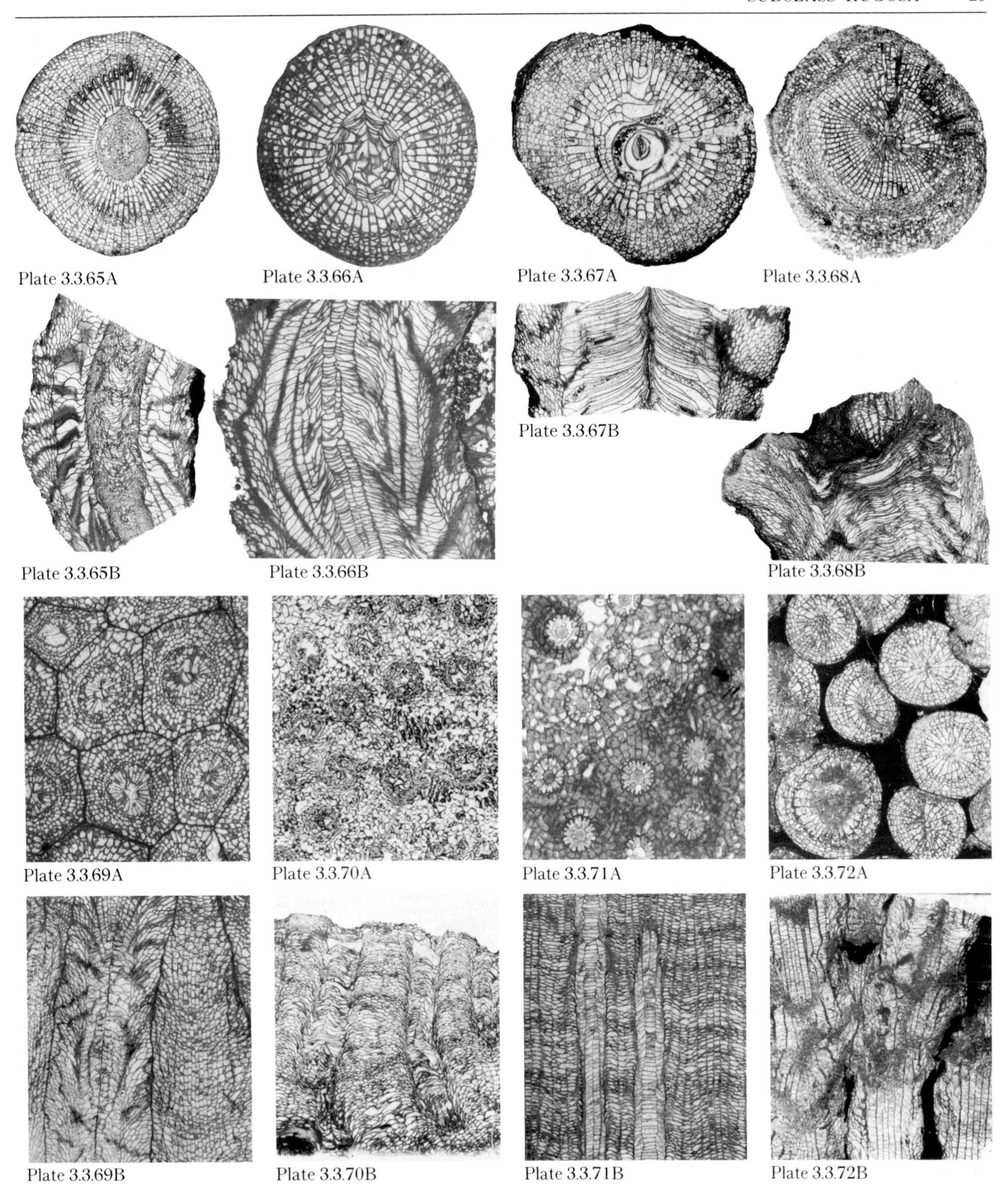

Plate 3.3.65A Plate 3.3.66A Plate 3.3.67A Plate 3.3.68A

Plate 3.3.67B

Plate 3.3.65B Plate 3.3.66B Plate 3.3.68B

Plate 3.3.69A Plate 3.3.70A Plate 3.3.71A Plate 3.3.72A

Plate 3.3.69B Plate 3.3.70B Plate 3.3.71B Plate 3.3.72B

usually with counter septum only. Some with an aulos or no axial structure. Dissepimentarium typically normal with small globose dissepiments, but occasionally lonsdaleoid. Tabular floors flat-topped domes or conical (with columella). Cardinal fossula not seen. L. Carboniferous–U. Permian.

FAMILY LITHOSTROTIONIDAE

Subfamily Lithostrotioninae

Pl. 3.3.69. *Lithostrotion* Fleming, 1828

Cerioid, with long, thin major septa and axial, slender, lath-like columella continuous with counter or both cardinal and counter septa. Minor septa short to long. Dissepiments small, normal; lonsdaleoid dissepiments rare to absent. Tabular floors conical, tabulae complete or incomplete. (Note: Fasciculate '*Lithostrotion*' referred to *Siphonodendron* M'Coy, 1849.)

L.–U. Carboniferous, shallow-water limestones or calcareous shales. Europe–N. Africa–Asia–Australia–N. America.

Lithostrotion araneum (M'Coy): Viséan, Settle, England, × $1\frac{3}{4}$.

Pl. 3.3.70. *Orionastraea* Smith, 1917

Astraeoid, thamnasterioid or aphroid, normally with long major and minor septa which may be discontinuous peripherally. Columella sometimes present. Dissepiments small, normal except peripherally in aphroid forms. Tabulae conical, complete or

incomplete.
L. Carboniferous, shallow-water limestones. Europe–Asia–Australia.
Orionastraea phillipsi (M'Coy): Viséan, Corwen, Wales, × 2.

Subfamily Aulininae
Pl. 3.3.71. *Aulina* Smith, 1917
Cerioid, astraeoid, thamnasterioid or aphroid with axial aulos formed by ends of major septa. Major and minor septa may be weakly carinate or zigzag. Dissepiments small, normal, except peripherally in aphroid forms. Tabularium with flat axial tabellae in aulos and peripheral abaxially declined tabellae.
L.–U. Carboniferous, shallow-water limestones. Europe–Asia–N. America.
Aulina rotiformis Smith: Namurian, Northumberland, England, × 3½.

FAMILY DURHAMINIDAE
Pl. 3.3.72. *Durhamina* Wilson & Langenheim, 1962
Fasciculate with axial structure a median plate which may be discontinuous in later stages and replaced by loose, irregular septal lamellae and tabellae. Major septa may be thickened in tabularium. Minor septa weakly developed and rare third-order septa may appear. Dissepimentarium narrow, with herringbone to lonsdaleoid dissepiments. Tabular floors arched axially, tabulae incomplete.
U. Carboniferous–L. Permian, shallow-water limestones. Asia–N. and S. America.
Durhamina sp.: Carboniferous, Sierra de Perija, Venezuela, × 1¼.

Suborder Lonsdaleiina

Solitary or colonial, typically with lonsdaleoid dissepiments but normal dissepiments in some. Axial structure of septal lamellae and tabellae, the latter declined abaxially. Peripheral tabulae flat or sagging. Third or higher orders of septa present in some. L. Carboniferous–U. Permian.

FAMILY AXOPHYLLIDAE
Pl. 3.3.73. *Axophyllum* Edwards & Haime, 1850
Solitary with axial column of irregular curving septal lamellae, a median plate and irregular conical tabellae. Septa may thicken peripherally and a lonsdaleoid dissepimentarium may develop. Peripheral tabulae flat or sagging.
L. Carboniferous, shallow-water limestones and calcareous shales. Europe–N. Africa–Asia–Australia.
Axophyllum lonsdaleiforme (Salee): Viséan, Montagne Noire, France, × 2.

Pl. 3.3.74. *Lonsdaleia* M'Coy, 1849
Phaceloid with marginarial, non-parricidal increase. Well-defined axial column with median plate, derived from cardinal septum, together with septal lamellae and conically disposed tabellae. Dissepimentarium lonsdaleoid. Pericolumnar tabulae slightly sagging or flat, gently declined abaxially or adaxially. (*Note:* Cerioid '*Lonsdaleia*' referred to *Actinocyathus* d'Orbigny, 1849.)
L.–U. Carboniferous, shallow-water limestones and calcareous shales. Europe–Asia–N. America.
Lonsdaleia duplicata (Martin): Viséan, Minera, N. Wales, × 1½.

FAMILY WAAGENOPHYLLIDAE
Subfamily Waagenophyllinae
Pl. 3.3.75. *Waagenophyllum* Hayasaka, 1924
Fasciculate with irregularly cylindrical axial column consisting of a median plate, a few septal lamellae and strongly domed tabellae stacked one on top of another. Dissepimentarium normal with small globose dissepiments. Pericolumnar tabulae more or less flat with prominent, elongate tabellae sloping steeply adaxially from dissepimentarium wall.
L.–U. Permian, shallow-water limestones and calcareous shales. Europe–Asia–New Zealand.
Waagenophyllum indicum (Waagen & Wentzel): U. Permian, Salt Range, Pakistan, × 2½.

Pl. 3.3.76. *Ipciphyllum* Hudson, 1958
Cerioid with axial column composed of thin, irregular axial plate, septal lamellae and strongly domed axial tabellae. Major septa long, slightly thickened just within tabularium. Dissepimentarium wide with small normal dissepiments. Periaxial tabulae an inner zone of flat plates and an outer zone of elongate tabellae sloping steeply adaxially from dissepimentarium wall.
L.–U. Permian, shallow-water limestones. Asia.
Ipciphyllum ipci Hudson: Permian, Chalki, N. Iraq, × 2.

Subfamily Wentzelellinae
Pl. 3.3.77. *Wentzelella* Grabau in Huang, 1932
Cerioid with dense axial column of median plate, septal lamellae and broadly conical tabellae. Major septa long, narrowly wedge-shaped. Minor, third-order and, rarely, fourth-order septa present. Dissepimentarium normal. Pericolumnar tabellae an inner zone of flat plates and an outer zone of elongate tabellae steeply inclined adaxially from dissepimentarium wall.
U. Permian, shallow-water limestones. Asia.
Wentzelella salinaria (Waagen & Wentzel): Permian, Kundal, Pakistan, × 1½.

Pl. 3.3.78. *Polythecalis* Yabe & Hayasaka, 1916
Mixed aphroid–cerioid with axial column consisting of a median plate, septal lamellae and conical axial tabellae. Major septa few, with minor, third- and fourth-order septa. Dissepimentarium lonsdaleoid. Pericolumnar tabellae steeply inclined adaxially, usually with inner zone of flat tabellae.
L.–U. Permian, shallow-water limestones. Europe–Asia.
Polythecalis japonica Yabe & Minato: Permian, Chalki, N. Iraq, × 3.

FAMILY PSEUDOPAVONIDAE
Subfamily Pseudopavoninae
Pl. 3.3.79. *Pseudopavona* Yabe, Sugiyama & Eguchi, 1943
Thamnasterioid or partly aphroid or pseudomeandroid. Solid columella originating from cardinal septum. Major and minor septa normally thickened. Dissepimentarium wide, composed of small dissepiments and occasional lonsdaleoid dissepiments. Tabulae adaxially declined peripherally and subhorizontal adjacent to columella.
U. Carboniferous–?Lower Permian, shallow-water limestones. Asia.
Pseudopavona s.p.: U. Carboniferous, Akiyoshidai, Japan, × 4.

Subclass Heterocorallia

Elongate solitary corals with 4 protosepta. Later septa attached at their axial ends to these primary septa so that the 4 original interseptal loci remain undivided. Epitheca absent. Tabulae complete; no dissepiments. U. Devonian–U. Carboniferous.

(Note: The heterocorals are a very small group of corals which may be related to the Rugosa (Hill 1981) or may represent the independent acquisition of a skeleton by a separate group of

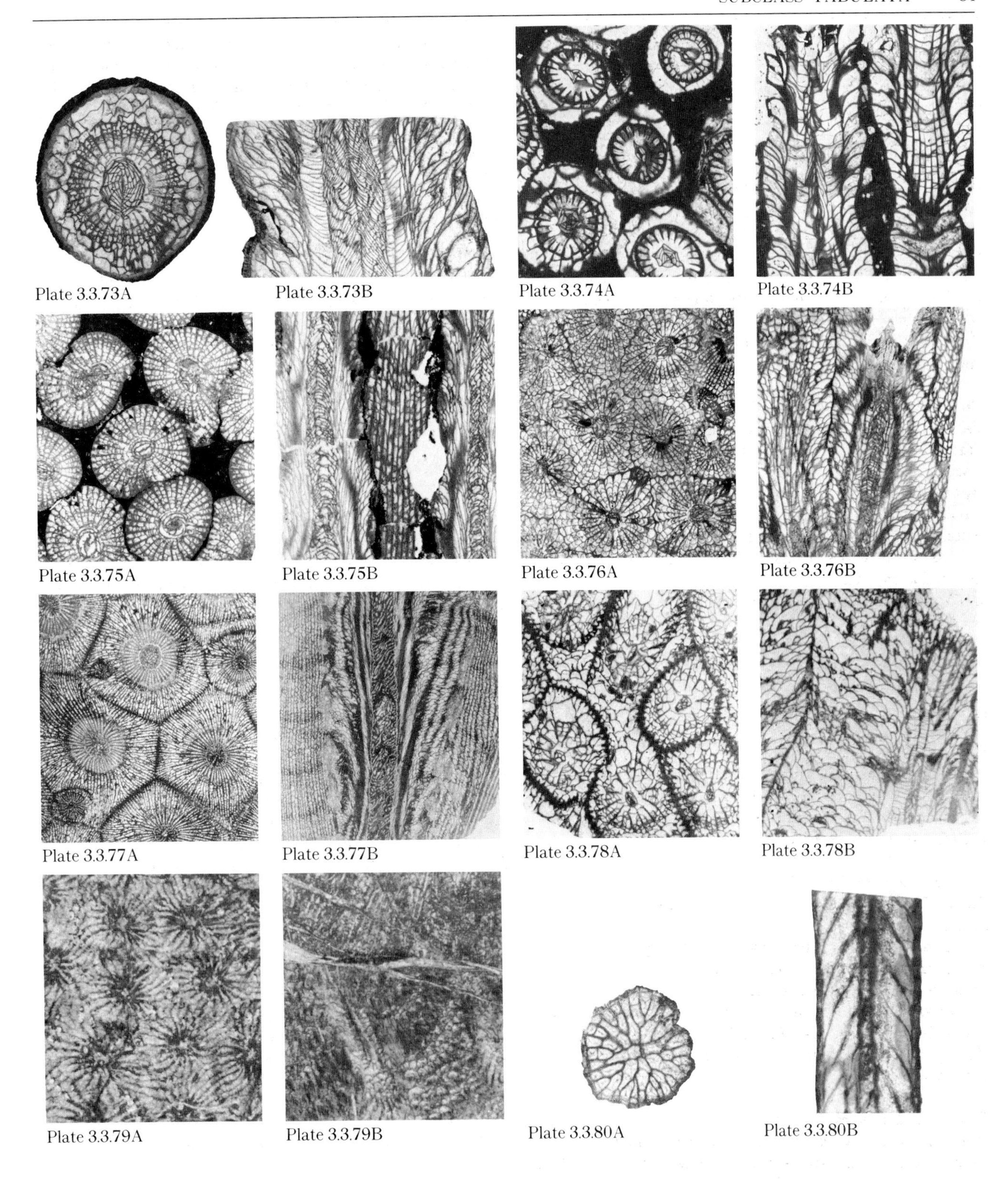

Plate 3.3.73A Plate 3.3.73B Plate 3.3.74A Plate 3.3.74B

Plate 3.3.75A Plate 3.3.75B Plate 3.3.76A Plate 3.3.76B

Plate 3.3.77A Plate 3.3.77B Plate 3.3.78A Plate 3.3.78B

Plate 3.3.79A Plate 3.3.79B Plate 3.3.80A Plate 3.3.80B

anthozoans. There is only 1 family and genera are distinguished by wall and septal characteristics.)

Order Heterocorallia

As for subclass.

FAMILY HETEROPHYLLIIDAE

Pl. 3.3.80. *Heterophyllia* M'Coy, 1849

Heterocorals with numerous septa and a narrow, trabeculate stereozone.

U. Devonian–L. Carboniferous, shallow-water limestones and calcareous shales. Europe–N. Africa–Asia.

Heterophyllia grandis M'Coy: Viséan, Northumberland, England, × 4.

Subclass Tabulata

Colonial epithecate corals with slender, elongate corallites. Septa absent or short, equal, often 12 in number and almost exclusively spinose although lamellar bases sometimes present. Walls may have pores, or fasciculate coralla connecting tubules. Tabulae commonly complete. Tabularia may be separated by coenenchyme in some. L. Ordovician–U. Permian.

Terminology and classification, except in the details mentioned below, follow the recently published revision of the *Treatise on Invertebrate Paleontology* (Hill 1981). Important morphological terms are defined in the glossary and the reader is referred to the *Treatise* for further information.

Suprageneric classification of tabulate corals is not readily amenable to representation by key. The evidence of morphological criteria is balanced by deductions of phylogenetic relationships and many structural conditions are thought to have evolved more than once. Important features used in classification are corallite form and disposition in the colony, type of increase, presence or absence of interconnections between corallites, presence or absence of coenenchyme, nature and distribution of tabulae, and the form and development of septa when present. All tabulate corals are colonial.

The type material of some tabulate corals is still very imperfectly known. Diagnoses given here reflect the generally accepted definition of such genera. The chaetetids, formerly usually classified as tabulate corals, are here regarded as sponges. The heliolitids and halysitids are treated as separate orders of tabulate corals rather than as suborders of the order Heliolitida.

Order Lichenariida

Cerioid, occasionally fasciculate, with slender corallites. Walls imperforate or with rare pores. Septa present in some. Tabulae sparse, complete. Increase lateral. L.–U. Ordovician.

FAMILY LICHENARIIDAE

Pl. 3.3.81. *Lichenaria* Winchell & Schuchert, 1895
Small, hemispherical, attached corals, predominantly cerioid but may be fasciculate in places. Slender corallites with thin, radially tufted walls, aseptate. Tabulae sparse, horizontal and complete.
L.–M. Ordovician, ?U. Ordovician, shallow-water limestones and calcareous shales. N. America.
Lichenaria major Bassler: M. Ordovician, Virginia, USA, × 4.

Pl. 3.3.82. *Foerstephyllum* Bassler, 1941
Cerioid, with dense median plane in common corallite walls. Septa variably developed, short, subequal, longitudinal ridges with spinose axial edges. Mural pores absent or very sparse. Tabulae horizontal, complete. Increase lateral.
M.–U. Ordovician, shallow-water limestones and calcareous shales. Asia–N. America.
Foerstephyllum vacuum (Foerste): U. Ordovician, Kentucky, USA, × 2½.

Order Tetradiida

Corallum variable in form. Corallites very slender, typically quadrate in form, but may be polygonal and also partly alveolitoid. Characteristically with axial, quadripartite increase. Corallite walls aseptate, aporose. Tabulae complete, horizontal, sparse. M.–U. Ordovician.

FAMILY TETRADIIDAE

Pl. 3.3.83. *Tetradium* Dana, 1846
Corallum cerioid, tollinoid or phaceloid. Corallites very slender, quadrate, usually with laminar projections from midpoints of walls which eventually meet in axis to effect quadripartite increase. Corallite walls aseptate, aporous. Tabulae complete, horizontal, sparse.
M.–U. Ordovician, shallow-water limestones (including small bioherms), and calcareous shales. Europe–Asia–Australia–N. America.
Tetradium approximatum Bassler: U. Ordovician, Kentucky, USA, × 5.

Order Sarcinulida

Cerioid (massive or ramose), phacelo-cerioid, tollinoid or astraeoid coralla with slender corallites. Tabularia interconnected by interseptal spaces when adjacent, or by canals or channels on coenenchymal platforms. Septa short, stout peripherally, conjunct or discrete monacanthine trabeculae. Tabulae almost always horizontal. M. Ordovician–Devonian.

FAMILY SYRINGOPHYLLIDAE

Subfamily Lyoporinae

Pl. 3.3.84. *Lyopora* Nicholson & Etheridge, 1878
Massive coralla with corallites surrounded by about 20 longitudinal rows of thick, slightly inclined trabeculae forming septal ridges. Those of adjacent corallites may alternate or be back to back, and zones of irregular rounded pores may form where the trabeculae thin. Tabulae distant, slightly sagging.
M.–U. Ordovician, shallow-water limestones and calcareous shales. Europe–Asia–Australia–N. America.
Lyopora favosa (M'Coy): Caradoc, Girvan, Scotland, × 3.

Subfamily Calapoeciinae

Pl. 3.3.85. *Calapoecia* Billings, 1865
Coenenchymate colony, with tabularial walls formed by greatly thickened, periodically contiguous trabeculae leaving wall pores in regular horizontal and vertical rows. Septa short, commonly spinose and 20 in number. Coenenchyme varies from wide to narrow to absent when corallites are polygonal. Tabulae mainly complete, horizontal or slightly sagging, sometimes with peripheral tabellae.
M.–U. Ordovician, shallow-water limestones and calcareous shales. Europe–Asia–Australia–N. America.
Calapoecia canadensis Billings: U. Ordovician, Anticosti Island, Canada, × 3.

Subfamily Syringophyllinae

Pl. 3.3.86. *Sarcinula* Lamarck, 1816
Corallites cylindrical, thick-walled, connected by well-spaced platforms. Septa 20 to 24 short trabeculate ribs which may be adaxially spinose, and which extend as low ridges across intercorallite platforms. Wall pores also extend as canals across platforms. Tabulae wide spaced, horizontal to sagging.
U. Ordovician, shallow-water limestones and calcareous shales. Europe–Asia–N. America.
Sarcinula organum (Linné): U. Ordovician, Herö, Norway, × 3.

FAMILY THECIIDAE

Pl. 3.3.87. *Thecia* Edwards & Haime, 1849
Encrusting or tabular, cerioid, astraeoid or thamnasterioid corallum. In basal parts and in axes of lobes on corallum surface, corallites are thin-walled with a wide, median, dense plane, and rarely septate. In much thicker distal zones, corallites with commonly 12 long and greatly thickened septa composed of monacanthine trabeculae, which close or almost close the lumen. A second order of septa may develop. Mural pores present. Tabulae thin, complete.
L.–U. Silurian, shallow-water limestones and calcareous shales. Europe–Asia–N. America.
Thecia expatiata (Lonsdale): Wenlock, Dudley, England, × 4½.

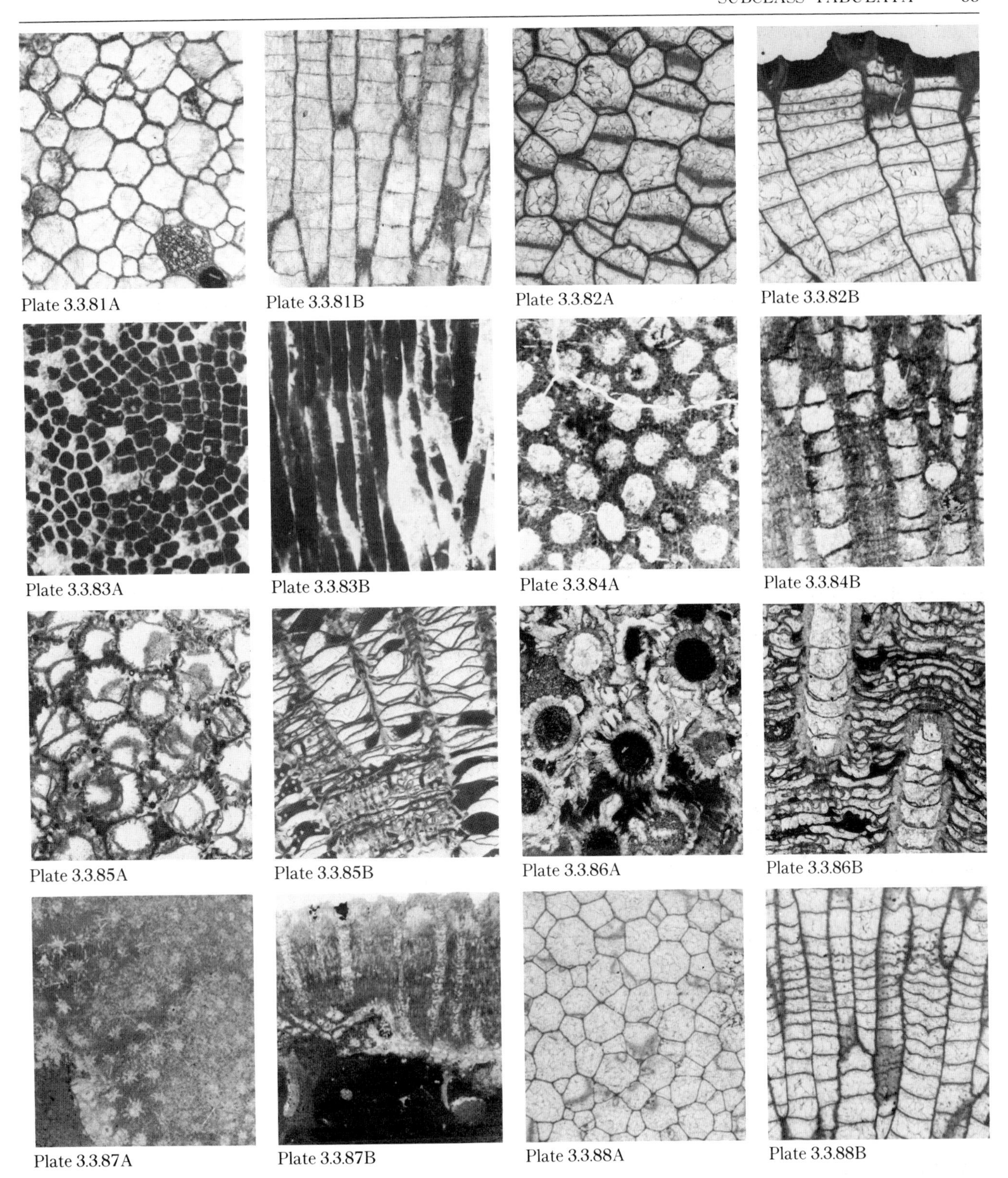

Plate 3.3.81A Plate 3.3.81B Plate 3.3.82A Plate 3.3.82B

Plate 3.3.83A Plate 3.3.83B Plate 3.3.84A Plate 3.3.84B

Plate 3.3.85A Plate 3.3.85B Plate 3.3.86A Plate 3.3.86B

Plate 3.3.87A Plate 3.3.87B Plate 3.3.88A Plate 3.3.88B

Order Favositida

Cerioid or alveolitoid with erect or reclined corallites. Septa spinose or absent or represented by squamulae or combs. Mural pores present. Corallite walls with thin median plane. Tabulae commonly complete, horizontal. M. Ordovician–U. Permian.

Suborder Favositina

Favositida with corallites polygonal in section. M. Ordovician–U. Permian.

SUPERFAMILY FAVOSITICAE
FAMILY FAVOSITIDAE
Subfamily Favositinae

Pl. 3.3.88. *Favosites* Lamarck, 1816
Corallum cerioid, of wide-ranging growth form. Corallites thin-walled, polygonal, usually with septa that are longitudinal rows of spines. Mural pores confined to faces of corallite walls, in up to 4 longitudinal rows. Tabulae complete.
U. Ordovician–M. Devonian, shallow-water limestones (inc. bioherms) and calcareous shales. Cosmopolitan.
Favosites multipora Lonsdale: Wenlock, Much Wenlock, England, × 4.

Subfamily Paleofavositinae

Pl. 3.3.89. *Paleofavosites* Twenhofel, 1914

Corallum cerioid, massive, with thin-walled polygonal corallites. Usually with septa that are longitudinal rows of spines. Mural pores dominantly adjacent to corallite angles, or located in the angles with vertically superposed pores opening alternately in opposite corallites of a group of 4. Pores confined to faces of corallite walls may also be present. Tabulae thin, usually complete and horizontal.

M. Ordovician–U. Silurian, shallow-water limestones (inc. bioherms) and calcareous shales. Europe–Asia–Australia–N. America.

Paleofavosites asper (d'Orbigny): Ludlow, Aymestry, England, × 4.

FAMILY MICHELINIIDAE

Subfamily Micheliniinae

Pl. 3.3.90. *Michelinia* de Koninck, 1841

Corallum cerioid, sometimes with supporting rootlets. Corallites large, polygonal to rounded with variably thickened walls. Short septal spines scattered on walls and tabulae. Mural pores large, sparse. Tabulae incomplete, somewhat globose.

L. Devonian–U. Permian, shallow-water limestones and calcareous shales. Europe–N. Africa–Asia–Australia–N. America.

Michelinia sp. nov.: L. Carboniferous, Kendal, England,(A) × 2½; (B) × 1½.

Pl. 3.3.91. *Pleurodictyum* Goldfuss, 1829

Corallum small, discoid or domal, cerioid with large corallites. Walls thick with numerous mural tunnels and rows of septal ridges, spines or spinose ridges. Tabulae typically absent, but complete or incomplete when present. Frequently with tube of commensal worm *Hicetes* in centre of basal part.

U. Silurian–M. Devonian, shallow-water limestones, calcareous shales and fine sandy sediments. Europe–N. Africa–Asia–Australia–N. America.

Pleurodictyum problematicum Goldfuss: L. Devonian, Eifel district, W. Germany, × 2.

FAMILY VAUGHANIIDAE

Pl. 3.3.92. *Vaughania* Garwood, 1913

Small, discoid, free or attached. Corallites very shallow, rounded, with thickened walls and floors of dense fibrous tissue. Ring canals encircle the base of each corallite into which they open by branch canals. They are interconnected by (?)mural pores. No tabulae.

L. Carboniferous, shallow-water calcareous shales and limestones. Europe.

Vaughania cleistoporoides Garwood: Tournaisian, Ravenstonedale, England, × 1½.

FAMILY PALAEACIDAE

Pl. 3.3.93. *Microcyathus* Hinde, 1896

Small discoid, usually attached corallum. Corallites short, circular, separated by ridged and canaliculate trabeculate coenenchyme. Lumen lined by aperforate fibrous tissue. Tabulae absent.

L. Carboniferous, shallow-water calcareous shales and limestones. Europe–N. America.

Microcyathus cyclostoma (Phillips): Carboniferous, Alnwick, England, × 3.

SUPERFAMILY PACHYPORICAE

FAMILY PACHYPORIDAE

Pl. 3.3.94. *Thamnopora* Steininger, 1831

Corallum ramose. Corallites, rounded in section, diverge from branch axes, except near tip of branch to open perpendicularly to the surface, except near tip of branch. Corallite walls thickened, often showing growth increments: thickening increases from branch axes to the surface. Mural pores common. Septal spines rare. Tabulae thin, complete, often widely spaced.

L.–U. Devonian, shallow-water limestones and calcareous shales. Cosmopolitan.

Thamnopora cervicornis (de Blainville): M. Devonian, Torquay, England, × 2.

Suborder Alveolitina

Favositida with corallites commonly inclined, opening to the surface at an angle and alveolitoid, rounded-polygonal, compressed-polygonal or meandroid in section. L. Silurian–U. Devonian.

FAMILY ALVEOLITIDAE

Subfamily Alveolitinae

Pl. 3.3.95. *Alveolites* Lamarck, 1801

Corallum massive, encrusting, occasionally with finger-like outgrowths. Corallites reclined, long, narrow, opening obliquely at colony surface with an alveolitoid (crescentic or irregularly angular) section. Walls thin basally, evenly thickened elsewhere. Mural pores uniserial. Septal spines small, thin, scattered, but with single row of larger spines associated with longitudinal increase. Tabulae thin, complete.

M. Silurian–U. Devonian, shallow-water limestones and calcareous shales. Cosmopolitan.

Alveolites suborbicularis Lamarck: M. Devonian, Paffrath, W. Germany, × 4.

FAMILY COENITIDAE

Pl. 3.3.96. *Coenites* Eichwald, 1829

Corallum of very slender branches. Corallites polygonal in section axially, diverging with thickened walls to open at branch surface obliquely. Calices slit-like, deflected by 1 upper median and 2 lower lateral ridges (? of septal origin). Mural pores sparse. Tabulae thin, complete.

M. Silurian–M. Devonian, shallow-water limestones and calcareous shales. Europe–Asia–N. America.

Coenites intertextus Eichwald: Wenlock, Dudley, England, × 4.

Order Heliolitida

Corallum sheet-like, encrusting, branching or massive, coenenchymal. Tabularia, commonly with complete tabulae, separated by tubular, dissepimental or trabeculate coenenchyme. Tabularia aseptate or more commonly with 12 spinose septa which may have laminar bases. M. Ordovician–M. Devonian.

SUPERFAMILY HELIOLITICAE

FAMILY HELIOLITIDAE

Pl. 3.3.97. *Heliolites* Dana, 1846

Corallum branching or massive. Tabularia circular in section, smooth-walled or formed of 12 scallop-shaped segments with or without 12 septa, laminar basally, spinose adaxially, arising from the ridges at the junction of adjacent scallops. Tabulae horizontal, complete. Coenenchyme of prismatic tubules with transverse diaphragms.

M. Ordovician–M. Devonian, shallow-water limestones (inc. bioherms) and calcareous shales. Cosmopolitan.

Heliolites megastoma (M'Coy): Wenlock, Much Wenlock, England, × 4.

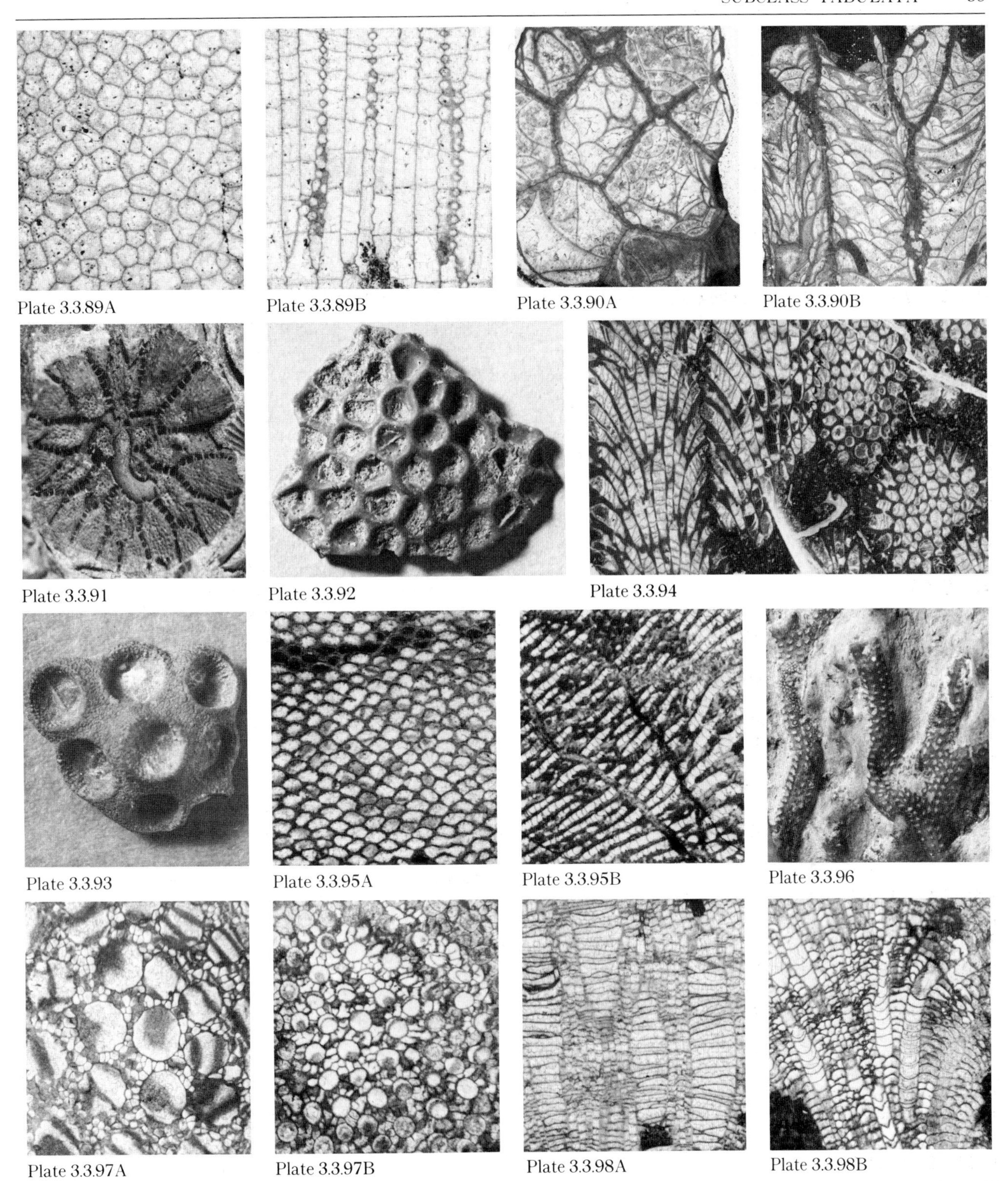

Plate 3.3.89A Plate 3.3.89B Plate 3.3.90A Plate 3.3.90B

Plate 3.3.91 Plate 3.3.92 Plate 3.3.94

Plate 3.3.93 Plate 3.3.95A Plate 3.3.95B Plate 3.3.96

Plate 3.3.97A Plate 3.3.97B Plate 3.3.98A Plate 3.3.98B

SUPERFAMILY PROPORICAE
FAMILY PROPORIDAE

Pl. 3.3.98. *Propora* Edwards & Haime, 1849

Corallum with tabularia separated by dissepimental coenenchyme and variably developed discrete trabeculae. Tabularia circular, smooth-walled or scalloped in section, with 12 rows of septal spines. Tabulae horizontal, sagging or slightly domed.

M. Ordovician–U. Silurian, shallow-water limestones and calcareous shales. Cosmopolitan.

Propora edwardsi Nicholson & Etheridge: Llandovery, Girvan, Scotland, × 4.

FAMILY PLASMOPORIDAE

Pl. 3.3.99. *Plasmopora* Edwards & Haime, 1849

Corallum with tabularia surrounded by an aureole of 12 coenenchymal tubules. Tabularia with smooth or scalloped circular section, with or without septal spines. Tabulae complete, sagging. Coenenchyme dominantly dissepimentate with vertical spines, rods or plates outlining imperfect tubuli.

?M. Ordovician, L.–U. Silurian, shallow-water limestones and calcareous shales. Europe–Australia–N. America.

Plasmopora petalliformis (Lonsdale): Wenlock, Walsall, England, × $2\frac{1}{2}$.

SUPERFAMILY COCCOSERIDICAE
FAMILY COCCOSERIDIDAE

Pl. 3.3.100. *Coccoseris* Edwards & Haime, 1851
Corallum of thin sheets, commonly encrusting. Corallites separated by coenenchyme of thick, vertical contiguous trabeculae. Trabeculae of 12 septa also contiguous, and with multi-element columella, completely infill lumen. No tabulae.
M.–U. Ordovician, shallow-water calcareous shales and limestones. Europe–Australia–N. America.
Coccoseris ungerni (Eichwald): Ashgill, Robeston Wathen, Wales, × 4.

Order Halysitida

Corallites thick-walled and arranged in uniserial ranks which join to enclose lacunae. When present, septal spines in 12 longitudinal rows. Tabulae commonly complete. Corallites may or may not be separated by coenenchyme consisting of individual tubuli or vesicular tissue. Increase lateral, intermural or coenenchymal. M. Ordovician–U. Silurian.

FAMILY HALYSITIDAE
Subfamily Halysitinae

Pl. 3.3.101. *Halysites* Fischer von Waldheim, 1828
Corallites rounded to elliptical in section, arranged in uniserial ranks with interstitial coenenchyme of single tubuli subrectangular in section. Ranks fuse to enclose irregular lacunae. Septal spines weakly developed or absent. Tabulae complete. Tubuli with closer spaced, complete diaphragms.
M. Ordovician–U. Silurian, shallow-water limestones (inc. bioherms) and calcareous shales. Cosmopolitan.
Halysites catenularius (Linné): Wenlock, Much Wenlock, England, × 3.

Pl. 3.3.102. *Cystihalysites* Chernyshev, 1941
Corallites rounded to elliptical in section, arranged in uniserial ranks with interstitial coenenchyme of vesicular tissue. Ranks fuse to enclose irregular lacunae. Septal spines sparse or absent. Tabulae complete.
L.–U. Silurian, shallow-water limestones and calcareous shales. Europe–Asia–N. and S. America.
Cystihalysites blakewayensis Sutton: Wenlock, Much Wenlock, England, × 3.

Subfamily Cateniporinae

Pl. 3.3.103. *Catenipora* Lamarck, 1816
Corallites elliptical in section and arranged in uniserial ranks without interstitial coenenchyme. Ranks fuse to enclose irregular lacunae. Septal spines in 12 longitudinal rows commonly well developed. Tabulae complete.
M. Ordovician–U. Silurian, shallow-water limestones and calcareous shales. Europe–Asia–Australia–N. America.
Catenipora escharoides Lamarck: Llandovery, Gotland, Sweden, × 4.

Order Auloporida

Corallites narrow, conical or tubular, offsetting in chains to form a prostrate or adherent network. In some, long cylindrical corallites may arise from the basal network to form a fasciculate or phacelo-cerioid colony. Mural pores may or may not develop in phacelo-cerioid forms and connecting tubuli are characteristic of fasciculate colonies. Septa very fine spines when present. Tabulae infundibuliform in most Syringoporicae, otherwise variable in number to sparse and even absent. ?L. Ordovician, M. Ordovician–U. Permian.

SUPERFAMILY AULOPORICAE
FAMILY AULOPORIDAE

Pl. 3.3.104. *Aulopora* Goldfuss, 1829
Corallites small, conical to tubular, reptant, commonly adherent, joined in linear chains or anastomosing networks. Walls moderately thick and calices slightly raised above substrate. Septal spines may be present. Tabulae commonly absent or sparse.
?L. Ordovician, M. Ordovician–U. Permian, shallow-water limestones and calcareous shales. Cosmopolitan.
Aulopora sp.: Wenlock, Gotland, Sweden, × 2½.

FAMILY PYRGIIDAE

Pl. 3.3.105. *Cladochonus* M'Coy, 1847
Proximal parts of corallum prostrate, or annular around crinoid stems. Distal part of erect branches that may fork. Corallites curved, conical, each attached by narrow base to side of, and opening into, next earlier corallite. Walls thick, sometimes with small spines. Tabulae absent or sparse.
M. Devonian–U. Permian, shallow-water calcareous shales and limestones. Cosmopolitan.
Cladochonus sp.: Viséan, Clitheroe, England, × 2.

SUPERFAMILY SYRINGOPORICAE
FAMILY SYRINGOPORIDAE

Pl. 3.3.106. *Syringopora* Goldfuss, 1826
Corallum fasciculate. Corallites long, cylindrical, thick-walled, interconnected by irregularly distributed but usually common horizontal tubuli. Septa spinose, in longitudinal rows, or possibly absent. Tabulae infundibuliform, usually forming an axial syrinx. Increase lateral.
U. Ordovician–L. Carboniferous, ?U. Carboniferous, ?L. Permian, shallow-water calcareous shales and limestones. Cosmopolitan.
Syringopora geniculata Phillips: Carboniferous, Derbyshire, England, × 3.

FAMILY THECOSTEGITIDAE

Pl. 3.3.107. *Thecostegites* Edwards & Haime, 1849
Corallum massive and encrusting. Corallites cylindrical, slender, thick-walled, perforate, united by successive, irregular, platform-like expansions which may be epithecate both above and below. Septal spines irregular in development. Tabulae irregular in shape, horizontal or oblique, concave, sometimes with short axial tubes. Tabulae also fill lateral expansions.
U. Silurian–L. Carboniferous, shallow-water limestones and calcareous shales. Europe–Asia–Australia–N. America.
Thecostegites bouchardi (Michelin): Frasnian, Gourdinne, Belgium, × 3.

Subclass Zoantharia

Order Scleractinia

Solitary or colonial corals. Paired mesenteries. Fundamentally hexameral, sometimes bihexameral, biradial or pseudoradial in transverse symmetry. Calcareous exoskeleton. Septa mostly plate-like, but sometimes as rudimentary spines or spine systems; at least six; further septa inserted more or less cyclically in all six primary septal spaces, and often differentiated into size orders. Corallite walls, intercorallite tissue and dissepiments present or absent.

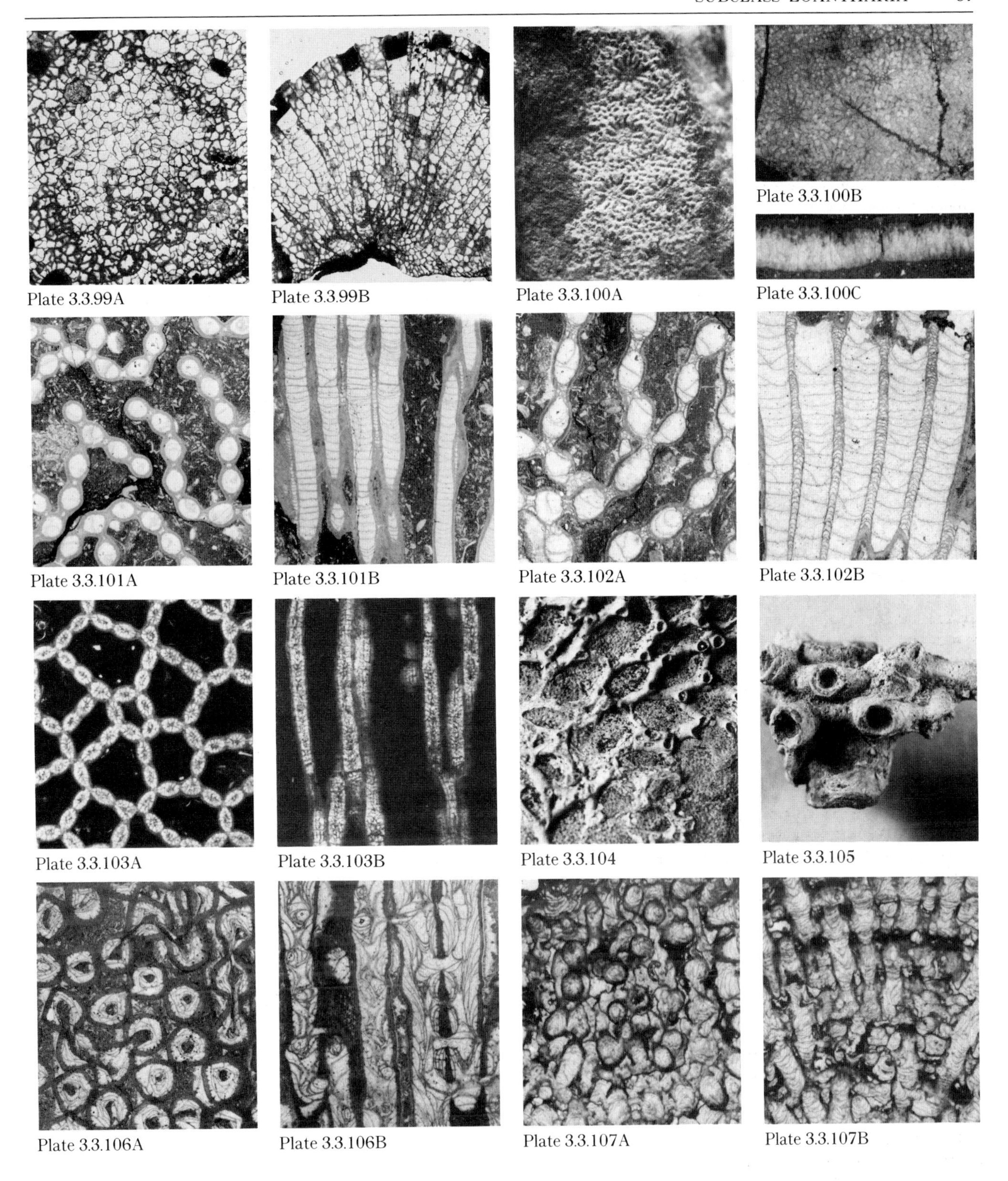

Plate 3.3.99A Plate 3.3.99B Plate 3.3.100A Plate 3.3.100B Plate 3.3.100C

Plate 3.3.101A Plate 3.3.101B Plate 3.3.102A Plate 3.3.102B

Plate 3.3.103A Plate 3.3.103B Plate 3.3.104 Plate 3.3.105

Plate 3.3.106A Plate 3.3.106B Plate 3.3.107A Plate 3.3.107B

Scleractinian skeleton originates as a transverse basal plate on which septa and epitheca are initiated. Other features are essentially transverse or longitudinal derivations of these primary features. They are formed beneath and round the coral as it grows in an oral direction, either as regularly repeated features like dissepiments or as continuous features like walls. Columellae and costae are septal. Dissepiments are epitheca-like. Walls may be septal, epithecal, dissepimental, etc. or heterogeneous. New corallites appear either within the parent corallite wall, or outside it. Parent corallites often stay incompletely divided and thereby permanently many-centred, with either linear confluent centres (meandroid valleys, e.g. Pl. 3.3.114) or radial confluent centres (circumoral systems). Polyps may be folded into edge-zone round exoskeleton, to enclose much of the skeleton, in which case epitheca is poorly developed or macroscopically absent.

For English-language terminology see Wells (1956), but for additional illustrations and a different approach see also Alloiteau (1952). Classification is unstable, there being two principal approaches. Both give importance to septal microstructure as the main criterion, but are biased towards different stratigraphic levels. Most English-language workers use Wells's (1956) approach, which is most readily applicable to Cainozoic Scleractinia. European workers mostly use, and are currently

Septa of fibres radiating outwards from a median plane; centres absent							Without carina-like ornament		Pl. 3.3.108. *Retiophyllia* Coryphyllidae L. Beauvais, 1980
							With carina-like ornament (*menianes*)		Pl. 3.3.109. *Astraeomorpha* Volzeiidae L. Beauvais, 1980
Septa of fibres radiating outwards from centres; median plane absent	Fibres radiate from upwardly continuous axis-like centre to form concentrically layered units			Fusion of cylindrical structures into septa incomplete					Pl. 3.3.110. *Stylophyllopsis* Stylophyllidae Volz, 1895
	Fibres radiate outwards from individual centres to form spherulitic units	Spherulitic units are fused into longitudinal granulated rods disposed more or less vertically ('simple trabeculae')	Axes of rods are aligned in a single linear system; rods fused into a sheet (i.e. a septum)	Fusion of rods into septa complete		Rods very small; numerous centres almost like a median line in transverse section	Without carina-like ornament		Pl. 3.3.111. *Stylocoenia* Astrocoeniidae Koby, 1890
							With carina-like ornament (*auricules*)		Pl. 3.3.112. *Stylina* Stylinidae d'Orbigny, 1851
						Rods large and distinct	Without carina-like ornament	Rods fused into a single linear series (one-fan system)	Pl. 3.3.113. *Tarbellastraea* Pl. 3.3.114. *Colpophyllia* Pl. 3.3.115. *Hydnophora* Faviidae Gregory, 1900
								Rods fused into several linear series (multiple-fan system) themselves fused linearly	Pl. 3.3.116. *Scolymia* Mussidae Ortmann, 1890
							With carina-like ornament	Without lateral lamellar thickening; carina-like features are pennular	Pl. 3.3.117. *Gablonzeria* Tropiphyllidae L. Beauvais, 1980
								With lateral lamellar thickening tending to obscure carina-like, strong longitudinal ridges	Pl. 3.3.118. *Montlivaltia* Pl. 3.3.119. *Thecosmilia* Montlivaltiidae Dietrich, 1926
				Fusion of rods into septa incomplete	Septa of spines when not complete				Pl. 3.3.120. *Acropora* Acroporidae, Verrill, 1902
					Septa perforate	Rods numerous, irregularly fused	Without carina-like ornament		Pl. 3.3.121. *Dendrophyllia* Dendrophylliidae Gray, 1847
							With carina-like ornament (*pennules, menianes*)		Pl. 3.3.122. *Microsolena* Microsolenidae Koby, 1890
						Rods very few, with palar rods also	With synapticular ornament		Pl. 3.3.123. *Actinacis* Actinacididae Vaughan & Wells, 1943 Pl. 3.3.124. *Porites* Poritidae Gray, 1842
			Axes of rods are commonly aligned in several systems more or less in parallel and fused into a sheet (i.e. a septum)					Rods fused into a single system (one-fan system)	Pl. 3.3.125. *Diploctenium* Meandrinidae Gray, 1847 Pl. 3.3.126. *Turbinolia* Caryophylliidae Gray, 1847 Turbinoliinae Milne Edwards & Haime, 1848
								Rods fused into two linear series (multiple-fan system) themselves fused linearly	Pl. 3.3.127. *Caryophyllia* Caryophylliidae Gray, 1847 Caryophylliinae Gray, 1847
		Spherulitic units are more or less fused vertically into horizontal rings or clusters each of which is fused into longitudinal globular rods disposed more or less vertically ('compound trabeculae')		Fusion of rods into septa incomplete	Septa perforate				Pl. 3.3.128. *Cyclolites* Cyclolitidae d'Orbigny, 1851

Table 3.3.1

extending Alloiteau's (1952, 1957) approach which is most readily applicable to Mesozoic Scleractinia. Even within the European school there are sharp differences, especially in the interpretation and terminology of septal microstructure. Some of this disagreement is probably semantic. This even applies to the supposedly basic microstructural units, trabeculae. There are also nomenclatural problems, because the diagenetic state of many important type specimens precludes their microstructural investigation.

Notwithstanding all these problems, L. Beauvais (1980) has attempted to combine the principal approaches with an emphasis on Mesozoic corals; but with significant anomalies in her treatment of Cainozoic corals, her scheme cannot be directly followed here. In lieu of a formal classification, the genera treated here are arranged in a sequence of generally increasing septal complexity based on a combination of L. Beauvais's (1980) and Wells's (1956) schemes (Table 3.3.1). Some of the details of septal structure can be seen in the present illustrations, mostly as external septal morphology. For internal details and their interpretation, in taxonomic context, see the illustrations, especially the line drawings, in the following works: Cuif (1968, 1972–76, 1980) for Triassic and some Cainozoic corals; M. Beauvais (1982) for Cretaceous corals; Russo (1979) and Chevalier (1962, 1971, 1975) for Cainozoic corals; see also Gill's work on Jurassic corals cited by these authors. For the scleractinian fossil record as a whole see Alloiteau (1952, 1957), Vaughan and Wells (1943) and Wells (1956). A new French treatise on Cnidaria (Grassé) is currently in preparation as Vol. III.2 of *Traité de zoologie*.

Most authors of neontological taxonomy apart from Chevalier (1971, 1975) make little direct reference to septal microstructure, nor use sectional views. It is therefore difficult to apply most neontological works to fossil corals except those with well-preserved calicinal detail.

Within each kind of familial (septal) microstructure, all classifications define genera similarly by making use of particular kinds of solitary or colonial habit, and the manner in which new daughter polyps arise within colonies. Most families therefore consist of a series, not always complete, of genera of the same septal microstructure, ranging from simple solitaries, through simpler colonials to more complex or more integrated colonials. This is shown for example in the relative loss of corallite identity (Pl. 3.3.122, 123, 124) representing integration, or in the grouping of corallites into higher order colony structures representing complexity, as in ramose branch development (Pl. 3.3.120, 124). Meander systems (Pl. 3.3.114, 125) represent integration within the meanders and complexity within the colony as a whole. The extreme of colony development is seen in integrated corals with ramose form (Pl. 3.3.124). There are even ramose forms of the highly developed meandroid coral *Hydnophora* (Pl. 3.3.115, but ramose form not shown here).

Other features of classificatory importance include wall structure, and the nature of dissepiments and columellae. Most of the features used at generic level are repeated in numerous families and on their own are unreliable for identification unless septal characters are also used (compare Pl. 3.3.109 with 122; Pl. 3.3.110 with 116 and with 118; Pl. 3.3.112 with 113 and with 123).

About half the scleractinian genera are colonial, and among the living forms about half are also zooxanthellate (i.e. have symbiotic algae). Most living zooxanthellates are colonial, usually showing greater complexity or integration. The lesser number of zooxanthellate solitaries attain a larger size than non-zooxanthellate solitaries. These patterns suggest a broad relationship between ecological habit, classification and evolution within families.

In the descriptions below, and Table 3.3.1, reference to trabeculae has been minimized because of the difficulties already mentioned. Stratigraphic and geographic distributions are based mostly on Wells (1956) or L. Beauvais (1980) and are subject to the nomenclatural problems discussed above. Indication of the ecologically important symbiosis with algae in entirely extinct forms is here tentatively inferred from general morphology by analogy with living zooxanthellates.

Table 3.3.1. Key to genera referred to, by septal structure. This key introduces principles of scleractinian classification as illustrated by selected genera. It is based on those characters of septal structure which are usually used in family classification, adapted where necessary to specify the particular genus or generic group. Although the relative position of genera is similar in places to that in published classifications, the key is not a proper diagnosis or classification of families. Many families, moreover, are not represented. The sequence of genera is broadly one of increasing septal complexity, but the distinctions between small and large 'rods', and between perforate and imperforate, are in part arbitrary. The characters used are essentially internal to septa and not usually visible in the accompanying illustrations except in part where they are expressed as external morphological details.

Glossary of Selected Terms

Terms of generally similar meaning for all coral groups are explained in the introduction to Rugosa, etc. Those included below have distinct scleractinian usage or apply only to scleractinians. Wherever possible, the genera which illustrate a feature are cited as examples and in most cases the feature is explained in the diagnosis or is visible in the illustrations, or both. Some very specialized terms are explained in the text and in Table 3.3.1.

Ahermatypic See zooxanthellate.

Ambulacrum A flat or trough-shaped coenosteal area between meandroid valley systems; see also ploco-meandroid (Pl. 3.3.114 *Colpophyllia*).

Branching See phaceloid, etc. and ramose.

Cerioid Corallite arrangement in which a single wall structure is shared by adjacent corallites, i.e. not two laterally fused walls with epitheca between them (Pl. 3.3.111 *Stylocoenia*, Pl. 3.3.117 *Gablonzeria*).

Cerio-meandroid Cerioid corals whose corallites are also meandroid (Pl. 3.3.115 *Hydnophora*, but note that its walls are also discontinuous).

Coenosteum Intercorallite tissue; strictly applicable to corals with walls, e.g. plocoid forms (Pl. 3.3.112 *Stylina*, Pl. 3.3.113 *Tarbellastraea*, Pl. 3.3.123 *Actinacis*). See also exotheca.

Columella Almost any axial structure. May be a styliform rod (Pl. 3.3.126 *Turbinolia*) or more complex combination of numerous elements (Pl. 3.3.116 *Scolymia*, Pl. 3.3.127 *Caryophyllia*).

Costa Continuation of septum beyond the corallite wall, seen as external longitudinal ridges in solitary corals (Pl. 3.3.126 *Turbinolia*) and in phaceloid and dendroid corals, and as septal prolongations in transverse sections of plocoid corals (Pl. 3.3.112 *Stylina*, Pl. 3.3.113 *Tarbellastraea*, Pl. 3.3.123 *Actinacis*). See also septo-costa.

Dendroid Corallites with irregularly spreading free branches (see also phaceloid and phacelo-dendroid).

Dendro-plocoid As dendroid, but corallite branches short and with partial development of intercorallite tissue around corallite bases (Pl. 3.3.121 *Dendrophyllia*).

Endotheca Skeletal elements of which interior of corallite is composed, e.g. endothecal dissepiments; used to distinguish from exothecal elements in plocoid corals.

Exotheca Skeletal elements of which coenosteum in plocoid corals is composed, e.g. exothecal dissepiments (Pl. 3.3.112 *Stylina*, Pl. 3.3.113 *Tarbellastraea*).

Flabellate Corallites whose transverse section is elongated in a single plane, with a single centre (compare flabello-meandroid).

Flabello-meandroid As flabellate, but with more than one centre within the corallite (Pl. 3.3.125 *Diploctenium*). The corallite may then be straight or truly meandering.

Hermatypic See zooxanthellate.

Hydnophoroid A special case of cerio-meandroid (or ploco-meandroid) in which the walls are projecting and discontinuous, and the valleys continuous (Pl. 3.3.115 *Hydnophora*). Also used for discontinuous ridge development in septo-costal corals without true walls.

Meandroid Corallites with distinct walls whose laterally elongated polyps contain many mouths, seen more or less distinctly in the skeleton as septal or columellar centres along the corallite axis (Pl. 3.3.114 *Colpophyllia*).

Monticule The discontinuous upstanding wall feature in hydnophoroid corals, especially when conical in form; often thickened by stereome (Pl. 3.3.115 *Hydnophora*).

Non-zooxanthellate See zooxanthellate.

Palus A longitudinal rod or sometimes a plate of septal origin separated from main septal structure and situated more or less close to the axis; often developed in conjunction with septal convergence (Pl. 3.3.123 *Actinacis*, Pl. 3.3.124 *Porites*, Pl. 3.3.127 *Caryophyllia*).

Parathecal wall Wall structure composed of dissepiments (Pl. 3.3.116 *Scolymia*, Pl. 3.3.118 *Montlivaltia*, Pl. 3.3.119 *Thecosmilia*).

Phacelo-dendroid See phaceloid and dendroid (Pl. 3.3.108 *Retiophyllia*, Pl. 3.3.119 *Thecosmilia*).

Phaceloid Corallites with more or less parallel free branches (see also dendroid, phacelo-dendroid).

Plocoid Corallites with more or less distinct wall structures separated from but connected to each other by intercorallite tissue (coenosteum) (Pl. 3.3.112 *Stylina*, Pl. 3.3.113 *Tarbellastraea*, Pl. 3.3.123 *Actinacis*).

Ploco-meandroid Plocoid corals whose corallites are also meandroid (Pl. 3.3.114 *Colpophyllia*).

Pourtalès plan A particular pattern of converging septa which in plan view of corallites is geometrically petal-like, see Wells (1956) (Pl. 3.3.121 *Dendrophyllia*).

Ramose A development of massive corals in which systems of corallites are grouped into columns, i.e. ramose-columnar (Pl. 3.3.111 *Stylocoenia*) or branches, i.e. ramose-branching (Pl. 3.3.120 *Acropora*, Pl. 3.3.124 *Porites*). *Note:* 'Branching' is ambiguous unless dendroid to phaceloid branching and ramose branching are distinguished.

Septo-costa The septum of thamnasterioid corals (mainly). Thamnasterioid corallites have no walls and there is therefore no obvious point at which septa pass into costae (Pl. 3.3.122 *Microsolena*).

Septothecal wall Wall structure composed of septal structures, generally lateral outgrowths from septal centres of calcification, or stereome thickening in marginal region of septa, or both (Pl. 3.3.108 *Retiophyllia* has inner septothecal wall; Pl. 3.3.112 *Stylina*).

Synapticula Lateral process on septal faces consisting of one or more centres of calcification; commonly occur as bridge-like fusions between adjacent septa (Pl. 3.3.123 *Actinacis*, Pl. 3.3.124 *Porites*).

Synapticulothecal wall Wall structure composed of synapticulae and typically perforate (Pl. 3.3.123 *Actinacis*, Pl. 3.3.124 *Porites*).

Thamnasterioid Corallites whose septa are continuous (confluent) between adjacent corallite centres, without intervening wall structures (Pl. 3.3.122 *Microsolena*).

Valley The elongated meander-system or meandering corallite of meandroid corals; generally trough-like in calicinal appearance. Term tends to be used for calicinal preservation only (Pl. 3.3.114 *Colpophyllia*; Pl. 3.3.115 *Hydnophora*).

Zooxanthellate Coral with endodermal symbiosis with dinoflagellate algae. Zooxanthellates are restricted to warm, clear, shallow tropical waters, about 15°C or more, and less than about 100 m depth (Pl. 3.3.114 *Colpophyllia*, Pl. 3.3.115 *Hydnophora*, Pl. 3.3.116 *Scolymia*, Pl. 3.3.120 *Acropora*, Pl. 3.3.124 *Porites*). Non-zooxanthellates are not so restricted (Pl. 3.3.121 *Dendrophyllia*, Pl. 3.3.127 *Caryophyllia*). 'Hermatypic' and 'ahermatypic' correspond approximately, but are also used in ecological and sedimentological sense of reef-dwelling or reef-building. The symbiosis, or its absence, in extinct genera is inferred indirectly, as indicated in generic entries.

Pl. 3.3.108. *Retiophyllia* Cuif, 1966
Colonial. Corallites phacelo-dendroid up to about 1 cm in diameter. Septa with uneven surface; 2 or more orders; up to about 4 cycles; as Table 3.3.1, with median plane undulating and fibres radiating slightly from its convexities; facial ornament of granular to spiny outgrowths in rows parallel to growing edge of septa; thickened by stereome towards margin where adjacent septa sometimes fuse to form inner septothecal wall; sometimes rhopaloid. Columella weak to absent. Outer wall epithecal. Dissepiments numerous, vesicular and inward sloping marginally, tabular internally. (Name proposed by Cuif following revision of Triassic *Thecosmilia*.)
Triassic–L. Jurassic, Eurasia. Common coral in Triassic reef facies.
Retiophyllia fenestrata (Reuss): U. Triassic, (A) Styria, Austria, TS; (B) Tyrol, Austria (BMNH R 33645) (British Museum (Nat. Hist.)) LS; (C) septal details of (A). (A and C after Cuif.)

Pl. 3.3.109. *Astraeomorpha* Reuss, 1854
Colonial, in small nodules. Corallites thamnasterioid, centres about 5 mm apart. Septa thick with smooth surfaces; up to 3 cycles; as Table 3.3.1 with strong facial ornamentation of slightly upturned horizontal carina-like ledges (*menianes*) often fused to columella and to each other between adjacent septa. Columella styliform when present.
Triassic, Eurasia. Colony form similar to living zooxanthellates (cf. *Pavona*).
Astraeomorpha crassisepta Reuss: (A) Zlambach Schichten, Triassic, Gosau, Austria (BMNH R 14441). TS Skeleton is light coloured in illustration; (B) LS Skeleton is dark coloured and corallites horizontal in illustration. (After Cuif.)

Pl. 3.3.110. *Stylophyllopsis* Frech, 1890
Solitary, cup-like to cylindrical, up to about 3 cm in diameter. Septa thin to thick with spiny irregular margins; numerous cycles and orders; composed of cylindrically structured rod-like units seen as spines (as in Table 3.3.1) fused into septal sheets except towards the axis where they remain as separate spines; without facial ornamentation. Columella absent. Dissepiments absent (cf. also *Oppelismilia*).
Triassic–L. Jurassic, Eurasia.
Stylophyllopsis mucronata (Duncan): Lias, England. (A) (BMNH R 13071) general view (note that septa are broken); (B) (BMNH R 30372) TS septal details.

Pl. 3.3.111. *Stylocoenia* Milne Edwards & Haime, 1849
Colonial, in small, encrusting, massive, nodular or ramose-columnar growths. Corallites cerioid with strong striate columniform projections at junctions of adjacent corallites; small, up to 5 mm in diameter. Septa thin, relatively few, up to about 3 cycles; as Table 3.3.1 with facial ornament slight but acute dentations on margins. Walls septothecal, structurally continuous with septa. Dissepiments tabular, thin.
Palaeocene–Miocene, Eurasia and Caribbean. Colony form similar to living zooxanthellates (cf. *Stylocoeniella*), often with central tube indicating growth round soft organisms (? plants) not preserved.
Stylocoenia spp.: (A) Eocene, Grignon, France (BMNH R 35392) surface; (B) Oligocene, Willoughby Bay, Antigua (BMNH R 34335) TS ramose branch; (C) Eocene, Hautville, France (BMNH R 50894) LS; (D) TS corallite details of (B).

Pl. 3.3.112. *Stylina* Lamarck, 1816
Colonial, usually massive or ramose columnar. Corallites plocoid, projecting, about 5 mm in diameter. Septa thin, uneven, up to 3 cycles and orders; structure as Table 3.3.1 with upper margins smooth to beaded and inner margins with pores and vertical carina-like processes (*auricules*) developed intermittently; *auricules* seen transversely as Y-fork axial terminations; facial

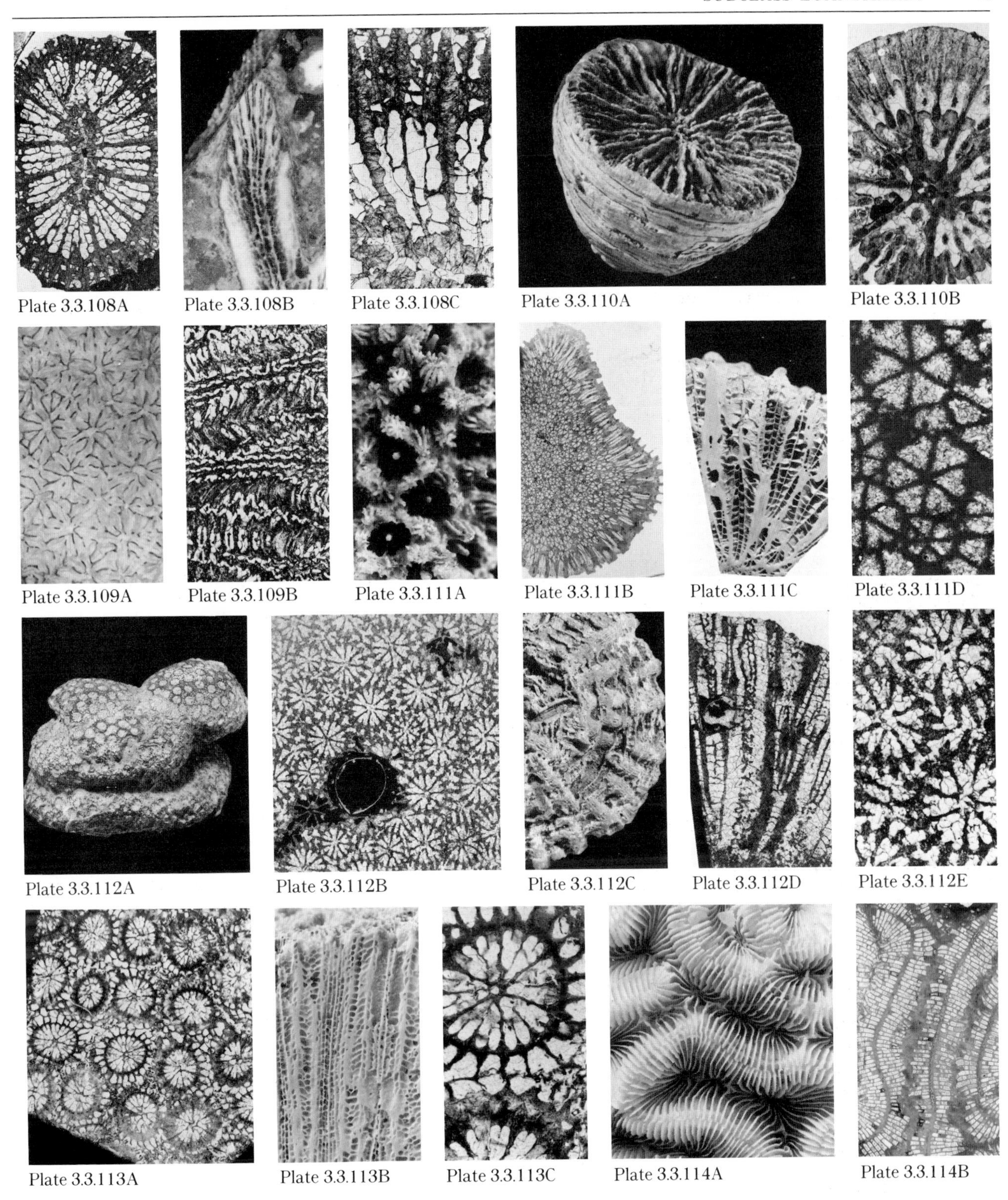

ornamentation irregularly spiny or granular; sometimes fused by axial processes (not the *auricules*) to a styliform columella if present. Walls septothecal. Costae strong. Corallites connected by costae and strongly tabular dissepiments. Endothecal dissepiments thin and tabular.

L. Jurassic–L. Cretaceous, cosmopolitan. Colony form similar to living zooxanthellates (cf. *Cyphastrea*).

Stylina spp.: (A) M. Jurassic, Jumara, India (BMNH R 5276) colony view; (B) (BMNH R 18871) TS; (C) U. Jurassic, Steeple Ashton, England (BMNH R 8403) longitudinal view; (D) cut LS of (B); (E) TS corallite detail of (B).

Pl. 3.3.113. *Tarbellastraea* Alloiteau, 1950

Colonial, massive. Corallites plocoid, projecting, small, up to about 5 mm in diameter and 1 cm apart. Septa thin, uneven, in 3 cycles and 2 to 3 orders; as Table 3.3.1 with facial ornament of fine irregular granulations and margins irregularly dentate. Columella weak to absent, formed by lamellar fusion of a few septa. Walls parathecal, costate, thickened by stereome. Endothecal dissepiments numerous, vesicular and inward sloping at margins, tabular internally. Corallites connected by costae and numerous exothecal dissepiments. Division outside corallites.

Miocene, Caribbean, Eurasia and Indo-Pacific margins. Colony

form similar to living zooxanthellates (like its close Recent relatives *Montastrea* and *Favia*). Important reef-builder.
(A) *Tarbellastraea reussiana* (Milne Edwards & Haime): Miocene, Balza di Rocca, Sicily (BMNH R 40009) TS; (B) U. Miocene, Sicily (BMNH R 35575) LS; (C) TS detail of (A).

Pl. 3.3.114. *Colpophyllia* Milne Edwards & Haime, 1848
Colonial, massive. Corallites ploco-meandroid consisting of long, broad, meandering valley systems up to 2 cm wide separated by two close walls, sometimes separated by a narrow ambulacrum. Septa straight, thin, even, 2 to 3 orders, projecting above walls and sloping down steeply to valley axes, about 10 per mm; as Table 3.3.1. Columella of septal lamellae laterally curved to form axial centres. Walls septothecal. Endothecal dissepiments vesicular and sloping inwards. Adjacent valleys connected by costae and narrow, tabular exothecal dissepiments.
Eocene–Recent, Europe, Caribbean. Zooxanthellate. Reef-builder.
(A) *Colpophyllia natans* (Houttuyn): Recent, Cayman Islands (BMNH 1976.4.14.27) general view; (B) *Colpophyllia* sp.: Oligocene, Antigua (BMNH R 35655) TS; (C) *C. natans*: Pleistocene, Rio Bueno Bay, Jamaica (BMNH R 50886) LS; (D) TS septal detail of (B).

Pl. 3.3.115. *Hydnophora* Fischer de Waldheim, 1807
Colonial; massive, incrusting, free plates, ramose-columnar or ramose-branching. Corallites cerio-meandroid with discontinuous walls (hydnophoroid); meanders continuous, up to about 5 mm wide in circular to elliptical units surrounding isolated upstanding conical points or ridges of wall (monticules). Septa thick or thin, finely frosted; 2 to 3 orders, often strongly alternating; as Table 3.3.1 with synapticular outgrowths axially; facial ornamentation of small granulations in rows indicating orientation of fan system; margins of very small spinulose dentations with a larger tooth axially. Columella discontinuous, of septal lamellae and synapticulae. Walls projecting, discontinuous, thickened by stereome, with fine septal ridges sloping down from summits. Dissepiments vesicular, sloping towards valley axes. (Note: The coral is 'inside out', its apparent centres being wall monticules and its apparent walls being columellae.)
Cretaceous–Recent, cosmopolitan. Zooxanthellate. Reef-builder.
(A) *Hydnophora exesa* (Pallas): Recent, Seychelles (BMNH R 50899) surface view; (B) *H. regularis* (Kühn): L. Miocene, Tanzania (BMNH R 41546) TS; (C) LS; (D) TS corallite detail of (B).

Pl. 3.3.116. *Scolymia* Haime, 1852
Mostly solitary, rarely colonial with a few centres within a single corallite; cup-shaped to cylindrical, large, up to about 7 cm in diameter; calicinal surface shallow, flat to slightly domed. Septa smooth, thick, margins strongly toothed with lobulate to spiny undulations; 7 cycles and numerous orders; as Table 3.3.1 with each fan system represented by a marginal tooth; facial ornamentation finely granular. Columella large, spongy, of individual septal rods. Walls parathecal, with costae and epithecae. Several centres if present linked by lamellae. Dissepiments numerous, arched marginally, sloping inwards internally.
Miocene–Recent, Caribbean, Eurasia, Indo-Pacific margins. Zooxanthellate, usually in deeper parts of reefs.
Scolymia spp.: (A) Miocene, Jamaica (BMNH R 40412) calicinal surface; (B) Miocene, Turkish Armenia (BMNH R 10646) TS; (C) septal detail of (A).

Pl. 3.3.117. *Gablonzeria* Cuif, 1976
Colonial, massive. Corallites polygonal, cerioid, with 1 to 3 centres, up to about 1 cm in diameter. Septa thin, uneven, strongly ornamented, up to about 4 cycles; 2 to 3 orders with additional rudimentary order within wall; as Table 3.3.1 with fan system vertical at margins and inward pointing axially; facial ornamentation of strong rounded to spinose granulations, sometimes of short, axially inclined carina-like flanges (*pennules*). Columella absent. Walls structurally the same as septa but thickened by stereome. Dissepiments very fine, numerous, small, vesicular. (Name proposed by Cuif for certain Triassic '*Isastrea*'.)
Triassic, Eurasia. Colony form like living zooxanthellates (cf. *Goniastrea*).
Gablonzeria major (Frech): ?Triassic, locality not known (BMNH R 13493). (A) TS; (B) LS; (C) TS septal details.

Pl. 3.3.118. *Montlivaltia* Lamouroux, 1821
Solitary, cup-shaped to cylindrical, large, up to about 10 cm in diameter. Septa straight, even, numerous, close, projecting above wall; as Table 3.3.1 with centres extended outwards into strong longitudinal carina-like ridges or strong spines; upper margins strongly dentate and inner margins smooth. Columella absent. Wall internally parathecal, of large arched dissepiments, and externally epithecal. Dissepiments numerous.
L. Jurassic–Cretaceous, cosmopolitan. Form and size similar to modern zooxanthellates (cf. *Scolymia*).
(A) *Montlivaltia slatteri* Tomes: Bathonian, Fairford, England (BMNH R 9656) general view; (B) *Montlivaltia* sp.: Bathonian, Jumara, India (BMNH R 5296) TS septal details.

Pl. 3.3.119. *Thecosmilia* Milne Edwards & Haime, 1848
Colonial. Corallites phacelo-dendroid, about 1 to 2 cm in diameter. Septa and other features like *Montlivaltia* (see also Table 3.3.1).
M. Jurassic–Cretaceous, cosmopolitan. Important Jurassic reef-builder and probably zooxanthellate.
(A) *Thecosmilia annularis* (Fleming): Oxfordian, Steeple Ashton, England (BMNH R 8297) general view; (B) *Thecosmilia* sp.: U. Jurassic, Weymouth, England (BMNH R 7890) TS; (C) *T. annularis* (Fleming): U. Jurassic, Lyneham, England (BMNH R 7848) LS.

Pl. 3.3.120. *Acropora* Oken, 1815
Colonial, encrusting, platy, massive, but most usually in ramose branches which may be 'elkhorn', 'stagshorn', bushy or anastomosed horizontally into tables. Corallites plocoid and usually strongly projecting, 1 to 2 mm inner diameter; dimorphic, with a more fully developed axial corallite terminating each ramose branching unit and surrounded by radials. Septa thin, irregular, inconspicuous, few, not more than 2 cycles; as Table 3.3.1 with spines pointing inwards and upwards from walls, sometimes fused into septa, sometimes as spines only; facial ornamentation of small granulations and margins irregular; perforations irregular. Columella weak to absent. Walls synapticulothecal, perforated. Corallites connected by finely reticulate tissue of septal origin, including synapticulae.
Eocene–Recent, Eurasia, Caribbean, Indo-Pacific. Zooxanthellate. Important reef-builder especially since Miocene; typical of well-circulated optimal conditions.
Acropora humilis (Dana): Recent, Mahé, Seychelles (BMNH 1981.3.5.948). (A) View of ramose branch; (B) broken TS axial corallite detail (SEM); (C) LS of ramose branch.

Pl. 3.3.121. *Dendrophyllia* de Blainville, 1830
Colonial. Corallites dendroid to dendro-plocoid, about 5 mm in diameter. Septa thin, sometimes uneven, about 4 cycles, ordered, convergent in geometric petal-like arrangement in transverse section (Pourtalès plan); as Table 3.3.1 with irregular fan system; facial ornamentation strongly granulate and margins smooth,

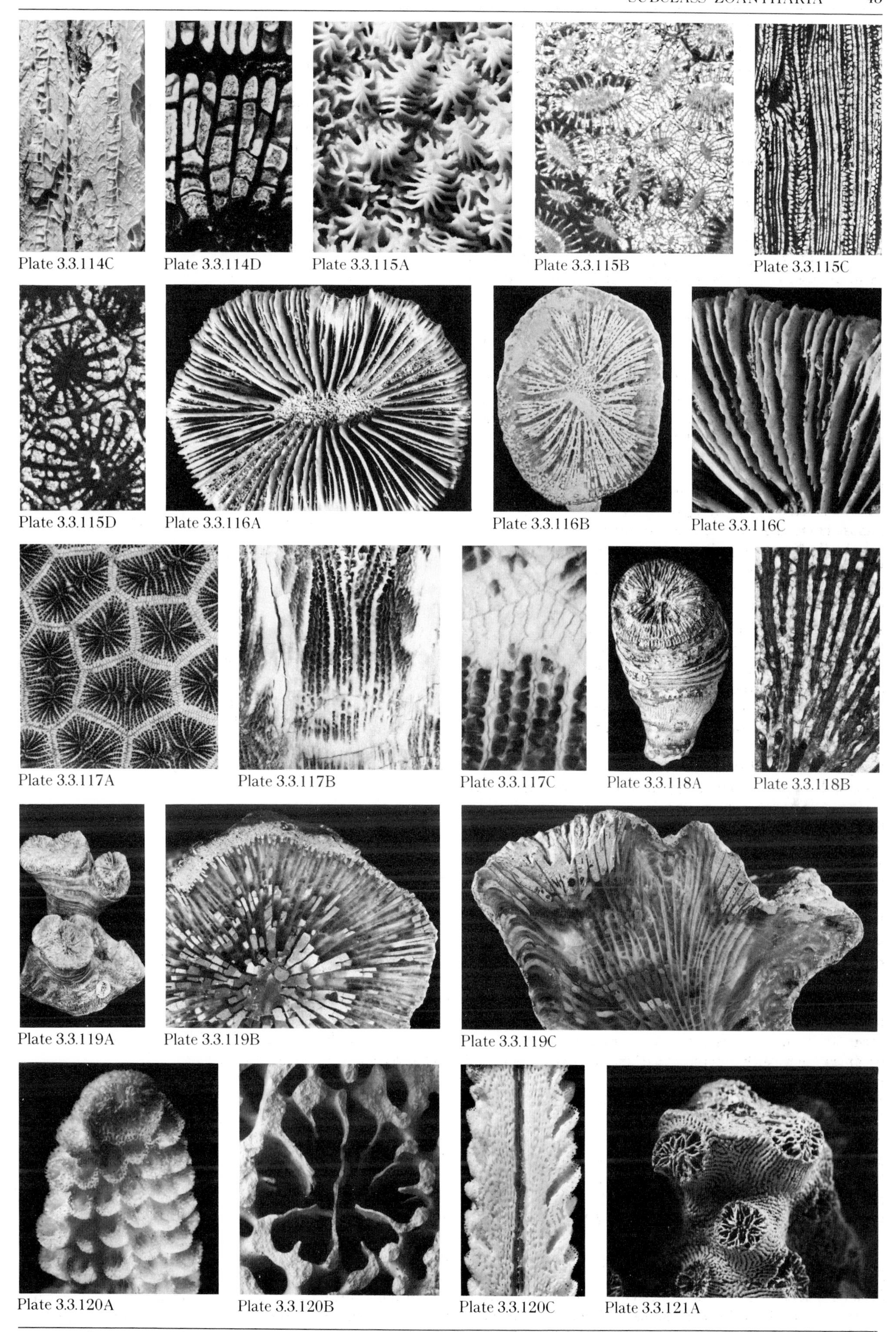

Plate 3.3.114C
Plate 3.3.114D
Plate 3.3.115A
Plate 3.3.115B
Plate 3.3.115C
Plate 3.3.115D
Plate 3.3.116A
Plate 3.3.116B
Plate 3.3.116C
Plate 3.3.117A
Plate 3.3.117B
Plate 3.3.117C
Plate 3.3.118A
Plate 3.3.118B
Plate 3.3.119A
Plate 3.3.119B
Plate 3.3.119C
Plate 3.3.120A
Plate 3.3.120B
Plate 3.3.120C
Plate 3.3.121A

granulate or dentate. Columella weak, spongy. Walls septothecal and synapticulothecal, regularly perforate or thickened by stereome, finely costate and granulate. Corallites more or less connected by porous tissue of costal elements especially towards bases of corallites. Dissepiments (endothecal) rare, tabular.
Eocene–Recent, cosmopolitan. Non-zooxanthellate; depth range 10 to 1200 m, temperature range 7 to 27 °C; sometimes contributes to deep-water coral bank construction.
Dendrophyllia dendrophylloides Milne Edwards & Haime: Eocene, Bracklesham, England. (A) (BMNH R 42060) general view; (B) (BMNH R 2667) TS corallite detail; (C) LS of 2 corallites.

Pl. 3.3.122. *Microsolena* Lamouroux, 1821
Colonial; massive or in sheets or plates. Corallites thamnasterioid up to about 5 mm in diameter, centres up to about 1 cm apart, scattered. Septa in numerous cycles with no obvious orders, confluent between centres, convergent within centres; as Table 3.3.1 with strongly developed facial ornament of flanged and beaded *pennules* and *menianes*, close and regular, giving septal sections a repeatedly bicuspate, zigzag or sinusoidal appearance. Columella absent. Walls absent, tissue between centres being septocostal only.
M. Jurassic–M. Cretaceous, cosmopolitan. Colony form similar to living zooxanthellates (cf. *Coscinaraea*); sometimes associated with deeper reef facies.
Microsolena sp.: U. Jurassic, S. Kilwa district, Tanzania (BMNH R 50375); (A) TS; (B) TS septal details.

Pl. 3.3.123. *Actinacis* d'Orbigny, 1849
Colonial, in nodular, encrusting or ramose-columnar growths. Corallites plocoid, slightly projecting, small, 1 to 4 mm in diameter, centres up to 5 mm apart. Septa irregularly perforate, thin, up to 3 cycles usually grouped into wedge-shaped convergences in transverse section; as Table 3.3.1 with innermost septal rods free as 6 to 8 pali; facial ornament of fine granulations and rod-like lateral outgrowths (synapticulae) sometimes fused between adjacent septa and costae, especially in wall region. Columella weak, mostly palar. Walls synapticulothecal, perforate. Costae discontinuous diverging outwards. Corallites connected by discontinuous tissue, vermicular or spongy in transverse section, reticulate in longitudinal section, consisting of costae and synapticulae.
Cretaceous–Oligocene, cosmopolitan. Colony form similar to living zooxanthellates (cf. *Porites*). Important Palaeogene reef-builder.
Actinacis parvistella Oppenheim: Turonian, Gosau, Austria. (A) (BMNH R 3453) TS; (B) (BMNH R 6859) LS with corallites oriented horizontally; (C) TS corallite detail of (A).

Pl. 3.3.124. *Porites* Link, 1807 (including subgenus *Synaraea* Verrill, 1864)
Colonial; encrusting, massive, corallith, ramose-columnar, ramose-branching, platy or in combinations of these, often very large, several metres in extent. Corallites small, usually 1 to 2 mm, cerioid (*Porites*) to plocoid (*Synaraea*), depressed. Septa 12 or fewer, thick irregular, very frosted and granular, discontinuous, grouped into wedge-shaped convergences; as Table 3.3.1 with very few rods (1 to 4) and regular perforations. Marginal ornamentation of spinulose columnar granulations. Columella palar, small. Walls synapticulothecal, usually in 3 rows, perforate. Corallites in *Synaraea* connected by densely granular porous tissue, longitudinally rectilinear.
Eocene–Recent, cosmopolitan. Zooxanthellate. Important late Cainozoic and modern reef-builder; tolerates extremes of temperature, salinity, turbidity and sedimentation.
(A) *Porites porites* (Pallas): Recent, Bermuda. (BMNH 1983.3.2.5) colony view; (B) *Porites* sp.: Oligocene, Wadi Tamet, Libya (BMNH R 42464) TS; (C) LS; (D) calicinal surface detail of (A); (E) oblique corallite detail of (B).

Pl. 3.3.125. *Diploctenium* Goldfuss, 1827
Colonial, but superficially solitary; a single straight valley system of almost indistinguishable centres (flabello-meandroid), curved outwards and downwards towards aboral point. Valley up to 5 mm in width and up to several cm in length. Septa fine, straight, smooth; 2 or more orders; as Table 3.3.1 with facial ornamentation of fine granulations and margins with small teeth. Columella thin, lamellar, continuous, deep. Walls septothecal, with numerous fine costae in orally diverging system.
M.–U. Cretaceous, Europe, N. Africa, Caribbean. Similar in general form and ?habitat to some living species of the non-zooxanthellate solitary coral *Flabellum* (e.g. *F. chunii* Marenzeller).
Diploctenium conjungens Reuss: (A) Santonian, Lerida, Spain (BMNH R 41676) general view; (B) Senonian, Gosau, Austria (BMNH R 22752) tangential LS parallel to valley; (C) Santonian, Lerida, Spain (BMNH R 41673) oral view.

Pl. 3.3.126. *Turbinolia* Lamarck, 1816
Solitary, small, less than 5 mm diameter, conical. Septa smooth, few, 2 cycles, projecting; as Table 3.3.1 with facial ornamentation of fine granulations in arcuate rows parallel to upper margins. Columella styliform. Walls septothecal and synapticulothecal, regularly perforated or pitted between strongly developed costae which almost obscure wall. Epitheca absent indicating that polyp invested whole skeleton.
Eocene–Oligocene, Europe, W. Africa, Americas. Solitary form similar to living non-zooxanthellates like *Trematotrochus* suggesting habitats which include deeper cooler waters and slightly coarse soft substrates.
Turbinolia sp(p).: Eocene. (A) Bracklesham, England (BMNH 49701) general view; (B) Barton, England (BMNH R 1875) TS.

Pl. 3.3.127. *Caryophyllia* Lamarck, 1801
Solitary, horn-shaped to cylindrical, sometimes compressed or polygonal, up to about 2 cm in diameter. Septa smooth, up to about 5 cycles, strongly ordered, projecting above wall; as Table 3.3.1 with rows of centres becoming meandering near walls (in transverse section), and inner fan system in each septum separated from main fan as a palus; facial ornamentation of fine granulations in arcuate rows parallel to upper margins. Pali opposite third cycle in one crown, or before second order of septa where hexameral symmetry is lost. Columella fascicular, of corkscrew-like laths intergrown with pali. Walls septothecate with costae.
?U. Jurassic, Miocene–Recent, cosmopolitan. Non-zooxanthellate; depth range 0–2475 m, temperature range 2.8 to 27 °C, rocky and slightly coarse soft substrates.
Caryophyllia smithii Stokes & Broderip: Recent, no locality (BMNH R 50898) general view of longitudinal cut specimen (with aboral end broken off).

Pl. 3.3.128. *Cyclolites* Lamarck, 1801
Solitary, discoidal to dome-shaped with prominent groove-like mouth region, sometimes elliptical in plan; up to 12 cm in diameter. Septa very numerous, fine to thick, close, granular to beaded, perforate; first few orders sometimes more prominent; as Table 3.3.1. Columella absent. Wall is flat aboral surface, synapticulothecal and epithecal; epitheca finely concentrically ridged and complete.
Cretaceous–Eocene, Eurasia, N. Africa, Caribbean. Form and

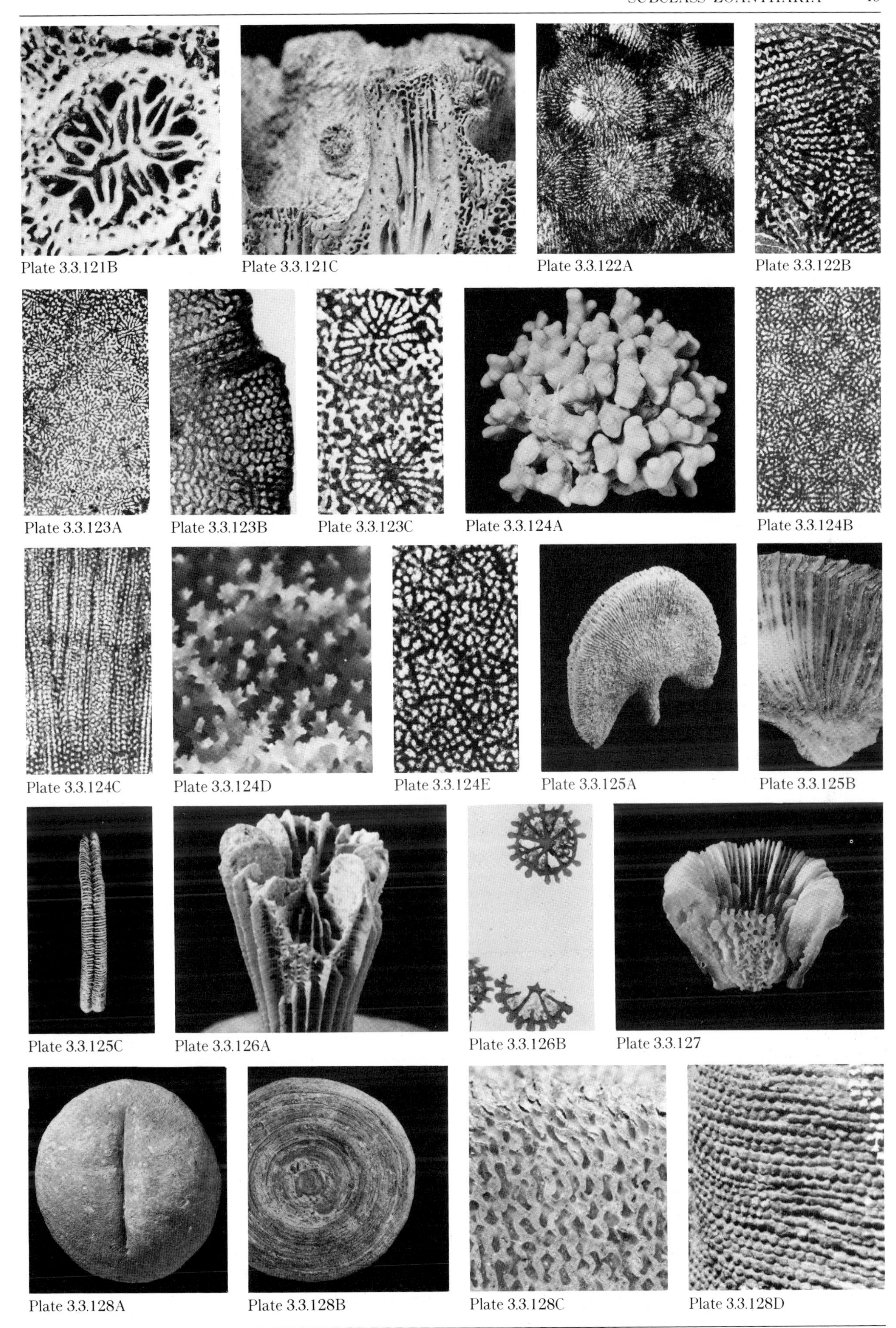

Plate 3.3.121B Plate 3.3.121C Plate 3.3.122A Plate 3.3.122B

Plate 3.3.123A Plate 3.3.123B Plate 3.3.123C Plate 3.3.124A Plate 3.3.124B

Plate 3.3.124C Plate 3.3.124D Plate 3.3.124E Plate 3.3.125A Plate 3.3.125B

Plate 3.3.125C Plate 3.3.126A Plate 3.3.126B Plate 3.3.127

Plate 3.3.128A Plate 3.3.128B Plate 3.3.128C Plate 3.3.128D

size similar to living zooxanthellates (cf. *Fungia*); morphology typical of soft substrates.
Cyclolites spp.: (A) Cretaceous, Corbières, France (BMNH R 7080) oral view; (B) aboral view; (C) (BMNH R 7077) LS septal detail dark in illustration; (D) surface septal detail of (A).

3.4 CLASS CONULATA

?Cnidarians with a dominantly tetramerous, cone-shaped, elongate pyramidal or subcylindrical form, mostly enclosed in a thin chitinophosphatic periderm. Test may bear transverse and/or longitudinal ridges or striae or be smooth. Some have attachment disc at pointed (aboral) extremity. Oral aperture may be protected by 4 flaps of periderm. Marginal tentacles preserved in some forms. U. Precambrian–Triassic.

The conulariids are a moderately uncommon group of uncertain affinity, long included with the Scyphozoa because of their tetramerous symmetry, the presence in one case of 4 branching longitudinal 'septa' and the rare preservation of marginal tentacles. Two orders are distinguished, the more common narrowly conical conulariids falling in the Conulariida and the very broadly diverging forms with marginal tentacles in the Conchopeltida. The latter are almost certainly cnidarian, but may be less closely related to the former than presently supposed. For the moment they are kept together and treated as a separate cnidarian class (Scrutton 1979: 172–4).

Order Conulariida

Narrowly conical or pyramidal, generally 4 sided conulatans with thin chitinophosphatic periderm bearing faint to strong transverse ridges usually interrupted or modified at mid-line of faces and at corners, the latter either rounded or depressed. Some juveniles show attachment disc at aboral extremity. Oral aperture may be closed by 4 flaps of periderm. M. Cambrian–Triassic.

Plate 3.4.1

FAMILY CONULARIIDAE
Subfamily Paraconulariinae
Pl. 3.4.1. *Paraconularia* Sinclair, 1940
Conulariids with transverse ribs moderately strong, sometimes tuberculate, abruptly bent adorally in the corner furrows. Mid-line on faces marked by a weak adoral chevron pattern in ribs and occasionally by a low, longitudinal ridge.
M. Silurian–M. Permian, shallow to moderately deep marine muds, ?pelagic as adults. Europe–Australia–N. America.
Paraconularia derwentensis (Johnston): L.–M. Permian, Tasmania, Australia, × ½.

CHAPTER 4

Bryozoa

by P. D. Taylor

The Bryozoa are an exclusively colonial phylum with a rich fossil history extending back to the L. Ordovician. Three classes are now living: the soft-bodied Phylactolaemata, with no significant fossil record; the Stenolaemata, represented by four extinct orders (Cystoporata, Trepostomata, Cryptostomata, Fenestrata) and one extant order (Cyclostomata); and the Gymnolaemata, with two extant orders (Cheilostomata, Ctenostomata). All stenolaemates and gymnolaemates possess calcareous skeletons except ctenostomes.

For definitions of morphological terms the second edition of the bryozoan *Treatise on Invertebrate Paleontology* (Boardman *et al.* 1983) and Ryland (1970) should be consulted.

Class level division is based on differences in zooid body plan, especially those related to the mode of hydrostatic eversion of the tentacles which may be reflected in skeletal morphology. Below class level various characters, mostly skeletal, are used but often inconsistently. External characters predominate in identification and classification of cheilostomes, cyclostomes and fenestrates, whereas internal characters, revealed by orientated thin sections, are more usually employed in trepostomes, cystoporates and cryptostomes. Colony form tends to be given greater emphasis in stenolaemates than in cheilostomes where features of the zooecial frontal surface are emphasized. Other important characters include zooecial budding pattern, form and distribution of polymorphs (e.g. gonozooecia in cyclostomes, avicularia in cheilostomes), orifice shape (especially in ascophoran cheilostomes) and intrazooecial structures (e.g. diaphragms in trepostomes) (Figs. 4.1, 4.2).

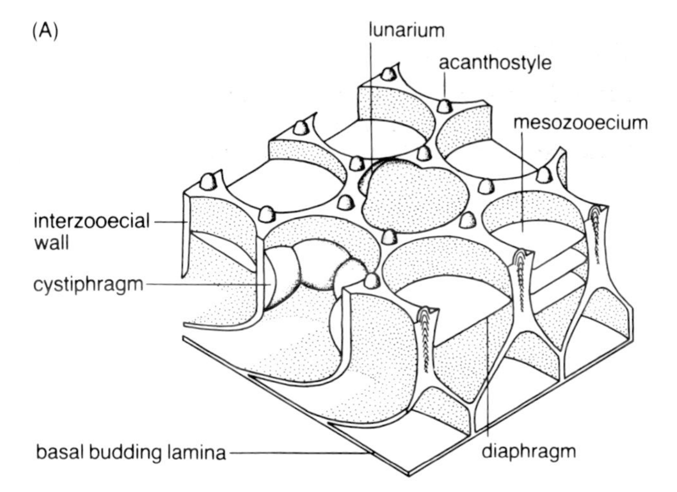

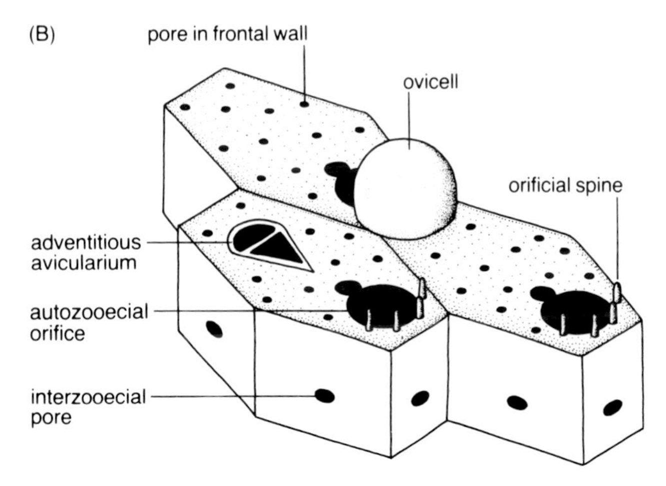

Fig. 4.1. Bryozoan morphology. (A) Cut-away diagram of a hypothetical stenolaemate; (B) diagram of three zooecia of an ascophoran cheilostome.

KEY

1. Zooecial aperture polygonal, circular or elliptical, rarely D-shaped and equipped with a calcified operculum; zooecia generally tubular; ancestrula with a hemispherical protoecium .... 2 (CLASS Stenolaemata)
   Zooecial aperture shaped otherwise, often indented by teeth, etc.; zooecia generally box-shaped; avicularia and small brood chambers (ovicells) usually present.. 6 (ORDER Cheilostomata)
2. Zooecia with calcified exterior frontal walls (usually pseudoporous) and/or interior walls pierced by small, regular pores; large brood chambers usually present either as dilated gonozooecia or extrazooecial chambers .... ORDER Cyclostomata
   Zooecia lacking calcified exterior frontal walls; pores usually absent, but when present large and irregular 3
3. Extrazooecial vesicles present between zooecia and/or zooecia with lunaria; large, irregular pores sometimes present in interior walls; autozooecia regularly patterned, their apertures widely spaced; maculae usually developed in large colonies........................... ORDER Cystoporata
   Otherwise.. 4
4. Zooecial budding zones one- or two-dimensional; colonies erect, typically with delicate branches 5
   Zooecial budding zones extensive; zooecia elongate, thin-walled proximally (in the endozone), thick-walled distally (in the exozone), and typically containing diaphragms; apertures usually polygonal and closely spaced without apparent pattern; acanthostyles, mesozooecia and maculae (including monticules) commonly developed .... ORDER Trepostomata
5. Apertures on one side only of erect colony branches, widely spaced and commonly in longitudinal rows; colony usually reticulate or pinnate, sometimes developing thick secondary calcification .... ORDER Fenestrata
   Apertures on both sides of bifoliate branches or around the entire circumference of narrow cylindrical branches, and regularly arranged, generally in a rhombic pattern or in longitudinal rows; zooecial budding within a narrow axial budding zone, from both sides of a median lamina, or from the outside of an axial tube; colony sometimes jointed .... ORDER Cryptostomata
6. Orifice either set within a wide frontal membrane (leaving a large aperture in fossils) or restricted, typically D-shaped and located at the distal end of a concave frontal cryptocyst (sometimes with paired opesiules) or a costate frontal shield; orifice rarely sinuate; avicularia usually interzooecial... SUBORDER Anasca
   Orifice set within an extensively calcified frontal wall, often sinuate and surrounded by a peristome; frontal shield usually convex, pierced by numerous pores and/or a medial spiramen, and commonly developing thick secondary calcification that obscures zooecial boundaries and may occlude the orifice and pores during late ontogeny; avicularia often adventitious .... SUBORDER Ascophora

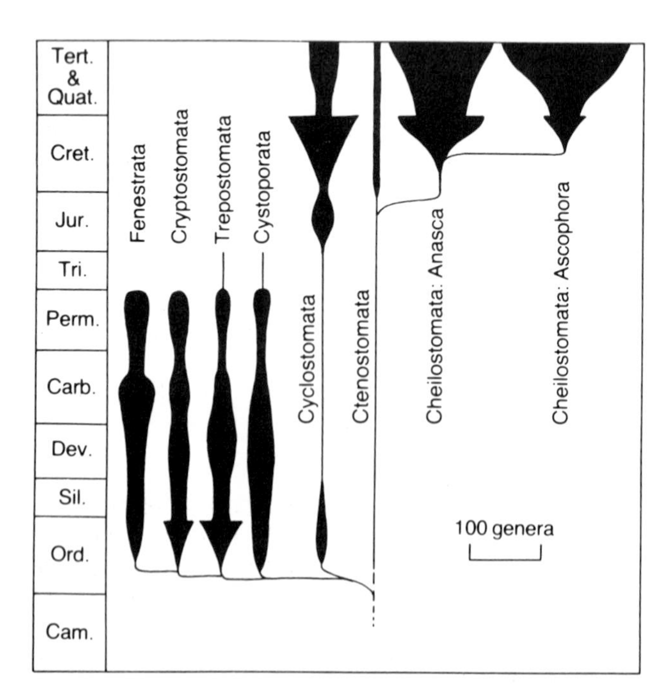

Fig. 4.2. Clade diagram showing stratigraphical ranges, phylogenic relationships and estimated generic diversity in major groups of Bryozoa.

Class Stenolaemata

4.1 Order Cyclostomata

Pl. 4.1.1. *Voigtopora* Bassler, 1952
Colony encrusting with uniserial, bifurcating branches of zooecia occasionally giving rise to lateral branches; zooecial frontal wall broad, somewhat fusiform, pseudoporous and about 1 mm long; apertures terminal, small and circular; polymorphism lacking.
Cretaceous, opportunistic encruster of shells and stones.
Voigtopora calypso (d'Orbigny): (A) L. Cretaceous, Faringdon, England; (B) U. Cretaceous, Le Mans, France, showing origin of lateral branch (lower left).

Pl. 4.1.2. *Hornera* Lamouroux, 1821
Colony erect with subcylindrical branches, about 1 to 2 mm wide, typically bifurcating in 1 plane to give a stagshorn-like appearance; branch obverse occupied by autozooecia surrounded by small, tubular cancelli, reverse by cancelli only; autozooecia elongate, club-shaped, lacking a calcified exterior wall; apertures circular to elliptical; gonozooecia bulbous, formed of porous interior wall, and originating on branch obverse but opening either laterally or on branch reverse.
U. Cretaceous–Recent.
Hornera farehamensis Gregory: Eocene, Fareham, England.

4.2 Order Cystoporata

Pl. 4.2.1. *Fistulipora* McCoy, 1849
Colony initially an encrusting discoidal expansion, sometimes becoming dendroid (solid or hollow) or massive; zooecia thin-walled, tubular, partitioned by diaphragms, usually budded from the basal lamina and rising to meet the colony surface more or less at 90°; apertures circular to elliptical with a poorly developed lunarium; extrazooecial vesicles between zooecia; maculae sometimes present with sparse zooecia and centripetally arranged lunaria.
Silurian–Permian.
Fistulipora incrustans (Phillips): L. Carboniferous, Cracoe, England; (A) tangential section; (B) longitudinal section.

Pl. 4.2.2. *Favositella* Etheridge & Foord, 1884
Colony encrusting, often becoming massive or dome-shaped; zooecia budded mostly from the basal lamina, elongate and partitioned by thin diaphragms; minutely crenulate zooecial walls pierced by large, irregular pores; apertures about 0.3 to

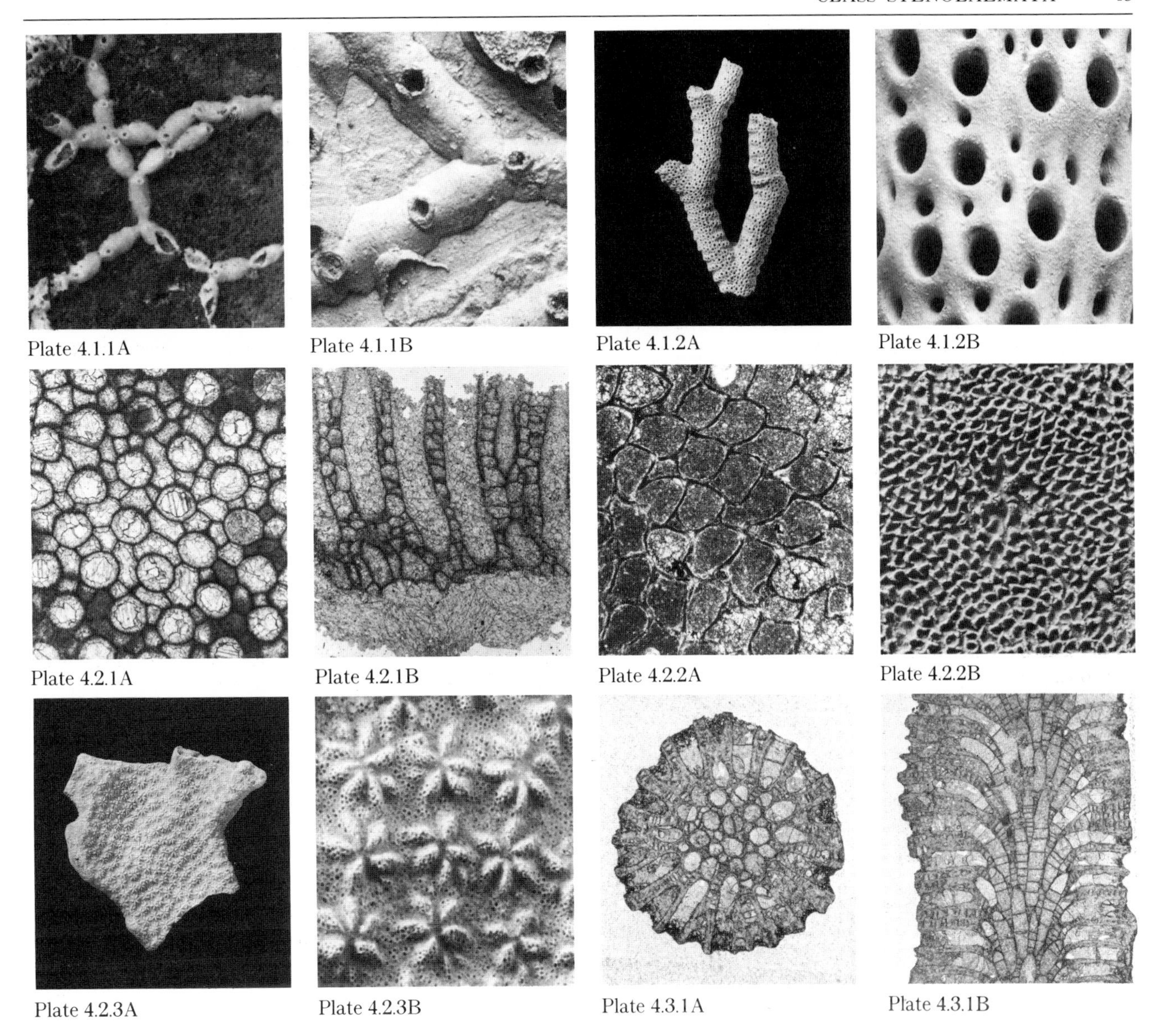

Plate 4.1.1A Plate 4.1.1B Plate 4.1.2A Plate 4.1.2B

Plate 4.2.1A Plate 4.2.1B Plate 4.2.2A Plate 4.2.2B

Plate 4.2.3A Plate 4.2.3B Plate 4.3.1A Plate 4.3.1B

0.6 mm in diameter with moderately well-developed lunarium; maculae have centripetally arranged lunaria and numerous small zooecia; phosphatic pearls commonly found within zooecial chambers, probably formed as a reaction to the presence of foreign inclusions.
Silurian.
Favositella squamata (Lonsdale): Silurian, Dudley, England; (A) external; (B) tangential section.

Pl. 4.2.3. *Constellaria* Dana, 1846
Colony erect, frondose or dendroid, with surface ornamented by star-shaped maculae spaced about 2 to 3 mm apart; zooecia long, thin-walled, partitioned by diaphragms, and separated by extrazooecial vesicles that also form depressed centres of maculae and their radiating channels; lunaria lacking; acanthostyles small, located within walls and roofs of vesicles.
Ordovician.
Constellaria antheloidea Hall: U. Ordovician, Cincinnati, USA.

4.3 Order Trepostomata

Pl. 4.3.1. *Hallopora* Bassler, 1911
Colony erect, dendroid with bifurcating cylindrical branches forming bushes up to 30 cm across; autozooecia budded within the endozone, long, club-shaped, initially polygonal but becoming rounded in cross-section, and partitioned by numerous diaphragms in the endozone but fewer in the exozone; apertures about 0.1 to 0.3 mm in diameter; mesozooecia numerous, budded at periphery of endozone, partitioned by closely spaced diaphragms; acanthostyles lacking.
Parvohallopora has smaller zooecia, especially mesozooecia.
Ordovician–Devonian, often associated with reefs in the British Wenlock.
Hallopora elegantula (Hall): Silurian, Benthall Edge, England; (A) transverse; (B) longitudinal section.

Pl. 4.3.2. *Anisotrypa* Ulrich, 1883
Colony erect, dendroid with bifurcating cylindrical branches, commonly <1 cm in diameter, solid or hollow, sometimes monticulate; zooecia budded within the endozone, long, club-shaped, partitioned by ring diaphragms, and thin-walled distally; apertures polygonal, about 0.3 mm in diameter; acanthostyles and mesozooecia lacking. *Tabulipora* differs in having acanthostyles.
Carboniferous, USA and USSR.
Anisotrypa solida Ulrich: L. Carboniferous, Alabama, USA: (A) external; (B) transverse section; (C) longitudinal section.

4.4 Order Cryptostomata

Pl. 4.4.1. *Rhabdomeson* Young & Young, 1874
Colony erect with bifurcating branches about 1 to 2 mm in diameter, circular in transverse section and containing an axial tube; zooecia budded from wall of axial tube, moderately long and club-shaped; apertures longitudinally elliptical, regularly arranged and surrounded by mega- and microacanthostyles that may project as prominent spines on colony surface.
Carboniferous–Permian, branch fragmentation may have served as a means of reproduction in some species.
Rhabdomeson sp.: Permian, Leonardian, Texas, USA.

Pl. 4.4.2. *Ptilodictya* Lonsdale, 1839
Colony erect, a single bifoliate branch, 2 to 14 mm wide, elliptical or compressed diamond-shaped in transverse section, gently curved, separated by an annular ridge from a short proximal cone that articulated with a socket on the colony base; zooecia rectangular in surface view, budded from a median lamina, rapidly acquiring thick, convexly laminated walls, and arranged in well-defined rows on colony surface, often with a central series of rows parallel to branch length flanked by oblique lateral series.
Ordovician–Devonian, colony bases may occur cemented to hardgrounds.
Ptilodictya lanceolata (Goldfuss): Silurian, Dudley, England.

4.5 Order Fenestrata

Pl. 4.5.1. *Penniretepora* d'Orbigny, 1849
Colony erect, delicate, pinnate with short secondary branches arising alternately from either side of a primary branch about 0.2 to 0.8 mm wide; zooecia short with circular to elliptical apertures arranged in 2 longitudinal rows on obverse of primaries and 1 or 2 rows on secondaries; branch reverse commonly ornamented by longitudinal striae.
Devonian–Permian, usually found in fine-grained, quiet-water deposits.
Penniretepora normalis Olaloye: L. Carboniferous, Carrick Lough, N. Ireland.

Pl. 4.5.2. *Archimedes* Owen, 1838
Colony erect, consisting of a reticulate platform radiating in a continuous spiral from a screw-shaped axis (up to 50 cm high) of thickened laminated calcite; branches, bearing 2 rows of zooecial apertures, linked by dissepiments to enclose rectangular to oval fenestrules; zooecia short, pentagonal in tangential section, with circular or elliptical orifices.
L. Carboniferous–L. Permian, *in situ* colonies often grew immediately leeward of migrating calcarenite dunes from where resistant axes were transported into coarser sediments. USA and USSR.
Archimedes lativolvis Ulrich: L. Carboniferous, Illinois, USA.

Pl. 4.5.3. *Archaeofenestella* Miller, 1962
Colony erect, reticulate, fan-shaped or conical, with wide branches linked by narrow dissepiments to enclose rectangular fenestrules about 0.3 by 0.15 mm; branch obverse bears 2 rows of apertures separated by a prominent carina bearing nodes; zooecia short, rectangular or rhomboidal in tangential section, possessing curved diaphragms and circular or elliptical apertures. *Rectifenestella*, one of several similar genera, has pentagonal zooecia in tangential section and lacks curved diaphragms.
Silurian, zooids probably filtered water through fenestrules from obverse to reverse.
Archaeofenestella rigidula (McCoy): Silurian, Dudley, England.

Class Gymnolaemata

Order Cheilostomata

4.6 Suborder Anasca

Pl. 4.6.1. *Wilbertopora* Cheetham, 1954
Colony encrusting, multiserial; zooecia subhexagonal, about 0.6 to 0.8 mm long, with a narrow area of gymnocyst proximally and laterally, and a raised, finely crenulate mural rim surrounding a large oval opesiae; lateral walls of zooecia shallow, each with a single pore; ovicell small, globular, having a large opening perpendicular to zooecial frontal surface; small kenozooecia and vicarious, spatulate avicularia sometimes developed.
Cretaceous.
Wilbertopora mutabilis Cheetham: L. Cretaceous, Albian, Denton County, Texas, USA.

Pl. 4.6.2. *Onychocella* Jullien, 1882
Colony encrusting and multiserial or, more often, erect and bifoliate with branches about 3 to 5 mm wide; autozooecia with extensive, depressed cryptocyst containing a D-shaped opesiae indented proximo-laterally for the passage of parietal muscles; avicularia vicarious, asymmetrical with a long, curved rostrum and winged mandible; ovicells immersed.
U. Cretaceous–Recent.
Onychocella inelegans (Lonsdale): U. Cretaceous, Bromley, Kent, England.

Pl. 4.6.3. *Lunulites* Lamarck, 1816
Colony free-living, cup-shaped, generally about 5 to 10 mm in diameter, with zooecia opening on the upper convex surface only; autozooecia rectangular to hexagonal, generally arranged in radial rows, with a depressed cryptocyst surrounding a wide circular to rhomboidal opesiae; avicularia vicarious, scattered or in radial rows, typically smaller than autozooecia, with an elongate rostrum often asymmetrical; brooding zooecia large, sometimes with ovicells.
U. Cretaceous–Recent, free-living colonies supported above the sea-bed by mandibles of marginal avicularia. Some species of the related *Selenaria* have mobile colonies.
Lunulites tenax Brydone: U. Cretaceous, Campanian, Wiltshire, England.

Pl. 4.6.4. *Castanopora* Lang, 1906
Colony generally encrusting, multiserial; autozooecia large (often > 1 mm long), oval in frontal outline, with an extensive frontal shield of radially arranged costae fused laterally at intervals with adjacent costae to leave small intercostal pores, and possessing numerous fractured vertical prolongations (pelmata and smaller pelmatidia); orifice D-shaped, surrounded by oral spines; avicularia adventitious, generally distally directed and paired on either side of autozooecial orifices, and having elongate rostra; ovicells extend on to frontal shield of next distal zooecium.
U. Cretaceous–Palaeocene.
Castanopora magnifica (d'Orbigny): U. Cretaceous, Campanian, Norwich, England.

4.7 Suborder Ascophora

Pl. 4.7.1. *Smittina* Norman, 1903
Colony generally encrusting, multiserial; autozooecia rectangular to hexagonal in frontal outline, generally 0.5 to 1 mm long,

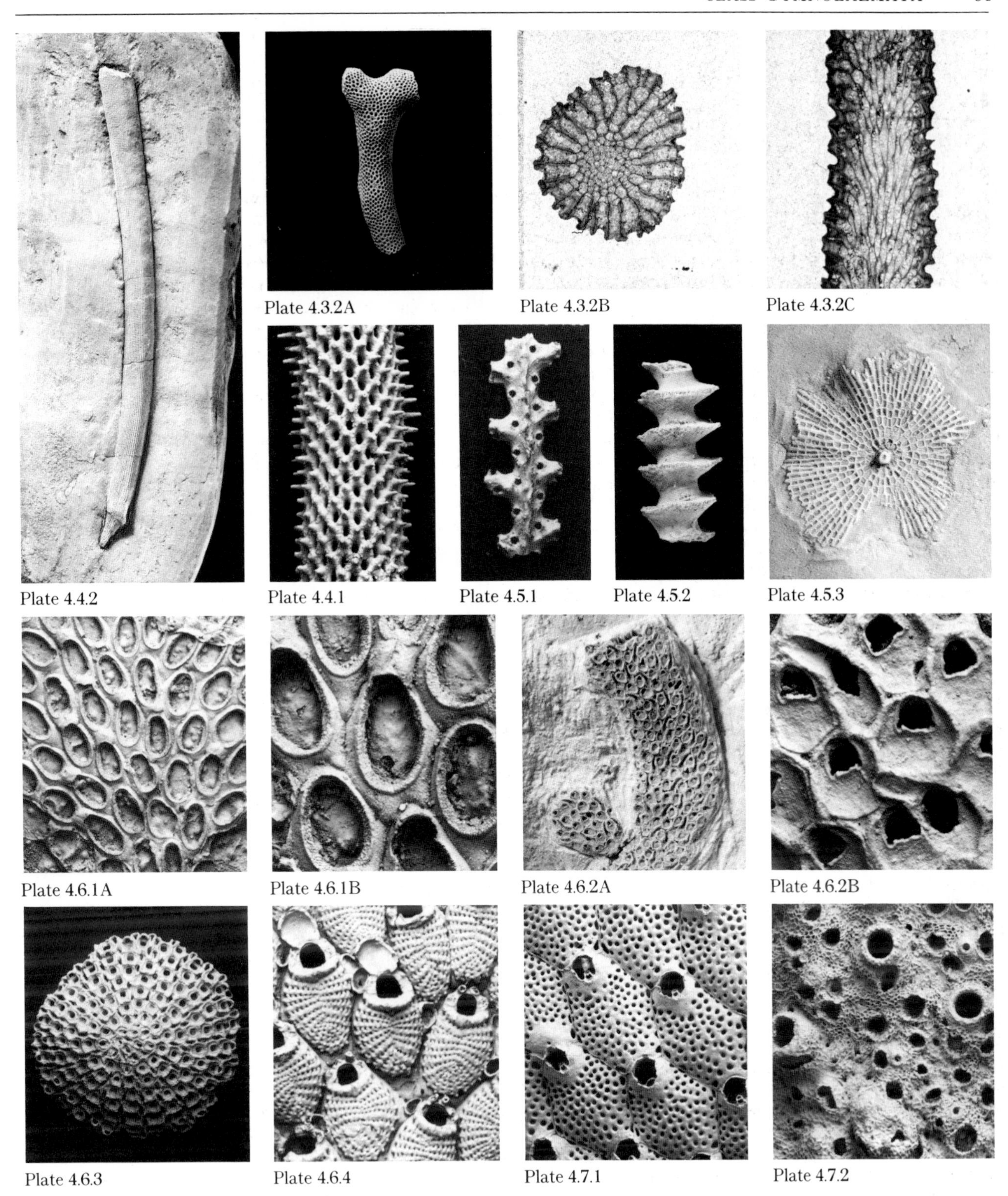

Plate 4.4.2 Plate 4.3.2A Plate 4.3.2B Plate 4.3.2C Plate 4.4.1 Plate 4.5.1 Plate 4.5.2 Plate 4.5.3 Plate 4.6.1A Plate 4.6.1B Plate 4.6.2A Plate 4.6.2B Plate 4.6.3 Plate 4.6.4 Plate 4.7.1 Plate 4.7.2

with extensive, convex cryptocyst porous over its entire surface; primary orifice with a median tooth, peristome and sometimes oral spines; avicularia adventitious, small, ovate with a narrow pivotal bar, and located medially close to proximal border of each autozooecial orifice and directed proximally; ovicell porous.

Smittoidea differs in having an imperforate cryptocyst except for a border of slit-like areoae.

Eocene–Recent.

Smittina exertaviculata Rogick: Holocene, Ross Ice Shelf, Antarctica.

Pl. 4.7.2. *Porina* d'Orbigny, 1852

Colony generally erect, bifoliate with branches a few mm wide; autozooecia elongate, indistinct, with extensive cryptocyst uniformly porous, containing a centrally placed spiramen, and with reticulate micro-ornamentation; primary orifice surrounded by a long peristome and sometimes adventitious avicularia; ovicell rapidly obscured by secondary calcification which also occludes pores and orifices of older zooecia.

U. Cretaceous–Recent.

Porina filograna (Goldfuss): U. Cretaceous, Campanian, Norwich, England.

Pl. 4.7.3. *Metrarabdotos* Canu, 1914

Colony erect and bifoliate, rarely encrusting; autozooecia rectangular to claviform in frontal outline, generally < 1 mm long, with extensive frontal shield bordered by pores located in wide pits; orifice immersed, having a distal oral shelf and proximal denticles, occluded by secondary calcification in old zooecia; avicularia adventitious, usually dimorphic with a pair of small avicularia on each side of the autozooecial orifice and scattered larger avicularia; brooding zooecia with perforate, costate ovicell and a wide, compressed orifice.

U. Eocene–Recent.

Metrarabdotos moniliferum (Milne Edwards): Pliocene, Suffolk, England.

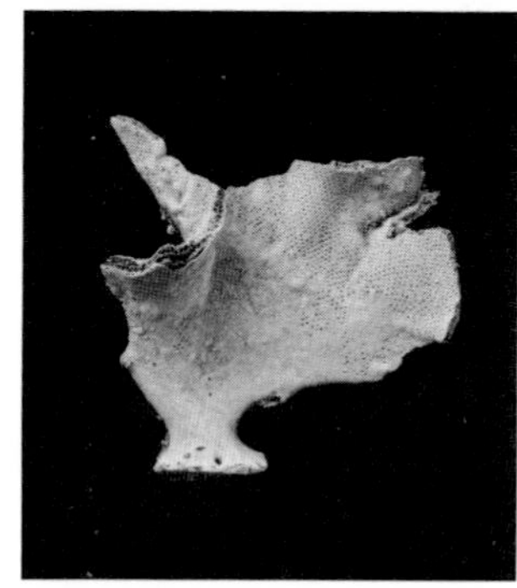

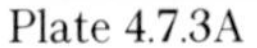

Plate 4.7.3A

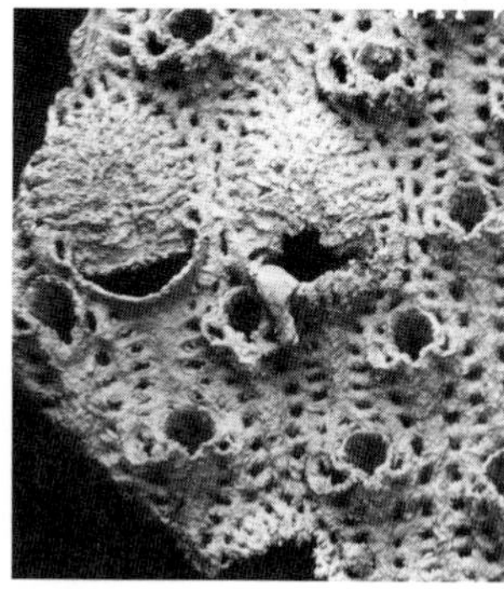

Plate 4.7.3B

CHAPTER 5

Brachiopoda

by L. R. M. Cocks

In many Palaeozoic rocks brachiopods form the bulk of the macrofauna, both in numbers of individuals and in variety of species. There are more than 3400 brachiopod genera known from the earliest Cambrian to the present day, and the selection of only just over 100 genera for inclusion in this book can only be arbitrary. The chief criteria for inclusion have been twofold: firstly, the most well-known and oldest-described genera, and secondly some other genera which illustrate some of the immense diversity of the phylum. Even so, it has not been found practicable to include a minimum of a single genus from each superfamily, let alone family, in this review. Hundreds, perhaps thousands, of genera, whose individuals are overwhelmingly abundant in some rocks, have been omitted.

For those readers relatively unfamiliar with brachiopods, an excellent introduction to them is by Rudwick (1970), where a readable account is given of their zoology, ecology and general history. The technical terms used in describing their morphology are partly summarized in Fig. 5.1 here, but are more exhaustively defined in the *Treatise* (Williams *et al.* 1965). Since the publication of the *Treatise*, and partly because of the impetus from it, the number of brachiopod genera has increased enormously, and a more recent list of these can be found in Doescher (1981).

Brachiopods possess two separate valves, which are known as the brachial valve and the pedicle valve, since in most (but not all) genera the fleshy pedicle protrudes through a hole in the pedicle valve, and the lophophore, or nutrient-gathering apparatus, is attached to the brachial valve. The majority of the Brachiopoda have these two valves physically linked by various forms of articulation, and are thus known as the **Articulata**, while those whose valves are joined merely by muscles are the **Inarticulata**. The lophophore has large numbers of small cilia on it which perform the double function of, firstly, beating rhythmically to cause inhalent and exhalent water currents in the space between the shells, and, secondly, of trapping nutrient particles and passing them to the mouth at the posterior end of the lophophore. The sea-water is separated from the viscera by the mantle, which also lines the inside of the shells, and from which more shell is deposited round the valve margins during growth. Also protruding from the mantle edge are setae, which project beyond the valve edges and act as the only external sensors which the animal possesses. The valves are operated by two separate sets of muscles, the adductors to close the valves together and the diductors to open them. In articulates, the

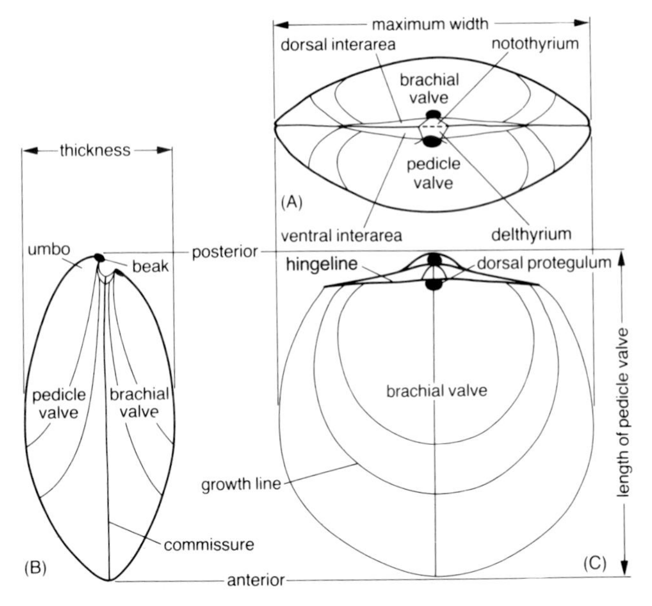

Fig. 5.1. Morphological terms used for brachiopods.

diductors usually run from the central or posterior part of the pedicle valve to a small knob or knobs at the posterior end of the brachial valve and overhanging the hinge line, known as the cardinal process. Although brachiopods are bisexual, sexual differences are rarely directly reflected in the shell morphology.

Studies on living and fossil brachiopods have been published since well before the time of Linnaeus in the eighteenth century, but it was in the nineteenth century that the bulk of collection and simple species description was achieved, particularly in Europe and eastern North America, and in our own century that a satisfactory classification has been forged, at least for the articulate brachiopods. The classification of the inarticulates, of which only just over 200 genera are known, is less certain, chiefly because of the smaller number of distinctive structures many possess. The publication of the *Treatise on Invertebrate Paleontology* (Williams *et al.* 1965) marked a turning-point in brachiopod studies, since it was able to summarize the work of many authors, notably Williams himself, and integrate the ultrastructural studies of the brachiopod shell with an inherently natural scheme of classification. Thus the seven orders of the Articulata securely embrace all but two of the articulate superfamilies known, and our knowledge of the phylogeny of the class may be summarized with some confidence (Fig. 5.2).

The zoological relationships of the Articulata to the Inarticulata and other groups of lophophorates remain obscure. Wright (1979) has postulated descent from several related soft-bodied ancestors comparable with the phoronid worms, but our knowledge of the latest Precambrian and earliest Cambrian animals of these groups is sparse. Several quite distinct groups of brachiopods, the Orthida, Lingulida, Obolellida, Acrotretida, Paterinida and Kutorginida, are all present in rocks of L. Cambrian age, and the relationships between them form the subject of an elegant analysis by Rowell (1982), who concludes that the origin of the brachiopods was probably monophyletic, with one cluster (of the Lingulida, Obolellida and Acrotretida) possibly more primitive than a second cluster (of the Paterinida, Kutorginida and Orthida) from which other articulates evolved.

The ecology of the brachiopods has varied with time. Most of the Cambrian forms appear to have lived chiefly on the shallower parts of the shelf, but the phylum slowly diversified during the L. Palaeozoic into more varied niches, until by early Devonian times they were able to live on a variety of substrates at all depths on the continental shelf and probably the upper part of the continental slope (McKerrow 1978). From late Palaeozoic times to the present, they are even recorded rarely from abyssal depths. Most brachiopods are epifaunal, standing clear of the sea-floor or clinging to rocks or other objects with their functional pedicles; but some have no functional pedicles as adults and lived free on the sea-floor, relying on the weight of their valves, mainly in softer substrates, to allow them to keep in a lifelong attitude which would keep their anterior commisures clear of the potentially choking sediment. *Lingula* and its allies are unique in the phylum in developing a burrowing habit. Since Permian times, brachiopods have been overtaken by molluscs in diversity and abundance, but even today they may be found in great numbers at many localities over a wide range of environments. The average brachiopod lives to an age of between five and seven years.

5.1 Class Inarticulata

All nine inarticulate superfamilies had evolved by M. Ordovician times, but only three, the Lingulacea, Discinacea and Craniacea, survived the Devonian. There are five orders, largely defined on shell structure and composition: the Obolellacea (L.–M. Cambrian), Paterinacea (L. Cambrian–M. Ordovician) and Kutorginacea (L.–M. Cambrian) each have their own order but are not dealt with further here. The shell structure of inarticulates is variable, and includes calcite, aragonite and phosphate with various organic additions.

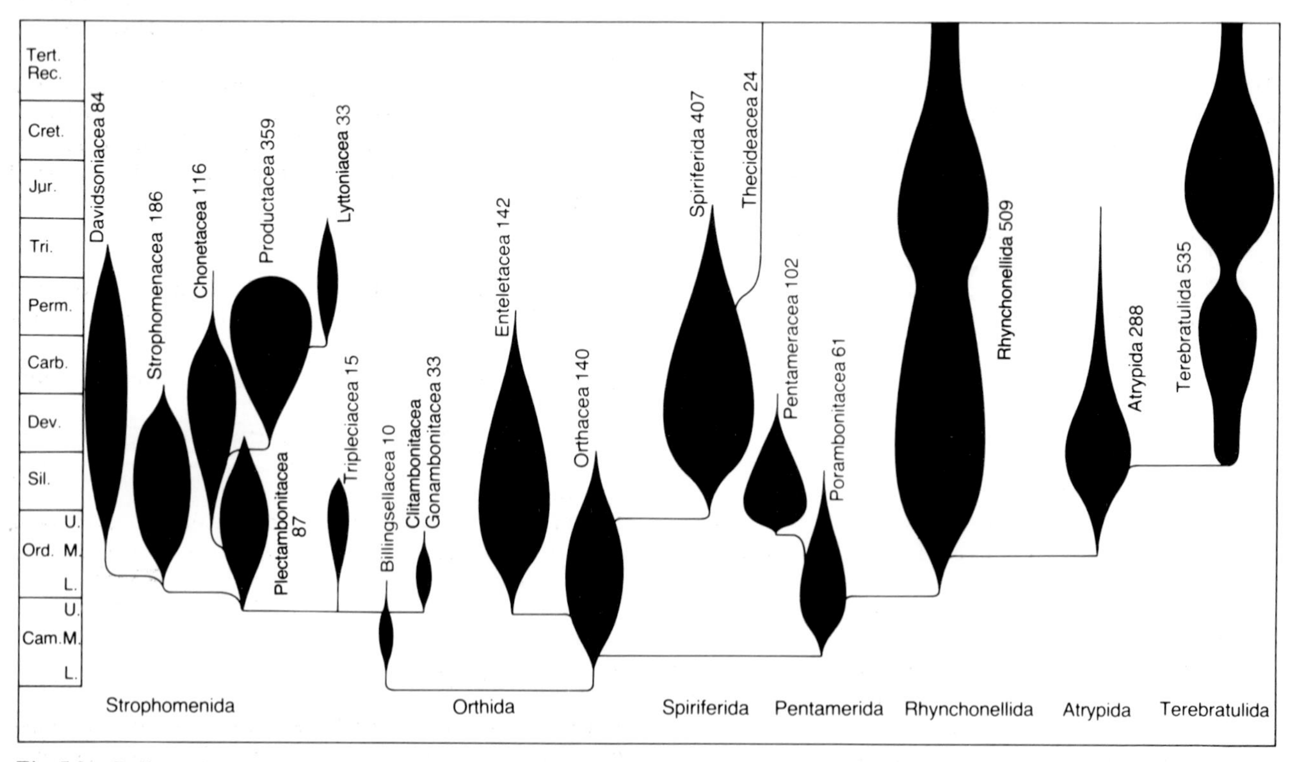

Fig. 5.2. Balloon diagram to show the diversity and stratigraphic range of articulate brachiopod orders and superfamilies.

Plate 5.1.1A Plate 5.1.1B Plate 5.1.2A Plate 5.1.2B Plate 5.1.3A

Plate 5.1.3B Plate 5.1.3C Plate 5.1.4A Plate 5.1.4B

Order Lingulida

Biconvex inarticulate brachiopods with the pedicle emerging between the 2 valves at the posterior ends. Shell substance variable, usually chitinophosphatic but sometimes calcareous and usually impunctate. Lingulides have the longest history of any animal group and are known from the Lower Cambrian to the present.

SUPERFAMILY LINGULACEA
Shells of calcium phosphate: pedicle emerging from between valves.

Pl. 5.1.1. *Lingula* Bruguière, 1797
Biconvex; different species more or less equivalve: suboval to spade-like outlines; ornament of numerous extremely fine subequal ribs. The fleshy pedicle can be as long as the shell. Interiors of both valves have a pseudointerarea at the apex; that of the pedicle valve with a broadly triangular groove for the pedicle. Average adult shell length 1 to 3 cm.
Ordovician (?Caradoc)–Recent, cosmopolitan. Distinctive ecology of burrowing in various (often badly sorted) substrates; intertidal to deep-water.
Lingula symondsi Davidson: Coalbrookdale Beds (Wenlock), Buildwas, Shropshire, England; pedicle and side views of conjoined valves.

Pl. 5.1.2. *Lingulella* Salter, 1866
Shallowly biconvex; elongately suboval to subrectangular outline; no external ornament, but inner shell layers have fine radial striae. Internally differs from *Lingula* in pseudointerarea divided into 2, with an inner proparea. Average adult length 1 to 3 cm.
L. Cambrian–Ordovician (Ashgill), cosmopolitan, usually semi-infaunal, though later species may have burrowed; more common in shallower-water sediments.
Lingulella ampla Owen: St Croix Sandstone (U. Cambrian), Dresbach, Minnesota, USA; pedicle and brachial valve exteriors.

SUPERFAMILY TRIMERELLACEA
This superfamily is unique among brachiopods in possessing an aragonitic shell.

Pl. 5.1.3. *Trimerella* Billings, 1862
Biconvex, with subtriangular pedicle valve outline and subcircular brachial valve; large pseudointerarea in pedicle valve; no ornament. Complex system of septa and umbonal cavities in interior of both valves, which probably served as muscle-attachment platforms. Average adult width 4 to 6 cm.
Silurian (Wenlock–Pridoli), Europe, Asia, N. America. Occurs as bioherm builder, subvertical with umbones downwards on chiefly lime-mud substrates.
Trimerella ohioensis Meek: Ludlow, Otwa County, Ohio, USA; pedicle and brachial views of natural mould of conjoined valves; *T. lindstroemi* (Dall): Klinteberg Limestone (Ludlow), Gotland, Sweden, exterior of brachial valve (beneath) and interarea of pedicle valve.

Pl. 5.1.4. *Dinobolus* Hall, 1871
Gently biconvex with subcircular outline; maximum width at about half valve length; very low pseudointerarea; ornament only of lamellose growth lines. Interior with diagonal platforms (presumably muscle supports) in both valves. Average adult width 3 to 5 cm.
Silurian (Llandovery–Ludlow), Europe, Asia, N. America. Sometimes solitary, sometimes in clumps on sand, silt and mud substrates.
Dinobolus davidsoni (Salter): Coalbrookdale Fm. (Wenlock), Walsall, West Midlands, England; partly exfoliated brachial and pedicle valves.

Order Acrotretida

Subcircular inarticulate brachiopods with the pedicle opening, when present, confined to the pedicle valve. Shell substance variable: phosphatic or calcareous with punctae. There are four superfamilies, two with representatives described here, and also the Acrotretacea (L. Cambrian–Devonian), in which most genera have conical pedicle valves, and which tend to be of very small size, and the Siphonotretacea (U. Cambrian–M. Silurian), which have spines. All have phosphatic shells, apart from the calcareous Craniacea.

SUPERFAMILY DISCINACEA

This superfamily is distinguished by the holoperipheral growth of the pedicle valve, which lacks a pseudointerarea.

Pl. 5.1.5. *Trematis* Sharpe, 1848
Subcircular to suboval outline; pedicle valve with triangular notch for pedicle in juveniles. Distinctive ornament of pits, chiefly developed in middle shell layers – these pits can be arranged in various geometrical patterns in different species. Relatively simple interior with slightly impressed muscle scars. Average adult width 2 to 4 cm.
Ordovician (Llandeilo–Ashgill), cosmopolitan attached to variable substrates by functional pedicle; usually shallower-water.
Trematis norvegica Cocks: Langøyene Fm. (Ashgill), Oslo, Norway; pedicle valve and brachial valve (with epifaunal cricoconariid); *T. terminalis* (Emmons): Trenton Limestone (Caradoc), Trenton Falls, New York, USA; close up to show pits on partly exfoliated brachial valve.

Pl. 5.1.6. *Orbiculoidea* d'Orbigny, 1847
Subcircular outline; brachial valve gently conical; pedicle valve subconical with slit for pedicle (open posteriorly in juveniles, closed in adults). Ornament of accentuated concentric growth lines. Interior with low median muscle support ridge in brachial valve. Average adult width 1 to 2 cm.
Ordovician (Caradoc)–Permian, cosmopolitan, attached singly to variable substrates in mid-shelf by functional pedicle.
Orbiculoidea rugata (J. de C. Sowerby): Whitcliffe Beds (Ludlow), Shropshire; exterior and exfoliated interior of pedicle valve and brachial valve exterior.

SUPERFAMILY CRANIACEA

This superfamily, members of which such as *Crania* itself are still living, is unique in possessing no pedicle. Some genera lived free, others were cemented to the substrate by all or part of their pedicle valves.

Pl. 5.1.7. *Ancistrocrania* Dall, 1877
Subcircular outline with straight posterior margin; apex posterior of valve centre; ornament of concentric pustules. Interior with holoperipheral rim; pair of circular muscle scars on both valves, with additional smaller scars; brachial valve interior with pair of processes near apex; prominent vascular markings. Average adult width 1 cm.
U. Cretaceous–?Recent, Europe. Cemented by valve exterior to algae or other objects above chiefly lime-mud substrates.
Ancistrocrania tuberculata (Nilsson): U. Danian (Palaeocene), Copenhagen, Denmark; exterior and interior views of pedicle valves.

5.2 Class Articulata

Articulate brachiopods all have calcite shells, apart from a very thin exterior organic layer known as the periostracum which is very rarely fossilized. All 7 orders have representatives described here, as well as the Eichwaldiacea and the Thecideacea, whose ordinal position is less certain.

Order Orthida

This order includes the root-stock of all articulate brachiopods. Apart from the Enteletacea and the Gonambonitacea, all the superfamilies have impunctate shells.

SUPERFAMILY BILLINGSELLACEA

Billingsellaceans are among the earliest fossils of any phyla known from the basal Cambrian. They have impunctate shells, and a delthyrium covered by an arched pseudodeltidium.

Pl. 5.2.1. *Billingsella* Hall & Clarke, 1892
Rectangular to subpentagonal outline; maximum width at hinge line; large interarea with large delthyrium partly covered by apical plate. Ornament of rounded radial ribs. Interior with simple teeth and sockets; single-lobed cardinal process; suboval impressed muscle fields. Average adult width 1 to 1.5 cm.
M. Cambrian–Ordovician (Arenig), cosmopolitan, umbones downwards on sand, silt or lime-mud substrates with functional pedicle.
Billingsella perfecta Ulrich & Cooper: U. Cambrian, Teton Creek, Wyoming, USA; pedicle valve interior; *B. corrugata* Ulrich & Cooper: U. Cambrian, Fort Sill, Oklahoma, USA, brachial valve interior.

SUPERFAMILY ORTHACEA

Orthaceans derived from billingsellaceans in the early Cambrian. They have impunctate shells and usually possess an open delthyrium, or one with additionally secreted plates.

Pl. 5.2.2. *Orthis* Dalman, 1828
Subcircular outline, with relatively short hinge line; maximum width at about half valve length; pedicle valve convex, brachial valve gently convex or flat; simple open delthyrium. Ornament of numerous sharp-crested subequal ribs. Interior with simple teeth and sockets and simple single cardinal process; suboval pedicle valve muscle field, and subcircular, sometimes divided, brachial valve muscle field. Average adult width 2 cm.
Ordovician (Arenig–Llandeilo), cosmopolitan, umbones downwards, with functional pedicle on variable substrates.
Orthis calligramma Dalman: L. Ordovician, Pavlovsk, Leningrad, USSR; brachial, pedicle and side views of conjoined valves.

Pl. 5.2.3. *Nicolella* Reed, 1917
Semicircular outline with maximum width at hinge line; pedicle valve convex, brachial valve flat or gently concave; simple open delthyrium. Ornament of numerous sharp-crested subequal ribs, and a tendency to frills at some anterior growth lines. Interior with simple teeth and sockets; simple cardinal process supported anteriorly by a low median swelling. Average adult width 2 to 3 cm.
Ordovician (Llandeilo–Ashgill), cosmopolitan, umbones downwards with functional pedicle over sand, silt and lime-mud substrates.
Nicolella actoniae (J. de C. Sowerby): Acton Scott Beds (Caradoc), Shropshire, England; internal mould of pedicle valve and internal and external views of brachial valve.

Pl. 5.2.4. *Glyptorthis* Foerste, 1914
Subquadrangular outline with maximum width at about half valve length; biconvex. Distinctive ornament of numerous rounded ribs and accentuated growth lines with frilly lamellae. Interior with stout simple teeth and sockets; single thin blade-like median septum; pair of suboval muscle scars in both pedicle and brachial valves. Average adult width 2 cm.
Ordovician (Llandeilo)–Silurian (Wenlock), cosmopolitan,

Plate 5.1.5A

Plate 5.1.5B

Plate 5.1.5C

Plate 5.1.6A

Plate 5.1.6B

Plate 5.1.6C

Plate 5.1.7A

Plate 5.1.7B

Plate 5.2.1A

Plate 5.2.1B

Plate 5.2.2A

Plate 5.2.2B

Plate 5.2.2C

Plate 5.2.3A

Plate 5.2.3B

Plate 5.2.3C

Plate 5.2.4A

Plate 5.2.4B

Plate 5.2.4C

umbones downwards attached by functional pedicle to a variety of sand, silt and mud substrates.
Glyptorthis pulchra Wang: Maquoketa Fm. (Ashgill), Winn County, Iowa, USA; pedicle and brachial valve interiors; *G. bellarugosa* (Conrad): Rye Cove, Virginia, USA; pedicle valve exterior.

Pl. 5.2.5. *Skenidioides* Schuchert & Cooper, 1931
Subpyramidal shape, with very large triangular interarea with large open delthyrium and convex pedicle valve; brachial valve flat to gently convex with a slight anterior sulcus; maximum width near hinge line. Ornament of numerous ribs. Interior with simple articulation; blade-like cardinal process continuous with prominent brachial valve median septum; spondylium in pedicle valve; suboval muscle field in brachial valve. Average adult width 0.5 to 1 cm.
Ordovician (Llanvirn)–Devonian (Gedinnian), cosmopolitan, attached by functional pedicle in various attitudes to other shells, algae and small particles on a variety of substrates.
Skenidioides lewisii (Davidson): Tickwood Beds (Wenlock), Shropshire, England; brachial and oblique views of conjoined valves; *S. woodlandiensis* (Davidson): Newlands Fm. (Llandovery), Girvan, Scotland, mould of brachial valve interior.

Pl. 5.2.6. *Platystrophia* King, 1850
Subrectangular outline with maximum width either at hinge line or at mid-valve length; small interarea; biconvex with prominent pedicle valve sulcus and brachial valve fold. Ornament of numerous sharp-crested ribs. Interior with simple teeth and sockets, but widely divergent brachiophore supports; prominent bilobed pedicle valve muscle field with lateral and posterior bounding area of thicker shell. Average adult width 3 to 5 cm.
Ordovician (Caradoc)–Silurian (Wenlock), cosmopolitan; umbones downwards, resting obliquely on pedicle valve with functional pedicle on various sand to mud substrates.
Platystrophia biforata (Schlotheim): Hudson River Group (Caradoc), Cincinnati, Ohio, USA; pedicle and side views of conjoined valves and pedicle valve interior.

SUPERFAMILY ENTELETACEA
Like Orthacea, but with punctate shell structure.

Pl. 5.2.7. *Dalmanella* Hall & Clarke, 1892
Subcircular outline; convex pedicle valve with small interarea and incurved beak, gently convex brachial valve with slight median sulcus in some species. Ornament of numerous rounded curved ribs with new ribs arising anteriorly. Interior with simple teeth and sockets, the teeth supported by dental plates, and the sockets merging with small erect brachiophores and the slight median ridge in the brachial valve. Average adult width 1 to 2 cm.
Ordovician (Llandeilo)–Silurian (Llandovery), cosmopolitan; attached by functional pedicle to small particles over a variety of substrates.
Dalmanella testudinaria (Dalman): Langøyene Sandstone (Ashgill), Oslo, Norway; brachial view of exterior of conjoined valves and natural moulds of pedicle and brachial valve interiors.

Pl. 5.2.8. *Dicoelosia* King, 1850
Subtriangular outline, distinctively bilobed; short hinge line; convex pedicle valve with incurved beak; medium-sized interarea and open delthyrium; brachial valve gently convex or concave in some species. Ornament of numerous fine branching curved ribs, and often of prominent growth lines as well. Interior with simple teeth and sockets; short cardinal process and long blade-like brachiophore plates. Average adult width 0.4 to 0.8 cm.
Ordovician (Caradoc)–Devonian (Emsian), cosmopolitan, attached by functional pedicle in a variety of attitudes to bryozoan twigs, etc. or small fragments in chiefly fine-grained substrates.
Dicoelosia biloba (Linnaeus): Wenlock Shale, Dudley, West Midlands, England; exterior of conjoined valves and brachial and pedicle valve interiors.

Pl. 5.2.9. *Heterorthis* Hall & Clarke, 1892
Subcircular outline with maximum width near half valve length; gently convex pedicle valve, flat brachial valve; relatively small interareas. Ornament of fine and numerous ribs over whole valve surfaces. Interior with simple teeth and sockets; dental plates blending anterolaterally into muscle bounding ridges; prominent muscle scars in both valves; simple cardinal process between prong-like brachiophore bases. Average adult width 2.5 to 3.5 cm.
Ordovician (Llandeilo–Ashgill), cosmopolitan, umbones downwards with functional pedicle in common clumps on silt or lime-mud substrates.
Heterorthis alternata (J. de C. Sowerby): Alternata Limestone (Caradoc), Horderley, Shropshire, England; interior views of natural moulds of pedicle and brachial valves.

Pl. 5.2.10. *Hirnantia* Lamont, 1935
Subcircular outline with maximum width at half valve length; low triangular interarea with open delthyrium; gently biconvex. Ornament of numerous relatively fine ribs. Interior with large simple teeth and sockets, the former supported by dental plates forming the posterolateral border of the pedicle valve muscle field; strong diverging brachiophore plates in the brachial valve and small cardinal process. Average adult width 1.5 to 4 cm.
Ordovician (Caradoc)–Silurian (Llandovery), cosmopolitan, commonest in latest Ashgill *Hirnantia* Fauna, umbones downwards with functional pedicle on variable substrates.
Hirnantia sagittifera (M'Coy): Langøyene Fm. (Ashgill), Oslo, Norway, interior views of natural moulds of pedicle and brachial valves, and brachial valve exterior.

Pl. 5.2.11. *Rhipidomella* Oehlert, 1890
Subcircular outline with maximum width at about half valve length; biconvex; short hinge line; small interareas; incurved umbones. Ornament of numerous rounded ribs. Interior with relatively large simple teeth and sockets, the former merging anterolaterally with a ridge surrounding the subcircular bilobed pedicle valve muscle field; cardinal process prominent and globose; brachial valve muscle field bilobed. Average adult width 1 to 2 cm.
Devonian (Gedinnian)–U. Permian, cosmopolitan, umbones downwards, held by small but functional pedicle to small particles in silts and muds.
Rhipidomella vanuxemi (Hall): Hamilton Group (M. Devonian), Erie County, New York, USA; brachial and side views of conjoined valves and brachial valve interior.

Pl. 5.2.12. *Schizophoria* King, 1850
Subcircular to subquadrangular outline with maximum width at half valve length; relatively small interareas; unequally biconvex, with greater convexity in brachial valve, leading anteriorly to a broad brachial valve fold and pedicle valve sulcus. Fine, unequally parvicostellate ribbing. Interior with strong simple teeth and sockets, the teeth supported by dental plates extending into muscle bounding ridges; large cardinal process. Average adult width 3 to 5 cm.
Silurian (Pridoli)–Permian, cosmopolitan, umbones downwards

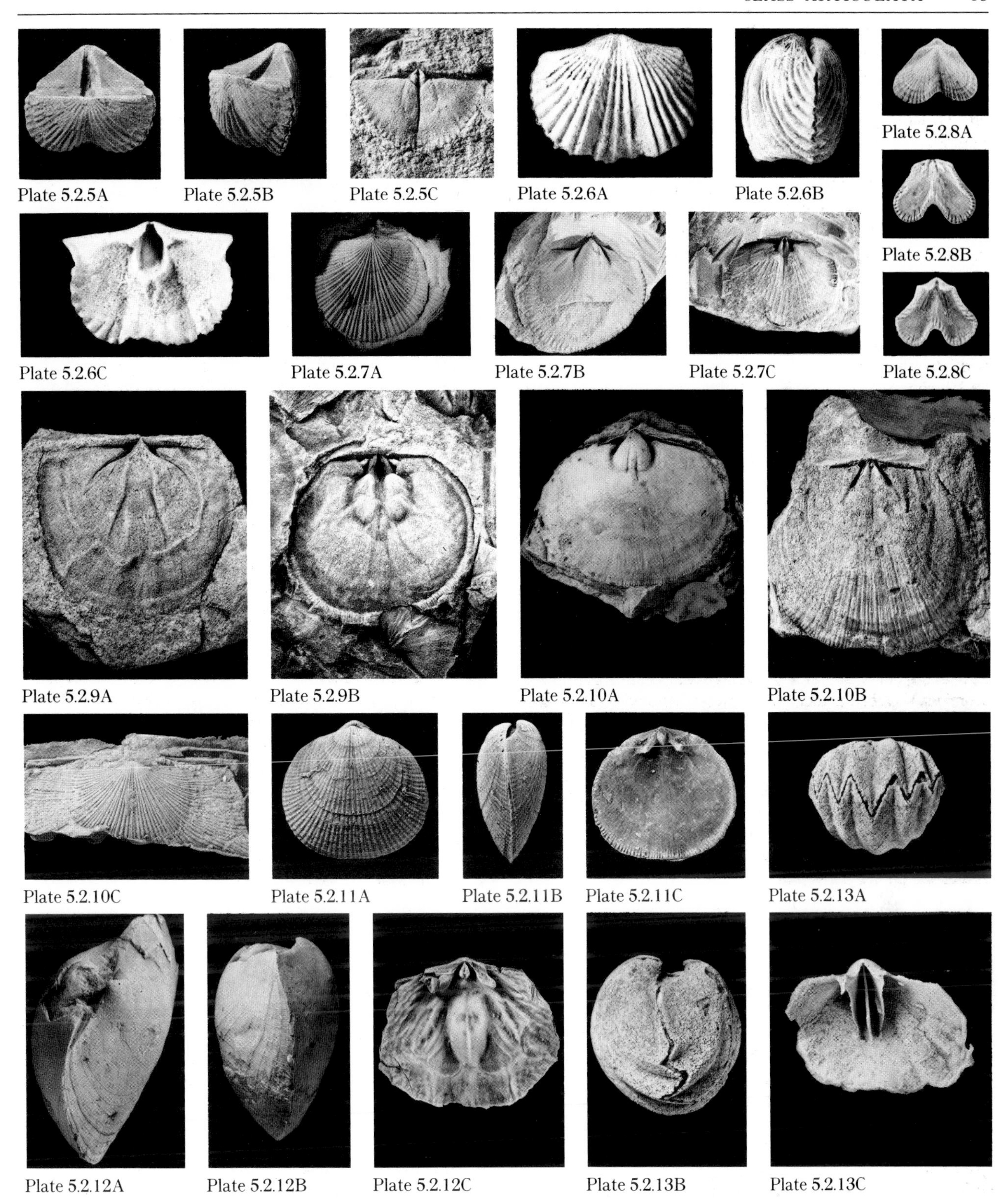

Plate 5.2.5A Plate 5.2.5B Plate 5.2.5C Plate 5.2.6A Plate 5.2.6B Plate 5.2.8A Plate 5.2.8B Plate 5.2.6C Plate 5.2.7A Plate 5.2.7B Plate 5.2.7C Plate 5.2.8C Plate 5.2.9A Plate 5.2.9B Plate 5.2.10A Plate 5.2.10B Plate 5.2.10C Plate 5.2.11A Plate 5.2.11B Plate 5.2.11C Plate 5.2.13A Plate 5.2.12A Plate 5.2.12B Plate 5.2.12C Plate 5.2.13B Plate 5.2.13C

and resting obliquely on brachial valve on chiefly lime-mud substrates.
Schizophoria resupinata (Martin): L. Carboniferous (Viséan), Visé, Belgium; oblique and side views of conjoined valves; Viséan, Cam Beck, Yorkshire, England; interior view of brachial valve.

Pl. 5.2.13. *Enteletes* Fischer de Waldheim, 1825
Subtriangular outline with both valves very convex; maximum width near anterior; short hinge line but large open delthyrium. Coarse ornament of 7 to 9 sharply crested ribs best developed anteriorly. Interior with large teeth and sockets; large thin dental plates and pedicle valve median septum; brachial valve with strong socket plates and large brachiophores curving upwards into the pedicle valve. Average adult width 3 to 4 cm. U. Carboniferous–U. Permian, cosmopolitan, umbones downwards with functional pedicle on variable substrates.
Enteletes subcircularis Cooper & Grant: Hess Fm. (Permian), Texas, USA; anterior and side views of conjoined valves and pedicle valve interior.

SUPERFAMILY CLITAMBONITACEA

Impunctate shells. Dental plates on spondylium merging with pedicle valve median septum. The superfamily is confined to the Ordovician.

Pl. 5.2.14. *Clitambonites* Agassiz, 1846
Subquadrangular outline with maximum width at or near hinge line; convex pedicle valve, flat to gently convex brachial valve; large interarea with delthyrium covered by pseudodeltidium with pedicle opening at apex; chilidium on brachial valve interarea. Ornament of numerous fine ribs and accentuated frilly growth lines. Interior with strong simple teeth and sockets; large spondylium; brachial valve with strong socket plates; low median septum and small simple cardinal process. Average adult width 2 to 3 cm.
Ordovician (Arenig–Caradoc), Europe, Asia, umbones downwards with functional pedicle on a variety of substrates.
Clitambonites maximus (Pahlen): Kukruse Fm. (Caradoc), Kohtla-Järve, Estonia, USSR; interiors of pedicle and brachial valves and exterior of conjoined valves.

SUPERFAMILY GONAMBONITACEA
Like clitambonitaceans but with pseudopunctate shell structure.

Pl. 5.2.15. *Kullervo* Öpik, 1932
Subpyramidal shape with convex pedicle valve; very large triangular interarea; delthyrium with large pedicle foramen with lip round it apical to a substantial pseudodeltidium. Ornament of numerous irregular ribs and prominent raised growth lines. Interior with pedicle valve divided into 3 parts by the spondylium and median septum; simple teeth and sockets; low brachial valve median ridge. Average adult width 0.7 to 1.5 cm.
Ordovician (?Llandeilo–Ashgill), cosmopolitan, attached by functional pedicle, probably lying on large interarea on chiefly lime-mud substrates.
Kullervo complectens (Wiman): Portrane Limestone (Ashgill), Portrane, Co. Dublin, Ireland; exterior, posterior and interior views of pedicle valve.

SUPERFAMILY TRIPLECIACEA
Tripleciaceans have variable external morphology, but are united in possessing a distinctive long forked cardinal process. Shell substance impunctate.

Pl. 5.2.16. *Triplesia* Hall, 1859
Subcircular to suboval outline; maximum width at about half valve length; biconvex and globose, with large brachial valve fold and corresponding pedicle valve sulcus; small interarea; no ornament. Interior with prominent dental plates, teeth and sockets; brachial valve with short, flaring brachiophores merging with base of massive cardinal process. Average adult width 2 to 4 cm.
Ordovician (Caradoc)–Silurian (Wenlock) cosmopolitan, attached by small functional pedicle umbones downwards, chiefly in softer and finer substrates.
Triplesia extans (Emmons): Trenton Group (Caradoc), Watertown, New York, USA, anterior, posterior and brachial views of conjoined valves.

Pl. 5.2.17. *Streptis* Davidson, 1881
Suboval outline; maximum width at mid-valve length; biconvex, both valves sulcate medianly with variable convexities on either side of the sulci, so that one half of the shell is deflected upwards and the other half downwards. Ornament of concentric lamellose frills. Interior with pedicle tube, dental plates, simple teeth and sockets; divergent brachiophore plates merging with the base of the massive cardinal process. Average adult width 1 cm.
Ordovician (Ashgill)–Silurian (Wenlock), cosmopolitan, attached by functional pedicle to small items on various substrates.
Streptis grayii (Davidson): Wenlock Limestone, Walsall, West Midlands, England; brachial, pedicle and anterior views of conjoined valves.

Order Uncertain

SUPERFAMILY EICHWALDIACEA
This group of 4 genera, ranging in age from the M. Ordovician to the Permian, is unique in possessing an inset smooth triangular plate in the exterior of the umbo of the pedicle valve. Its affinities are uncertain; they may lie among early Orthida or Pentamerida.

Pl. 5.2.18. *Dictyonella* Hall, 1868
Subtriangular outline; biconvex, with very gentle brachial valve fold; little interarea; distinctive criss-cross ornament of small pits. Interior; pedicle valve with umbonal and posterior overhanging ledges; brachial valve with median septum; no teeth or dental plates, articulation was by grooves and ridges along the posterolateral edges of both valves; rudimentary knob as cardinal process. Average adult width 1 cm.
Ordovician (Ashgill)–Silurian (Ludlow), cosmopolitan, a chitinous pad on the triangular plate probably attached the shell to the substrate.
Dictyonella reticulata (Hall): Waldron Shale (Wenlock), Waldron, Indiana, USA; brachial and side views of conjoined valves; *D. gibbosa* (Hall): Decatur Fm. (Ludlow), Linden, Tennessee, USA; interior of brachial valve.

Order Strophomenida

These brachiopods are the only ones with pseudopunctate shells. The order diversified greatly during the Palaeozoic, and is classified into 8 superfamilies. Strophomenaceans in the Ordovician to Devonian and productaceans in the later Palaeozoic dominated the shelf benthos in many assemblages.

SUPERFAMILY PLECTAMBONITACEA
Early strophomenides with a trifid cardinal process.

Pl. 5.2.19. *Leangella* Öpik, 1933
Shallowly convex pedicle valve and concave brachial valve; relatively large interarea. Ornament of 5 to 15 widely spaced costellae with smaller parvicostellae between them. Pedicle interior with bilobed muscle bounding ridges; brachial valve interior with 2 raised concentric ridges of secondary calcite, 1 near the valve rim, the inner 'W' shape anteriorly and posteriorly merging with the base of the socket plates. Average adult width 0.5 to 1.5 cm.
Ordovician (Caradoc)–Silurian (Ludlow), cosmopolitan, either attached or oblique on sea-floor on pedicle valve with small but functional pedicle.
Leangella scissa (Davidson): Haverford Fm. (Llandovery), Haverfordwest, Dyfed, Wales; pedicle and brachial valve interiors.

Pl. 5.2.20. *Sowerbyella* Jones, 1928
Pedicle valve convex, brachial valve concave. Ornament of up to 25 primary costae with 6 to 10 parvicostellae between adjacent costellae. Interior; hinge line smooth; simple pedicle valve teeth locking into brachial valve sockets. Thin, small median septum confined to posterior of pedicle valve; prominent muscle scars. Pair of divergent septa in brachial interior. Average adult width 0.7 to 1.5 cm.
Ordovician (Llandeilo–Ashgill), cosmopolitan, adults free-lying

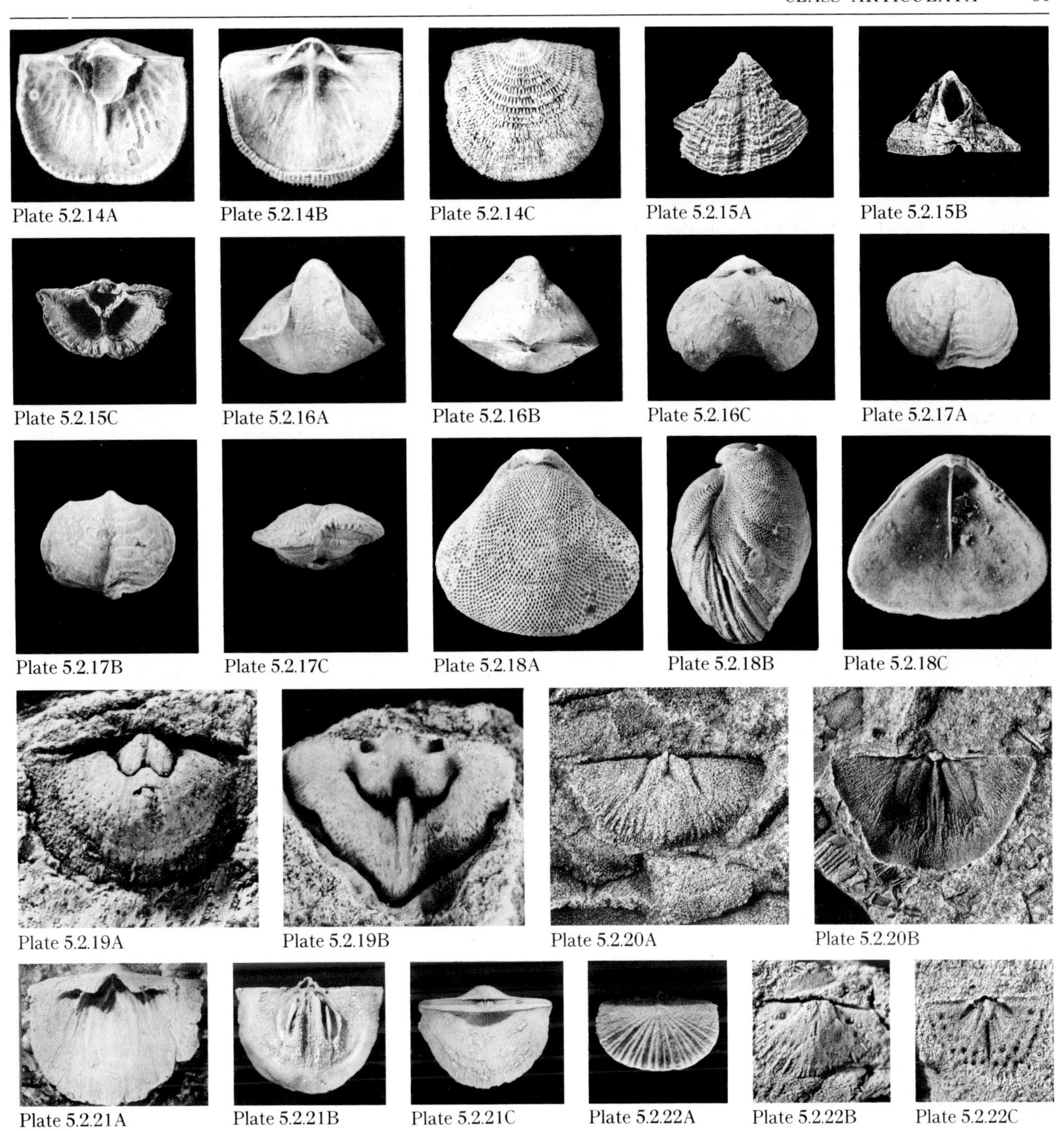

Plate 5.2.14A Plate 5.2.14B Plate 5.2.14C Plate 5.2.15A Plate 5.2.15B

Plate 5.2.15C Plate 5.2.16A Plate 5.2.16B Plate 5.2.16C Plate 5.2.17A

Plate 5.2.17B Plate 5.2.17C Plate 5.2.18A Plate 5.2.18B Plate 5.2.18C

Plate 5.2.19A Plate 5.2.19B Plate 5.2.20A Plate 5.2.20B

Plate 5.2.21A Plate 5.2.21B Plate 5.2.21C Plate 5.2.22A Plate 5.2.22B Plate 5.2.22C

on pedicle valve; pedicle functional in youth, on sand, silt and mud substrates.

Sowerbyella sericea (J. de C. Sowerby): Caradoc, Shropshire, England; natural moulds of pedicle and brachial valve interiors.

Pl. 5.2.21. *Eoplectodonta* Kozlowski, 1929

Pedicle valve very convex, with incurved umbo; brachial valve concave; similar ornament to *Sowerbyella*. Interior; there is a row of denticles along the hinge line of both valves; teeth absent; otherwise pedicle valve interior like *Sowerbyella*; brachial valve interior has 2 or 3 pairs of thick trans-muscle septa. Average adult width 0.7 to 1.5 cm.

Ordovician (Caradoc)–Silurian (Ludlow), cosmopolitan, lay on pedicle valve with atrophied pedicle in adults; may have snapped valves to feed.

Eoplectodonta transversalis (Wahlenberg): Visby Beds (Llandovery), Gotland, Sweden, pedicle and brachial valve interiors and brachial view of exterior of conjoined valves.

Pl. 5.2.22. *Aegiria* Öpik, 1933

Slightly convex pedicle valve; flat brachial valve; relatively large interarea; ornament of 8 to 10 sharply plicate primary costellae, between and from which other ribs of equal size arise anteriorly. Interior simple, with teeth and sockets, small median septum in central part of brachial valve; relatively few large papillae scattered over valve outside the smooth muscle field. Average adult width 0.5 cm.

Silurian (Llandovery–Pridoli), cosmopolitan, attached or epi-planktonic with functional pedicle attached to seaweed, floating fragments, etc.

Aegiria grayi (Davidson): Purple Shale (Llandovery), Shropshire, England; exterior view of conjoined valves; pedicle valve and brachial valve interior moulds.

SUPERFAMILY STROPHOMENACEA

The articulation varies from a simple tooth and socket system to a toothless hinge with many small denticles (stropheodontid denticulation). Stropheodontid denticulation arose polyphyletically at least 4 separate times within the superfamily. The cardinal process is bifid.

Pl. 5.2.23. *Strophomena* de Blainville, 1825
Resupinate shape (brachial valve convex; pedicle valve concave except at posterior); maximum width at hinge line; ornament of subequal, rather fine ribs. Interior with massive teeth in the pedicle valve, the base of which merges anteriorly into a pair of prominent muscle bounding ridges which first diverge and then curve round to nearly unite anteriorly; brachial valve interior with strong socket plates and several low transmuscle septa up to one-third valve length. Average adult width 3 to 4 cm.
Ordovician (Llandeilo–Ashgill), cosmopolitan, resting obliquely on posterior end of brachial valve in soft muds; pedicle not functional in adults.
Strophomena planumbona (Hall): U. Ordovician, Madison, Indiana, USA, conjoined valves and pedicle interior; *S. cancellata* (Portlock): U. Ordovician, Girvan, Scotland, mould of brachial valve interior.

Pl. 5.2.24. *Rafinesquina* Hall & Clarke, 1892
Uniformly convex pedicle valve, and flatter but concave brachial valve; outline semicircular; ornament of fine parvicostellae with the main costellae separated by several fine ribs; some species have a more pronounced central costella. Pedicle valve interior simple, with medium-sized teeth and prominent suboval muscle field; brachial valve with massive cardinal process, the lateral edges of which form part of the socket system. Average adult width 3 to 4 cm.
Ordovician (Llandeilo–Ashgill), cosmopolitan, rested on pedicle valve; pedicle non-functional in adults, on soft lime-mud substrates.
Rafinesquina nasuta (Conrad): M. Ordovician, Cincinnati, Ohio, USA, brachial and pedicle exteriors of conjoined valves, and brachial valve interior.

Pl. 5.2.25. *Leptaena* Dalman, 1828
Pedicle valve slightly convex and brachial valve flat until both valves bend sharply (geniculate) anteriorly in a brachial direction. Ornament of fine parvicostellate ribs and concentric waves (rugae); semicircular outline with prominent ears. Pedicle valve interior with oval muscle field with lateral muscle bounding ridges; brachial valve interior with a variety of septal structures. Average adult width 2 to 5 cm.
Ordovician (Llandeilo)–Devonian (Frasnian), cosmopolitan, mode of life varies with species, but most lay free on sea-floor on their pedicle valve, with pedicle atrophied in adults; mud-free sea water entered through the long trail.
Leptaena martinensis Cocks: Haverford Mudstone Fm. (Ashgill), Haverfordwest, Dyfed, Wales; natural mould and latex cast of pedicle valve interior, latex cast of brachial valve interior.

Pl. 5.2.26. *Christiania* Hall & Clarke, 1892
Very convex pedicle valve with incurved umbo and slightly concave brachial valve. Hinge line narrow relative to length of shell; no ornament except growth lines. Pedicle valve interior with simple teeth and bilobed muscle field; brachial interior with a prominent series of long septa running most of the valve length and curving round anteriorly, sometimes with additional septa subparallel to hinge line. Average adult width 0.6 to 1 cm.
Ordovician (Llandeilo–Ashgill), cosmopolitan, found alone or in clumps, attitude uncertain, functional pedicle.
Christiania subquadrata (Hall): Lenoir Fm. (M. Ordovician), Friendsville, Tennessee, USA, brachial and side views of conjoined valves, and brachial valve interior.

Pl. 5.2.27. *Strophodonta* Hall, 1850
Gently convex pedicle valve and concave brachial valve; semicircular outline; ornament of numerous subequal ribs over the whole valve area. Interior with denticulate hinge line in both valves; no large teeth or sockets, but substantial cardinal process; pedicle valve muscle field suboval to triangular. Average adult width 3 to 5 cm.
Devonian (Siegenian–Givetian) cosmopolitan, lay free on pedicle valve on sea-floor, with pedicle functional only in juveniles.
Strophodonta demissa (Conrad): M. Devonian, Alpena, Michigan, USA, brachial view of conjoined valves' exterior and brachial valve interior; *S. hemispherica* (Grabau): M. Devonian, Silvania, Ohio, USA, pedicle valve exterior.

Pl. 5.2.28. *Strophonella* Hall, 1879
Shield-shaped outline; pedicle valve gently convex at first, becoming sharply concave anteriorly; brachial valve flat posteriorly and convex anteriorly. Radial ornament unequally parvicostellate. Interior with denticulate hinge line and well-impressed subrectangular muscle scars in pedicle valve and prominent cardinal process. Average adult width 3 to 5 cm.
Silurian (Llandovery)–Devonian (Emsian), cosmopolitan. Lived free on sea-floor, probably obliquely when young, and resting on brachial valve when adult.
Strophonella euglypha (Dalman): Wenlock Limestone, Dudley, West Midlands, England; brachial valve exterior and pedicle valve interior.

Pl. 5.2.29. *Leptostrophia* Hall & Clarke, 1892
Semicircular outline; pedicle valve gently convex; brachial valve flat. Radial ornament of unequal parvicostellae. Interior with denticulate hinge line and simple bilobed cardinal process; pedicle valve muscle field triangular, open anteriorly, but with more or less straight muscle bounding ridges laterally. Brachial valve muscle field suboval. Average adult width 3 to 4 cm.
Silurian (Llandovery)–Devonian (Emsian), cosmopolitan, probably subvertical when young, resting obliquely on pedicle valve when older, on sand, silt or mud substrates.
Leptostrophia tenuis Williams: Llandovery type area, Dyfed, Wales; pedicle valve exterior and mould of pedicle valve interior.

Pl. 5.2.30. *Pholidostrophia* Hall & Clarke, 1892
Convex pedicle valve with incurved umbo and gently concave brachial valve; small interareas; semicircular outline. Ornament either absent or of very fine parvicostellate ribs. Interior with denticulate stropheodontid hinge line; simple bilobed cardinal process; simple triangular pedicle valve muscle field merging with valve floor anteriorly. Average adult width 0.8 to 1.3 cm.
Ordovician (Ashgill)–Devonian (Givetian), cosmopolitan, rested obliquely on pedicle valve; atrophied pedicle in adults, small pedicle tube functional in juveniles.
Pholidostrophia salopiensis Cocks: Purple Shale (Llandovery), Shropshire, England, interior of pedicle valve and anterior view of pedicle valve mould; brachial valve exterior also showing cardinal process.

SUPERFAMILY DAVIDSONIACEA

Articulation of simple tooth and socket system; pre-Devonian members are impunctate, but their presumed U. Palaeozoic descendants are pseudopunctate. Some late Palaeozoic genera have their pedicle valves cemented to the substrate.

Pl. 5.2.31. *Coolinia* Bancroft, 1949
Gently biconvex; slightly resupinate in adults of some species; semicircular outline, with variable development of ears;

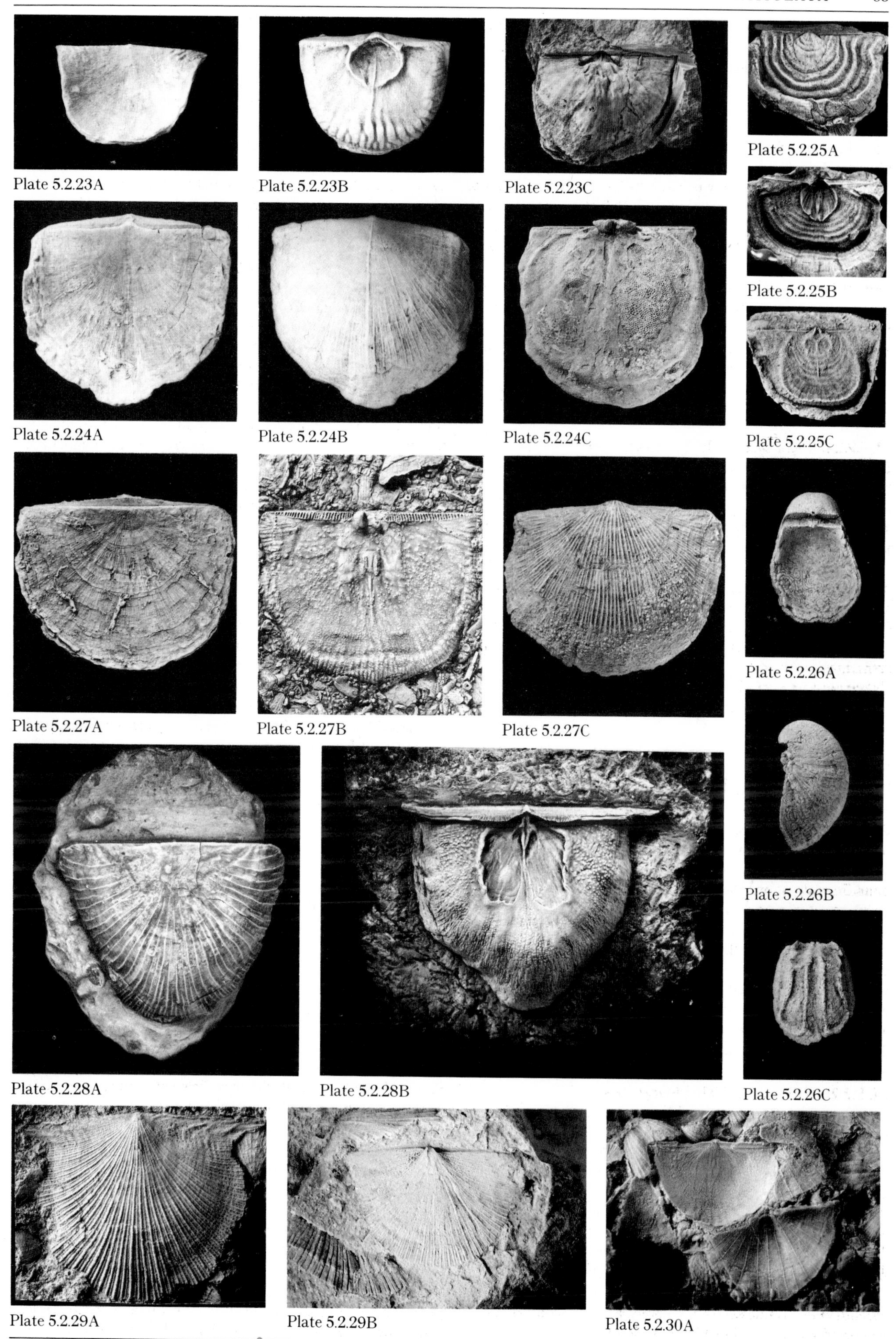

Plate 5.2.23A

Plate 5.2.23B

Plate 5.2.23C

Plate 5.2.25A

Plate 5.2.25B

Plate 5.2.24A

Plate 5.2.24B

Plate 5.2.24C

Plate 5.2.25C

Plate 5.2.27A

Plate 5.2.27B

Plate 5.2.27C

Plate 5.2.26A

Plate 5.2.26B

Plate 5.2.28A

Plate 5.2.28B

Plate 5.2.26C

Plate 5.2.29A

Plate 5.2.29B

Plate 5.2.30A

ornament of subequal ribs. Interior with strong tooth and socket system and prominent cardinal process; muscle scars rarely impressed. Average adult width 3 to 5 cm.
Ordovician (Ashgill)–Silurian (Ludlow), cosmopolitan, subvertical in juveniles and young adults on a variety of substrates; gerontic individuals resting on brachial valve.
Coolinia dalmani Bergström: Husbergøya Fm. (Ashgill), Oslo, Norway; mould of pedicle valve interior and brachial valve exterior; *C.* aff. *pecten* (Linnaeus): Yartleton Beds (Llandovery), May Hill, Gloucestershire, England, natural mould of brachial valve interior.

Pl. 5.2.32. *Schellwienella* Thomas, 1910
Gently convex, nearly flat valves; semicircular outline; pedicle valve sulcus and brachial valve fold in large specimens; ornament of fine costellae. Interior with strong teeth and sockets, the former supported by divergent dental plates. Cardinal process fused to socket plates. Triangular pedicle valve muscle field. Average adult width 3 to 5 cm.
?U. Devonian–Carboniferous (Viséan), cosmopolitan, cemented to hard substrates by pedicle valve umbo.
Schellwienella radialis (Phillips): Carboniferous Limestone (Viséan), pedicle valve exterior from Derbyshire; brachial valve interior from Co. Fermanagh, N. Ireland.

SUPERFAMILY CHONETACEA
Chonetids differ from all other strophomenides in possessing spines projecting from the hinge line, but not from the rest of the valve exteriors.

Pl. 5.2.33. *Rugosochonetes* Sokolskaya, 1950
Semicircular outline; convex pedicle valve and concave brachial valve; broad interarea with chilidium and pseudodeltidium. Ornament of equal costellae and stubby hinge-line spines. Interior with teeth and sockets; median septa in both valves to just over half valve length; curved socket plates and pair of oblique trans-muscle septa in brachial valve; numerous coarser papillae near valve margin. Average adult width 0.9 to 1.5 cm.
Carboniferous (Tournaisian–Westphalian), cosmopolitan, resting obliquely on pedicle valve with spines under silt or lime-mud substrate.
Rugosochonetes celticus Muir Wood: L. Carboniferous, Beith, Strathclyde, Scotland, brachial and pedicle exterior views and interior of pedicle valve.

Pl. 5.2.34. *Anoplia* Hall & Clarke, 1892
Small; semicircular outline, with convex pedicle valve and flat or concave brachial valve; small interarea; spines small; ornament only of growth lines. Interior with relatively small teeth and sockets; thin pedicle valve median septum to one-third valve length; pair of diverging trans-muscle septa in brachial valve; faint diaphragm; papillae coarser towards valve margin. Average adult width 0.4 to 0.8 cm.
Devonian (Gedinnian–Emsian), N. America, Europe, N. Africa, Australia. Ecology uncertain, possibly epiplanktonic.
Anoplia nucleata (Hall): Camden Chert (L. Devonian), Camden, Tennessee, USA, external of pedicle valve and interiors of pedicle and brachial valve.

Pl. 5.2.35. *Delepinea* Muir Wood, 1962
Large; semicircular to alate outline; convex pedicle valve (usually thickened posteriorly in adults) and gently concave brachial valve. Spines scarcely seen except in juveniles; ornament of fine parvicostellae. Interior with denticulate hinge line and with delicate median septa in both valves; strong subtriangular to bilobate pedicle valve muscle field; prominent papillae. Average adult width 6 to 10 cm.
M. Devonian–M. Carboniferous, cosmopolitan, resting free on pedicle valve, with pedicle functional only in very small specimens and spines functional only in juveniles.
Delepinea destinezi (Vaughan): Dartry Fm. (Visean), Co. Fermanagh, N. Ireland, pedicle valve interior and brachial view of conjoined valves with epifauna.

SUPERFAMILY STROPHALOSIACEA
The three following superfamilies, Strophalosiacea, Productacea and Richthofeniacea, can be grouped together as 'productids' in having spines over the whole valve area and not confined to the hinge line.

Pl. 5.2.36. *Dasyalosia* Muir Wood & Cooper, 1960
Subcircular outline, with short hinge line, convex pedicle valve and concave or flat brachial valve. Numerous spines of various lengths cover both valves, except in the interarea. Interior with strong, simple teeth and sockets; prominent cardinal process; median septum extending over half brachial valve length; bilobed subcircular pedicle valve muscle field. Average adult width 2 to 3 cm.
Permian (Zechstein), Europe, semi-infaunal, with spines of pedicle valve buried in soft calcilutite substrate.
Dasyalosia goldfussi (Münster): Permian, Gara, W. Germany, brachial and pedicle views of conjoined valves, and brachial valve interior.

SUPERFAMILY PRODUCTACEA
Pl. 5.2.37. *Productella* Hall, 1867
Subcircular outline with relatively short hinge line; very convex pedicle valve and gently concave brachial valve. Spines scattered at intervals over exterior of pedicle valve; ornament of fine subequal parvicostellae. Simple interior, with relatively small teeth and sockets, and low, widely divergent socket plates; fine median septum developed to over half brachial valve length. Pedicle valve muscle field triangular; suboval in brachial valve. Average adult width 0.7 to 2 cm.
Devonian (Emsian–Famennian), Europe, Asia, N. America, resting obliquely on pedicle valve on a variety of mud, silt or sand substrates.
Productella hallana Walcott: Hackberry Fm. (U. Devonian), Rockford, Iowa, USA, pedicle valve exterior viewed from above and side, and brachial valve interior.

Pl. 5.2.38. *Productus* J. Sowerby, 1814
Brachial valve subcircular in outline and flat to slightly concave; pedicle valve with relatively short hinge line, very convex initially and with substantial trail in some adults. Ornament of simple ribs and irregular rugae; spines rarely preserved but relatively few and stubby on pedicle valve only. Interior with brachial valve median septum, and brachial valve suboval muscle field. Average adult width 3 to 4 cm.
Carboniferous (Tournaisian–Westphalian), Europe, Asia, resting on convex pedicle valve, usually on lime-mud substrate.
Productus productus (Martin): Carboniferous Limestone (Viséan), Derbyshire, England, brachial and pedicle view of conjoined valves of small adult, and oblique view of larger adult with substantial trail.

Pl. 5.2.39. *Antiquatonia* Miloradovich, 1945
Brachial valve semicircular to transverse and flat to concave; pedicle valve transverse and very convex leading to trail, and with slight median sulcus. Ornament of regular ribs and rugae on both valves; a few large spines (seldom preserved) on flanks of pedicle valve, smaller ones scattered over whole pedicle valve

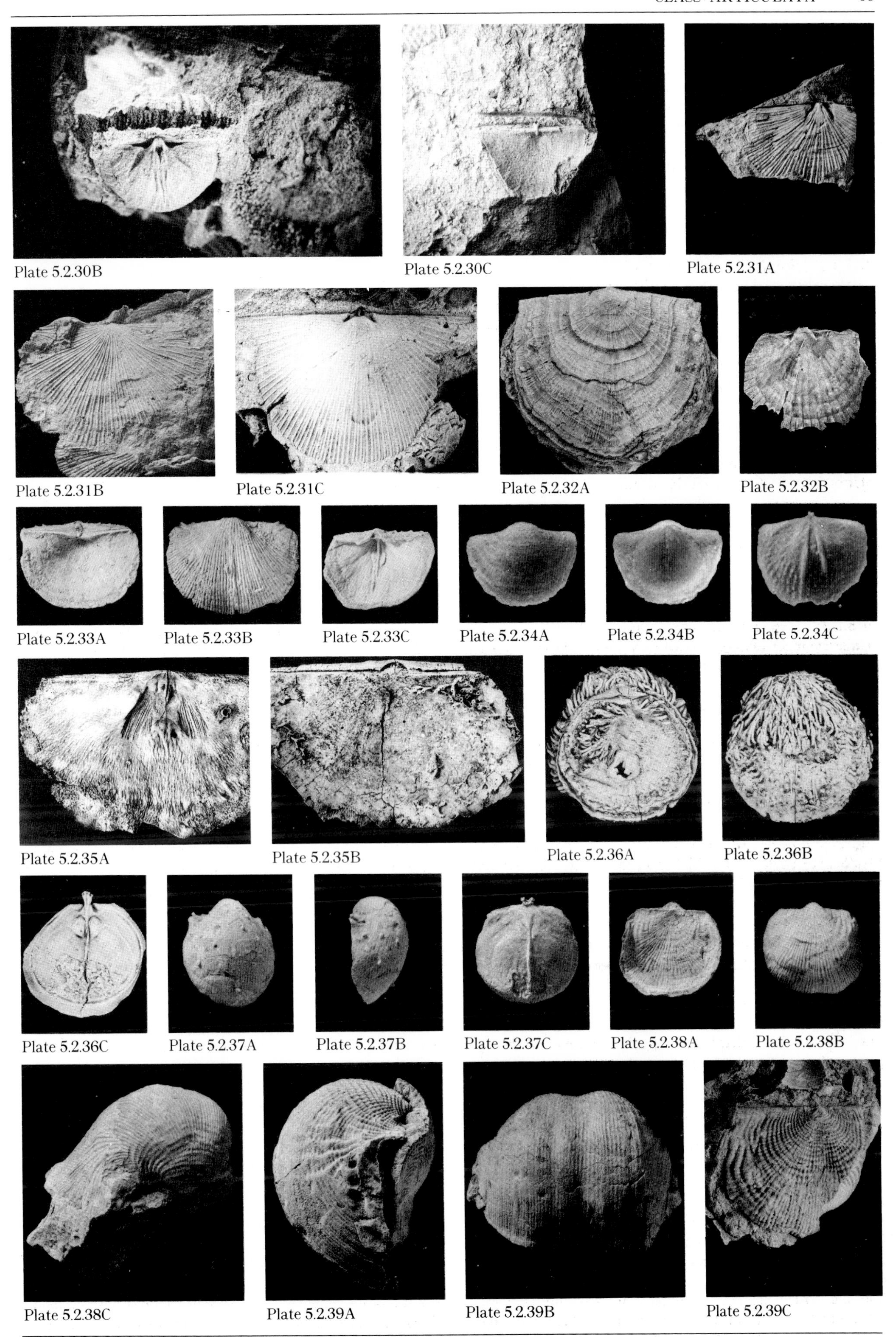

Plate 5.2.30B

Plate 5.2.30C

Plate 5.2.31A

Plate 5.2.31B

Plate 5.2.31C

Plate 5.2.32A

Plate 5.2.32B

Plate 5.2.33A

Plate 5.2.33B

Plate 5.2.33C

Plate 5.2.34A

Plate 5.2.34B

Plate 5.2.34C

Plate 5.2.35A

Plate 5.2.35B

Plate 5.2.36A

Plate 5.2.36B

Plate 5.2.36C

Plate 5.2.37A

Plate 5.2.37B

Plate 5.2.37C

Plate 5.2.38A

Plate 5.2.38B

Plate 5.2.38C

Plate 5.2.39A

Plate 5.2.39B

Plate 5.2.39C

surface. Interior with relatively small cardinal process; small brachial valve median septum; bilobed brachial valve muscle field; more prominent papillae anterolaterally. Average adult width 3 to 6 cm.
Carboniferous (Tournaisian–Westphalian), Europe, Asia, Australia, semi-infaunal, resting on convex pedicle valve on silt or lime-mud substrates.
Antiquatonia antiquata (J. Sowerby): Carboniferous Limestone (Viséan), Park Hill, Staffordshire, England, side and anterior views of pedicle valve exterior and brachial valve exterior.

Pl. 5.2.40. *Levitusia* Muir Wood & Cooper, 1960
Large productid with initial semicircular outline; very convex pedicle valve curving round to long trail anteriorly in adults; concave brachial valve. Ornament of posterior rugae and very faint ribs; spines rare on pedicle valve only. Interior with massive cardinal process; delicate brachial valve median septum; pedicle valve heavily thickened posteriorly with deeply impressed muscle fields and pair of conical hollows in brachial valve. Average adult width 4 to 6 cm.
Carboniferous (Viséan), Europe, Asia, resting semi-infaunally on convex pedicle valves in lime-mud substrates.
Levitusia humerosa (J. Sowerby): Carboniferous Limestone (Viséan), N. Staffordshire, England; posterior and side views of pedicle valve exterior, and brachial view of exterior of conjoined valves.

Pl. 5.2.41. *Gigantoproductus* Prentice, 1950
Very large transverse shells, with thick, convex pedicle valve and gently concave brachial valve. Irregularly costate, with 2 orders of costellae; often rugose near hinge line and laterally. Interior with massive bilobed pedicle valve muscle field; rounded elevations in brachial valve corresponding to spirals of soft original lophophore. Average adult width 15 to 25 cm.
Carboniferous (Viséan–Westphalian), cosmopolitan, resting free on convex pedicle valve on soft lime-muds, atrophied pedicle in adults.
Gigantoproductus giganteus (J. Sowerby): Carboniferous Limestone (Viséan), Clwyd, Wales, pedicle and side views of pedicle valve; Muirkirk, Strathclyde, Scotland; internal mould of pedicle valve, showing muscle scars.

SUPERFAMILY RICHTHOFENIACEA
Aberrant productids with conical pedicle valves aping corals.

Pl. 5.2.42. *Prorichthofenia* King, 1931
Pedicle valve conical and covered with root-like spines; subcircular top into which fitted the flat brachial valve with short hinge line. The upper, open end of the pedicle valve often developed spines, or a skeletal mesh arching over the opening. Interior with median septa in both valves and strongly impressed muscle scars. Average adult height 3 to 4 cm.
L. Permian, Europe, N. America, subvertical with cone downwards in biohermal environments.
Prorichthofenia permiana (Shumard): Word Fm. (L. Permian), Texas, USA, side view of two pedicle valves and interior of pedicle valve.

SUPERFAMILY LYTTONIACEA
This bizarre but widespread group of fewer than 20 genera flowered in the late Carboniferous and Permian, and lingered on into the Triassic. The brachial valve was sometimes vestigial, barely covering the lophophore, and the pedicle valve was usually cemented to the substrate.

Pl. 5.2.43. *Leptodus* Kayser, 1882
Subcircular to irregularly elongate outline of thick pedicle valve, with thin serrated-edged brachial valve. Massive posterior flap on pedicle valve umbo used for cementation. Interior of pedicle valve with lateral ridges (into which the brachial valve fitted) and with median septum; hinge line short; brachial valve with median channel. Average adult length 3 to 5 cm.
L.–M. Permian, cosmopolitan, cemented on to hard substrates on pedicle valve.
Leptodus americanus Girty: Word Fm. (M. Permian), Texas, USA, interior of pedicle valve.

Order Pentamerida

Biconvex brachiopods with impunctate shells and with a pair of diverging plates in the brachial valve and very often a median septum in the pedicle valve.

SUPERFAMILY PORAMBONITACEA
Pl. 5.2.44. *Porambonites* Pander, 1830
Equivalve, semicircular outline; incurved pedicle umbo, brachial valve fold and pedicle valve sulcus. Ornament of rows of pits, otherwise smooth. Interior with strong teeth and sockets. Dental plates initially diverging, converging anteriorly to form sessile spondylium; brachiophore plates uniting anteriorly to form low septalium. Average adult length 3 to 5 cm.
Ordovician (Arenig–Ashgill); Baltic early, but cosmopolitan later. Ecology uncertain, but sealed non-functional pedicle in adults.
Porambonites aequirostris (Schlotheim): L. Ordovician, Leningrad, USSR, brachial and side views of conjoined valves; *P. alta* Pander: L. Ordovician, Tallinn, Estonia; interior view of conjoined valves, brachial valve above.

Pl. 5.2.45. *Lycophoria* Lahusen, 1886
Equivalve, subcircular outline, small umbones; simple anterior commissure. Ornament of faint, even ribs. Interior with strong teeth and sockets, subparallel dental plates; tripartite cardinal process with fused brachiophore plates. Average adult length 2 to 5 cm.
Ordovician (Arenig–Llanvirn); Baltic. Semi-infaunal in carbonate muds; no functional pedicle in adults.
Lycophoria nucella (Dalman): Arenig, Leningrad, USSR; brachial and side views of conjoined valves.

SUPERFAMILY PENTAMERACEA
In latest Ordovician to Devonian times, pentameraceans dominated the mid-shelf benthos like oyster reefs today, and were in discrete depth-related bands in the early Silurian.

Pl. 5.2.46. *Holorhynchus* Kiaer, 1902
Nearly equivalve, subcircular to pentagonal outline; incurved pedicle umbo; simple anterior commissure; no ornament. Interior; small pedicle valve median septum in juveniles (absent in adults) anterior to spondylium in umbonal area; brachiophore apparatus largely clear of valve floor, with delicate inner plates and vestigial outer plates. Average adult length 6 to 10 cm.
Ordovician (Ashgill); Baltic, USSR, China. Epifaunal in clumps in carbonate muds.
Holorhynchus giganteus Kiaer: Ashgill, Oslo, Norway; brachial and side views of conjoined valves; mould of internal of brachial valve.

Pl. 5.2.47. *Pentamerus* J. Sowerby, 1813
Nearly equivalve, subcircular to elongately pentagonal outline; prominent pedicle umbo; often trilobate anteriorly; no ornament. Interior with prominent long pedicle valve median septum with spondylium posteriorly; two prominent subparallel

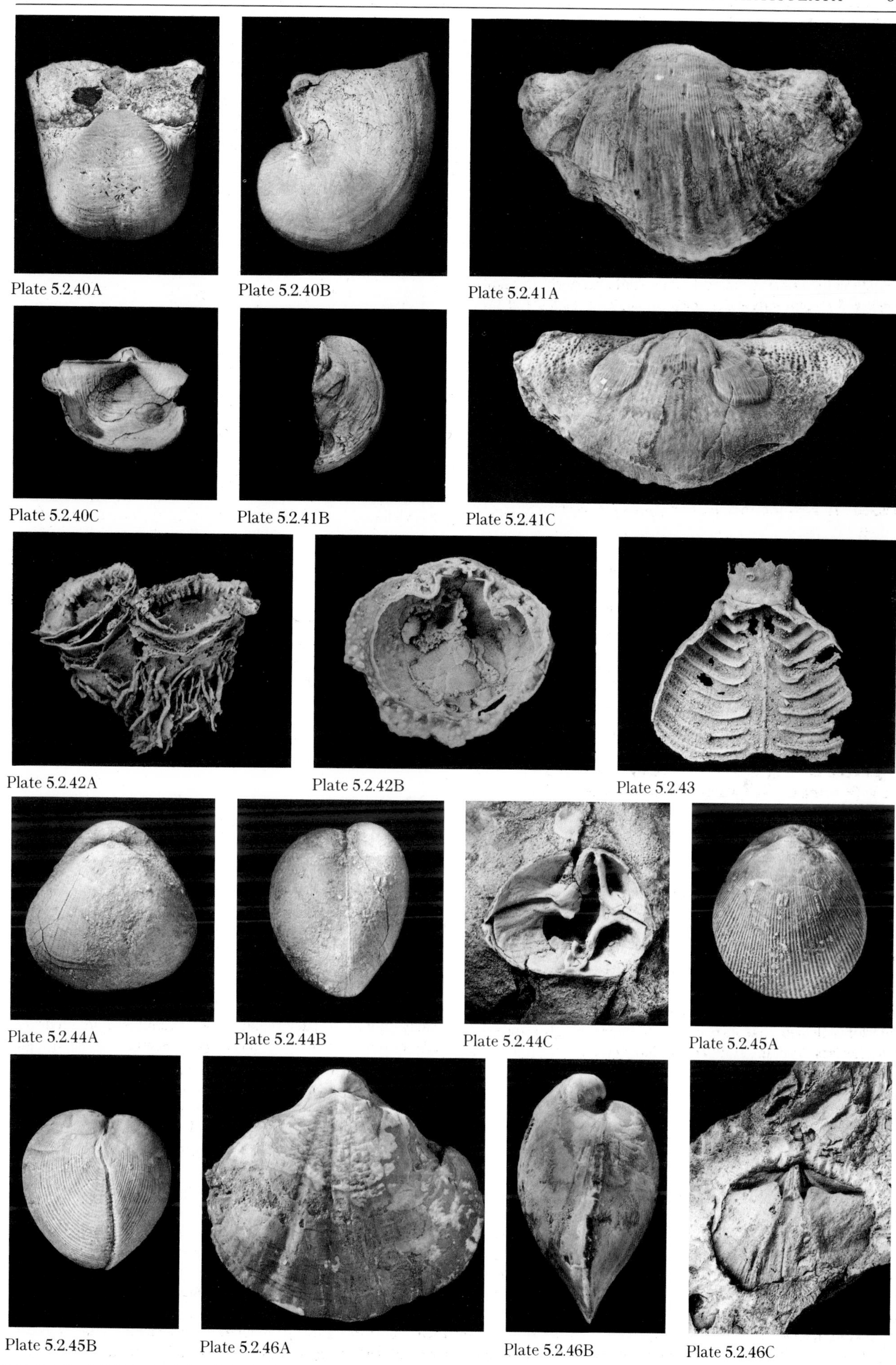

Plate 5.2.40A

Plate 5.2.40B

Plate 5.2.41A

Plate 5.2.40C

Plate 5.2.41B

Plate 5.2.41C

Plate 5.2.42A

Plate 5.2.42B

Plate 5.2.43

Plate 5.2.44A

Plate 5.2.44B

Plate 5.2.44C

Plate 5.2.45A

Plate 5.2.45B

Plate 5.2.46A

Plate 5.2.46B

Plate 5.2.46C

septa in brachial valve (uniting anteriorly to form cruralium in descendant *Pentameroides*). Average adult length 3 to 9 cm.
Silurian (commonest in late Llandovery), cosmopolitan (except S. America, Africa). Epifaunal in clumps with umbones down on variable mid-shelf sand–silt–mud substrates. Non-functional pedicle in adults.
Pentamerus oblongus J. de C. Sowerby: Llandovery type area, Wales, cast of pedicle interior and brachial view of conjoined valves; *P. asiaticus* Cocks, Wenlock, Iran, side view.

Pl. 5.2.48. *Kirkidium* Amsden, Boucot & Johnson, 1967
Large pedicle valve, differentially even larger in older specimens, with progressively incurved pedicle valve umbo; hexagonal to quadrangular outline, simple anterior commissure; ornament of strong simple ribs. Interior includes prominent long median pedicle valve septum with spondylium posteriorly; 2 prominent but shorter diverging septa in brachial valve. Average adult length 6 to 10 cm.
Silurian (Ludlow), Europe, N. America. Epifaunal with umbones downwards or oblique on pedicle umbo in clumps on carbonate muds – can be bioherm builder. Non-functional pedicle in adults.
Kirkidium knightii (J. Sowerby): Ludlow, Aymestry, England; half-grown specimen; brachial and side views of gerontic conjoined valves.

Pl. 5.2.49. *Stricklandia* Billings, 1859
Nearly equivalve, subcircular to pentagonal in outline; small umbones; tendency to trilobation anteriorly in adults; no ornament. Interior; relatively short pedicle valve median septum and small spondylium; brachiophore apparatus similar to *Holorhynchus*. Average adult length 3 to 7 cm.
Silurian (Llandovery–Wenlock), cosmopolitan, except S. America, Africa. Epifaunal in clumps on variable substrates in mid-shelf. Evolving species useful for dating.
Stricklandia lens (J. de C. Sowerby): Jupiter Fm. (Llandovery), Anticosti, Canada; conjoined valves; internal moulds of conjoined valves, Woodland Fm. (Llandovery), Girvan, Scotland.

Pl. 5.2.50. *Clorinda* Barrande, 1879
Unequally biconvex, with large, globose pedicle valve with incurved umbo, and thinner, flatter brachial valve; rectangular fold in brachial valve and sulcus in pedicle valve. No ornament. Interior with thin median septum to one-third pedicle valve length, partly supported by a small thin spondylium; brachial valve septa thin, short and widely diverging. Average adult length 2 to 3 cm.
Silurian (Llandovery)–Devonian (Eifelian), cosmopolitan, semi-infaunal and usually solitary on fine clastics in deeper shelf; non-functional pedicle in adults.
Clorinda undata (J. de C. Sowerby): Newlands Fm. (Llandovery), Girvan, Scotland; internal mould of pedicle valve and brachial and anterior views of brachial valve.

Pl. 5.2.51. *Gypidula* Hall, 1867
Unequally biconvex with prominent incurved pedicle valve umbo; subcircular outline. Ornament of median ribs, smooth laterally. Interior with strong median septum to half pedicle valve length, with small spondylium posteriorly; pair of divergent brachial valve septa to half valve length. Average adult length 2 to 4 cm.
Silurian (Wenlock)–Devonian (Frasnian), cosmopolitan, semi-infaunal in small clusters, usually on lime-mud; non-functional pedicle in adults.
Gypidula galeata (Dalman): Wenlock Limestone, Dudley, West Midlands, England; brachial, pedicle and side views of conjoined valves.

Order Rhynchonellida

This group has been successful from L. Ordovician to Recent times and contains over 500 genera. It is distinguished from all others in possessing crura – a pair of projections in the brachial valve from which the soft lophophore is supported. The vast majority of the genera are in the primitive and simple Rhynchonellacea, but there are a few in the Stenoscismatacea, which have a special brachial valve structure, and a few in the punctate Rhynchoporacea: both the latter are confined to the Palaeozoic and are not represented in this book.

SUPERFAMILY RHYNCHONELLACEA

Pl. 5.2.52. *Stegerhynchus* Foerste, 1909
Subtriangular outline; globose profile, with convex pedicle valve with large sulcus and convex brachial valve with corresponding fold. Ornament of simple sharp-crested ribs. Interior with strong teeth and sockets, dental plates and brachial valve median septum. Average adult width 1 to 2 cm.
Ordovician (Ashgill)–Silurian (Ludlow), cosmopolitan, attached with functional pedicle, but usually solitary, on variable substrates and usually in shallow water.
Stegerhynchus borealis (Schlotheim): Wenlock Limestone, Wenlock Edge, Shropshire, England, brachial, side and anterior views of conjoined valves.

Pl. 5.2.53. *Rhynchotreta* Hall, 1879
Triangular outline with prominent characteristic elongation of both valves; pedicle valve flatter and sulcate anteriorly; brachial valve more convex and globose with anterior fold; ribs sharp-crested and prominent. Large pedicle opening. Interior with prominent parallel dental plates, strong teeth and sockets; divided hinge plate and slender crura. Average adult width 0.5 to 1.5 cm.
Silurian (Llandovery–Ludlow), cosmopolitan, orientation variable, but attached by functional pedicle to bryozoan twigs, etc.
Rhynchotreta cuneata (Dalman): Wenlock Limestone, Dudley, West Midlands, England, brachial, pedicle and side views of conjoined valves.

Pl. 5.2.54. *Sphaerirhynchia* Cooper & Muir Wood, 1951
Circular to subpentagonal outline; very biconvex, producing a spherical profile. Widely separated but shallow ribs, almost smooth near umbones; square-edged prominent brachial valve fold and pedicle valve sulcus; small, but open pedicle foramen. Interior with small dental plates, no cardinal process, median septum in brachial valve. Average adult width 0.7 to 2.5 cm.
Silurian (Llandovery)–Devonian (Emsian), cosmopolitan, attached by functional pedicle in variable soft substrate with umbones downwards.
Sphaerirhynchia davidsoni (M'Coy): Wenlock Limestone, Dudley, West Midlands, England, brachial, side and anterior views of conjoined valves.

Pl. 5.2.55. *Eocoelia* Nikiforova, 1961
Subcircular outline with convex pedicle valve and flat brachial valve; no fold or sulcus. Sharp-crested, even ribs, becoming less prominent in stratigraphically younger species; open pedicle foramen. Interior with complex teeth and sockets; faint muscle field. Average adult width 0.7 to 1.4 cm.
Silurian (Llandovery–Wenlock), cosmopolitan; evolutionary species useful for dating; attached by functional pedicle in various orientations to algae or particles on sea-floor in shallower open shelf.
Eocoelia curtisi Ziegler: Camregan Fm. (Llandovery), Girvan, Scotland, internal moulds of pedicle and brachial valves.

Plate 5.2.47A
Plate 5.2.47B
Plate 5.2.47C
Plate 5.2.48A
Plate 5.2.48B
Plate 5.2.48C
Plate 5.2.49A
Plate 5.2.49B
Plate 5.2.50A
Plate 5.2.50B
Plate 5.2.50C
Plate 5.2.51A
Plate 5.2.51B
Plate 5.2.51C
Plate 5.2.52A
Plate 5.2.52B
Plate 5.2.52C
Plate 5.2.53A
Plate 5.2.53B
Plate 5.2.53C
Plate 5.2.54A
Plate 5.2.54B
Plate 5.2.54C
Plate 5.2.55A
Plate 5.2.55B

Pl. 5.2.56. *Eatonia* Hall, 1857
Subcircular to hexagonal outline; pedicle valve convex initially, becoming flatter anteriorly with sulcus; brachial valve convex, trilobed anteriorly with even fold. Rounded ribs varying from numerous and fine to fewer and stronger. Interior with small teeth and sockets; large complex cardinal process; pedicle muscle field prominent and subpentagonal, bounded by encircling ridge; thin brachial valve median septum. Average adult width 1.5 cm.
Devonian (Gedinnian–Siegenian), N. America, probably resting on brachial valve with functional pedicle more important in early growth.
Eatonia singularis Vanuxem: Schoharie Fm. (L. Devonian), New York, USA, brachial and side views of conjoined valves; *E. medialis* (Vanuxem): Helderberg Fm. (L. Devonian), Maryland, USA, interior of pedicle valve.

Pl. 5.2.57. *Leiorhynchoidea* Cloud, 1944
Outline circular to subpentagonal; biconvex with inturned pedicle umbo and very large, rounded pedicle valve sulcus and brachial valve fold. Shell mostly smooth, though faint but large costae developed medianly. Interior with complex articulation; strong median septum to over half brachial valve length; suboval muscle field. Average adult width 1 to 2 cm.
Carboniferous (U. Mississippian)–U. Permian, N. America, functional pedicle with umbones or brachial valve downwards into mud substrates.
Leiorhynchoidea carboniferum (Girty): Moorfield Fm. (L. Carboniferous), Fort Gibson, Oklahoma, USA, brachial, side and anterior views of conjoined valves.

Pl. 5.2.58. *Pugnax* Hall & Clarke, 1893
Outline triangular; general shape subtetrahedral; pedicle valve initially convex, but concave anteriorly to single sharp sulcus; brachial valve semiglobose with large anterior fold; ornament of numerous faint ribs. Interior with dental plates; complex but delicate crural plates in brachial valve. Average adult width 1 to 3 cm.
Devonian (Famennian)–U. Carboniferous, Europe, often occurs in intertwined nests, or attached to substrate fragments with functional pedicle.
Pugnax acuminatus (J. Sowerby): Carboniferous Limestone (Viséan), Derbyshire, posterior, side and anterior views of conjoined valves.

Pl. 5.2.59. *Rhynchonella* Fischer, 1809
Outline subtriangular, general shape subtetrahedral, with single sharp brachial valve fold and pedicle valve sulcus. Ornament ranging from nearly smooth to numerous sharp distinct ribs. Medium-sized pedicle foramen. Interior with strong dental plates; shallow septalium, leading anteriorly into short brachial valve median septum. Average adult width 1 to 1.5 cm.
Jurassic (Portlandian)–Cretaceous (Hauterivian), Europe, in intertwined nests or attached as single individuals to other items with functional pedicle.
Rhynchonella speetonensis Owen: Speeton Clay (Hauterivian), Speeton, Yorkshire, England; brachial, side and anterior views of conjoined valves.

Pl. 5.2.60. *Tetrarhynchia* Buckman, 1918
Subtriangular outline; pedicle valve convex at first, with small incurved beak, becoming concave anteriorly in large sulcus; brachial valve globose with anterior fold with several sharp ribs at its crest. Ribs developed near anterior margins; smooth posteriorly. Interior with complex interlocking mechanism, but simple crura. Average adult width 0.8 to 1.4 cm.
Jurassic (Sinemurian–Bajocian), Europe, N. America, occurs in nests on lime-mud, silt or sand substrates.
Tetrarhynchia tetrahedra (J. Sowerby): M. Lias (Pliensbachian), Delby Magna, Leicestershire, England; brachial, side and anterior views of conjoined valves.

Pl. 5.2.61. *Kallirhynchia* Buckman, 1918
Subtriangular outline, pedicle valve convex with erect beak; brachial valve more convex; brachial valve fold and corresponding pedicle valve sulcus best developed anteriorly, square-edged, with several ribs at crest. Ribs sharp-crested. Short median septum in brachial valve. Average adult width 1 to 2 cm.
Jurassic (Bathonian–Callovian): cosmopolitan, usually solitary, resting on umbones or above sea-floor with functional pedicle.
Kallirhynchia concinna (J. Sowerby): Cornbrash, Yaxley, Northamptonshire, England; brachial, side and anterior views of conjoined valves.

Pl. 5.2.62. *Acanthothiris* d'Orbigny, 1850
Subcircular outline; biconvex with small, incurved beak, slight fold and sulcus. Ornament of numerous rounded ribs bearing long, hollow spines. Interior with dental plates and complex articulation; no cardinal process; median septum in brachial valve. Average adult width 1 to 1.5 cm.
Jurassic (Bajocian–Bathonian), Europe, Asia, resting on brachial valve with functional pedicle; spine purpose uncertain, but they may have carried sensory organs.
Acanthothiris spinosa (Linnaeus): U. Inferior Oolite (Bajocian), Rodborough, Cotswold Hills, England; brachial valve exterior with exceptionally preserved spines, and pedicle and side views of more normal preservation with only spine bases visible.

Pl. 5.2.63. *Cyclothyris* M'Coy, 1844
Transverse, subtriangular outline; erect beak with large foramen; biconvex with rectangular brachial valve fold and pedicle valve sulcus. Numerous relatively small but sharp-crested ribs over whole valve. Interior with complex socket and hinge plates; very slight brachial valve median septum. Average adult width 1.5 to 3 cm.
Cretaceous (Aptian to Cenomanian), Europe, N. America, juveniles free over substrate; adults partly resting on brachial valves, all with functional pedicles.
Cyclothyris latissima (J. de C. Sowerby): Greensand (Aptian), Faringdon, Berkshire, England; brachial, side and anterior views of conjoined valves.

Pl. 5.2.64. *Orbirhynchia* Pettitt, 1954
Subcircular to pentagonal outline with globose shape; relatively low fold and sulcus; fairly large ribs becoming sharper and more prominent anteriorly. Small beak but medium-sized foramen. Interior with complex articulation, but no septalium or median septum. Average adult width 0.8 to 1.5 cm.
Cretaceous (Albian–Senonian), Europe, either in clusters, or separately with functional pedicle downwards on to small particles in lime-mud substrates.
Orbirhynchia mantelliana (J. de C. Sowerby): L. Chalk (Cenomanian), Dover, Kent, England; brachial, side and anterior views of conjoined valves.

Order Atrypida

This order has calcified spiralia and rounded hinges, unlike the straight hinge lines of the Spiriferida. There are 5 superfamilies; the 4 below and the Devonian to Triassic Athyrisinacea, which are like the Retziacea, but impunctate.

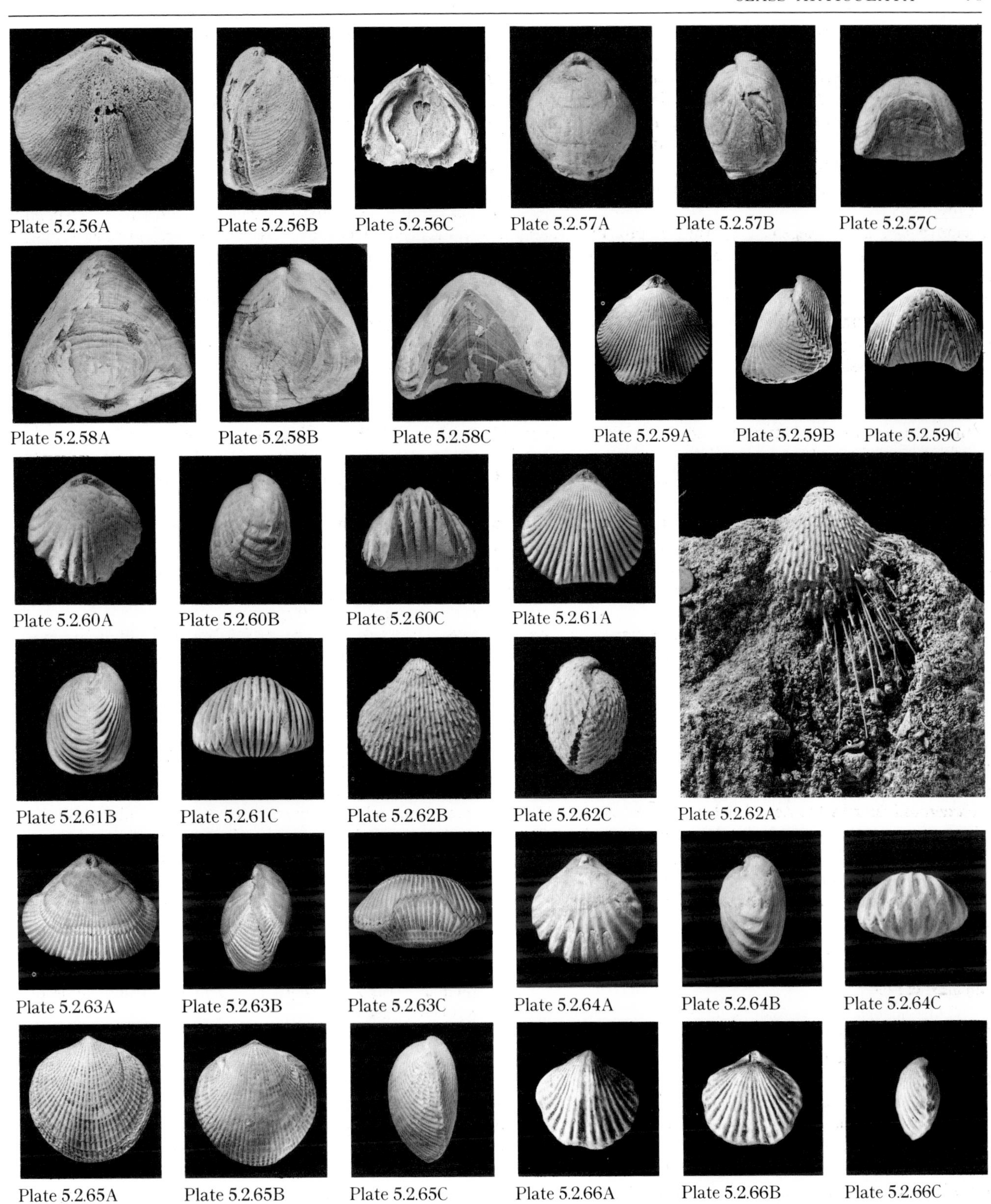
Plate 5.2.56A Plate 5.2.56B Plate 5.2.56C Plate 5.2.57A Plate 5.2.57B Plate 5.2.57C

Plate 5.2.58A Plate 5.2.58B Plate 5.2.58C Plate 5.2.59A Plate 5.2.59B Plate 5.2.59C

Plate 5.2.60A Plate 5.2.60B Plate 5.2.60C Plate 5.2.61A

Plate 5.2.61B Plate 5.2.61C Plate 5.2.62B Plate 5.2.62C Plate 5.2.62A

Plate 5.2.63A Plate 5.2.63B Plate 5.2.63C Plate 5.2.64A Plate 5.2.64B Plate 5.2.64C

Plate 5.2.65A Plate 5.2.65B Plate 5.2.65C Plate 5.2.66A Plate 5.2.66B Plate 5.2.66C

SUPERFAMILY ATRYPACEA

This group has the spiralia directed medially or dorso-medially.

Pl. 5.2.65. *Atrypa* Dalman, 1828

Biconvex, with inflated brachial valve; slight brachial valve fold and pedicle valve sulcus. Ornament of numerous fine rounded ribs, interrupted by concentric growth lines where frills are sometimes formed. Simple interior with strong teeth and sockets. Average adult length 1.5 to 2.5 cm.

Silurian (Llandovery)–Devonian (Frasnian), cosmopolitan, epifaunal, usually solitary; functional pedicle in youth, but oldest specimens rest on brachial valve with non-functional pedicle.

Atrypa reticularis (Linnaeus): Wenlock Limestone, Wenlock Edge, Shropshire, England; pedicle, brachial and side views of conjoined valves.

Pl. 5.2.66. *Zygospira* Hall, 1862

Convex pedicle valve, flatter brachial valve; subcircular to pentagonal outline; weak brachial valve sulcus with small medial fold. Strongly ribbed. Interior with no dental plates, but disjunct hinge plates. Average adult length 1 cm.

Ordovician (Caradoc–Ashgill), Europe, N. America, solitary and

epifaunal, attached with functional pedicle.
Zygospira modesta (Say): Cincinnati Group (Ashgill), Taylor Station, Kentucky, USA; pedicle, brachial and side views of conjoined valves.

SUPERFAMILY DAYIACEA
This group has spiralia directed ventrally, laterally or planospirally parallel to the median plane. Some formerly attributed genera, e.g. *Eocoelia*, are now known to be rhynchonellides.

Pl. 5.2.67. *Dayia* Davidson, 1881
Convex pedicle valve; flat brachial valve with sulcus; no ornament. Interior with much secondary shell in pedicle valve across which runs lateral muscle field channels; median septum in brachial valve; complex teeth and socket system. Average adult length 0.7 to 1.2 cm.
Silurian (Ludlow)–Devonian (Gedinnian); Europe, Asia, N. Africa. Epifaunal in clusters and clumps; pedicle opening small, but presumably pedicle functional. The shell probably partly rested on the thicker pedicle valve.
Dayia navicula (J. de C. Sowerby): Ludlow Beds, Aymestry, Hereford and Worcester, England; exterior of conjoined valves, and interiors of natural moulds of pedicle and brachial valves.

SUPERFAMILY RETZIACEA
This group has laterally directed spiralia and the shell is punctate.

Pl. 5.2.68. *Homoeospira* Hall & Clarke, 1893
Biconvex, strongly ribbed, with finer ribs in median sector; brachial valve fold and pedicle valve sulcus; incurved umbo with medium to large-sized pedicle foramen. Interior with complex articulation; small brachial valve median septum. Average adult length 0.7 to 1.5 cm.
Silurian (Wenlock–Ludlow), Europe, N. America. Epifaunal and solitary, with functional pedicle.
Homoeospira baylei (Davidson): Wenlock Limestone, Benthall Edge, Shropshire, England; brachial, anterior and side views of conjoined valves.

SUPERFAMILY ATHYRIDACEA
This group has laterally directed spiralia, and crura united with primary spires by a pair of loops.

Pl. 5.2.69. *Cryptothyrella* Cooper, 1942
Biconvex, elongate; simple anterior commissure; incurved pedicle umbo. No ornament. Pedicle valve interior with long, slightly diverging dental plates with deeply impressed muscle field between them. Complex articulation; short brachial valve median septum. Average adult length 1 to 3 cm.
Ordovician (Ashgill)–Silurian (Llandovery), cosmopolitan, resting obliquely singly or in small clumps on shallow shelf varied substrates; pedicle functional in small individuals, atrophied in large adults.
Cryptothyrella quadrangularis (Foerste): Indian Fields Fm. (Llandovery), Dunkinsville, Ohio, USA; brachial, anterior and side views of conjoined valves.

Pl. 5.2.70. *Meristina* Hall, 1867
Subequally biconvex with brachial valve fold and pedicle valve sulcus; incurved umbones, almost no ornament. Interior with complex articulation; prominent divergent dental plates in pedicle valve enclosing well-impressed muscle field; median septum in brachial valve. Average adult length 3 to 4 cm.
Silurian (Wenlock)–Devonian (Frasnian), cosmopolitan, single or in small clumps in mid-shelf, mostly lime-mud substrates; resting obliquely on brachial valve with functional pedicle.
Meristina obtusa (J. Sowerby): Wenlock Limestone, Walsall, West Midlands, England; brachial and side views of conjoined valves, and brachial valve interior showing spiralia.

Pl. 5.2.71. *Athyris* M'Coy, 1844
Biconvex with brachial fold and pedicle valve sulcus; outline subcircular to pentagonal. Ornament only of weakly lamellose growth lines. Interior with complex articulation and spiralia; short dental plates present; no median septum. Average adult length 3 cm.
Devonian (Siegenian)–Triassic, cosmopolitan, resting singly and obliquely on brachial valve, chiefly on mid-shelf lime-muds, with functional pedicle.
Athyris spiriferoides (Eaton): Hamilton Fm. (Givetian), Moscow, New York, USA, brachial, side and anterior views of conjoined valves.

Pl. 5.2.72. *Nucleospira* Hall, 1859
Biconvex; circular outline; small, tightly incurved umbones; slight sulcus in both valves; ornament only of very fine tubercles. Interior with complex articulation and median ridges in both pedicle and brachial valves extending for over half the shell length. Average adult length 0.7 to 1.3 cm.
Silurian (Wenlock) to L. Carboniferous, cosmopolitan, solitary on fine lime-mud and silt mid-shelf substrates; pedicle functional.
Nucleospira pisum (J. de C. Sowerby): Wenlock Limestone, Benthall Edge, Shropshire, England; brachial and anterior views of conjoined valves.

Order Spiriferida

Biconvex brachiopods in which the lophophore is supported by calcareous looped ribbons termed spiralia: shell substance usually impunctate, but rarely punctate. The current state of suprafamilial classification within this order is less certain than with most other brachiopods, but there are 5 undoubted superfamilies, from each of which representatives are described below, all of which have calcified spiralia. The Cadomellacea is also included here, though its systematic position is less certain.

SUPERFAMILY CYRTIACEA
Impunctate shells, often with fine radial ornament.

Pl. 5.2.73. *Cyrtia* Dalman, 1828
Pyramidal shape, with conical pedicle valve and large, triangular interarea with pedicle foramen in centre; gently convex brachial valve with small fold. Ornament of very fine subequal radial ribs. Pedicle valve interior with strong dental plates; brachial valve interior with short crural plates; no median septa. Average adult length 1.5 to 2.5 cm.
Silurian (Llandovery)–Devonian (Emsian), cosmopolitan. Ecology variable; usually solitary and semi-infaunal with pedicle valve apex downwards in silt or lime-mud mid-shelf substrates; functional pedicle.
Cyrtia exporrecta (Wahlenberg): Wenlock Limestone, Dudley, West Midlands, England; brachial, side and posterior views of conjoined valves.

Pl. 5.2.74. *Eospirifer* Schuchert, 1913
Biconvex, with incurved pedicle umbo; outline laterally suboval; brachial valve fold and corresponding pedicle valve sulcus; ornament of fine ribs. Pedicle interior with divergent dental plates; brachial valve interior very similar to *Cyrtia*. Average adult length 2 cm.

Silurian (Llandovery–Pridoli), cosmopolitan, resting obliquely on brachial valve with functional pedicle on lime-muds, silt and sand on mid-shelf.

Eospirifer radiatus (J. de C. Sowerby): Wenlock Limestone, Dudley, West Midlands, England; brachial, anterior and side views of conjoined valves.

Pl. 5.2.75. *Crurithyris* George, 1931
Unequally biconvex, subcircular outline; larger pedicle valve with incurved umbo; open delthyrium; ornament only of minute tubercles. Interior; no dental plates, complex articulation, triangular cardinal process; large crural plates to half brachial valve length. Average adult width 0.5 cm.
Devonian (Eifelian)–Permian, cosmopolitan, attached by functional pedicle to small particles or above chiefly lime-mud substrates.
Crurithyris urei (Fleming): Dartry Limestone (Viséan), Co. Fermanagh, N. Ireland; pedicle valve exterior, posterior view of conjoined valves, and brachial valve interior.

SUPERFAMILY SUESSIACEA
Like Cyrtiacea, but with punctate shells.

Pl. 5.2.76. *Cyrtina* Davidson, 1858
Subpyramidal form like *Cyrtia*, with large triangular interarea but more apical pedicle opening; brachial valve gently convex; fold and sulcus present, sometimes with some extra plications laterally. Interior with prominent teeth and sockets; spondylium and median septum in pedicle valve. Average adult width 2 cm.
Devonian (Gedinnian)–Permian, cosmopolitan, attached by functional pedicle with large interarea downwards and anterior commissure upwards.
Cyrtina hibernica Benton: Dartry Fm. (Viséan), Co. Fermanagh, N. Ireland, brachial view of conjoined valves, pedicle interior and brachial valve interior.

SUPERFAMILY SPIRIFERACEA
No fine radial ornament in early (Silurian–Devonian) forms; costate in later genera; shell substance usually impunctate.

Pl. 5.2.77. *Howellella* Kozlowski, 1946
Biconvex with incurved pedicle umbo; large interarea with open delthyrium; subquadrangular outline; coarse plications and lamellose growth lines as ornament. Interior with strong divergent dental plates and short brachiophore plates; no median septum. Average adult width 1 to 2 cm.
Silurian (Llandovery)–Devonian (Emsian), cosmopolitan, attached with functional pedicle, anterior upwards on fine sand, silt and mud substrates or to other objects.
Howellella elegans (Muir Wood): Wenlock Limestone, Dudley, West Midlands, England; brachial, pedicle and side views of conjoined valves.

Pl. 5.2.78. *Mucrospirifer* Grabau, 1931
Very transverse valves with maximum width at hinge line; incurved umbo with small pedicle opening surrounded by small complex plates in delthyrium; brachial valve fold and pedicle valve sulcus. Ornament of rounded ribs and frilly growth lamellae. Interior with short dental plates and no median septum. Average adult width 4 to 6 cm.
Devonian (Emsian–Givetian), cosmopolitan, solitary and epifaunal, resting obliquely with umbones downwards and with functional pedicle.
Mucrospirifer mucronatus (Conrad): Arkona Shale (M. Devonian), Ontario, Canada; brachial, anterior and side views of conjoined valves.

Pl. 5.2.79. *Syringothyris* Winchell, 1863
Pyramidal shape with large triangular interarea and large delthyrium mostly filled by complex plate with interior tube for pedicle (plate absent in photo); punctate shell fabric. Ornament of numerous rounded ribs except on smooth pedicle valve sulcus and brachial valve fold. Interior with strong dental plates. Average adult width 4 to 5 cm.
Devonian (Famennian)–L. Carboniferous, cosmopolitan, pedicle valve downwards with functional pedicle; semi-infaunal in lime-mud substrates.
Syringothyris cuspidata (J. Sowerby): Carboniferous Limestone (Viséan), Derbyshire, England; anterior, posterior and side views of conjoined valves.

Pl. 5.2.80. *Spirifer* J. Sowerby, 1816
Biconvex with semicircular transverse outline; incurved umbones but substantial interarea; brachial valve fold and pedicle valve sulcus; ornament of numerous ribs. Interior; short stout dental plates in pedicle valve; no median septum or crural plates in brachial valve. Average adult width 6 to 12 cm.
L.–U. Carboniferous, cosmopolitan, umbones downwards, oblique on brachial valve with functional pedicle on silt, mud or lime-mud substrates.
Spirifer striatus (Martin): Carboniferous Limestone (Viséan), Settle, Yorkshire, England; brachial and side views of conjoined valves.

SUPERFAMILY RETICULARIACEA
Biconvex spiriferides with short hinge lines; commonly lacking primary costa at umbo, but with micro-ornament.

Pl. 5.2.81. *Phricodothyris* George, 1932
Unequally biconvex; subcircular outline; larger pedicle valve with incurved umbo; open delthyrium. Ornament of double-barrelled spines arranged concentrically. Interior; no dental plates or median septa; normal teeth and sockets; very short crural plates in brachial valve. Average adult width 1 cm.
L. Carboniferous–Permian, cosmopolitan, attached by functional pedicle to particles or above chiefly lime-mud substrate.
Phricodothyris verecunda George: Dartry Limestone (Viséan), Co. Fermanagh, N. Ireland; oblique and side views of conjoined valves and brachial valve interior.

Pl. 5.2.82. *Martinia* M'Coy, 1844
Biconvex; elliptical outline; incurved umbones; pedicle valve sulcus and brachial valve fold. Apparently smooth, but with concentric rows of small pits. Interior; no dental plates, median septa or crural plates; longitudinally striate cardinal process. Average adult width 2 to 3 cm.
Carboniferous, cosmopolitan, umbones downwards obliquely on brachial valve with functional pedicle clinging to small particles on lime-muds.
Martinia glabra (J. Sowerby): Carboniferous Limestone (Viséan), Co. Kildare, Ireland; brachial, anterior and side views of conjoined valves.

SUPERFAMILY SPIRIFERINACEA
Like Spiriferacea, but with punctate shells.

Pl. 5.2.83. *Spiriferina* d'Orbigny, 1847
Biconvex, subpentagonal outline; incurved umbones; large triangular interarea with open delthyrium. Ornament of large rounded ribs, the central rib accentuated to form brachial valve fold and pedicle valve sulcus. Micro-ornament of numerous small spines. Interior with median septum to half pedicle valve length; pair of strong dental plates; no crural plates. Average adult width 2 to 3 cm.
Triassic–Jurassic (Lias), cosmopolitan, umbones downwards with functional pedicle on silt or mud substrates.
Spiriferina walcotti (J. Sowerby): L. Lias (Sinemurian), Radstock, Somerset, England; brachial, anterior and side views of conjoined valves.

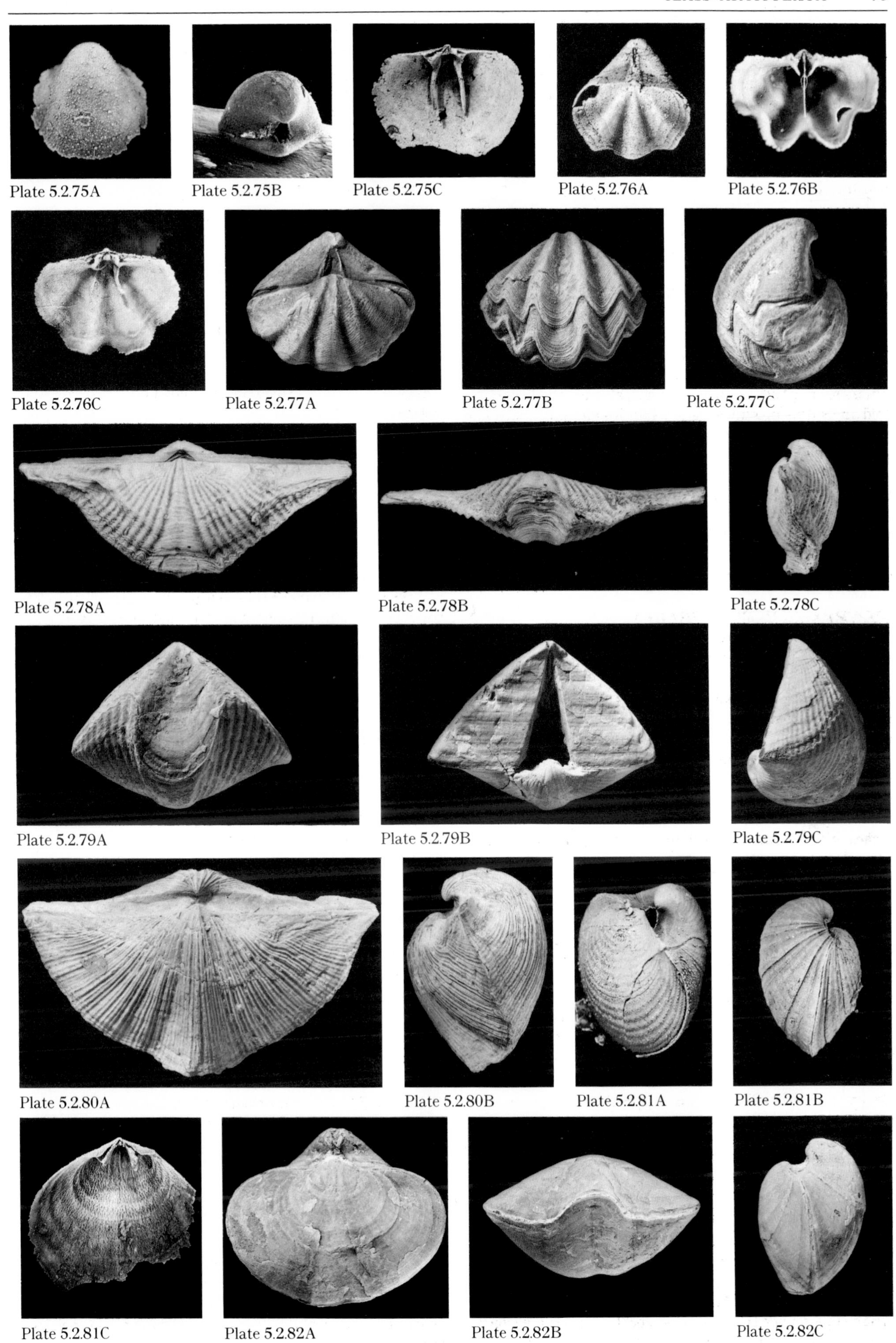

Plate 5.2.75A Plate 5.2.75B Plate 5.2.75C Plate 5.2.76A Plate 5.2.76B

Plate 5.2.76C Plate 5.2.77A Plate 5.2.77B Plate 5.2.77C

Plate 5.2.78A Plate 5.2.78B Plate 5.2.78C

Plate 5.2.79A Plate 5.2.79B Plate 5.2.79C

Plate 5.2.80A Plate 5.2.80B Plate 5.2.81A Plate 5.2.81B

Plate 5.2.81C Plate 5.2.82A Plate 5.2.82B Plate 5.2.82C

SUPERFAMILY CADOMELLACEA

This distinctive superfamily has been classified with the Strophomenida because of its shape and supra-apical foramen; however, it is now usually classified with the Spiriferida because of its shell structure and its calcified spiralia.

Pl. 5.2.84. *Cadomella* Oehlert, 1887

Convex pedicle valve and concave brachial valve; semicircular outline with maximum width at hinge line. No ornament. Small pedicle opening above interarea. Interior with low median septum in each valve; simple teeth and socket system; no dental plates. Average adult width 1.3 to 2 cm.

Jurassic (Pliensbachian–Bajocian), Europe, probably resting obliquely on pedicle valve with functional pedicle on silt or mud substrates.

Cadomella davidsoni (Deslongchamps): U. Lias, (Toarcian), May, France; brachial and pedicle views of conjoined valves and conjoined valves with most of the brachial valve removed to expose the spiralia.

Order Terebratulida

The order possesses calcified loops which act as supports for the fleshy lophophore. The type of loop characterizes the various superfamilies, representatives from each of which are included here apart from the late Palaeozoic Cryptonellacea.

SUPERFAMILY STRINGOCEPHALACEA

Confined to the U. Palaeozoic, this superfamily has a distinctive loop form known as centronelliform.

Pl. 5.2.85. *Stringocephalus* Defrance, 1825

Biconvex with prominent but incurved pedicle valve umbo; subcircular outline; no ornament. Large interarea with relatively small pedicle opening below apex. Interior with median septa in both valves; loop with spines. Average adult length 6 to 10 cm.

Devonian (Givetian), Europe, N. America, Asia, umbones downwards, obliquely resting on brachial valve with functional pedicle.

Stringocephalus burtini (Defrance): M. Devonian, Paffrath, W. Germany, brachial and side views of conjoined valves.

SUPERFAMILY DIELASMATACEA

Pl. 5.2.86. *Beecheria* Hall & Clarke, 1893

Biconvex with flatter brachial valve; elongate elliptical outline; very faint broad fold and sulcus; erect umbo with pedicle opening at apex; no ornament. Interior with complex articulation; dental plates, and complex cardinal plate behind the loop. Average adult length 3 to 5 cm.

Carboniferous (Tournaisian)–U. Permian, cosmopolitan, attached by functional pedicle to firm substrate or small particles on various substrates.

Beecheria cf. *hastata* (J. de C. Sowerby): Carboniferous Limestone (Viséan), Co. Clare, Ireland, pedicle, brachial and side views of conjoined valves, the pedicle valve left unsprayed to show original colour banding.

SUPERFAMILY TEREBRATULACEA

This superfamily includes all of the Mesozoic to Recent terebratulides with relatively short loops.

Pl. 5.2.87. *Epithyris* Phillips, 1841

Biconvex with erect beak and large apical pedicle opening; subcircular outline; 2 broad folds in brachial valve and intermediate sulcus in pedicle valve are variably developed in different species, some sharp-crested, others rounded. No ornament. Interior with low cardinal process; complex articulation and lophophore support bases; no dental plates or median septa. Average adult length 3 to 4 cm.

Jurassic (Bajocian–Bathonian), in clumps in various attitudes over lime-mud substrates, attached to small particles and each other.

Epithyris submaxillata (Morris): Inferior Oolite (Bajocian), Notgrove, Gloucestershire, England, brachial, side and anterior views of conjoined valves.

Pl. 5.2.88. *Gibbithyris* Sahni, 1925

Biconvex, globose and subcircular outline; small incurved pedicle valve umbo with relatively small pedicle opening; no ornament. Interior with no median septa or dental plates; convex hinge plates with crural bases starting from under them. Average adult width 2 to 2.5 cm.

Cretaceous (Cenomanian–Turonian), Europe, Asia, solitary, umbones downwards on soft lime-muds with functional pedicle.

Gibbithyris semiglobosa (J. Sowerby): M. Chalk (Turonian), Warminster, Wiltshire, England; brachial, side and anterior views of conjoined valves.

Pl. 5.2.89. *Plectothyris* Buckman, 1918

Biconvex; subcircular outline; erect beak with large apical pedicle foramen. Distinctive ornament of numerous rounded ribs confined to the anterior third of adult valves. Interior; no dental plates or median septa; complex articulation and bases to lophophore support. Average adult width 3 to 4 cm.

Jurassic (Bajocian), Europe, attached singly or in clumps over chiefly lime-mud substrates by stout functional pedicle; variable orientation.

Plectothyris fimbria (J. Sowerby): Oolite Marl (Bajocian), Birdlip, Gloucestershire, England; brachial, side and anterior views of conjoined valves.

Pl. 5.2.90. *Dictyothyris* Douvillé, 1879

Biconvex with erect beak and large pedicle opening; subpentagonal outline; 2 medial folds on crest of large plication in pedicle valve; corresponding structures on pedicle valve. Microornament of fine ribs and minute spines. Interior with large cardinal process; no median septa or dental plates. Average adult width 1 to 1.5 cm.

Jurassic (Bathonian–Kimmeridgian), Europe, umbones downwards and attached with stout functional pedicle over a variety of substrates.

Dictyothyris coarctata (Parkinson): Great Oolite (Bathonian), Bath, Avon, England; brachial, side and anterior views of conjoined valves.

Pl. 5.2.91. *Pygites* Buckman, 1906

Biconvex; subtriangular outline; small incurved pedicle umbo with large pedicle opening; bilobate, fused anteriorly in adults to form central hole; plane anterior commissure; no ornament. Simple interior; no median septa or dental plates; short hinge plates and small complex articulation. Average adult width 4 to 5 cm.

Cretaceous (Neocomian), Europe, N. Africa, Arctic (Tethyan region), obliquely on pedicle valve with functional pedicle.

Pygites diphyoides (d'Orbigny), L. Neocomian, Ardèche, France; pedicle and brachial views of conjoined valves.

SUPERFAMILY ZEILLERIACEA

Members of this superfamily all have long loops which are not attached to a brachial valve median septum in adults.

Plate 5.2.83A Plate 5.2.83B Plate 5.2.83C Plate 5.2.84A Plate 5.2.84B Plate 5.2.84C

Plate 5.2.85A Plate 5.2.85B Plate 5.2.86A Plate 5.2.86B Plate 5.2.86C

Plate 5.2.88A Plate 5.2.87A Plate 5.2.87B Plate 5.2.87C

Plate 5.2.88B

Plate 5.2.88C Plate 5.2.89A Plate 5.2.89B Plate 5.2.89C Plate 5.2.90A

Plate 5.2.90B Plate 5.2.90C Plate 5.2.91A Plate 5.2.91B

Plate 5.2.92A Plate 5.2.92B Plate 5.2.92C

Plate 5.2.94A Plate 5.2.94B Plate 5.2.94C

Plate 5.2.96A Plate 5.2.96B Plate 5.2.96C

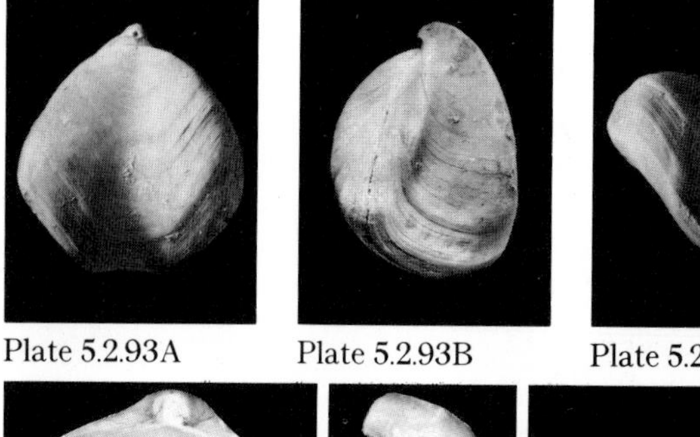

Plate 5.2.93A Plate 5.2.93B Plate 5.2.93C

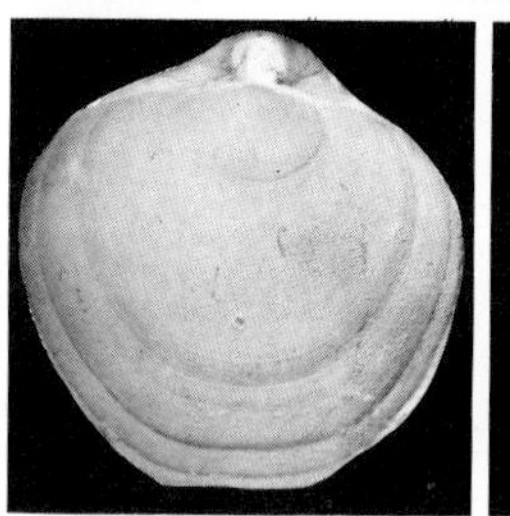

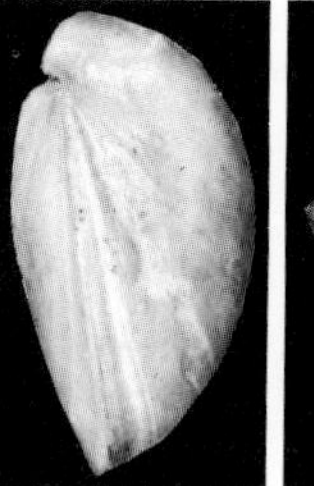

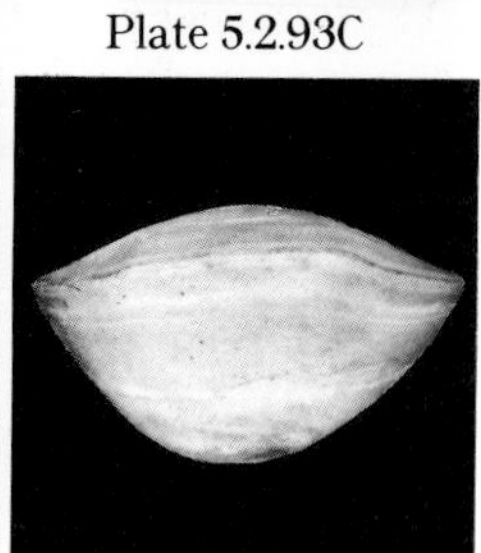

Plate 5.2.95A Plate 5.2.95B Plate 5.2.95C

Pl. 5.2.92. *Obovothyris* Buckman, 1927
Biconvex, subpentagonal outline with rectangular anterior commissure; incurved pedicle umbo with pedicle opening; no ribs or ornament. Interior with short dental plates; complex articulation; long brachial valve median septum to two-thirds valve length. Average adult width 1.5 cm.
Jurassic (Bathonian), Europe, attached with functional pedicle at various attitudes to fragments on lime-mud or silt substrates.
Obovothyris magnobovata Buckman: L. Cornbrash (Bathonian), Rushden, Northamptonshire, England; brachial, side and anterior views of conjoined valves.

Pl. 5.2.93. *Aulacothyris* Douvillé, 1879
Subpentagonal outline; convex pedicle valve with large fold, matched by brachial valve sulcus extending over most of the valve area; small incurved umbo. No ornament. Interior with median septum to half brachial valve length; short dental plates; complex hinge plates and crural bases. Average adult width 1 to 2 cm.
Triassic–Jurassic (Kimmeridgian), cosmopolitan, attached by functional pedicle to small fragments in sands, silts and muds.
Aulacothyris resupinata (J. Sowerby): M. Lias (Pliensbachian), Ilminster, Somerset, England; brachial, side and anterior views of conjoined valves.

Pl. 5.2.94. *Eudesia* King, 1850
Biconvex; subcircular to suboval outline; erect beak with relatively large pedicle opening; no fold or sulcus. Ornament of about 20 sharply crested ribs. Interior with dental plates; median septum in brachial valve; complex cardinal process and hinge plates. Average adult width 1.5 to 2 cm.
Jurassic (Bathonian), Europe, Asia, N. America (chiefly Tethyan region), attached by functional pedicle in various attitudes to particles on silt and lime-mud substrates.
Eudesia cardium (Valenciennes): Bathonian, Normandy, France; brachial, side and anterior views of conjoined valves.

SUPERFAMILY TEREBRATELLACEA
All terebratellaceans have long loops which are developed in association with a brachial valve median septum.

Pl. 5.2.95. *Kingena* Davidson, 1852
Biconvex with flatter brachial valve; erect umbo with relatively large pedicle opening; subcircular outline; faint, broad brachial valve fold. Ornament only of minute granules. Interior; dental plates present; small cardinal process; complex loop and loop supports on brachial valve median septum. Average adult length 2 to 3 cm.
Cretaceous (Albian–Maastrichtian), cosmopolitan, attached by functional pedicle in various attitudes over silt, mud and lime-mud substrates.
Kingena blackmorei Owen: U. Chalk (Turonian), Southampton, Hampshire, England; brachial, side and anterior views of conjoined valves.

Order Uncertain

SUPERFAMILY THECIDEACEA
This morphologically compact superfamily of 24 Triassic to Recent genera, all small, has been classified with the Strophomenida, Terebratulida and Spiriferida; most modern authors choose the latter on analogies of shell structure, but their final classification remains uncertain.

Pl. 5.2.96. *Thecidella* Oehlert, 1887
Semicircular outline; thickened and distorted but generally convex pedicle valve; gently concave brachial valve; relatively large interarea; no ornament. Interior with simple teeth and sockets; well-impressed bilobed pedicle valve muscle field; massive cardinal process; raised bilobed brachiophore support ridges in brachial valve. Average adult width 0.3 to 0.6 cm.
Triassic (Rhaetic)–Jurassic (Toarcian), Europe, cemented by pedicle valve to hard substrates.
Thecidella leptaenoides (Deslongchamps): U. Lias (Toarcian), May, Normandy, France; brachial view of conjoined valves and interiors of brachial and pedicle valves.

CHAPTER 6

Mollusca

The great diversity of fossil and living molluscs bears testimony to their success in adapting to many different modes of life, ranging from benthic (infaunal and epifaunal) to nektonic and planktonic. They mainly live in marine waters but some live in brackish, some in hypersaline, others in fresh waters and still others live on land. Their feeding strategies range from deposit and detritus feeding, through suspension feeding, scavenging and grazing, to predation. In size they range from the microscopic to the gigantic, but the majority are of quite modest dimensions. The emphasis here is on those forms with hard parts.

6.1 Class Monoplacophora

Monoplacophorans are generally bilaterally symmetrical, univalved molluscs with an anterior head and posterior anus. The nervous system is not torted, i.e. it is not twisted into the figure-of-eight pattern characteristic of primitive gastropods. Soft parts in living species show a pseudometamerism, with several pairs of discrete muscle scars, gills and kidneys. The shell varies from cap-shaped, with subcentral or overhanging apex (Fig. 6.1.1), to strongly planispirally coiled, with or without a median dorsal sinus. Monoplacophorans are most common from the Cambrian to the Silurian in shallow-water deposits. They are not certainly recorded as fossils since the Devonian, but a few species have been identified from Recent seas, generally in deep water.

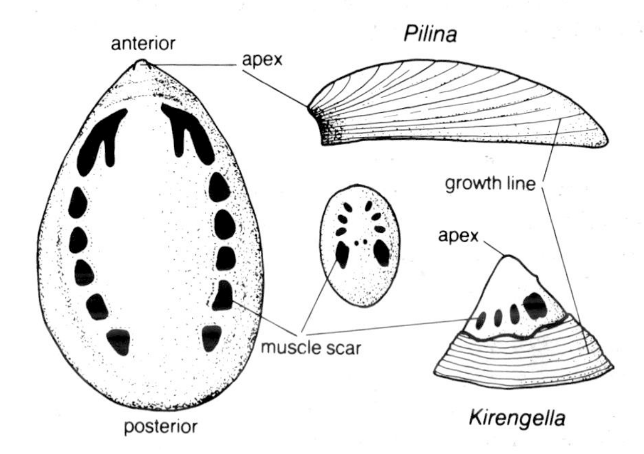

Fig. 6.1.1. *Pilina* Koken, 1925 (Ordovician–Silurian) and *Kirengella* Rosov, 1968 (U. Cambrian) in dorsal and lateral views showing principal morphological features of class Monoplacophora. Muscle scars are visible on moulds of the shell interior.

Opinions are currently divided as to the content of the class Monoplacophora and a satisfactory subdivision is not available. A conservative approach restricts the class to 'classic' forms with cap-shaped shells and (generally) several pairs of muscle scars, such as *Pilina* (Fig. 6.1.1, Pl. 6.1.2), and loosely to tightly coiled planispiral species without inductural deposits, such as *Sinuites* (Fig. 6.1.2). Some authors assign all the bellerophontiform molluscs (Fig. 6.1.2; Pl. 6.1.5; Pl. 6.6.1–5) to the Monoplacophora, but this complex of bilaterally symmetrical, planispirally coiled molluscs appears to contain both monoplacophorans and gastropods. A bellerophontiform shell assigned to the Monoplacophora would be oriented with the anal sinus at the posterior and the coil above the head. In a bellerophontiform gastropod the anal sinus or slit is anterior, over the head, as a result of torsion, and the coil is over the posterior of the animal.

Plate 6.1.1

Plate 6.1.2

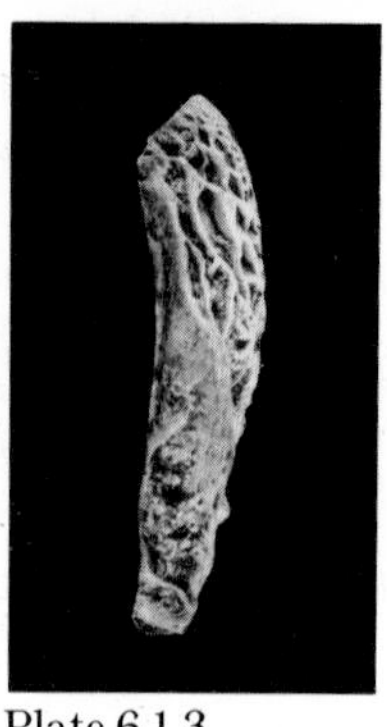
Plate 6.1.3

Plate 6.1.4

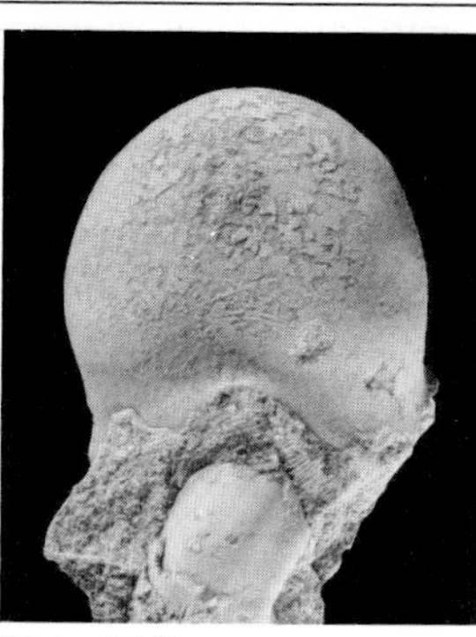
Plate 6.1.5

Pl. 6.1.1. *Scenella* Billings, 1872
Cap-shaped, subcircular, reticulate ornament; interior with 6 or 7 pairs of muscle scars; maximum length 1.5 cm.
Cambrian.
Scenella sp.: M. Cambrian, Canada.

Pl. 6.1.2. *Pilina* Koken, 1925
Elongate, with anterior apex. Shell exterior with fine growth lines; interior with 6 pairs of muscle scars, the anterior pair compound; maximum length 5 cm.
Ordovician–Silurian.
Pilina cheyennica Peel: U. Ordovician, Oklahoma, USA, internal mould showing muscle scars (see also Fig. 6.1.1).

Pl. 6.1.3, 4. *Tryblidium* Lindström, 1880
As *Pilina* (Pl. 6.1.2), but more shallow and with irregular lamellose ornament; maximum length 4 cm.
Ordovician–Silurian.
Tryblidium reticulatum Lindström: M. Silurian, Gotland, Sweden.

Pl. 6.1.5. *Sylvestrophaera* Peel, 1980
Planispirally coiled, globose with closed umbilici and dorsal sinus; lacking the lateral shields characteristic of *Sinuites* (Fig. 6.1.2); one compound muscle scar on each umbilical shoulder half a whorl back from aperture; maximum length about 3 cm.
Silurian.
Sylvestrophaera lemchei Peel: U. Silurian, England.

lateral shield
growth line
umbilicus
muscle scar
sinus indicated by growth lines
anterior
posterior

Fig. 6.1.2. *Sinuites* Koken, 1896 (Ordovician) in lateral and dorsal aspects, showing muscle scars on the internal mould which are considered to indicate monoplacophoran affinities.

6.2 Class Amphineura

The class Amphineura includes two subclasses of bilaterally symmetrical marine molluscs, namely the Aplacophora and the Polyplacophora. Aplacophorans are worm-like, naked and have no fossil record. In the Polyplacophora or chitons, the upper surface is usually covered by 8 overlapping calcareous plates set in a muscular girdle (Figs 6.2.1, 2) which is often ornamented by scales, spicules or hairs. A large foot on the underside is well

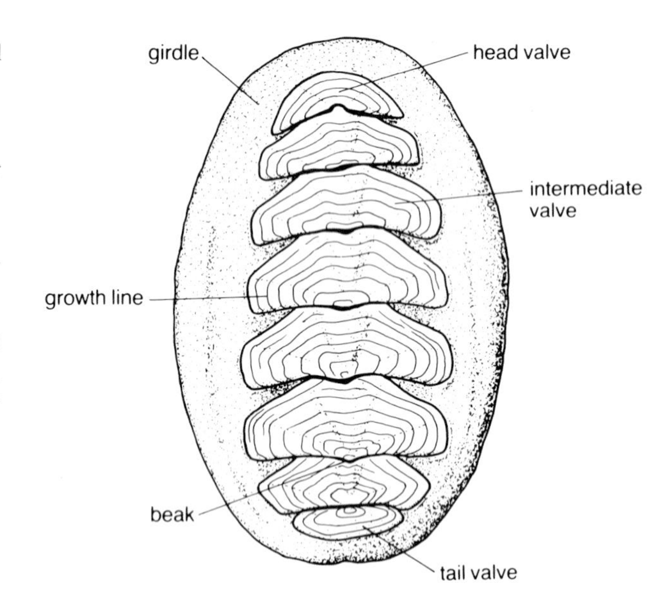

Fig. 6.2.1. *Mopalia* Gray, 1847 (Polyplacophora: Neoloricata: Pleistocene–Recent) showing morphological terms.

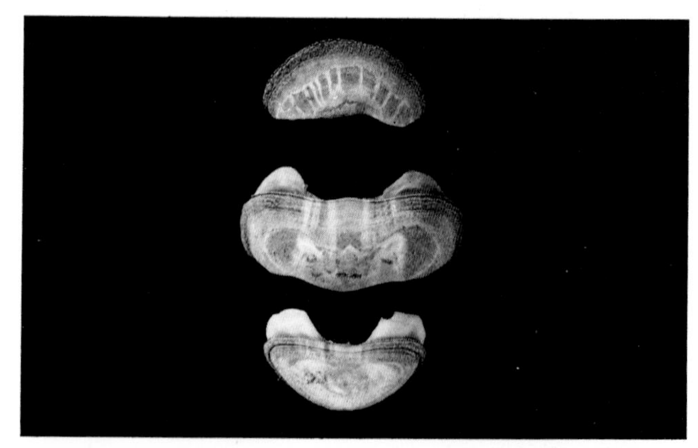

Fig. 6.2.2. Disarticulated valves of a recent neoloricate polyplacophoran showing insertion plates on intermediate and tail valves.

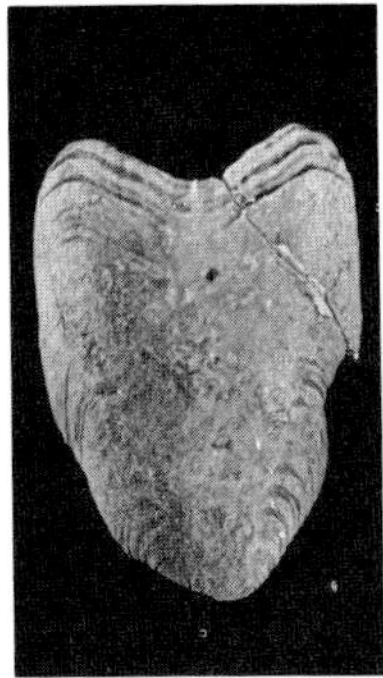
Plate 6.2.1

Plate 6.2.2

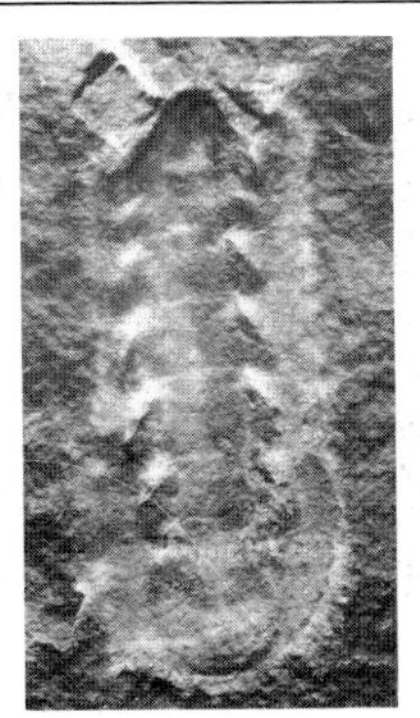
Plate 6.2.3

adapted to clinging to rocky substrates in high-energy environments. The mouth, which contains a well-developed radula, is anterior, the anus posterior; there are two kidneys and the heart has two auricles. Many have two gills located near the anus in the elongate mantle cavity which occurs between the foot and the girdle. In others, bunches of gills occupy most of the mantle cavity. The sexes are separate. Average size range is from 2 to 8 cm, rarely up to 30 cm. Polyplacophorans occur rarely as fossils from the U. Cambrian to Recent, usually as disarticulated valves. There are about 600 living species.

Two orders of polyplacophorans are recognized on the basis of valve structure – the presence or absence of an internal shell layer termed the 'articulamentum' which makes up the articulating insertion plates visible in Fig. 6.2.2.

Order Paleoloricata

Valves generally thick and massive; articulamentum, and therefore insertion plates, absent. U. Cambrian–U. Cretaceous.

Pl. 6.2.1, 2. *Chelodes* Davidson & King, 1874
Intermediate valves massive, heart-shaped with posterior elongation; maximum length of valve about 1.5 cm.
L. Ordovician–Silurian.
Chelodes gotlandicus Lindström; M. Silurian, Gotland, Sweden (Pl. 6.2.1); *Chelodes* sp.: L. Ordovician, Peary Land, N. Greenland (Pl. 6.2.2).

Order Neoloricata

Articulamentum, and hence insertion plates, present. Carboniferous–Recent.

Pl. 6.2.3. *Pterochiton* Carpenter *in* Dall, 1882
Eight articulated valves surrounded by a wide girdle which is studded with spicules, probably of aragonite; intermediate valves posterolaterally angular, with median posterior beak; head valve posteriorly sinuate; tail valve with low boss; length about 3 cm.
Pterochiton concinnus (Richardson): U. Carboniferous, Will–Kankakee Counties, Illinois, USA.

6.3 Class Scaphopoda

Scaphopods are marine, bilaterally symmetrical molluscs in which the shell consists of a tapering, curved tube, convex ventrally and open at both ends. In life, the anterior, apertural part of the shell is buried in sediment, while the tapered

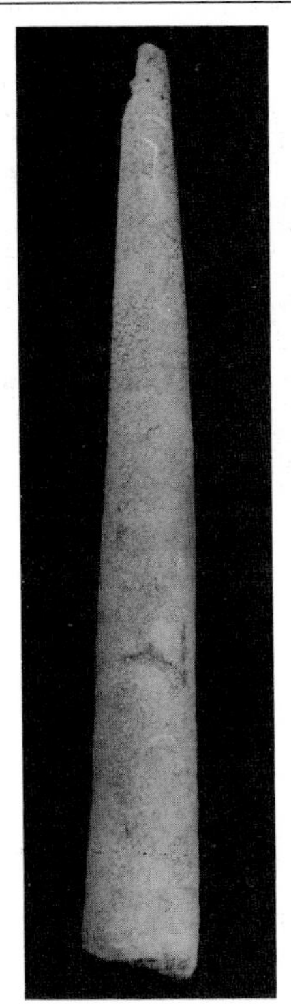
Plate 6.3.1

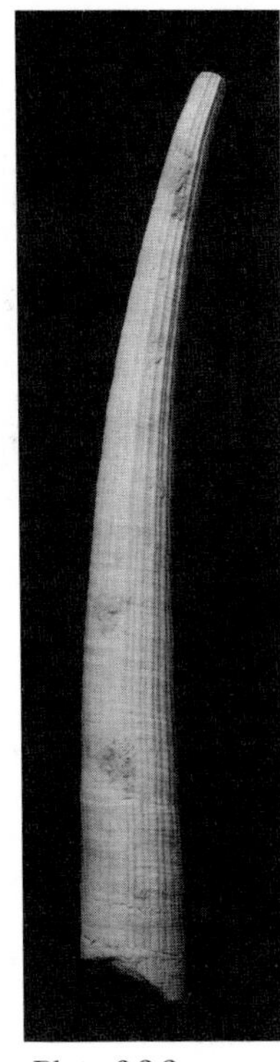
Plate 6.3.2

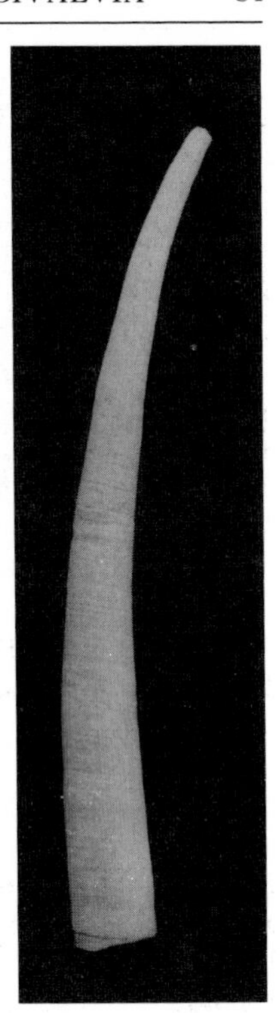
Plate 6.3.3

posterior, the apex, protrudes into the water. The head and radula, and a tentaculate feeding organ, the captacula, are well developed; gills are absent. The sexes are separate.
Ordovician–Recent, most abundant at the present day.

Pl. 6.3.1. *Plagioglypta* Pilsbry & Sharp, 1897
Closely spaced, oblique concentric cords near aperture; deep slit at apex; maximum length about 10 cm.
U. Devonian–U. Cretaceous.
Plagioglypta canna (White): Permian, Nevada, USA.

Pl. 6.3.2. *Dentalium* Linné, 1758
Longitudinal ribs prominent, especially near apex which may be polygonal in cross-section; maximum length about 15 cm.
U. Cretaceous–Recent.
Dentalium sp.: Miocene, Germany.

Pl. 6.3.3. *Antalis* Adams & Adams, 1854
Fine ribs and growth lines; apex with notch and inner pipe; maximum length about 10 cm.
M. Triassic–Recent.
Antalis grande (Deshayes): Eocene, Paris basin, France.

6.4 Class Bivalvia

Primitively and predominantly, bivalves are bilaterally shelled molluscs that burrow in marine sediments. Major secondary adaptations include epifaunal and boring life habits as well as invasion of fresh water. The shell in the Bivalvia consists of two *lateral valves* (left and right, abbreviated throughout as LV and RV), connected at their *dorsal* margins by a resilient *ligament* (Pl. 6.4.36A). These commonly enclose the entire animal. Each valve is produced by a lobate outgrowth of tissue (*mantle lobe*) from the animal's dorsal surface. The lobe progressively adds new layers of shell material to the valve's inner surface, and around the greater part of its margins, so leaving *commarginal growth lines* on the valve's exterior (e.g. Pl. 6.4.51A). Each valve thus tends to form a rapidly expanding helicocone with little or no change of shape during growth. The earliest-formed part of the valve, or *beak*, is situated above and/or in front of the ligament on a dorsal prominence, resulting from the spiral growth, called the *umbo* (pl. *umbones*). Each beak may be slightly separated from the dorsal valve margin by a shelly surface supporting the ligament called a *cardinal area* (Pl. 6.4.14A), or it may touch it, separating crescentic areas fore and aft, the front pair in a shell making up the *lunule* and the back pair, usually flanking the ligament, the *escutcheon* (Pl. 6.4.46A, B). In life the two valves can be pulled together by two *adductor muscles*, situated fore and aft (reduced to one in some), whose attachment to the valves leaves distinctive *scars* on their inner surfaces (Pl. 6.4.46B). Adduction imposes a strain on the ligament, which counteracts by opening the valves when the muscles relax. In most species, the inner margins of the valves ventrally or otherwise adjacent to the ligament bear an array of interlocking *hinge teeth* and *sockets*, collectively called the *dentition* (Pl. 6.4.44A), which ensures accurate, shear-free closure of the valves. These may be sited on internally projecting ledges called *hinge plates* (Pl. 6.4.44A, B). The ventral part of each mantle lobe is usually connected to its valve along a long scar or series of scars called the *pallial line*. The shell itself is composed of $CaCO_3$, with a minor proteinaceous component, and is coated externally by a layer of tanned proteinaceous *periostracum*, which is produced around the margins of the mantle lobes and acts as a conveyor-belt-like foundation for the laying down of the calcareous shell. The shell carbonate is usually aragonite, but some or even most of it is calcite in certain species. However, the parts of the shell deposited beneath zones of mantle adhesion (usually associated with muscle attachment) are invariably aragonite.

Variants of these basic features can be used as bases for the classification of bivalve shells (though the proper classification of the Bivalvia of course incorporates features of the soft parts as well, but this information is largely unavailable in fossils). The most important shell features for classification are:

1. Dentition (at all taxonomic levels).
2. Form of ligament insertion on the valves (particularly at superfamily and family level).
3. State of adductor muscle scars (usually at order to superfamily level).
4. State of the pallial line (mainly at family level and below).
5. Shell shape (all levels from superfamily downwards).
6. Shell mineralogy and microstructure (mainly at superfamily level).

Like the pop music industry, bivalve evolution is sparing on real novelty, but succeeds by recycling old tricks; this probably reflects the perenially plastic simplicity of the starting material. Consequently, equivalent adaptive morphologies have emerged independently in several different stocks, and this means that no single feature is safe from occasional perversion as a basis for classification. It is thus important to consider many features together, so that deviant characters can be detected. For this reason it is virtually impossible to come up with a simple, fail-safe hierarchical key for classifying bivalves; such keys constrain the user to considering only one feature at a time, and thereby give scope for many fruitless misleading decisions. Exceptions could only be catered for by a host of qualifying clauses that would rapidly constipate the key. So in the guide to classification (Table 6.4.1), variations in the six features listed above are weighted equally.

Classification to the superfamily level has been chosen here as being the most practicable. These are moderately stable taxa, and, with some clear exceptions, probably represent more or less real phylogenetic clusters of species. Higher level taxa are, by and large, considered less reliable as reflections of phylogenetic clustering (though some currently employed subclasses are shown on Table 6.4.1), while lower level taxa are just too numerous, and would demand greater coverage than this work could offer. Certain minor superfamilies have been entirely omitted here. These are: Archanodontacea Weir, 1969; Chlamydoconchacea Dall, 1884; Gaimardiacea Hedley, 1961; and Hiatellacea Grey, 1824. Details of these can be found in the *Treatise* (Moore 1969, 1971). Moreover, some of the superfamilies discussed here have themselves been split up by certain authors to create new superfamilies. These are mentioned in the appropriate superfamily descriptions.

More detailed accounts of bivalve nomenclature and classification can be found in the *Treatise* on Bivalvia and other major works such as Pojeta (1971), Yonge and Thompson (1978) and Boss (1982). These works also contain data on the stratigraphic ranges of the superfamilies. But it should be noted that the range of the class has now been extended down to the L. Cambrian (see Pojeta, *in* Yonge and Thompson 1978).

Guide to classification

Table 6.4.1 can be used to classify bivalve specimens from five of the six shell features listed on p. 83; variants of these are illustrated down the left-hand side of the table. The sixth feature, shell mineralogy and microstructure, is dealt with at the end of this section. Along the top of the table are listed the 51 superfamilies discussed herein, and the distribution among these of the shell feature variants are indicated in the matrix making up the main body of the table.

In classifying a specimen, first decide which variant of each shell feature appears to be present, and then list these. The numbers at the left of the table will serve as useful codes. Note that the diagrams of the variants in the table are only intended to show basic arrangements of features, and that the features of any one specimen are likely to differ from them in detail. Sometimes it will not be possible to make a decision for a feature because of poor preservation, or because the specimen shows a peculiar form of the feature in question that is either difficult to relate to, or is not represented in the table. In such cases omit the feature for the time being, rather than guessing. Next, study the main body of the table to determine which superfamilies might exhibit the combination of variants you have listed. Remember that no feature takes precedence for systematic assignment; so the easiest way to compare your list with the table is to find which of the variants you have selected implicates the smallest number of superfamilies, and then to use the other listed variants to narrow the field down from there. In practice the search will often start with dentition simply because this has been split into the greatest number of variations. You should then end up with a few (hopefully even one) superfamilies. Comparison of your specimen with the superfamily descriptions and figures in the next section on p. 83 should then enable you to decide to which superfamily the specimen should be assigned. If a specimen fits the description and photographs of a particular genus tolerably well, that is no guarantee that it should in fact be assigned to that genus. The descriptions given here are necessarily brief and many details of lower level taxonomy have been omitted. Having found the right superfamily, you should refer to more detailed works, particularly the *Treatise* volumes on the Bivalvia (Moore 1969, 1971) to complete the classification.

Notes on taxonomic features

1. *Dentition.* In the diagrams on Table 6.4.1, teeth are shown up in white on black backgrounds representing hinge plates, or valve margins where these are lacking. Ligamentary pits (shown by heavy stippling) are included in the diagrams of isodont and mactroid dentition (types 5 and 11), as these form integral parts of those types. In the various kinds of heterodont dentition (types 8–12) it is the arrangement of the cardinal teeth that is important; lateral teeth may be more or less reduced from a maximum of two in front and behind in each valve.
2. *Ligament insertion.* Areas of insertion of lamellar ligament (which is purely organic) are shown in black, and those of *fibrous* ligament (which contains aragonite fibres), by stippled ornament. But note that in type 16, fibrous ligament is inserted on to the steep dorsal face of an elongate shelly ridge (*nymph*), which is demarcated here by a row of dots. The internally projecting ligament of the Pectinacea (included in type 21) is a highly modified form of type 19. The ligamentary support in the Pholadacea (included in type 22) is commonly obscure, but should not be confused with the prominent muscle support in members of this superfamily.
3. *Adductor scars.* These are shown in black.
4. *Pallial line.* These are also shown in black. This feature is commonly rather difficult to see, but will usually show up if the specimen is slowly moved to and fro in oblique light.
5. *Shell shape.* Broad and rather generalized categories are shown in diagrammatic outline. In type 31 the anterior end is generally reduced to a small lobe, while in type 32 it is significantly extended. In type 35, only one, or both valves may be attached to the tube.
6. *Shell mineralogy and microstructure.* Detailed studies of shell structure are relatively young, and so had little part to play in the original formulation of bivalve systematics. However, they can provide useful contributory evidence in classification. Most microstructures can be distinguished with a binocular microscope at ×50. The terminology used here follows that of the major study by Taylor, Kennedy and Hall (1969, 1973), with the following abbreviations. Aragonitic microstructures: P, simple prismatic; CP, composite prismatic; N, nacreous; CL, crossed-lamellar; CCL, complex cross-lamellar; H, homogeneous. Calcitic microstructures: P, simple prismatic; FP, fibrillar prismatic; F, foliated. A more detailed classification is provided by Carter (1980).

Preservation allowing, peels and/or thin sections can be used to identify shell microstructures in most cases, and the reader may wish to check assignment of a specimen to any particular superfamily on the basis of the other five features, thereby.

Most bivalves have an entirely aragonitic shell, and so are commonly fossilized as casts made of cavity-fill cement, or as moulds. The following superfamilies also exhibit calcitic shell layers (in which original or ghosted microstructure is frequently visible in fossil material): Mytilacea, Ambonychiacea, Pteriacea, Pinnacea, Limacea, Aviculopectinacea, Pectinacea, Buchiacea, Anomiacea, Ostreacea, Plicatulacea, Hippuritacea, (Chamacea, Veneracea in a few species).

Systematic descriptions

Each superfamily is characterized in terms of the six numbered features listed on p. 82, followed by a brief account of one or more representative genera. The numbering of the photographs corresponds with that of the generic description. The sequence of superfamilies more or less follows that of the *Treatise* (Moore 1969, 1971); any changes are intended to reflect more recent ideas concerning relationships. Those superfamilies marked with an 'X' are now extinct. The maximum size given for each genus refers to adult shell length, unless otherwise stated. Stratigraphic data are expressed in terms of Lower (L.), Middle (M.) and Upper (U.) parts of systems, greater accuracy commonly being unobtainable and/or unreliable. Geographical ranges should be taken with a pinch of salt, reflecting the paucity of work in many areas quite as much as real distributions. Finally, note that a number of minor exceptions to the diagnostic features cited for each superfamily are not mentioned, for reasons of space, but are indicated by small dots on Table 6.4.1.

SUPERFAMILY CTENODONTACEA X

1, Taxodont; 2, external, simple opisthodetic; 3, isomyarian; 4, integripalliate; 5, equivalve, equilateral; 6, ?aragonite.

Pl. 6.4.1. *Tancrediopsis* Beushausen, 1895
Subequilateral, trigonal; mid-dorsal beaks point inwards; primitive external ligament, semicylindrical and mounted in slender trough behind each umbo; up to 2 cm.
M.–U. Ordovician; deposit feeeder; shallow burrowing; N. America.
Tancrediopsis cuneata (Hall): U. Ordovician, east of Lake Huron, Canada. RV interior.

SUPERFAMILY NUCULACEA

1, Taxodont; 2, external opisthodetic, or internal; 3, isomyarian; 4, integripalliate; 5, equivalve, truncate posterior; 6, aragonite, outer CP, and middle and inner N layers.

Pl. 6.4.2. *Nucula* Lamarck, 1799
Inequilateral, subtrigonal; beaks point backwards; ligament internal on triangular pit beneath each beak; exterior may have fine radial ribs; valve margins crenulate; up to 3 cm.
L. Cretaceous–Recent; deposit feeder; burrowing just beneath muddy surface; cosmopolitan.
Nucula (Pectinucula) pectinata J. Sowerby: L. Cretaceous. (A) Badbury Wick, Wiltshire, England, RV interior; (B) Henfield, Sussex, England, LV exterior.

SUPERFAMILY NUCULANACEA

1, Taxodont; 2, external opisthodetic, or internal; 3, isomyarian; 4, usually sinupalliate; 5, equivalve, extended posterior; 6, aragonite, H inner and outer layers (inner layer N in some fossil species).

Pl. 6.4.3. *Portlandia* Mörch, 1857
Subequilateral, inflated, with gently furrowed rostrate posterior; beaks point inwards; ligament internal on triangular pit beneath each beak; up to 3 cm.
Tertiary–Recent; deposit feeder; shallow burrower; cosmopolitan.
Portlandia deshayesii (Nyst): Oligocene, Rupelmonde, Antwerp, Belgium. (A) LV interior; (B) RV exterior.

SUPERFAMILY SOLEMYACEA

1, Edentulous; 2, opisthodetic, on more or less internalized ridges; 3, heteromyarian (anterior muscle larger); 4, integripalliate (often obscure); 5, equivalve, inequilateral with elongate anterior; 6, aragonite, outer P and inner H layers, with a thick periostracum extending beyond valve margins.

KEY
○ Feature found in nearly all genera
● Feature found in many genera
• Feature found in a few genera
( ) Feature present in abnormal state
◄ anterior
Shell features, with examples

Shell features		Example	No.	Palaeo-taxodonta: Ctenodontacea	Palaeo-taxodonta: Nuculacea	Palaeo-taxodonta: Nuculanacea	'Cryptodonta': Solemyacea	'Cryptodonta': Praecardiacea	Isofilibranchia: Modiomorphacea	Isofilibranchia: Mytilacea	Pteriomorphia: Cyrtodontacea	Pteriomorphia: Arcacea	Pteriomorphia: Limopsacea	Pteriomorphia: Ambonychiacea	Pteriomorphia: Pteriacea	Pteriomorphia: Pinnacea
1. Dentition	Many small teeth along hinge plates	 Taxodont, Pl. 6.4.1, 14A	1	○	○	○						●	○			
		 Actinodont, Pl. 6.4.34	2			•										
		 Cyrtodont, Pl. 6.4.12, 16B	3								○			●	●	
		 Parallelodont, Pl. 6.4.13	4									●				
	Few prominent teeth beneath beaks	 Isodont, Pl. 6.4.24, 32	5													
		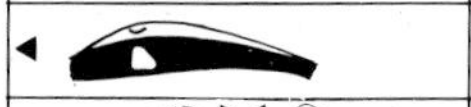 Simple tooth or teeth, Pl. 6.4. 80B	6						●	•	•					
		 Schizodont, Pl. 6.4.37B, 38B	7													
	Heterodont: up to three prominent *'cardinal teeth'* beneath each beak, with commarginal *'lateral teeth'* fore and aft	 Lucinoid Pl. 6.4. 40B, C, 44A, B	8													
		 Arcticoid, Pl. 6.4.57B, C	9													
		 Corbiculoid, Pl. 6.4.59B, C	10													
		 Mactroid, Pl. 6.4.51B	11													
		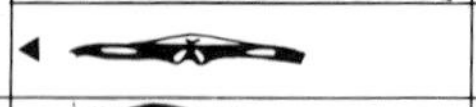 Reduced heterodont, Pl. 6.4.41B	12													
	Large, knobbly teeth beneath beaks	 Pachyodont, Pl. 6.4.64B	13													
	Teeth absent: margins may have tiny ridges	 Edentulous or denticulate, Pl. 6.4.29B, 69B	14				○	○	●	○				●	●	○
2. Ligament insertion	Wholly external (visible outside shell). Opisthodetic: groove behind each beak	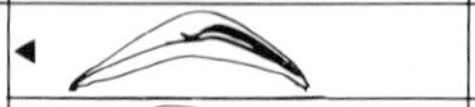 Simple groove, Pl. 6.4.1	15	○	●	●		?	○							
		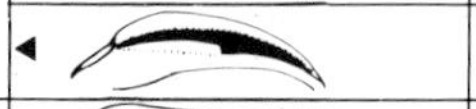 Nymph-supported, Pl. 6.4.44B, 57C	16			●	●			○						○
	Wholly external. Oblique: cardinal area mostly behind each beak	 With single or multiple pits, Pl. 6.4.19B, 18	17												○	
		 With many horizontal or chevron grooves, Pl. 6.4.11B, 12	18								○			○	•	
	Wholly external. Amphidetic: cardinal area fore and aft beneath each beak	 With central triangular pit, Pl. 6.4.15	19					(●)					○			
		 With multiple chevron grooves, Pl. 6.4.14A	20									●				
	Partly or wholly internal	 In sunken pit beneath each beak, Pl. 6.4.2A, 24, 46B	21		●	●										
		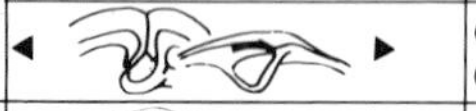 On projecting sub-umbonal process(es), Pl. 6.4.67, 79B	22				●									
3. Adductor scars		Isomyarian: scars ~ equal, Pl. 6.4.46B	23	○	○	○		?				○	○			
		 Heteromyarian; anterior scar larger, Pl. 6.4. 40A	24				○									
		 Heteromyarian; posterior scar larger, Pl. 6.4.6	25						○	○	○			?	●	○
		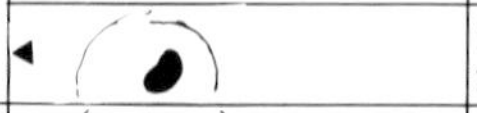 Monomyarian: only one adductor scar, Pl. 6.4.29B	26				•			•				●	●	
4. Pallial line		Integripalliate: simple arc, Pl. 6.4.2A	27	○	○	•	○	?	○	○	○	○	○			
		 Sinupalliate: sinus present, Pl. 6.4.52B	28			●										
		 Disjunct or wanting, Pl. 6.4.29B, 74	29											○	○	○
5. Shell shape	Equivalve: valves externally symmetrical to each other	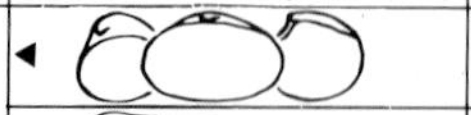 Equilateral: anterior and posterior ~ equal (but beaks commonly anterior), 6.4.1	30	○	●	○		●				●	○			
		 Anterior greatly reduced, Pl. 6.4.8	31					•	○	○	○	●		●		○
		 Anterior greatly expanded, Pl. 6.4.2A	32		●		○									
	Inequivalve: valves externally asymmetrical to each other	 Shell unattached, Pl. 6.4.25	33					●				•		●	○	
		 One valve of shell attached to substratum, Pl. 6.4.30A	34													
	Adult shell fused to tube	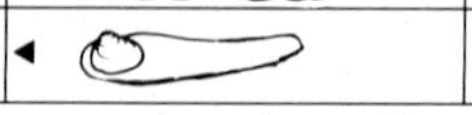 Pl. 6.4.82	35													

Table 6.4.1. Key to morphology and taxonomy of bivalved molluscs (see text for discussion).

							Heteroconchia																							Anomalodesmata								
Limacea	Aviculopectinacea	Pectinacea	Buchiacea	Anomiacea	Ostreacea	Plicatulacea	Cycloconchacea	Anthracosiacea	Unionacea	Trigoniacea	Babinkacea	Lucinacea	Cyamiacea	Leptonacea	Carditacea	Chamacea	Crassatellacea	Cardiacea	Tridacnacea	Mactracea	Solenacea	Tellinacea	Arcticacea	Glossacea	Corbiculacea	Dreissenacea	Veneracea	Megalodontacea	Hippuritacea	Edmondiacea	Pholadomyacea	Pandoracea	Poromyacea	Clavagellacea	Gastrochaenacea	Myacea	Pholadacea	
•									•																													1
							○		•																													2
																																						3
																																						4
	•	●				○																																5
								●		•	○	•																		•	•	•	●			●		6
										●																												7
												●			○		○	○	○			●	•		•		(•)											8
																							●	(○)														9
																									●		○											10
																				○																		11
													○	○			•				○	●					•											12
									●							○												○	○									13
○	○	●	○	○	○			●	●			•														○				○	●	○	•	○	○	●	○	14
							○				○																								●			15
								○	○	○		○	•		●	○	●	○	○		○	●	○	○	○	○	○	○	●	○	○	•	●	●	●			16
																																						17
																																						18
○	●		○		● (●)																																	19
	●																																					20
		(○)				○		•					●	○	●		●			○		●							●			●	●					21
				○																•									●			●	●			○	(○)	22
							○	●	○	○	○	●	○	○	●	○	○	○	•	○	●	●	○	○	○		○	○	●	○	○	○	○	●		○	○	23
												●									●	•							●									24
								●							●											○								(●)	○			25
○	○	○	○	○	○	○			•										○																			26
		●				●	○	○	●	○	○	○	○	○	○	○	●	●	○				●	●	●	●	•	○	○	○	•	●	●			•		27
									•	•							(•)	●		○	○	○	•	•	•	●	○				●	●	●		○	●	○	28
○	●	•	○	○	○																											•						29
	(•)	(●)					○	●	●	○	○	○	○	○	●		○	○	(○)	○	●	●	●	○	○		○	●		●	○	●	●			●	●	30
○								●	●						●				•		●		•			○	•			•					(○)		●	31
																				•		●																32
	●	●	○	•																		(●)						•			•	●	(•)			●		33
		•		(○)	○	○			•							○													○			•						34
																																		○			•	35

Pl. 6.4.4. *Solemya* Lamarck, 1818
Compressed with extended anterior and small oval posterior; depressed marginal umbones near posterior; ligament mainly behind umbones, between margin and sunken ledge (which may have low buttress skirting posterior muscle) in each valve; blunt radial ribs externally; muscle scar band rises dorsally from inner ventral corner of large anterior adductor scar; up to 7 cm.
L. Ordovician–Recent; suspension feeder, lives in deep Y-shaped burrow; cosmopolitan.

Solemya primaeva Phillips: U. Carboniferous, Stanhope, Durham, England. Internal mould of RV.

SUPERFAMILY PRAECARDIACEA X

1, Edentulous (or with denticles); 2, external, amphidetic on plain cardinal areas, or ?simple opisthodetic, or lacking; 3, 4, musculature uncertain; 5, equivalve to inequivalve, often radially ornamented, thin shells, usually circular to ovate with prominent (sometimes distinctly ornamented) umbones; 6, unknown.

Pl. 6.4.5. *Slava* Barrande, 1881
Large projecting umbones with broad commarginal undulations; outer part of shell (later growth stage) less inflated, circular, with radial riblets; short denticulate hinge line; up to 5 cm.
Silurian; found in muddy carbonates (ecology unknown); Europe.
Slava fibrosa (J. de C. Sowerby): Silurian, Dudley, Worcestershire, England. LV exterior.

SUPERFAMILY MODIOMORPHACEA X

1, Edentulous, or with 1 or more simple teeth; 2, external, opisthodetic, simple sheet connecting valves; 3, heteromyarian (anterior muscle reduced); 4, integripalliate; 5, equivalve, modioliform with reduced anterior; 6, ?aragonite.

Pl. 6.4.6. *Modiolopsis* Hall, 1847
Inequilateral, modioliform with low forwardly inclined umbones and maximum height of shell towards posterior; ligament-supporting ridges absent; fine commarginal sculpture; edentulous; up to 7 cm.
M.–U. Ordovician; suspension feeder, epifaunal byssate (as in mussels); cosmopolitan.
Modiolopsis modiolaris (Conrad): U. Ordovician, Waynesville, Ohio, USA. Internal mould of RV.

Pl. 6.4.7. *Modiomorpha* Hall and Whitfield, 1869
Like *Modiolopsis* in shape, but with ventral embayment and consequent preumbonal sulcus; single wedge-shaped tooth in LV; up to 6 cm.
M. Silurian–L. Permian, probably like *Modiolopsis*; widespread.
Modiomorpha mytiloides (Conrad): M. Devonian, Syracuse, New York, USA. RV exterior.

SUPERFAMILY MYTILACEA

1, Edentulous, or with marginal denticles; 2, external, opisthodetic, deep-set on elongate ridges to inside of valve margins; 3, heteromyarian (anterior muscle much reduced); 4, integripalliate; 5, equivalve, anterior reduced (mussel shape); 6, either entirely aragonite, with N outer and inner layers (inner layer may be CCL), or mixed, with an outermost layer of FP calcite.

Pl. 6.4.8. *Modiolus* Lamarck, 1799
'Modioliform', somewhat inflated with beaks slightly behind rounded anterior; long ligament; simple commarginal ornament; edentulous; up to 22 cm, but most species around 8 cm.
Carboniferous–Recent; suspension feeder; with anterior more or less embedded in sediment, and posterior projecting out; byssate attachment; cosmopolitan.
Modiolus ungulatus (Young & Bird): U. Jurassic, Malton, Yorkshire, England. RV exterior.

Pl. 6.4.9. *Musculus* Röding, 1798
Modioliform, with anterior and posterior radial zones bearing radial riblets, separated by an embayed smooth zone; margins crenulate around ribbed zones, hinge denticulations fore and aft of ligament; anterior adductor scar long and thin; up to 5 cm.
Jurassic–Recent; suspension feeder; byssate nestler, commonly among stones and algae.
Musculus elegans (J. Sowerby): Eocene, Bognor, Sussex, England. Internal mould of LV, showing impression of ligamentary support, forming a groove alongside the dorsal margin of the mould (upper right on figure).

Pl. 6.4.10. *Lithophaga* Röding, 1798
Subelliptical, modioliform with anterior beaks and cylindrical cross-section, but tapering posteriorly; smooth or with fine vertical striations; edentulous; shell margins smooth; up to 10 cm, but most up to about 3 cm.
?Carboniferous, Jurassic–Recent; suspension feeder; chemical borer into carbonate substrata (e.g. corals), making plump bullet-shaped crypt; cosmopolitan.
Lithophaga inclusa (Phillips): U. Jurassic, Lyneham, Wiltshire, England. LV exterior with moulds of crypts.

SUPERFAMILY CYRTODONTACEA X

1, Anterior teeth, arched over anterior adductor, separated by edentulous area from posterior teeth, parallel to valve margin; 2, external, posteriorly oblique on broad cardinal areas, with multiple parallel longitudinal grooves and ridges (may have chevron form in some genera); 3, heteromyarian (anterior scar slightly reduced); 4, integripalliate; 5, equivalve, ovoid with more or less prominent anterior umbones, and a rounded anterior, which may be reduced; 6, ?aragonite throughout.

Pl. 6.4.11. *Ptychodesma* Hall & Whitfield, 1872
Modioliform, with reduced lobate anterior and weak anterior umbones; ligament grooves arched beneath beaks, apparently in chevron form; finely commarginal external ornament; shell with outer P, middle N, and inner CCL layers; up to 5 cm.
Devonian (?M. Ordovician–U. Devonian); suspension feeder; ?semi-infaunal byssate; USA, Europe, ?Ghana, ?Australia.
Ptychodesma knappanum Hall & Whitfield: M. Devonian, Charlestown, Indiana, USA. (A) LV exterior; (B) RV cardinal area and LV.

Pl. 6.4.12. *Vanuxemia* Billings, 1858
Ovate to subcircular, inflated, with slightly reduced anterior, and forwardly directed umbones; anterior adductor scar embedded on subumbonal shelf; up to 3 cm.
M.–U. Ordovician, suspension feeder; semi-infaunal or cavity-dwelling nestler; N. America, Sweden.
Vanuxemia gibbosa Ulrich: Ordovician, Tennessee, USA. LV interior (Pojeta 1971: Pl. 7, Fig. 10).

SUPERFAMILY ARCACEA

1, Taxodont or with short oblique anterior, and elongate posterior teeth; 2, external, amphidetic, usually of chevron form (sometimes vertically striate) on broad cardinal areas; 3, isomyarian; 4, integripalliate; 5, equivalve, trapezoidal, with

Plate 6.4.1 Plate 6.4.2A Plate 6.4.2B Plate 6.4.3A

Plate 6.4.3B Plate 6.4.4 Plate 6.4.5 Plate 6.4.6

Plate 6.4.7 Plate 6.4.8 Plate 6.4.9 Plate 6.4.10 Plate 6.4.11A

Plate 6.4.11B Plate 6.4.12 Plate 6.4.13 Plate 6.4.14A Plate 6.4.14B

widely separated umbones (ark form), and usually radially ornamented; 6, aragonite, outer CL, and inner CCL layers, with tubules penetrating shell fabric.

Pl. 6.4.13. *Cosmetodon* Branson, 1942
Shell at least twice as long as high, with inwardly facing umbones, somewhat anterior; elongate cardinal areas; oblique anterior, and elongate posterior teeth tending to converge ventrally beneath umbones; up to 7 cm.
Jurassic; suspension feeder; semi-infaunal; Europe.
Cosmetodon cf. *undatus* (Walford): L. Jurassic, Byfield, Northamptonshire, England. RV interior.

Pl. 6.4.14. *Barbatia* Gray, 1842
Elongate and somewhat ovoid, inequilateral, each end rounded to subangular; low, elongate cardinal area; exterior with numerous closely spaced, beaded riblets; hinge with fine, comb-like taxodont teeth; up to 7 cm.
?Triassic, Jurassic–Recent; suspension feeder; byssate nestler among stones, branching coral, etc.; cosmopolitan.
Barbatia scabrosa (Nyst): Miocene, Touraine, France. (A) RV hinge; (B) RV exterior.

SUPERFAMILY LIMOPSACEA

1, Taxodont; 2, external amphidetic, of triangular form with a central fibrous zone flanked fore and aft by lamellar zones; 3, isomyarian; 4, integripalliate; 5, equivalve, orbicular to obliquely ovoid; 6, aragonite, outer CL, and inner CCL layers, with tubules penetrating shell fabric.

Pl. 6.4.15. *Limopsis* Sassi, 1827
Subequilateral, orbicular with slight forward obliquity; exterior and inner margins smooth or radially sculptured; up to 1.5 cm.
M. Jurassic–Recent; suspension feeder; shallow burrower; cosmopolitan.
Limopsis aurita (Brocchi): Miocene, Torquay, Victoria, Australia. RV interior.

SUPERFAMILY AMBONYCHIACEA X

1, A few small anterior and elongate posterior teeth, separated by an edentulous zone, or wholly edentulous; 2, external, posteriorly oblique, with multiple grooves as in cyrtodontaceans, or of chevron form; 3, monomyarian or ? heteromyarian with a tiny anterior scar in some; 4, integripalliate, often discontinuous; 5, equivalve to inequivalve, strongly inequilateral with no anterior lobe; 6, calcite outer P layer, and aragonite inner N layer.

Pl. 6.4.16. *Ambonychia* Hall, 1847
Obliquely ovoid with anterior umbones and with an anterior byssal gape; ligament insertion on elongate cardinal area with multiple grooves; ornament of simple radial costae; 2 or 3 small radial teeth beneath beaks and a few elongate posterior teeth at back end of hinge margin; single large adductor scar; up to 6 cm.
M.–U. Ordovician, suspension feeder; epifaunal byssate (often gregarious); eastern N. America, Europe.
(A) *Ambonychia radiata* Hall: U. Ordovician, Girvan, Ayrshire, Scotland. Internal mould of RV. (B, C) *Ambonychia radiata* Hall: U. Ordovician, Manitoulin Island, Lake Huron, Canada. (B) LV interior; (C) LV anterior.

Pl. 6.4.17. *Septimyalina* Newell, 1942
Rhomboidal, with slender beaks projecting anteriorly and rounded elongate ventral part of shell projecting directly down or obliquely backwards; shell thick and slightly inequivalve; broad chevron-form ligament; exterior smooth or rugose; edentulous; up to 3 cm.
L. Carboniferous–L. Permian; suspension feeder; epifaunal byssate (some related forms non-marine); USA, western Europe.
Septimyalina perattenuata (Meek & Hayden): U. Carboniferous, Baldwin, Kansas, USA. LV interior.

SUPERFAMILY PTERIACEA

1, Edentulous, or with small ridges along hinge fanning backwards from beaks; 2, external, posteriorly oblique, on elongate cardinal area in each valve with oblique triangular pit, or multiple pits for fibrous ligament and adjacent lamellar zones fore and aft, or (primitively) of chevron form; 3, monomyarian or heteromyarian with a small anterior scar; 4, disjunct insertions; 5, inequivalve (LV more convex), strongly inequilateral, with forwardly inclined umbones and a byssal notch; 6, calcite outer P layer, and aragonite middle and inner N layers.

Pl. 6.4.18. *Volviceramus* Stoliczka, 1871
Inequivalve with inflated LV spirally coiled, and cap-like RV; multiple pits for fibrous ligament; exterior with broad commarginal folds; edentulous; up to 20 cm (commonly large).
U. Cretaceous; suspension feeder; epifaunal, ?reclining on sediment; Europe, N. America.
Volviceramus involutus (J. de C. Sowerby): U. Cretaceous, Norfolk, England. RV exterior and LV cardinal area.

Pl. 6.4.19. *Pteroperna* Morris & Lycett, 1853
Oblique, with sharply pointed posterior wing and small anterior wing; LV umbo protruding; single fibrous ligament pit, thick hinge margin with anterior denticulations and up to 4 longitudinal grooves on posterior wing; up to 9 cm.
U. Triassic–Jurassic; suspension feeder; ?free-swinging byssate; cosmopolitan.
Pteroperna cf. *plana* Morris & Lycett: M. Jurassic, Dorset, England. (A) anterior of bivalve; (B) bivalve from R side.

Pl. 6.4.20. *Gervillella* Waagen, 1907
Slightly inequivalve, greatly elongated posteriorly, with obtuse posterior wing and smaller, pointed anterior wing, lacking byssal gape; several fibrous ligament pits; fine commarginal ornament; 2 to 4 anterior, and 1 to 2 posterior oblique teeth beneath ligament; up to 18 cm.
Triassic–Cretaceous; suspension feeder; semi-infaunal; cosmopolitan.
Gervillella siliqua (Deshayes): M. Jurassic, Dives, France. LV exterior and RV cardinal area, with close-up.

SUPERFAMILY PINNACEA

1, Edentulous; 2, deep-set external opisthodetic, with extended posterior part, of cross-fused periostracum; 3, heteromyarian with small anterior scars in umbones; 4, obsolete; 5, usually equivalve with elongate wedge, or ham shape, and pointed anterior beaks with a narrow byssal gape; 6, calcite outer P layer, and aragonite inner N layer.

Pl. 6.4.21. *Pinna* Linné, 1758
Wedge to ham-shaped with medial carinae on pointed anterior umbones; exterior usually radially ribbed and may have commarginal undulations ventrally; shell repair common; prominent central posterior adductor; inner layer divided medially into 2 lobes; up to 40 cm.
L. Carboniferous–Recent; suspension feeder; semi-infaunal, byssate with posterior projecting from sediment; cosmopolitan.
(A) *Pinna hartmanni* Zieten: L. Jurassic, Dorset, England. RV exterior. (B) *Pinna* sp.: U. Cretaceous, River Kakut, Alberta, Canada. Internal mould, RV side.

SUPERFAMILY LIMACEA

1, Edentulous or with weak taxodont teeth; 2, external amphidetic, with central fibrous zone flanked by lamellar zones, on triangular cardinal areas; 3, monomyarian; 4, restricted pallial insertions, or absent; 5, equivalve, ovate or orbicular, usually higher than long, ventral margin extended anteroventrally; 6, calcite, outer F layer and inner aragonite, CL, and sometimes CCL layer.

Pl. 6.4.22. *Plagiostoma* J. Sowerby, 1814
Obliquely ovate, moderately inflated, with obtuse posterior, and smaller anterior wings; broad, embayed anterior face which may have a small byssal gape; elongate cardinal areas; exterior smooth or radially ornamented; up to 12 cm.
M. Triassic–U. Cretaceous; suspension feeder; epifaunal byssate; cosmopolitan.
Plagiostoma buckmani Cox: M. Jurassic, Éterville, Calvados, France. (A) LV exterior; (B) LV cardinal area.

SUPERFAMILY AVICULOPECTINACEA X

1, Edentulous; 2, external, amphidetic, of chevron form, or with central fibrous zone flanked fore and aft by lamellar zones on

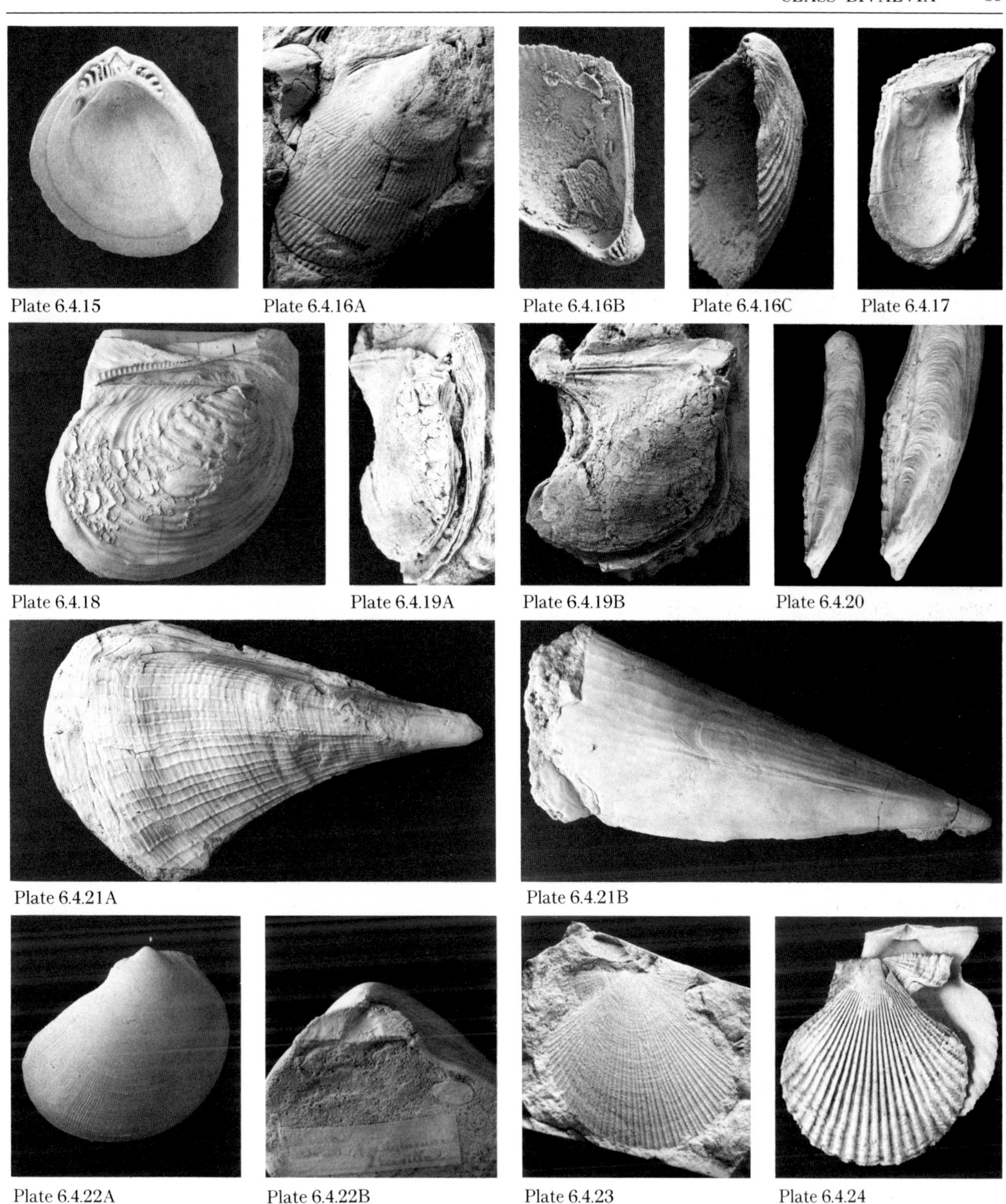

Plate 6.4.15 Plate 6.4.16A Plate 6.4.16B Plate 6.4.16C Plate 6.4.17

Plate 6.4.18 Plate 6.4.19A Plate 6.4.19B Plate 6.4.20

Plate 6.4.21A Plate 6.4.21B

Plate 6.4.22A Plate 6.4.22B Plate 6.4.23 Plate 6.4.24

broad cardinal areas; 3, monomyarian; 4, discontinuous; 5, usually inequivalve, orbicular shells with anterior and posterior wings; 6, calcite outer layer (P in some cases), with aragonite CL or N, and/or calcite F within.

Pl. 6.4.23. *Aviculopecten* M'Coy, 1851
Inequivalve (LV slightly larger), inequilateral, with postero-ventral margin usually slightly extended, and posterior wing as long as or longer than anterior; radial ribs on exterior increase by intercalation on LV and by bifurcation on RV; byssal notch in RV; up to 4 cm.

L. Carboniferous–U. Permian; suspension feeder, epifaunal byssate; cosmopolitan.
Aviculopecten plicatus (J. de C. Sowerby): L. Carboniferous, Co. Kildare, Ireland. LV exterior.

SUPERFAMILY PECTINACEA
1, Edentulous to isodont; 2, amphidetic, with external lamellar connection between dorsal margins and ventrally sunken pad of ligament (mostly lamellar) in triangular pit in each valve; 3, monomyarian; 4, integripalliate; 5, inequivalve to equivalve, byssate, cemented or free shells with RV against substrate, of

orbicular outline with anterior and posterior wings (scallop shape); 6, calcite outer F layer (RV may have outermost P layer), aragonite CL middle layer may be present, and an inner calcite F, or aragonite CCL layer.

Pl. 6.4.24. *Chlamys* Röding, 1798
Both valves convex, LV more than RV; tall, orbicular shell with large wings and, usually, a pronounced byssal notch beneath anterior wing of RV; strong radial ribbing, commonly spinose, especially on LV; scalloped margins; variable isodont teeth; up to 16 cm (usually < 9 cm).
Triassic–Recent; suspension feeder; epifaunal byssate, in fissures, or settling into depressions in coarse sediment, though some species are free and can swim.
Chlamys varia (Linné): Pliocene, Piacenza, Italy. RV exterior and LV interior.

Pl. 6.4.25. *Neithea* Drouet, 1825
RV inflated and LV almost flat, more or less equilateral; byssal notch shallow; exterior with 4 to 6 raised radial ribs separated by sets of 3 or 4 smaller ribs or with strong undifferentiated ribs; isodont teeth; up to 5 cm.
Cretaceous; suspension feeder; epifaunal, byssate; cosmopolitan.
Neithea quinquecostata (J. Sowerby): U. Cretaceous, Warminster, Wiltshire, England. Bivalve exterior, LV side.

Pl. 6.4.26. *Bositra* de Gregorio, 1886
Thin, flattish ovate, subequivalve with low umbones and rounded dorsal margins; wings very weak; exterior with commarginal undulations; edentulous; no byssal notch; up to 5 cm.
Jurassic; suspension feeder; epifaunal ?benthic (interpreted as swimmer by some); Europe, E. Africa.
Bositra somaliensis (Cox): U. Jurassic, Daghani, N. Somalia. Cluster of single valves (exteriors).

SUPERFAMILY BUCHIACEA X

1, Edentulous; 2, amphidetic; 3, monomyarian; 4, disjunct; 5, inequivalve (LV larger), inequilateral shell, obliquely ovate with short hinge and reduced posterior wing, but clear anterior wing in RV, height usually greater than length; 6, calcite outer P layer and inner F layer (cross-foliated outside the pallial line).

Pl. 6.4.27. *Buchia* Rouillier, 1845
Inflated, overarching LV and low RV, with extended postero-ventral margin; RV anterior wing bent towards LV, which has corresponding sinus; exterior with commarginal ridges; up to 3 cm.
M. Jurassic–U. Cretaceous; suspension feeder; epifaunal byssate; cosmopolitan (mainly boreal).
Buchia mosquensis (Von Buch): U. Jurassic, Tatarovo, Moscow, USSR. Bivalve exterior from RV side.

SUPERFAMILY ANOMIACEA

1, Edentulous; 2, invaginated from dorsal margin on buttresses (that in RV may be knobby); 3, monomyarian (+ byssal retractor scars in LV); 4, small ring around LV scars; 5, inequivalve with deep byssal notch in substrate-hugging RV for plug-like byssus, and with convex upper LV, or secondarily free and orbicular; 6, calcite outer F layer, with an outermost P layer at least in RV, with aragonite, inner CCL layer in some.

Pl. 6.4.28. *Pododesmus* Philippi, 1837
Attached shell with irregularly rounded outline; deep byssal foramen of variable size; RV ligament support large and knobby; exterior with irregular corrugations and radial ribs; one large byssal retractor scar in LV; up to 6 cm.
?Oligocene, Miocene–Recent; suspension feeder; epifaunal, attached; widespread.
Pododesmus zelandica Gray: Pliocene, Parimoa, New Zealand. LV exterior and part of RV interior.

SUPERFAMILY OSTREACEA

1, Edentulous; 2, external, amphidetic to prosodetic, with a central fibrous pad, flanked fore and aft by lamellar zones; 3 monomyarian; 4, absent in most; 5, inequivalve with LV cemented to substrate in most species, and flat RV as 'lid'; 6, F calcite, with a thin outermost layer of calcite prisms in the RV and perhaps also in the LV, shell may also incorporate chalky or vesicular layers.

Pl. 6.4.29. *Ostrea* Linné, 1758
Outline variable (usually orbicular); generally flattish shells; low beaks directed dorsally; cardinal areas high and triangular; LV with unequal rounded radial ribs with frilly growth squamae; RV exterior flat, but with lamellar squamae; marginal denticulations present; kidney-shaped adductor scar; up to 20 cm.
Cretaceous–Recent; suspension feeder; epifaunal cemented; cosmopolitan.
Ostrea bellovacina Lamarck: Eocene, Bracheux, Oise, France. (A) LV exterior; (B) RV interior.

Pl. 6.4.30. *Exogyra* Say, 1820
Strongly inequivalve with inflated LV and flat RV; pronounced spiral growth, with umbones coiling towards *posterior*; margins more or less orbicular; elongate prosodetic cardinal areas; LV with or without radial ribbing, RV usually with flaring commarginal growth squamae; marginal denticulations in many species; RV margin reflexed, fitting within LV margin; up to 21 cm.
Cretaceous, suspension feeder; epifaunal cemented; cosmopolitan.
Exogyra costata Say: U. Cretaceous, New Jersey, USA. (A) Bivalve, RV side; (B) RV interior.

Pl. 6.4.31. *Gryphaea* Lamarck, 1801
Strongly inequivalve with high, inflated LV hooked over flat or concave RV; LV umbo coils directly over hinge line; cardinal areas as in *Ostrea*; exterior with commarginal growth squamae, and LV with radial sulcus on posterior flank; marginal denticulations absent; attachment scar of shell usually small; up to 16 cm.
U. Triassic–U. Jurassic; suspension feeder; epifaunal, cemented in early life, later reclining on sediment surface; cosmopolitan.
Gryphaea arcuata Lamarck: L. Jurassic, Lyme Regis, Dorset, England. Bivalve, posterior view.

SUPERFAMILY PLICATULACEA

1, Isodont; 2, internal fibrous pad in ventrally sunk pit, with an external lamellar ligament dorsally; 3, monomyarian; 4, entire pallial scar; 5, inequivalve with more convex attached RV and variable outline; 6, calcite outer F layer, and aragonite middle and inner CL layers.

Pl. 6.4.32. *Plicatula* Lamarck, 1801
Subequivalve with oval, orbicular or subtrigonal shape; irregular margins; small, deep triangular pit for ligament, flanked fore and aft by straight, narrow teeth in each valve; exterior commarginally lamellose with broad radial ribs; up to 3 cm.
M. Triassic–Recent, suspension feeder; epifaunal, cemented; widespread.
Plicatula tubifera Lamarck: U. Jurassic, Neuvizy, Ardennes,

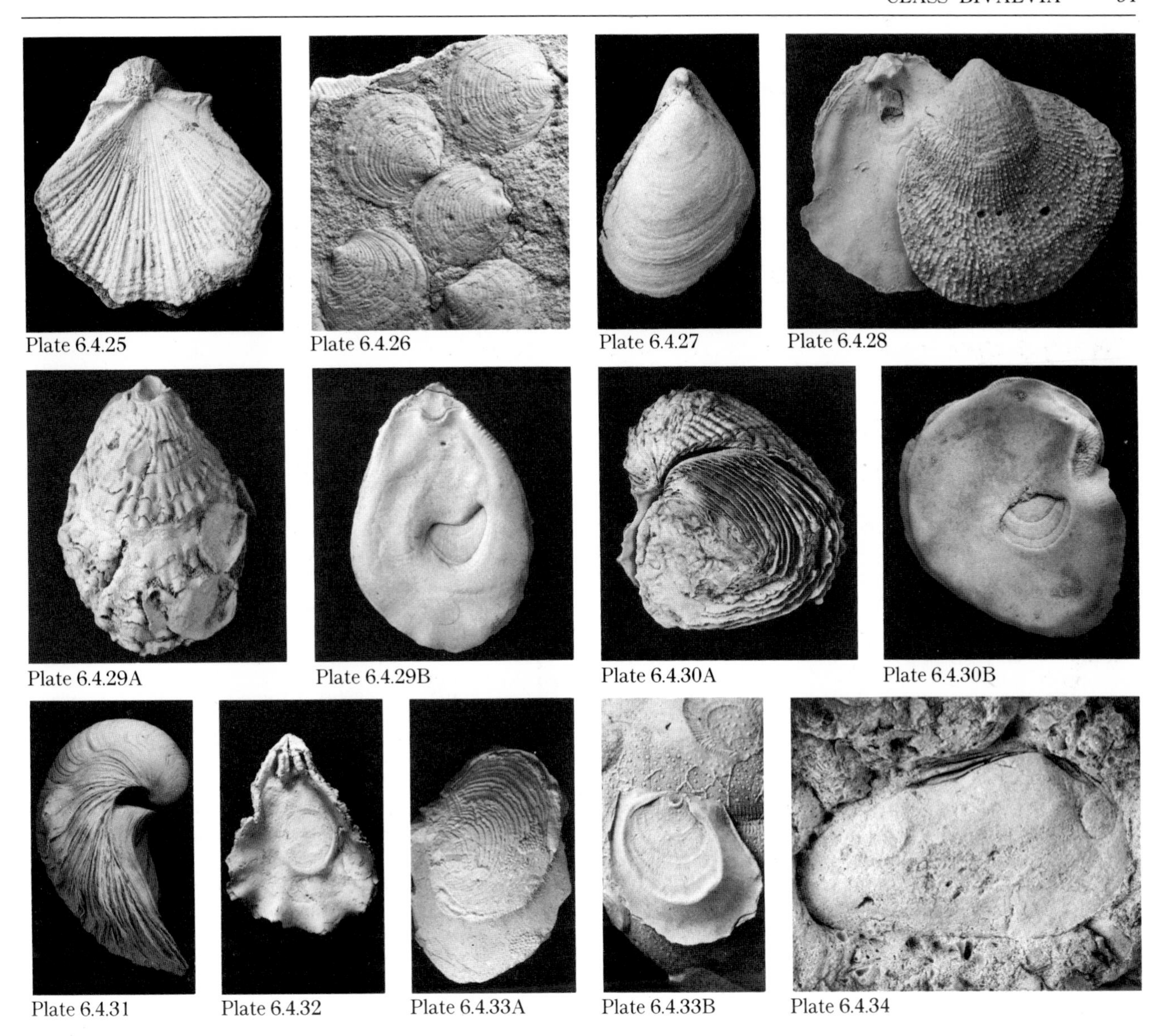

Plate 6.4.25 Plate 6.4.26 Plate 6.4.27 Plate 6.4.28

Plate 6.4.29A Plate 6.4.29B Plate 6.4.30A Plate 6.4.30B

Plate 6.4.31 Plate 6.4.32 Plate 6.4.33A Plate 6.4.33B Plate 6.4.34

France. RV interior.

Pl. 6.4.33. *Atreta* Étallon, 1862
Orbicular, with convex LV overlying flat, adhering RV; tiny pit for ligament with thin, short flanking ridges (rarely visible); LV with commarginally lamellose exterior; RV interior with reflexed rim, and raised central area bearing anastomosing radial striations; adductor scar unknown; up to 2 cm. (This may belong with a distinct superfamily Dimyacea Fischer, 1886; see Waller in Yonge and Thompson 1978.)
U. Triassic–U. Cretaceous; suspension feeder; epifaunal, cemented; Europe, N. America.
Atreta nilsonni (Hagenow): U. Cretaceous. (A) Chatham, Kent, England. LV exterior; (B) Norwich, Norfolk, England. RV interior.

SUPERFAMILY CYCLOCONCHACEA X
1, Actinodont; 2, external, opisthodetic, simple; 3, isomyarian; 4, integripalliate; 5, equivalve, ovoid, with submedian beaks, and lacking radial ornament; 6, ?aragonite.

Pl. 6.4.34. *Actinodonta* Phillips, 1848
Inequilateral elongate ovoid, with anteriorly biased beaks; about 9 teeth radiate down from beneath each beak, the medial ones short and those at each end longer; anterior adductor scar, slightly smaller than the posterior, deeply impressed; up to 4 cm.
M. Silurian–L. Devonian; ?suspension feeder; shallow infaunal, in inshore sands; UK.
Actinodonta cuneata Phillips: M. Silurian, St Marloes Bay, Dyfed, Wales. Internal mould of RV.

SUPERFAMILY ANTHRACOSIACEA X
1, One or 2 teeth in 1 or both valves, or with numerous tiny denticles, or edentulous; 2, external, opisthodetic, on long low nymphs but partly internal in some; 3, isomyarian to slightly heteromyarian; 4, integripalliate; 5, equivalve, commonly ovoid with blunt, anterior beaks; 6, unknown.

Pl. 6.4.35. *Carbonicola* M'Coy, 1855
Subtrigonally ovoid with anterior, erect umbones facing in towards one another; anterior part of ligament expanded down into triangular pit beneath each beak; hinge plate forms continuous arc along each valve, and may bear 1 or 2 teeth; up to 8 cm.
U. Carboniferous, suspension feeder; shallow burrower in non-marine sediments; western Europe, USSR.
Carbonicola acuta (J. Sowerby): U. Carboniferous, Longton, Lancashire, England. (A) RV exterior; (B) RV interior.

SUPERFAMILY UNIONACEA

1, Rugose cardinal and posterior lamellar teeth, or edentulous; 2, external, opisthodetic on elongate nymphs; 3, isomyarian; 4, usually integripalliate; 5, mostly equivalve (except in attached forms), ovoid, with beaks, only, commonly ornamented, shell coated by thick periostracum; 6, aragonite outer P, and middle and inner N layers.

Pl. 6.4.36. *Unio* Phillipsson, 1788
Equivalve with distinct posterior slopes; beaks anterior, facing inwards and with concentric sculpture; rest of shell smooth; usually 2 cardinal teeth and 2 posterior teeth in LV and 1 of each in RV; up to 8 cm.
Triassic–Recent; suspension feeder; shallow burrower in freshwater sediments; Old World.
(A) *Unio karrooensis* Cox: Triassic, Songea District, Tanzania. Bivalve exterior, dorsal view. (B) *Unio gibbsii* Morris, Oligocene, Headon Hill, Isle of Wight, England. Hinge of RV.

SUPERFAMILY TRIGONIACEA

1, Schizodont or a few simple teeth in some; 2, external, opisthodetic, on short nymphs; 3, isomyarian; 4, integripalliate; 5, equivalve, usually trigonal, with somewhat extended, truncate posterior bounded by carinae, and with erect inward or slightly backwardly facing beaks; 6, aragonite, outer P layer and middle and inner N layers.

Pl. 6.4.37. *Schizodus* de Verneuil & Murchison, 1844
Subtrigonally ovoid with slightly anterior, inward-pointing beaks and rounded posterior carinae; exterior smooth; LV with prominent bilobed tooth and small marginal anterior tooth, RV with single tooth; up to 5 cm.
Carboniferous–Permian, suspension feeder; shallow infaunal; cosmopolitan.
Schizodus harii Miller: U. Carboniferous, Kansas, USA. (A) LV exterior; (B) LV hinge.

Pl. 6.4.38. *Myophorella* Bayle, 1878
Trigonally ovoid with anterior, erect, inward-pointing beaks and obtuse posterior carinae; posterior slope on each valve bipartite with little ornament; flanks of shell with oblique rows of tubercles or tuberculate costae; LV with prominent bifid pivotal tooth and lamellar anterior tooth, RV with 2 diverging teeth; teeth with pronounced ridges; up to 11 cm.
L. Jurassic–L. Cretaceous; suspension feeder, shallow inshore burrower (cf. cockles); cosmopolitan.
Myophorella muricata (Goldfuss): U. Jurassic, Santa Cruz, Portugal. (A) LV exterior; (B) LV interior.

SUPERFAMILY BABINKACEA X

1, Small cardinals, 2 in LV, 1 in RV; 2, external, opisthodetic, simple; 3, isomyarian, accompanied by a row of pedal muscle scars between the adductor scars; 4, integripalliate; 5, equivalve, subequilateral, ovoid; 6, unknown.

Pl. 6.4.39. *Babinka* Barrande, 1881
Compressed shell with slightly expanded anterior; elongate subequal adductor scars, with row of up to 8 pedal scars running between their crests; up to 2 cm.
L. (L.–M.) Ordovician; feeding mode unknown; shallow infaunal; Europe.
Babinka prima Barrande: L. Ordovician, ?Cantabrians, Spain. Internal mould, RV side.

SUPERFAMILY LUCINACEA

1, Heterodont-lucinoid or more or less reduced, may be edentulous; 2, external, opisthodetic on more or less sunk nymphs; 3, subisomyarian to heteromyarian, with elongate anterior adductor; 4, integripalliate; 5, equivalve, subcircular to oval or subtrigonal with small, pointed beaks; 6, aragonite, outer CP layer, middle CL layer and inner CCL layer.

Pl. 6.4.40. *Miltha* H. & A. Adams, 1853
Compressed, discoidal; forwardly inclined, median beaks with embayed lunule; stout, deeply set nymphs; exterior commarginally ornamented; 2 cardinal teeth in each valve, the LV anterior and RV posterior teeth bifid; lateral teeth weak or wanting; very long anterior adductor scar; up to 4 cm.
Cretaceous–Recent; suspension feeder; active deep burrower, with anterior, mucus-lined inhalent tube; cosmopolitan.
Miltha (Eomiltha) pandata (Conrad): Eocene, Claiborne, Alabama, USA. (A) RV interior; (B) LV hinge; (C) RV hinge.

SUPERFAMILY CYAMIACEA

1, Small, sometimes bifid cardinals beneath beaks, with varied laterals; 2, internal pad, embayed on hinge plates usually present, with external opisthodetic part on small nymphs; 3, isomyarian; 4, integripalliate; 5, equivalve, commonly ovate and typically small; 6, aragonite, H. (*Note:* This small superfamily is allied with the larger Leptonacea Gray, 1847, which shares many features, though rarely possessing an external ligament, and having only a few long laterals. Their shell has aragonite outer CL and inner CCL layers. They are typically small and commonly commensal in habits.)

Pl. 6.4.41. *Sportella* Deshayes, 1858
Elliptical, almost equilateral, compressed; ligament largely external on long nymphs; exterior smooth; small, low cardinals and weak laterals; up to 2 cm.
Palaeocene–Pliocene; ?suspension feeder; possibly burrowing, or secured by byssal thread in some form of cavity; Europe, N. America.
Sportella dubia (Deshayes): Eocene, Neuilly-en-Vexin, France. (A) RV exterior; (B) RV interior.

SUPERFAMILY CARDITACEA

1, Heterodont, lucinoid; 2, external, opisthodetic, on strong nymphs (or internal pad in some forms); 3, isomyarian or heteromyarian with reduced anterior adductor (byssate species); 4, integripalliate; 5, equivalve, trigonal, trapezoidal, or mussel-shaped with strong radial sculpture, inner margin usually crenulate, and forward-pointing beaks; 6, aragonite, outer CL, and inner CCL layers.

Pl. 6.4.42. *Glans* Megerle von Mühlfeld, 1811
Quadrate to trapezoidal with anteriorly slanted umbones, shell somewhat inflated; external ligament; exterior with strong, nodular or scaly radial ribs; 2 strong cardinal teeth in each valve, the RV posterior one being excavated ventrally and that in the LV elongate; laterals weak to obsolete; up to 4 cm.
Palaeocene–Recent; suspension feeder; shallow infaunal; widespread.
Glans (Centrocardita) bazini (Deshayes): Oligocene, Ormoy, nr Étampes, France. (A) LV hinge; (B) RV hinge; (C) LV exterior.

SUPERFAMILY CHAMACEA

1, At least 1 large cardinal tooth in each valve; 2, external opisthodetic, on nymphs, anterior parts progressively split and overgrown by tangentially migrating shell growth increments; 3, isomyarian; 4, integripalliate; 5, inequivalve, attached by LV (sometimes RV), with umbones strongly coiled forward; 6, aragonite, CL outer, and CCL inner layers, with an outermost

Plate 6.4.35A Plate 6.4.35B Plate 6.4.36A Plate 6.4.36B Plate 6.4.37A Plate 6.4.37B

Plate 6.4.38A Plate 6.4.38B Plate 6.4.39 Plate 6.4.40A

Plate 6.4.40B Plate 6.4.40C Plate 6.4.41A Plate 6.4.41B Plate 6.4.42A Plate 6.4.42B

Plate 6.4.42C Plate 6.4.43A Plate 6.4.43B Plate 6.4.44A Plate 6.4.44B

layer of P calcite in a few species.

Pl. 6.4.43. *Chama* Linné, 1758

Attached by larger LV, RV cap-like; exterior commarginally foliaceous; prominent rugose tooth in LV; up to 10 cm, usually somewhat less.

?U. Cretaceous, Palaeocene–Recent; suspension feeder; epifaunal, attached (commonly to corals, etc. in reefs); tropical and contiguous areas (+Europe, N. America, as fossils).

Chama squamosa (Solander): Eocene, Barton, Hampshire, England. (A) Bivalve, anteroventral view; (B) LV hinge.

SUPERFAMILY CRASSATELLACEA

1, Heterodont, lucinoid (but may look corbiculoid); 2, external, opisthodetic on nymphs, or a prominent internal triangular pad with only a small external ligament; 3, isomyarian; 4, integripalliate or with a slight sinus; 5, equivalve, with forwardly pointed peaks and distinct lunule and escutcheon; 6, aragonite, outer CL, and inner H, or myostracal prismatic CCL inner layers.

Pl. 6.4.44. *Neocrassina* Fischer, 1887

Ovate to trapezoidal, inequilateral thick shell; beaks point forward; depressed lunule; nymphs broad and flat; exterior

commarginally ribbed, valve margins may be denticulate; 2 cardinal teeth in each valve, the posterior one in the RV being large and pivotal; prominent posterior lateral teeth; up to 6 cm.
L. Jurassic–U. Cretaceous; suspension feeder; shallow infaunal; Europe, Southern Africa.
Neocrassina elegans (J. Sowerby): M. Jurassic, Curcy, Calvados, France. (A) LV hinge; (B) RV hinge.

Pl. 6.4.45. *Opis* Defrance, 1825
Valve margins quadrate with dorsally extended, trigonal umbones and strong posteroventral angulations; narrow external ligament; exterior commarginally ribbed; elongate cardinals, 1 in RV, 2 in LV, and no laterals; up to 8 cm.
L. Jurassic–U. Cretaceous, suspension feeder; ?epifaunal, commonly around reefs; Europe, Madagascar, N. America, Japan.
Opis buvignieri d'Orbigny: U. Jurassic, Vieil-St Remi, Ardennes, France. Bivalve from R. side.

Pl. 6.4.46. *Crassatella* Lamarck, 1799
Subtrapezoidal, thick-shelled with somewhat anterior beaks; prominent internal triangular ligamentary pit in each valve; exterior commarginally ribbed with slight posterior angulation, 2 cardinal teeth in each valve, but the posterior in RV pivotal, and anterior small; moderate lateral teeth; valve margins finely crenulate; up to 6 cm.
U. Cretaceous–Miocene; suspension feeder; shallow infaunal; Europe, N. America.
Crassatella vadosa (Morton): U. Cretaceous, Coon Creek, Tennessee, USA. (A) LV hinge; (B) RV hinge; (C) LV exterior.

Pl. 6.4.47. *Cardinia* Agassiz, 1841
Trigonally suboval, with anteriorly turned umbones and steeply indented lunule and escutcheon, bordered by ridges; external ligament on deeply sunk nymphs; exterior commarginally ribbed or smooth; 1 cardinal tooth in RV only, but lateral teeth heavy; up to 20 cm.
U. Triassic–L. Jurassic; suspension feeder; shallow infaunal; cosmopolitan.
Cardinia listeri (J. Sowerby): L. Jurassic, Besford, Worcestershire, England. (A) LV interior; (B) LV exterior.

SUPERFAMILY CARDIACEA

1, Heterodont, lucinoid with compact cardinals and prominent laterals set well away from cardinals; 2, external, opisthodetic on short nymphs; 3, isomyarian; 4, integripalliate or with slight sinus; 5, equivalve, globose with strong radial sculpture (cockle form); 6, aragonite, outer CL, and inner CCL layers. Outer part of CL layer thrown into complex form by ribbing.

Pl. 6.4.48. *Protocardia* Von Beyrich, 1845
Rounded quadrate, equilateral; beaks directed inwards; posterior slope with radial ribs, rest of shell with fine commarginal ribs; up to 8 cm.
U. Triassic–U. Cretaceous, suspension feeder; shallow infaunal; Europe, Americas, Africa.
Protocardia hillana (J. Sowerby), L. Cretaceous, Bracquegnies, Belgium. RV exterior.

Pl. 6.4.49. *Acanthocardia* Gray, 1851
Obliquely quadrate; radial ribs nodose to spinose; valve margins crenulate; LV cardinals partly fused; up to 11 cm.
U. Cretaceous–Recent; suspension feeder; active, shallow burrower in inshore sands, capable of leaping; Europe, Asia, Americas.
Acanthocardia echinata (Linné): Pliocene, Palermo, Sicily. (A) RV exterior; (B) LV hinge.

SUPERFAMILY TRIDACNACEA

1, Two oblique, elongate cardinals and 1 or more laterals in each valve; 2, external, opisthodetic on nymphs; 3, usually monomyarian; 4, integripalliate; 5, equivalve, with coarse radial ribbing, anterior is rotated so that byssal gape lies directly in front of umbones; 6, aragonite, outer CL, and inner CCL layers.

Pl. 6.4.50. *Tridacna* Bruguière, 1797
Commonly large and massive, with a few strong ribs, which may be commarginally scaly; umbones submedial; rims of byssal gape sometimes plicate; valve margins scalloped; up to 135 cm.
?U. Cretaceous, Tertiary–Recent; suspension feeder (with symbiotic algae in tissues); byssate or free, commonly in excavations in coral on reefs; tropical, Old World (especially Indo-Pacific).
Tridacna squamosa Lamarck: Pleistocene, Jebel Zeit (Red Sea), Egypt. (Left) RV interior; (right) LV exterior.

SUPERFAMILY MACTRACEA

1, Two cardinals in RV, Λ-shaped cardinal in LV in front of internal ligament pit, as well as laterals and accessory cardinal laminae in most species; 2, internal pad in socket-like pit beneath beaks, with or without small external ligament; 3, isomyarian; 4, sinupalliate; 5, equivalve with small beaks; 6, aragonite, outer CL, and inner CCL layers. Both layers typically have fine structure.

Pl. 6.4.51. *Mactra* Linné, 1767
Subequilateral, trigonally oval, thin-walled shell with slightly forward-turned beaks; large posterior (siphonal) and narrow anterior (pedal) gapes; exterior usually smooth, or with commarginal ribs; smooth lateral teeth; oval pallial sinus; up to 10 cm, usually about 4 cm.
Eocene–Recent; suspension feeder; active burrower; cosmopolitan.
Mactra semisulcata Lamarck: Eocene, Parnes, Paris Basin, France. (A) LV exterior; (B) LV interior.

Pl. 6.4.52. *Lutraria* Lamarck, 1799
Elliptical, with anteriorly situated, low umbones; wide posterior and anterior gapes; broad ligamentary pits, somewhat projecting; prominent cardinals, but laterals obsolete; deep pallial sinus; up to 14 cm.
Miocene–Recent; suspension feeder; deep burrower, usually in sand; cosmopolitan.
Lutraria magna (da Costa): Pleistocene, Sicily. (A) LV exterior; (B) LV interior.

SUPERFAMILY SOLENACEA

1, One to 3 small cardinals, lateral teeth small or absent; 2, external, opisthodetic on slender nymphs; 3, subisomyarian with elongate anterior adductor; 4, sinupalliate; 5, equivalve, elongate flattened to cylindrical shell gaping at both ends (razor shell form); 6, aragonite, outer CL, and inner H layers. Both layers typically have fine structure.

Pl. 6.4.53. *Solen* Linné, 1758
Long, straight, compressed cylindrical shell with suppressed umbones at anterior end; anterior margin truncate; 1 small tooth in each valve; elongate anterior adductor; pallial sinus shallow; up to 15 cm.
Eocene–Recent; suspension feeder; active burrower in inshore fine sands; N. America, Europe, Pacific.
Solen vagina Linné: Pliocene, Antigiane (?). Bivalve, from LV side.

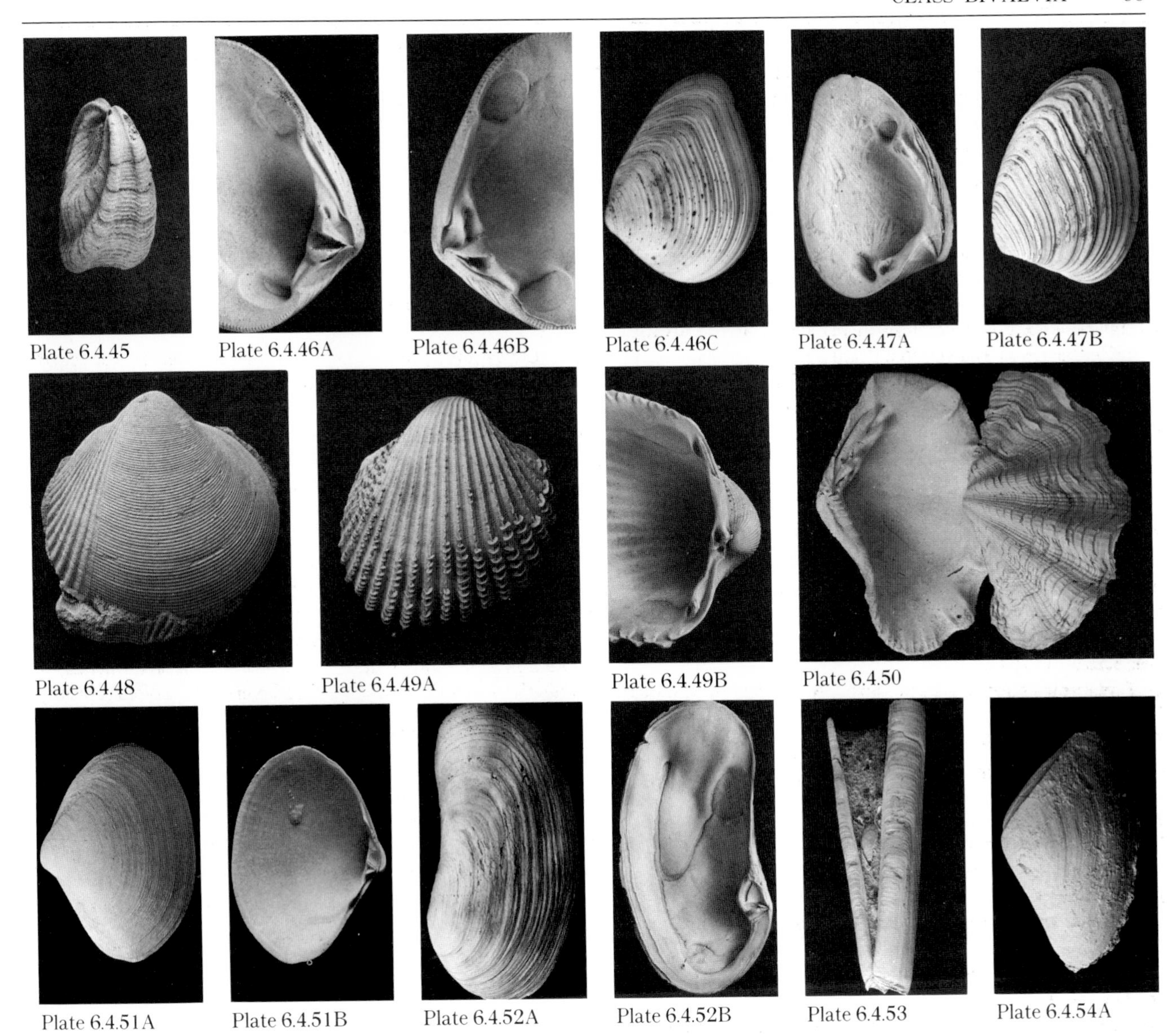
Plate 6.4.45 Plate 6.4.46A Plate 6.4.46B Plate 6.4.46C Plate 6.4.47A Plate 6.4.47B
Plate 6.4.48 Plate 6.4.49A Plate 6.4.49B Plate 6.4.50
Plate 6.4.51A Plate 6.4.51B Plate 6.4.52A Plate 6.4.52B Plate 6.4.53 Plate 6.4.54A

SUPERFAMILY TELLINACEA
1, Two cardinals in each valve, tending to be bifid, and laterals in most species; 2, external, opisthodetic on nymphs, may be accompanied by internal pad in pits beneath beaks; 3, isomyarian or with anterior scar slightly extended; 4, strongly sinupalliate; 5, equivalve to slightly inequivalve with flexed posterior, commonly gaping; 6, aragonite, most have outer CP, middle CL, and inner CCL or H layers.

Pl. 6.4.54. *Tancredia* Lycett, 1850
Subtrigonal with tapered anterior, and commonly with abruptly truncate posterior; posterior gape common; short external ligament; exterior smooth; 1 or 2 blunt cardinal teeth in each valve, with posterior laterals and weak to obsolete anterior laterals; adductor scars and pallial line set high in shell; weak pallial sinus; up to 6 cm.
U. Triassic–L. Cretaceous; feeding mode uncertain; infaunal; cosmopolitan.
Tancredia donaciformis Lycett: L. Jurassic, Stonehouse, Gloucestershire, England. (A) LV exterior; (B) LV hinge.

Pl. 6.4.55. *Solecurtus* de Blainville, 1824
Elongate-quadrate, subequilateral with wide gape at both ends; umbones weak; external ligament on long nymphs; exterior with spaced oblique striations; 2 small cardinals in RV, 1 in LV: lateral teeth wanting; large pallial sinus; up to 6 cm.
Eocene–Recent; infaunal, ?deposit feeder; cosmopolitan.
Solecurtus deshayesi des Moulins: Eocene, Bracklesham Bay, England. RV exterior.

Pl. 6.4.56. *Tellina* Linné, 1758
Usually subequilateral, suboval, more or less elongate, with posterior commonly flexed, especially RV; beaks small, facing inwards; ligament external; exterior smooth or weakly ornamented; up to 2 cardinal teeth in each valve, lateral teeth in at least 1 valve; pallial sinus deep; up to 12 cm, usually less than half that.
?Cretaceous, Tertiary–Recent, deposit feeder; active burrower; cosmopolitan.
(A) *Tellina (Quadrans) serrata* Renier: Pliocene, Rome, Italy. Bivalve, dorsal view. (B) *T. scalaroides* Lamarck, Eocene, Bracklesham Bay, England. RV interior.

SUPERFAMILY ARCTICACEA
1, Heterodont, usually arcticoid; 2, external, opisthodetic on long nymphs; 3, isomyarian; 4, usually integripalliate; 5, equivalve, with forward-pointing beaks; 6, aragonite outer CL, and inner CCL layers, or H throughout.

Pl. 6.4.57. *Venilicardia* Stoliczka, 1870
Inequilateral, trigonally suboval, solid, without lunule or escutcheon; exterior smooth; 3 cardinals in each valve, the central one in the RV incipient; solid laterals; up to 13 cm.
L. Cretaceous–Recent; suspension feeder; shallow burrower; Europe, N. America, N. Atlantic.
Venilicardia lineolata (J. Sowerby): L. Cretaceous, Blackdown, Devon, England. (A) RV exterior; (B) LV hinge; (C) RV hinge.

SUPERFAMILY GLOSSACEA
1, Heterodont, arcticoid, tangentially elongate; 2, external, as in Chamacea; 3, isomyarian; 4, mostly integripalliate; 5, equivalve, with forwardly coiled, inflated beaks; 6, aragonite, outer H or CL, and inner CCL/myostracal layers.

Pl. 6.4.58. *Glossus* Poli, 1795
Inflated, heart-shaped shell with indistinct lunule and escutcheon; ligament and dentition much affected by tangential growth of valves; exterior smooth or commarginally sculptured; up to 11 cm.
Palaeocene–Recent; suspension feeder; shallow burrower in offshore muddy sediments; widespread.
Glossus humanus (Linné): Pliocene, Sicily. (A) RV hinge; (B) bivalve, dorsal view.

SUPERFAMILY CORBICULACEA
1, Heterodont, usually corbiculoid; 2, external opisthodetic on nymphs; 3, isomyarian; 4, mostly integripalliate; 5, equivalve, rounded trigonal to ovate with commarginal sculpture; 6, aragonite outer CL, and inner CCL layers.

Pl. 6.4.59. *Polymesoda* Rafinesque, 1828
Rounded trigonal, plump, solid shell; prominent beaks turned inwards and slightly forwards; weak commarginal sculpture; 3 cardinals in each valve, RV central tooth pivotal; single laterals fore and aft in LV matched by pairs of laterals in RV; pallial sinus may be present; up to 10 cm, usually much less.
Eocene–Recent; suspension feeder; shallow burrower, commonly freshwater; cosmopolitan.
Polymesoda cordata (Morris): Eocene, Charlton, Kent, England. (A) RV exterior; (B) LV hinge; (C) RV hinge.

SUPERFAMILY DREISSENACEA
1, Edentulous, but septa cover umbonal cavities; 2, opisthodetic ligament on sunken nymphs, overarched dorsally by posterior extension of ligament; 3, heteromyarian with small anterior adductor inserting on umbonal septa; 4, with or without sinus; 5, equivalved, mussel-shaped to quadrate with anterior beaks (byssate); 6, aragonite outer CL, and inner CCL layers.

Pl. 6.4.60. *Congeria* Partsch, 1835
Subquadrate with smooth, thick valves; 2 scars on each septum, for anterior adductor and pedal retractor; no pallial sinus; up to 6 cm.
L. Oligocene–Pliocene; suspension feeder; epifaunal byssate, freshwater; Europe, W. Asia.
Congeria subcarinata Andrusov: Miocene, Susitza-Mehedintzi, Romania. (A) LV exterior; (B) LV interior.

SUPERFAMILY VENERACEA
1, Heterodont, corbiculoid; 2, external, opisthodetic, on long nymphs; 3, isomyarian; 4, sinupalliate; 5, equivalve, usually ovate with commarginal ornament and beaks directed forward; 6, aragonite, variable, may have CP outer layer, CL to H middle (or outer) layer, and H to CCL inner layer, commonly with sheets of myostracal prisms.

Pl. 6.4.61. *Petricola* Lamarck, 1801
Inequilateral, oval, with anterior umbones; exterior with commonly distorted radial ribbing; narrow hinge plates with small cardinals and no laterals; up to 7 cm.
Eocene–Recent; suspension feeder; byssate nestlers and physical borers into rock, mud, peat, etc.; widespread.
Petricola (Petricolaria) denticulata G. B. Sowerby: Pleistocene, San Quintin, Baja California, Mexico. (A) Bivalve, dorsal view; (B) LV hinge.

Pl. 6.4.62. *Circomphalus* Mörch, 1853
Inequilateral subtrigonal, compressed with impressed, weakly ornamented lunule and escutcheon; exterior with spaced commarginal lamellae; 3 cardinals in each valve, RV central tooth pivotal; posterior laterals absent; up to 6 cm.
Miocene–Recent; suspension feeder; shallow burrower; Europe, W. Africa.
Circomphalus foliaceolamellosa (Dillwyn): Pliocene, Piedmont, Italy. (A) RV exterior; (B) LV interior; (C) RV interior.

Pl. 6.4.63. *Pitar* Römer, 1857
Inequilateral, trigonally suboval; lunule weak and escutcheon unmarked; exterior smooth or with commarginal lamellae (some species also with long spines on posterior flanks); 3 cardinals and strong anterior laterals in each valve; pallial sinus usually deep; up to 8 cm.
Eocene–Recent; suspension feeder; shallow burrower; cosmopolitan.
Pitar sulcataria (Deshayes): Eocene, Bracklesham Bay, Sussex, England. RV exterior.

SUPERFAMILY MEGALODONTACEA X
1, Pachyodont; 2, external, as in Chamacea; 3, isomyarian; 4, integripalliate; 5, usually equivalve, with protruding gibbous umbones coiling strongly forwards and away from valve margins; 6, aragonite, H in some species.

Pl. 6.4.64. *Megalodon* J. de C. Sowerby, 1827
Usually equivalve, tall, heart-shaped shell with protrusive umbones, a wide lunule, and a tapered orbicular ventral margin; exterior smooth; massive hinge plates with a few knobby cardinals and slender posterior laterals; deep crescentic anterior adductor scar at front of each hinge plate; posterior scar on salient ledge in each valve; up to 5 cm.
Devonian and U. Triassic; suspension feeder; semi-infaunal, in clusters; tropical/Old World Tethyan.
Megalodon cucullatus J. de C. Sowerby: M. Devonian, Paffrath, near Köln, W. Germany. (A) Bivalve, anteroventral view; (B) LV interior.

SUPERFAMILY HIPPURITACEA X
1, Pachyodont; 2, external, as in Chamacea, or invaginated and more or less obsolete; 3, isomyarian, or with enlarged anterior scars in some; 4, integripalliate; 5, inequivalve, attached to substrate by RV in most, by LV in some, with at least 1 umbo (usually attached) greatly extended in spiral or open conical fashion; 6, calcite, outer FP, and aragonite, middle CL, and inner CCL/myostracal layers.
Note: hippuritacean, or 'rudist' shells are of highly modified form, with some species showing superficial similarity to corals and/or certain attached brachiopods. They may also reach

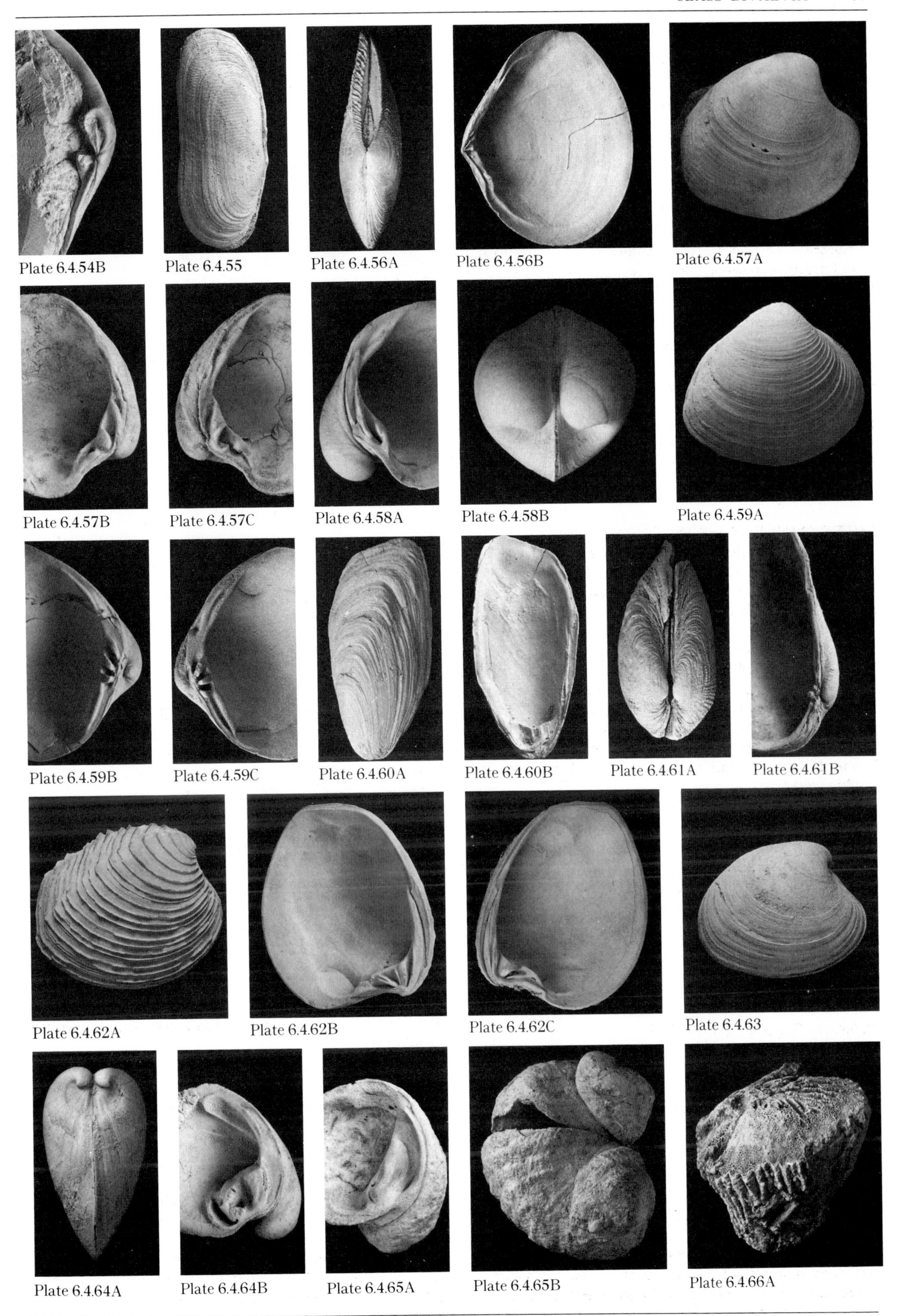

Plate 6.4.54B
Plate 6.4.55
Plate 6.4.56A
Plate 6.4.56B
Plate 6.4.57A
Plate 6.4.57B
Plate 6.4.57C
Plate 6.4.58A
Plate 6.4.58B
Plate 6.4.59A
Plate 6.4.59B
Plate 6.4.59C
Plate 6.4.60A
Plate 6.4.60B
Plate 6.4.61A
Plate 6.4.61B
Plate 6.4.62A
Plate 6.4.62B
Plate 6.4.62C
Plate 6.4.63
Plate 6.4.64A
Plate 6.4.64B
Plate 6.4.65A
Plate 6.4.65B
Plate 6.4.66A

considerable size. For a discussion of their evolution, see the chapter by Skelton in Yonge and Thompson (1978).

Pl. 6.4.65. *Epidiceras* Douvillé, 1935
Subequivalve, inflated, with circular margins, and spiralling umbones projecting forwards and outwards, that of LV attached to substrate; *Chama*-type ligament; LV radially ribbed, RV almost smooth, but both with growth rugae; massive hinge plates; 1 large tooth in LV, 1 large and 1 small (anterior) in RV; posterior adductor scar on salient ledge in each valve; up to 15 cm (across commissure).
U. Jurassic; suspension feeder; encrusting sediment or hard surfaces around reefs; Old World Tethyan.
Epidiceras sinistrum (Deshayes): U. Jurassic, Dompcevrin, Meuse, France. (A) LV interior; (B) bivalve, anteroventral view.

Pl. 6.4.66. *Hippurites* Lamarck, 1801
Straight, tubular, attached RV and operculiform LV, with apical umbones; ligament deeply invaginated or lost; RV radially ribbed, LV with porous exterior and underlying radial canals in outer shell layer; 2 pointed teeth and adductor-supports project from LV into RV; infolding of posterior flanks forms 2 pillars in RV and corresponding oscules in LV; up to 13 cm (across commissure).
U. Cretaceous; suspension feeder; epifaunal attached, commonly aggregative; Tethyan.
(A) *Hippurites striatus* Defrance: U. Cretaceous, Gosau, Austria. Bivalve, oblique dorsal view. (B) *H. radiosus* des Moulins: U. Cretaceous, Camérac, Charente, France. RV interior.

Pl. 6.4.67. *Radiolites* Lamarck, 1801
Biconical, with elongate, attached RV and low LV, and apical umbones; ligament deeply invaginated; exterior radially ribbed to squamose, with 2 distinctively ornamented radial bands on posterior flank; 2 pointed cardinals, and outward facing adductor-supports project from LV into RV; RV outer shell layer composed of stacked sheets of tiny prismatic cells; up to 8 cm (across commissure).
U. Cretaceous, suspension feeder; epifaunal attached, commonly aggregative; Tethyan.
Radiolites cf. *angeoides* de Lapeirouse: U. Cretaceous, Gosau, Austria. Oblique section of dorsal part of RV showing cellular outer layer (right) and ligamentary invagination (left).

Pl. 6.4.68. *Coralliochama* White, 1885
Long, conical, attached RV and cap-like LV; trace of ligamentary invagination marked externally by radial groove along each valve; exterior smooth; RV tooth flanked by 2 from LV; adductor scars on thickened ramps; aragonitic shell layers shot through with fine tabulate canals; up to 9 cm (across commissure).
U. Cretaceous, suspension feeder; epifaunal attached, usually aggregative; Baja California, Mexico.
Coralliochama orcutti White: U. Cretaceous, Baja California, Mexico. Bivalve, dorsal view.

SUPERFAMILY EDMONDIACEA X

1, Edentulous; 2, external, opisthodetic, on short nymphs, each buttressed by a longitudinal ridge; 3, isomyarian; 4, integripalliate; 5, equivalve, ovate with forward-slanted umbones, 6, unknown.

Pl. 6.4.69. *Edmondia* De Koninck, 1841
Elongate ovate, moderately inflated with closed margins; low beaks near anterior; plain exterior; long, low supporting ridge beneath nymph in each valve; up to 5 cm.
U. Devonian–U. Permian; ?suspension feeder; shallow infaunal, cosmopolitan.
Edmondia lacordaireana P. de Ryckholt: L. Carboniferous, Tournai, Belgium. (A) LV exterior; (B) LV hinge.

SUPERFAMILY PHOLADOMYACEA

1, Mostly edentulous; 2, external, opisthodetic on strong nymphs; 3, isomyarian; 4, usually sinupalliate; 5, equivalve, ovate to elongate, often with posterior gape; 6, aragonite, thin outer P, and middle and inner N layers, shell outer surface usually has radial rows of minute spiny granules.

Pl. 6.4.70. *Osteomya* Moesch, 1874
Elongate oblong, somewhat inflated shell, with slightly backward-facing, low beaks near anterior; posterior truncate, with wide gape, and may curve upwards; exterior with weak commarginal undulations; surface granules conspicuous; up to 10 cm.
Jurassic, suspension feeder; deep burrower; Europe, Madagascar, E. Africa.
Osteomya dilata (Phillips): M. Jurassic, Cheltenham, Gloucestershire, England. (A) Bivalve, LV side; (B) detail showing granules.

Pl. 6.4.71. *Pholadomya* G. B. Sowerby, 1823
Strongly inequilateral, ovate to subtrigonal, inflated shell with anterior, more or less prominent umbones; posterior gape variable, anterior gape narrow to absent; exterior with commarginal undulations crossed by spaced radial ribs, which may be tubercular; surface granules very fine; pallial sinus deep; up to 11 cm.
U. Triassic–Recent; suspension feeder; deep burrower; cosmopolitan.
Pholadomya ambigua (J. Sowerby): L. Jurassic, Chideock, Dorset, England. LV exterior + internal mould.

Pl. 6.4.72. *Ceratomya* Sandberger, 1864
Commonly subequivalve, inflated ovate shell, with anterior, large inward- and forward-facing beaks, one of which may project more than the other; no gape; ligament between recurved upper margin of LV and overlapping margin of RV; exterior with commarginal or oblique undulations, or smooth; pallial sinus weak or absent; up to 9 cm.
Jurassic; suspension feeder; infaunal; cosmopolitan.
Ceratomya bajociana (d'Orbigny): M. Jurassic, Cheltenham, Gloucestershire, England. Bivalve composite mould, LV side.

Pl. 6.4.73. *Grammysia* de Verneuil, 1847
Slightly inflated ovoid shell, with anteriorly turned beaks and clear lunule and escutcheon; elongate ligament on weak nymphs; exterior with commarginal undulations and 2 oblique radial sulci; no pallial sinus; up to 5 cm.
Devonian; ?suspension feeder; ?infaunal; cosmopolitan.
Grammysia bisulcata (Conrad): Devonian, Cayuga Lake, New York, USA. Open bivalve, dorsal view.

SUPERFAMILY PANDORACEA

1, Edentulous or with small teeth; 2, internal pad, with medial shelly wedge ('lithodesma'), supported between laminar buttresses or on spoon-like ledges, external ligament may also be present; 3, isomyarian; 4, sinus may be present; 5, inequivalve, usually thin and elongate, commonly gaping; 6, aragonite, outer P, and middle and inner N layers, but some H throughout, and many species have external granules (cf. Pholadomyacea). (Note:

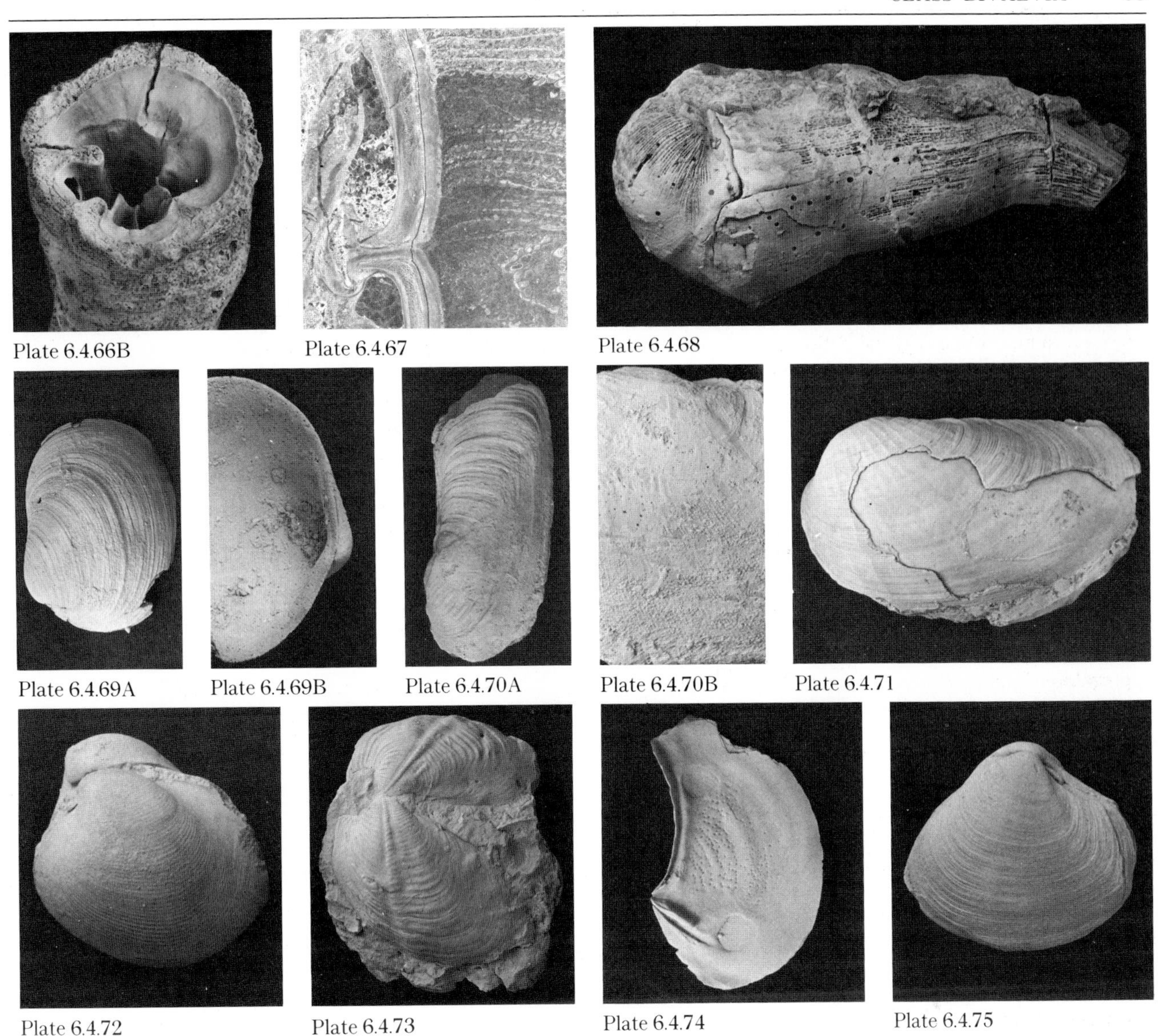

Plate 6.4.66B Plate 6.4.67 Plate 6.4.68

Plate 6.4.69A Plate 6.4.69B Plate 6.4.70A Plate 6.4.70B Plate 6.4.71

Plate 6.4.72 Plate 6.4.73 Plate 6.4.74 Plate 6.4.75

Some authors separate off the Thraciacea as a distinct superfamily (see Morton 1982)).

Pl. 6.4.74. *Pandora* Bruguière, 1797

Thin, flat, posteriorly rostrate suboval shell; RV flatter than LV; laminar buttresses diverge from beaks on shell interior, surrounding ligament pad; lithodesma may be wanting; exterior with weak commarginal sculpture; disjunct pallial line; up to 4 cm.

Oligocene–Recent; suspension feeder; lying on surface, or sluggishly burrowing just beneath; widespread.

Pandora (Heteroclidus) punctata Conrad: Pleistocene, San Diego, California, USA. RV interior.

Pl. 6.4.75. *Thracia* J. Sowerby, 1823

Subequilateral, subelliptical shell, with larger RV, and backward-turned, close umbones, which may interpenetrate; truncate posterior marked off by a low ridge in each valve; ligament pad (+ lithodesma) in spoon-like subumbonal supports; external ligament short; smooth exterior, with granules; edentulous; large pallial sinus; up to 9 cm.

Jurassic–Recent; suspension feeder, moderately deep burrower; widespread.

Thracia depressa (Phillips): U. Jurassic, Villers-sur-Mer, France.

SUPERFAMILY POROMYACEA

1, Thin hinge margins with tooth-like protuberances; 2, internal pad with lithodesma (as in Pandoracea) and/or external ligament; 3, isomyarian, small; 4, may be slightly sinupalliate; 5, equivalve to subequivalve, usually rounded to elongate, with little or no gape; 6, aragonite, outer P or H, and middle and inner N layers, or H throughout, usually with external granules (cf. Pholadomyacea). (Note: Some authors separate off the Cuspidariacea and Verticordiacea as distinct superfamilies (see Morton 1982).)

Pl. 6.4.76. *Cuspidaria* Nardo, 1840

More or less equivalve, thin-walled, plump, ovate shells with long posterior rostrum and inward-facing beaks; small supports for ligament pad; weak commarginal sculpture on exterior, with or without spaced radial ribs; hinge with 1 or more tooth-like protuberances; up to 3 cm.

U. Cretaceous–Recent; predator, living just beneath surface and spasmodically sucking in small crustaceans, worms, etc. by contracting muscular, bellow-like gills; widespread.

Cuspidaria subrostrata (Tate): Oligocene, Hamilton, Victoria, Australia. (A) LV exterior; (B) LV interior; (C) RV interior.

SUPERFAMILY CLAVAGELLACEA

1, Edentulous; 2, external to obsolete; 3, isomyarian to obsolete;

4, obsolete; 5, free when young, but later more or less fused on to elongate secondary calcareous tube constructed by the crevice- or burrow-dwelling animal's siphons; 6, aragonite, outer P, and inner N layers, tube of platy homogeneous microstructure.

Pl. 6.4.77. *Clavagella* Lamarck, 1818
Simple, subovate shell, 1 valve of which becomes entirely fused to tube; anterior end of tube sealed off in adult; its wall being produced into projecting tubules; up to 20 cm (including tube).
U. Cretaceous–Recent; suspension feeder; occupies crevice, usually in living coral, and builds out tube as latter grows; widespread, among many reefs.
Clavagella coronata Deshayes: Pliocene, Palermo, Sicily. Shell with anterior part of tube, LV side.

SUPERFAMILY GASTROCHAENACEA

1, Edentulous; 2, external, opisthodetic, in elongate groove in each valve; 3, heteromyarian (anterior reduced); 4, strongly sinupalliate; 5, equivalve, oblong, with wide anterior (pedal) gape and tapering posterior; 6, aragonite, outer CL and inner CCL or H layers.

Pl. 6.4.78. *Gastrochaena* Spengler, 1783
Elongate, with anterior, low umbones, and a wide, oval anterior gape; shell lies free in boring, but secretes calcareous lining around posterior end of boring, with 2 projecting tubes for siphons; exterior smooth, or with oblique radial furrow; up to 2.5 cm (shell).
U. Jurassic–Recent; suspension feeder; physically boring into coral and rock; widespread.
Gastrochaena recondita (Phillips): U. Jurassic, Ayton, Yorkshire, England. Bivalve, LV side, in bore.

SUPERFAMILY MYACEA

1, Usually edentulous, or with a small subumbonal tooth; 2, largely internal, between a broad subumbonal process projecting from LV and a recessed support beneath umbo of RV; 3, isomyarian; 4, deeply sinupalliate to integripalliate; 5, equivalve to inequivalve, elongate or subtrigonal, may have posterior gape; 6, aragonite, outer H, and middle (or outer) CL, and inner CCL or H layers.

Pl. 6.4.79. *Mya* Linné, 1758
Subequivalve (RV slightly larger), ovate to subquadrate shell with low, inward-turned, nearly median umbones and a broadly gaping, more or less truncate posterior; LV has large tongue-like projecting ligament support; exterior with commarginal growth lines and commonly wrinkled periostracum; edentulous; pallial sinus deep; up to 15 cm.
Oligocene–Recent; suspension feeder; sluggish, deep burrower; Europe, N. America, Japan.
Mya truncata Linné: Pleistocene, E. Southampton Island, Canada. (A) Bivalve, LV side; (B) LV interior; (C) RV interior.

Pl. 6.4.80. *Corbula* Bruguière, 1797
Inflated subtrigonal, sturdy shell with inturned umbones and rostrate posterior; LV smaller than RV, fitting *into* it; ligament pad between pit on internal projection just behind LV beak, and recessed area beneath RV beak; exterior smooth to commarginally ribbed; boss-like tooth in RV; pallial sinus weak; up to 4 cm. (Note: The family Corbulidae may be descendants of crassatellaceans that have convergently evolved myacean features (N. J. Morris pers. comm.).)
Cretaceous–Recent; suspension feeder; sluggish shallow burrower; cosmopolitan.
Corbula ephamilla Tate: Eocene, Adelaide, Australia. (A) LV interior; (B) RV interior; (C) bivalve, LV side.

SUPERFAMILY PHOLADACEA

1, Edentulous; 2, internal, on often obscure subumbonal supports; 3, usually isomyarian, but with anterior muscle on raised anterodorsal margin where it counteracts posterior muscle; 4, sinupalliate; 5, equivalve, inequilateral, with extra shelly elements in addition to valves; 6, aragonite outer P, middle CL and inner CCL or H layers, though outer layer is H in some, or even absent.

Pl. 6.4.81. *Cyrtopleura* Tryon, 1862
Elongate, subelliptical, with low anterior umbones; anterior pedal gape; small ligament supports; exterior with spiky radial ribs; spoon-like muscle support projects down from umbonal cavity in each valve; anterior adductor on flaring anterodorsal margins arching back above fronts of umbones; several accessory plates; up to 13 cm.
Miocene–Recent; suspension feeder; boring mechanically into stiff clay, rock, etc. in very shallow water; New World.
Cyrtopleura (Scobinopholas) costata (Linné): Pleistocene, Wailes Bluff, Maryland, USA. (A) LV exterior; (B) RV interior.

Pl. 6.4.82. *Teredina* Lamarck, 1818
Short, high shell with anterior and posterior gapes, which in the adult are, respectively, covered over by a bulbous calcareous wall, and fused on to an elongate calcareous lining to boring; umbones covered by broad accessory plate; up to 17 cm (with tube).
U. Cretaceous–M. Miocene; suspension feeder; boring into wood; Europe.
Teredina personata (Lamarck): Eocene, Épernay, France. Bivalve, internal mould (LV side) and tube.

6.5 Class Rostroconchia

Rostroconch growth geometry is characteristic: growth expansion of the lateral margins of a simple conical larval shell produced an adult shell with two distinct lateral lobes connected dorsally, looking like a bivalve shell. But unlike the latter, the shell remained a single unit with shell layers deposited continuously across the dorsal midline. The latter thus suffered continuous fracture and repair in most rostroconchs, though it seems to have become flexible in certain advanced forms. Rostroconchs also lacked adductor muscles. In early forms, moreover, the two lobes are joined internally by a dorsal transverse shelf, or *pegma*, which leaves a characteristic notch in internal moulds (Pl. 6.5.1B). For a fuller account, see Pojeta and Runnegar (1976), and the chapter by Runnegar in Yonge and Thompson (1978).

Pl. 6.5.1. *Ribeiria* Sharpe, 1853
Elongate, compressed, subovate shell with forward-pointing apex near front; straight to gently arched dorsally, and tapering posteriorly; a narrow gape may run ventrally from front to back or is pinched ventrally; exterior and margins smooth; short pegma slopes backwards beneath apex; up to 6 cm long.
U. Cambrian–U. Ordovician; ?deposit feeder; in offshore muddy carbonates; widespread (tropical).
Ribeiria apusoides Schuchert & Waagen: (A) U. Ordovician, Radodin, Czechoslovakia. Exterior, left side. (B) Ordovician,

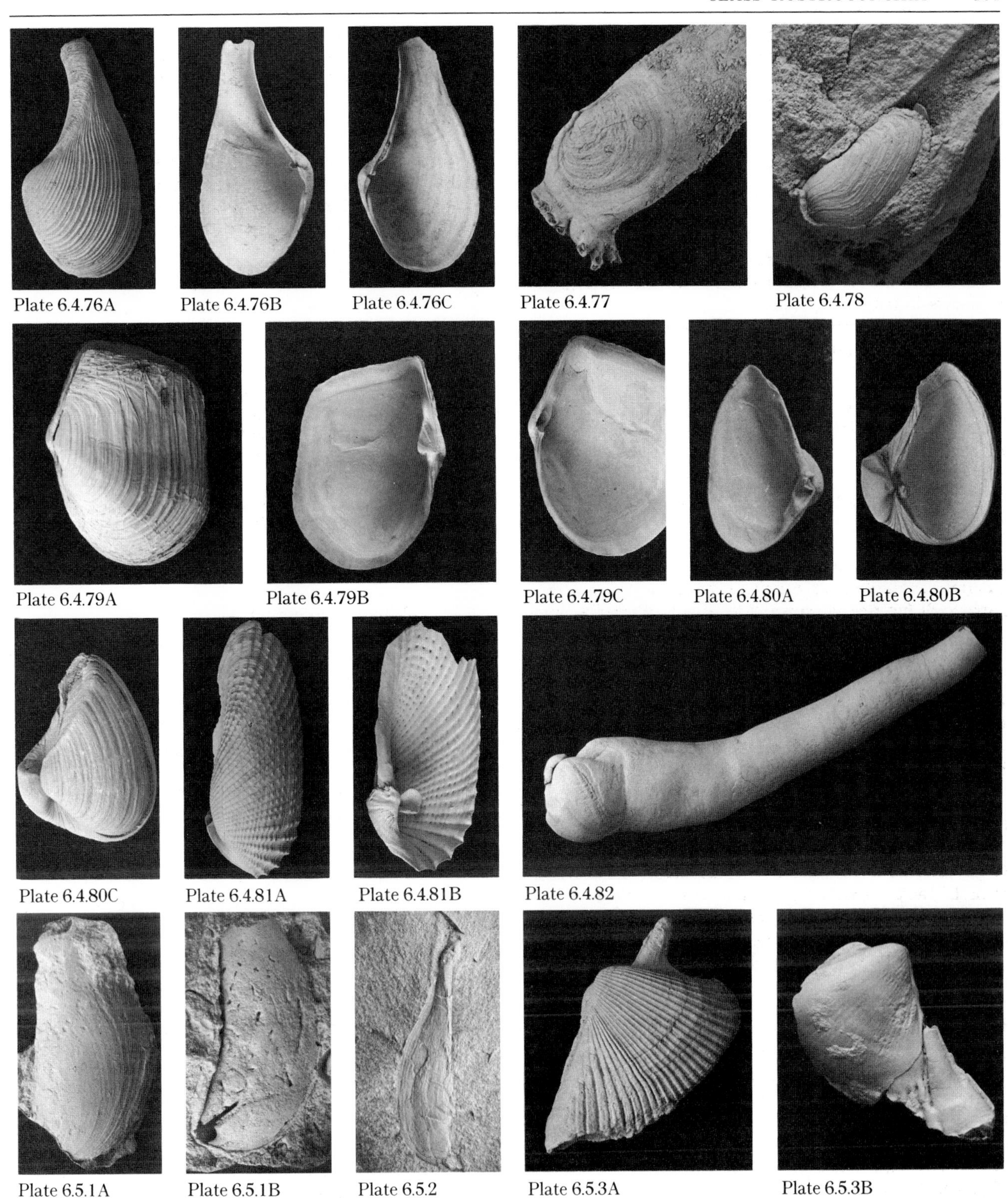

Plate 6.4.76A Plate 6.4.76B Plate 6.4.76C Plate 6.4.77 Plate 6.4.78

Plate 6.4.79A Plate 6.4.79B Plate 6.4.79C Plate 6.4.80A Plate 6.4.80B

Plate 6.4.80C Plate 6.4.81A Plate 6.4.81B Plate 6.4.82

Plate 6.5.1A Plate 6.5.1B Plate 6.5.2 Plate 6.5.3A Plate 6.5.3B

?Czechoslovakia. Internal mould, left side.

Pl. 6.5.2. *Pinnocaris* Etheridge, 1878
Highly elongate, compressed shell, straight to concave dorsally, with gently curved ventral margins, and tapering, rostrate posterior; low, slightly peaked apex a short way back from front; gape restricted to anterior and posterior; exterior smooth or commarginally ornamented; pegma present; up to 3 cm long.
U. Cambrian–U. Ordovician; ?deposit feeder; in fine clastics and carbonates; N. America, Scotland, Australia.
Pinnocaris lapworthi Etheridge: U. Ordovician, Girvan, Ayrshire, Scotland. Exterior, right-hand side.

Pl. 6.5.3. *Conocardium* Bronn, 1835
Strongly bilobate, each lobe rising to umbo-like crest either side of apparently organic-rich and flexible dorsal midline; anterior produced into triangular snout, and posterior into tubular rostrum; gapes only beneath snout and at end of rostrum; anterior margins crenulate; exterior with coarse radial ribs; up to 4 cm long.
L. Devonian–U. Carboniferous; ?sessile, ?deposit feeder; Europe, N. America.
Conocardium aliforme J. de C. Sowerby: L. Carboniferous. (A) Visé, Belgium. Exterior, left-hand side. (B) Redesdale, Northumberland, England. Internal mould, right-hand side.

6.6 Class Gastropoda

Gastropods are elongate molluscs with a well-developed head and a large, flattened foot. Most have an external shell (Fig. 6.6.1), which is usually helically coiled, but in many groups the shell is reduced, internal or absent. Gastropods are characterized by having undergone torsion, a process by which the primitively posterior gill-bearing mantle cavity and the anus are rotated in an anticlockwise direction to lie anteriorly above the head. Torsion produces internal anatomical asymmetry, with the nervous system being twisted into a figure-of-eight form. Most groups of gastropods have modified the process and have often lost one of each original pair of internal organs. A well-developed radula is present. The sexes are usually separate but advanced land snails are hermaphroditic.

Gastropods are the most abundant molluscs with a history extending from the Cambrian to the present day.

From a primitive mobile marine benthic existence, gastropods have subsequently adapted to pelagic, sedentary and parasitic modes of life. They are abundant in fresh water and are the only terrestrial molluscs.

Gastropod classification is based on features of the soft parts in living representatives. Fossils are placed into this scheme after comparison of shell morphologies with living species. Subclasses are recognized after the form of the mantle cavity. In the **Prosobranchia**, the mantle cavity is located anteriorly as a result of torsion, while modification of the effects of torsion and posterior placement (or eventual loss) of the mantle cavity is a feature of the **Opisthobranchia. Pulmonates** have an air-breathing lung.

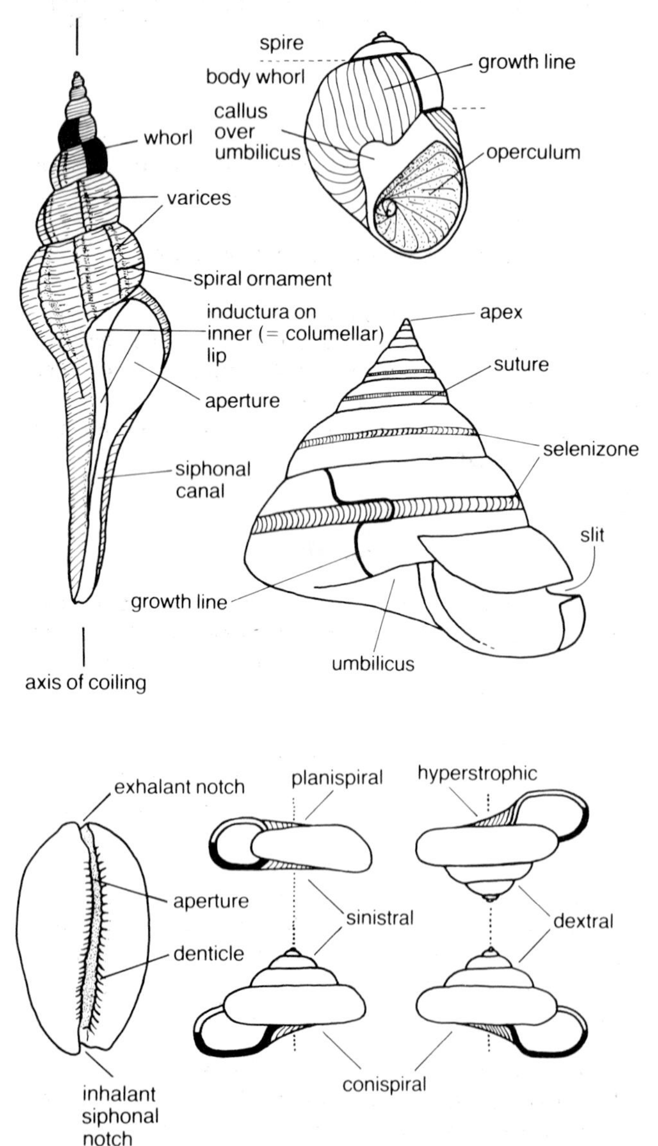

Fig. 6.6.1. Morphological features and coiling styles of gastropod shells.

Subclass Prosobranchia

Fully torted gastropods with anterior mantle cavity; 1 or 2 gills; shell conispiral or cap-shaped. Cambrian–Recent.

Order Archaeogastropoda

Conispiral, equidimensional to cap-shaped, only infrequently high-spired; aperture without inhalant siphonal notch but some with exhalant sinus or slit in outer lip; 1 or 2 bipectinate gills; heart with 2 auricles; sexes separate, but sexual products usually discharged into the sea. Cambrian–Recent. Most archaeogastropods are browsing herbivores, although some are scavengers or sluggish carnivores.

Suborder Bellerophontina

Planispirally coiled, bilaterally symmetrical; with few or many whorls and umbilicus closed to widely open; well-developed mid-dorsal sinus or slit. Cambrian–Triassic. Distribution of genera between this suborder and the class Monoplacophora is speculative.

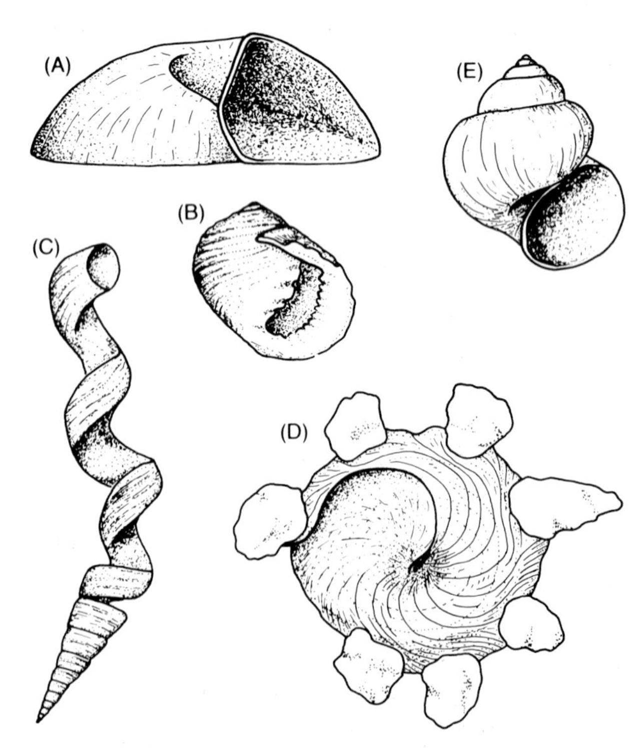

Fig. 6.6.2. Prosobranch gastropod shell morphologies. (A) *Maclurites* Leseur, 1818 (Ordovician, see also Pl. 6.6.7); (B) *Nerita* Linné, 1758 (U. Cretaceous–Recent); (C) *Vermicularia* Lamarck, 1799 (Cretaceous–Recent); (D) *Xenophora* Waldheim, 1807 (Cretaceous–Recent); (E) *Viviparus* Montfort, 1810 (Cretaceous–Recent).

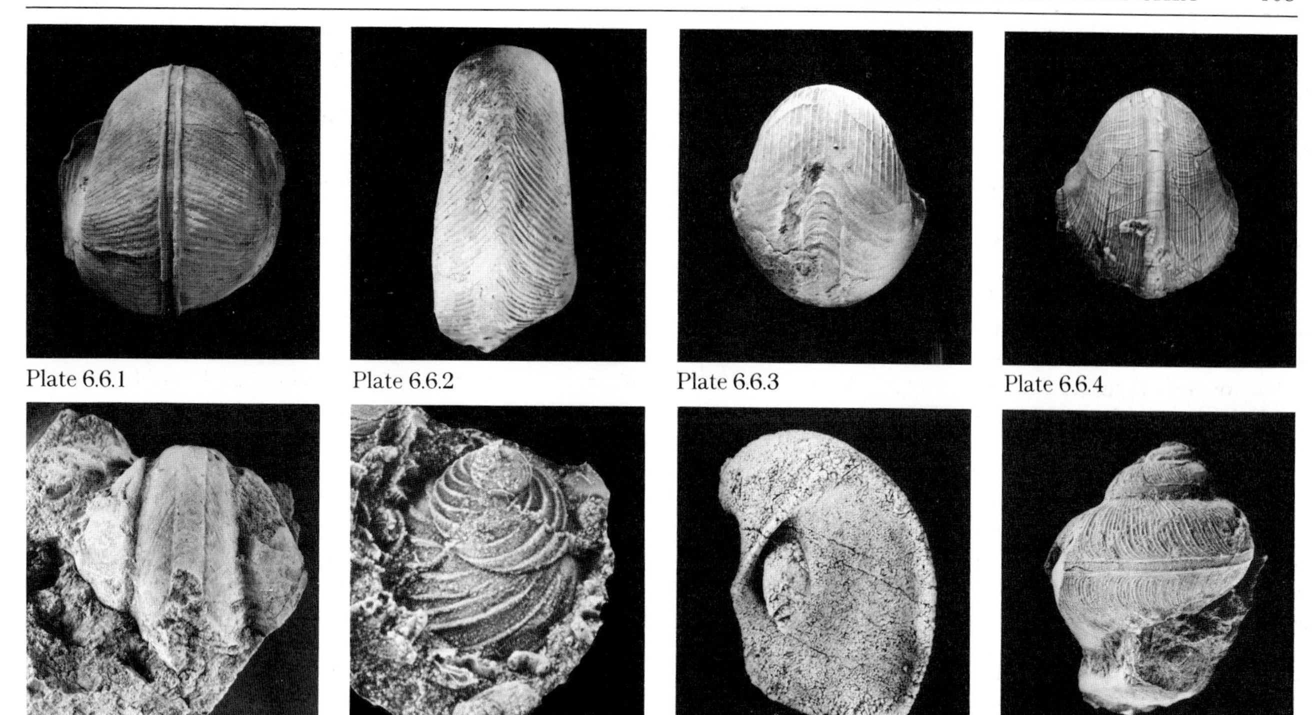

Plate 6.6.1 Plate 6.6.2 Plate 6.6.3 Plate 6.6.4

Plate 6.6.5 Plate 6.6.6 Plate 6.6.7 Plate 6.6.8

Pl. 6.6.1. *Bellerophon* Montfort, 1808
Broadly rounded with narrow umbilici; well-developed selenizone; transverse growth lines; maximum length 10 cm.
Silurian–Triassic.
Bellerophon sp.: L. Carboniferous, Belgium.

Pl. 6.6.2. *Modestospira* Yochelson, 1964
Wide umbilici and deep median sinus; prominent growth lamellae; maximum length 5 cm.
Ordovician.
Modestospira poulseni Yochelson: Ordovician, Bornholm, Denmark.

Pl. 6.6.3. *Euphemites* Warthin, 1930
Broadly rounded with broad selenizone; most of whorl enveloped in an inductural layer ornamented with spiral ribs; maximum length 4 cm.
Carboniferous–Permian, possibly an infaunal predator.
Euphemites jacksoni Weir: Carboniferous, Namurian, Cheshire, England.

Pl. 6.6.4. *Retispira* Knight, 1945
As *Bellerophon* (Pl. 6.6.1), but reticulate ornament; maximum length 4 cm.
Silurian (?)–Permian.
Retispira concinna (Weir): Carboniferous, Namurian, Cheshire, England.

Pl. 6.6.5. *Plectonotus* Clarke, 1899
Dorsum spirally trilobed with broad selenizone; ornament growth lines and spiral ribs; maximum length 3 cm.
Ordovician (?), Silurian–Devonian.
Plectonotus boucoti Peel: Silurian, near Llandeilo, Wales.

Suborder Macluritina

Hyperstrophic, basal spire low to high. Cambrian–Devonian.

Pl. 6.6.6. *Mimospira* Koken, 1925
Basal spire high with shallowly convex whorls; ornament of prominent oblique ribs; maximum height about 1 cm.
Ordovician–Silurian.
Mimospira abbae Peel: Silurian, Arisaig, Nova Scotia.

Pl. 6.6.7. *Maclurites* Leseur, 1818
Large, robust, with flat base (Fig. 6.6.2A, p. 102) and heavily calcified operculum; maximum length 30 cm, operculum 10 cm.
Ordovician, probably a sedentary ciliary feeder.
Maclurites sp. operculum: M. Ordovician, Kronprins Christian Land, N. Greenland.

Suborder Pleurotomariina

Conispiral, rarely cap-shaped, with exhalant sinus, slit or series of perforations generally near midwhorl. Heart with 2 auricles; mantle cavity with 2 gills, the right usually reduced in size.
U. Cambrian–Recent.

SUPERFAMILY PLEUROTOMARIACEA

Mainly conispiral, with sinus, slit or series of perforations; the slit generating a selenizone ornamented with crescentic lunulae.
U. Cambrian–Recent.

Pl. 6.6.8. *Mourlonia* de Koninck, 1883
Turbiniform, concave selenizone bordered by spiral cords; generally reticulate ornament; maximum height about 4 cm.
M. Ordovician–Permian.
Mourlonia sp.: Carboniferous, Oklahoma, USA.

Pl. 6.6.9. *Omospira* Ulrich *in* Ulrich & Scofield, 1897
Whorl profile step-like, with large final whorl; broad selenizone at whorl shoulder; ornament of growth lines; maximum height about 6 cm.
M. Ordovician–Silurian.
Omospira vitellia (Billings): Silurian, Ontario, Canada.

Pl. 6.6.10. *Phanerotrema* Fischer, 1885
Resembles *Omospira* (Pl. 6.6.9) but selenizone narrow, bordered by cords; ornament of spiral cords crossed by growth lines; maximum height about 6 cm.
Silurian–Devonian.
Phanerotrema lindstroemi (Boucot & Johnson): Silurian, Gotland, Sweden.

Pl. 6.6.11. *Glabrocingulum* Thomas, 1940
Turbiniform, conical or step-like spire; selenizone bordered by cords; reticulate ornament with nodes at intersections; maximum height about 2 cm.
Carboniferous–Permian.
Glabrocingulum grayvillense (Norwood & Pratten): U. Carboniferous, Texas, USA.

Pl. 6.6.12. *Ruedemannia* Foerste, 1914
Turbiniform, selenizone bordered by cords; strong spiral keel on upper whorl surface and commonly also on base; maximum height about 4 cm.
Ordovician–Devonian.
Ruedemannia sp.: Silurian, Wisconsin, USA.

Pl. 6.6.13. *Pleurotomaria* Defrance, 1826
Trochiform, with step-like profile; with or without umbilicus; broad selenizone on outer whorl face; tubercles at shoulder and sometimes on base; maximum height 12 cm.
L. Jurassic–L. Cretaceous.
Pleurotomaria sp.: M. Jurassic, Bayeux, France.

Pl. 6.6.14. *Euconospira* Ulrich *in* Ulrich & Scofield, 1897
Trochiform, selenizone between strong spiral cords; ornament generally reticulate; maximum height about 5 cm.
Silurian–Permian.
Euconospira claustrata (Lindström): Silurian, Gotland, Sweden.

Pl. 6.6.15. *Conotomaria* Cox, 1959
Conical, with or without umbilicus; narrow selenizone at or above midwhorl; ornament mainly of spiral cords; maximum height about 15 cm.
M. Jurassic–Palaeocene.
Conotomaria sp.: Palaeocene, Fakse, Denmark.

Pl. 6.6.16, 17. *Lophospira* Whitfield, 1886
Turbiniform with prominent spiral keels; sinus generally deep, often culminating in a short slit and selenizone at the angular midwhorl; ornament of growth lines or lamellae; maximum height about 10 cm. A variable genus with many species.
Ordovician–Silurian.
Pl. 6.6.16. *Lophospira gothlandica* Ulrich & Scofield: Silurian, Gotland, Sweden. Pl. 6.6.17. *Lophospira* sp: Silurian, British Columbia, Canada.

Pl. 6.6.18. *Baylea* de Koninck, 1883
Turbiniform with step-like profile; selenizone at whorl shoulder; ornament dominated by spiral ribs; maximum height 4 cm.
Carboniferous–Permian.
Baylea yvanii (Léveillé): L. Carboniferous, Belgium.

Pl. 6.6.19. *Trepospira* Ulrich & Scofield, 1897
Lenticular to subtrochiform, with partially closed umbilicus; selenizone just above periphery; ornament of growth lines and round subsutural nodes; maximum width about 4 cm. *Angyomphalus* Cossmann, 1916 has radially elongate nodes.
Devonian–Permian.
Trepospira sp.: Carboniferous, Oklahoma, USA.

Pl. 6.6.20. *Pyrgotrochus* Fischer, 1885
Conical with prominent tubercles at margin of base; selenizone broad, below midwhorl; ornament of spiral ribs and growth lines; maximum height about 10 cm.
L. Jurassic–Cretaceous.
Pyrgotrochus sp.: Jurassic, Bayeux, France.

Pl. 6.6.21. *Ptychomphalus* Agassiz, 1839
Sublenticular with closed umbilicus and peripheral selenizone; maximum width about 4 cm.
L. Jurassic.
Ptychomphalus expansus (Sowerby): L. Jurassic, France.

SUPERFAMILY FISSURELLACEA
Cap-shaped, with exhalant perforation or marginal slit; muscle scar U-shaped. Triassic–Recent.

Pl. 6.6.22. *Fissurella* Bruguière, 1789
Exhalant perforation near the central apex; bordered within by rounded callus; maximum length about 4 cm.
Eocene–Recent.
Fissurella sp.: Eocene, Grignon, France.

SUPERFAMILY TROCHONEMATACEA
Turbiniform, with notch within angulation at midwhorl; shallow sinus. M. Ordovician–M. Permian.

Pl. 6.6.23. *Trochonema* Salter, 1859
Resembles *Lophospira* (Pl. 6.6.17) but usually lower-spired; sinus shallow or absent; maximum height about 7 cm.
M. Ordovician–Devonian.
Trochonema umbilicata (Hall): M. Ordovician, Quebec, Canada.

Suborder Murchisoniina

Commonly high-spired with many whorls; exhalant sinus or slit at midwhorl probably indicates paired gills. U. Cambrian (?), Ordovician–Triassic.

Pl. 6.6.24. *Murchisonia* d'Archiac & de Verneuil, 1841
Selenizone bordered by spiral cords; maximum height about 5 cm.
Silurian–Permian.
Murchisonia bilineata (Dechen): M. Devonian, Paffrath, W. Germany.

Pl. 6.6.25. *Hormotoma* Salter, 1859
Whorls generally convex; deep sinus at midwhorl passes into a short slit; selenizone obscure, bordered by striae; maximum height about 15 cm.
Ordovician–Silurian.
Hormotoma whiteavesi Clarke and Ruedemann: Silurian, New York, USA.

Suborder Euomphalina

Mainly discoid with wide umbilicus; orthostrophic or hyperstrophic; notch within angulation near periphery suggests presence of 2 gills. L. Ordovician–L. Cretaceous. Many euomphalins were probably sedentary filter or ciliary feeders.

Pl. 6.6.26. *Euomphalus* Sowerby, 1814
Wide umbilicus and very low spire; channel-bearing angulation at upper margin of rounded whorls; thick shell with growth

Plate 6.6.9

Plate 6.6.10

Plate 6.6.11

Plate 6.6.12

Plate 6.6.13

Plate 6.6.14

Plate 6.6.15

Plate 6.6.16

Plate 6.6.17

Plate 6.6.18

Plate 6.6.19

Plate 6.6.20

Plate 6.6.21

Plate 6.6.22

Plate 6.6.23

Plate 6.6.24

Plate 6.6.25

Plate 6.6.26

lines only; maximum width 10 cm.
Silurian–Permian.
Euomphalus pentangulatus Sowerby: L. Carboniferous, Belgium.

Pl. 6.6.27. *Centrifugus* Bronn, 1834
Very low spired, with wide umbilicus; rounded whorls with flange at periphery; narrow subsutural selenizone; ornament of spiral cords and ribs crossed by growth lines; maximum width about 10 cm.
Silurian.
Centrifugus planorbis (Hisinger): U. Silurian, Gotland, Sweden.

Suborder Patellina

Cap-shaped, without perforation or marginal slit; internal surface with U-shaped muscle scar; living forms with single gill or differentiated circle of small gills around margin. Silurian–Recent.

Pl. 6.6.28. *Patella* Linné, 1758
Thick-shelled with prominent ridges radiating from subcentral apex; maximum length about 7 cm.
Cretaceous–Recent.
Patella sp.: Palaeocene, Nûgssuaq, W. Greenland.

Pl. 6.6.29. *Lepetopsis* Whitfield, 1882
Flat conical with subcentral apex; concentric growth lines sometimes with radiating ridges; maximum length 3 cm.
Carboniferous–Permian.
Lepetopsis retrorsus (Phillips): L. Carboniferous, Longnor, England.

Suborder Trochina

Conispiral with a single gill; aperture simple, without sinus or slit. L. Ordovician–Recent.

SUPERFAMILY PLATYCERATACEA
Generally robust, globose; some with irregular growth reflecting their coprophagous habit on echinoderms. L. Ordovician–Permian.

Pl. 6.6.30. *Holopea* Hall, 1847
Turbiniform with rounded whorls; ornament of growth lines; maximum height 5 cm.
M. Ordovician–Devonian.
Holopea rossbrookiensis Peel: Silurian, Arisaig, Nova Scotia, Canada.

Pl. 6.6.31. *Cyclonema* Hall, 1852
Final whorl relatively large; ornament of spiral ridges and threads crossed by growth lines; some species with irregular growth; maximum height about 6 cm.
M. Ordovician–L. Devonian, coprophage or scavenger.
Cyclonema boreale Poulsen: L. Silurian, Washington Land, N. Greenland.

Pl. 6.6.32. *Platyceras* Conrad, 1840
Naticiform to uncoiled, often with irregular coiling or ornamentation; growth lines and corrugations dominate ornament, but spiral ridges often present, particularly in earlier whorls; maximum height 10 cm.
Silurian–Permian, coprophage or scavenger.
Platyceras sp.: L. Silurian, Washington Land, N. Greenland.

SUPERFAMILY ORIOSTOMATACEA
Turbiniform to almost planispiral, often with wide umbilicus; strong spiral ornament. Silurian–Devonian.

Pl. 6.6.33, 34. *Oriostoma* Munier-Chalmas, 1876
Turbiniform to sublenticular, with spiral ridges and/or cords crossed by growth lines which may be lamellose; operculum round, multispiral; maximum width about 4 cm.
Silurian–Devonian. Pl. 6.6.33. *Oriostoma globosa* (Schlotheim): with operculum in place, U. Silurian, Gotland, Sweden. Pl. 6.6.34. *Oriostoma* sp.: U. Silurian, Gotland, Sweden.

SUPERFAMILY TROCHACEA
Conical to turbiniform. Triassic–Recent.

Pl. 6.6.35. *Tectus* Montfort, 1810
Generally higher than wide, no umbilicus; strong columellar fold; ornament of varices which slope forward from the suture, growth lines sweep strongly backward; maximum height about 8 cm.
U. Cretaceous–Recent.
Tectus ornatus (Lamarck): Eocene, Grignon, France.

SUPERFAMILY AMBERLEYACEA
Dextral or sinistral, trochiform to turbiniform; commonly with strong ornament; subordinal classification uncertain. M. Triassic–Oligocene.

Pl. 6.6.36, 37. *Amphitrochus* Cossmann, 1907
Trochiform; 2 rows of nodes just above periphery, a third round the narrow umbilicus; maximum height about 3 cm.
U. Triassic–Cretaceous.
Amphitrochus duplicatus (Sowerby): Jurassic, France.

Suborder Neritopsina

Globose, robust shells, commonly with denticles on the thickened inner lip (Fig. 6.6.2B, p. 102). Devonian–Recent. The only archaeogastropods with internal fertilization; marine, freshwater and (few) terrestrial.

Order Mesogastropoda

Prosobranchs in which the right gill is lost, left gill monopectinate; heart with 1 auricle; sexes separate, fertilization internal; shell usually conispiral, often with siphonal notch. M. Ordovician–Recent. Marine, freshwater, terrestrial, employing a variety of feeding patterns.

SUPERFAMILY ARCHITECTONICACEA
Low-spired to discoidal; commonly with wide umbilicus and strong spiral ornament. U. Cretaceous–Recent.

Pl. 6.6.38. *Architectonica* Röding, 1799
Spire slightly convex in profile; base flat with row of tubercles around wide umbilicus; ornament of broad, flat-topped spiral ridges crossed by growth lines; maximum width about 5 cm.
U. Cretaceous–Recent, carnivores on coelenterates.
Architectonica sp.: Tertiary, France.

SUPERFAMILY HIPPONICACEA
Conispiral with large body whorl and simple aperture, to cap-shaped; the latter with U-shaped muscle scar on shell interior. Permian–Recent.

Plate 6.6.27 Plate 6.6.28 Plate 6.6.29 Plate 6.6.30 Plate 6.6.31 Plate 6.6.32 Plate 6.6.33 Plate 6.6.34 Plate 6.6.35 Plate 6.6.36 Plate 6.6.37 Plate 6.6.38 Plate 6.6.39

Pl. 6.6.39. *Hipponix* Defrance, 1819
Cap-shaped with thick shell and overhanging apex; reticulate ornament; maximum length about 3 cm.
U. Cretaceous–Recent, selective deposit feeder or coprophage.
Hipponix cornucopiae (Lamarck): Eocene, Grignon, France.

SUPERFAMILY CERITHIACEA
Mainly high spired, with many whorls; some irregularly coiled due to cementation (Fig. 6.6.2C, p. 102); with or without siphonal notch; some with sinus on outer whorl face. Devonian–Recent. Generally algal browsers, but some ciliary feeders.

Pl. 6.6.40. *Turritella* Lamarck, 1799
Many whorls, commonly with spiral ribs or cords; aperture simple; maximum length about 15 cm.
Cretaceous–Recent.
Turritella sp.: Palaeocene, Nûgssuaq, W. Greenland.

Pl. 6.6.41. *Potamides* Brongniart, 1810
Spire rather flat-sided; ornament generally of 3 nodose cords; aperture with siphonal canal and notches in outer whorl face.
U. Cretaceous–Recent.
Potamides tricarinatus (Lamarck): Eocene, Paris basin, France.

SUPERFAMILY LOXONEMATACEA

Commonly high-spired with many whorls; some with an exhalant sinus; smooth or with transverse ribs or varices. M. Ordovician–M. Jurassic. Probably algal browsers.

Pl. 6.6.42. *Loxonema* Phillips, 1841
Resembles *Hormotoma* (Pl. 6.6.25), but selenizone replaced by an open sinus; maximum height about 5 cm.
M. Ordovician–Carboniferous.
Loxonema sp.: Silurian, Arisaig, Nova Scotia, Canada.

SUPERFAMILY EPITONIACEA

Usually high-spired with many whorls; aperture round, simple; ornament commonly of spiral ribs crossed by prominent lamellae or varices. Jurassic–Recent. Carnivores on coelenterates.

Pl. 6.6.43. *Coniscala* Boury, 1887
Whorls convex; ornament of prominent varices with spiral ribs; maximum height about 4 cm.
U. Cretaceous–Palaeocene.
Coniscala sp.: Palaeocene, Nûgssuaq, W. Greenland.

SUPERFAMILY CALYPTRACEA

Mainly cap-shaped, with curved apex, or slipper-shaped, usually with internal shelf; others trochiform with flat base, sometimes with stones and shells cemented to shell as camouflage (Fig. 6.6.2D, p. 102). Jurassic–Recent. Commonly ciliary feeders.

Pl. 6.6.44. *Lamelliphorus* Cossmann, 1915
Trochiform, with open umbilicus; aperture acuminate peripherally; ornament of radiating lamellose varices which project as short spines; maximum height about 2 cm.
Jurassic.
Lamelliphorus ornatissimus (d'Orbigny): M. Jurassic, Bayeux, France.

SUPERFAMILY STROMBACEA

Moderately high spired, with relatively few, often angular and ornamented whorls; aperture elongate, with siphonal notch or canal; outer lip often widely expanded or digitate. Jurassic–Recent. Many are infaunal selective herbivores.

Pl. 6.6.45. *Drepanochilus* Meek, 1864
Angular whorls with curved varices; expanded outer lip with a single apically directed digitation; siphonal canal short; maximum height about 4 cm.
U. Cretaceous–Recent.
Drepanochilus sp.: U. Cretaceous, N. Dakota, USA.

Pl. 6.6.46, 47. *Rimella* Agassiz, 1840
Spindle-shaped with siphonal notch; upper margin of aperture extended as a canal to near apex; ornament principally of varices; maximum height about 3 cm.
U. Cretaceous–Recent.
Rimella fissurella (Lamarck): Eocene, Paris basin, France.

SUPERFAMILY NATICACEA

Globose, smooth, with large body whorl; simple aperture. Triassic–Recent. Infaunal predators, shell borers.

Pl. 6.6.48, 49. *Gyrodes* Conrad, 1860
Low spire, with open umbilicus and globose body whorl; growth lines swept strongly back; row of nodes below suture and (often) at umbilical shoulder; maximum height about 5 cm.
Cretaceous.
Gyrodes supraplicatus (Conrad): Cretaceous, Tennessee, USA.

Pl. 6.6.50. *Polinices* Montfort, 1810
Pear-shaped, final whorl very large; aperture with thick callus in umbilical region; growth lines only; maximum height about 7 cm.
U. Cretaceous–Recent.
Polinices sp.: Palaeocene, Nûgssuaq, W. Greenland.

SUPERFAMILY CYCLOPHORACEA

Mantle cavity modified to functional lung, gill generally lost; generally convex whorls, but low- to high-spired or pupiform; Carboniferous–Recent. Aquatic and terrestrial (Fig. 6.6.2E, p. 102).

SUPERFAMILY TONNACEA

Often large, globose and strongly ornamented, with siphonal canal or notch; aperture often somewhat expanded and thickened.
U. Cretaceous–Recent. Active predators in sand or on rocky shores.

Pl. 6.6.51. *Semicassis* Mörch, 1852
Robust, with thickened outer lip and thick inductura on inner lip; ornament of spiral plications, cords and ribs, nodose, crossed by growth lines; maximum height 10 cm.
U. Cretaceous–Recent.
Semicassis sp.: Oligocene, Jutland, Denmark.

Pl. 6.6.52. *Cassidaria* Lamarck, 1812
Outer lip thickened; siphonal canal well developed; ornament of flat-topped spiral cords with nodes, especially at whorl shoulder; maximum height about 7 cm.
Eocene–Recent.
Cassidaria echinophora (Lamarck): Miocene, Jutland, Denmark.

Pl. 6.6.53. *Ficus* Röding, 1798
Body whorl large to very large, convex, with long siphonal canal; reticulate ornament; maximum height about 10 cm.
Palaeocene–Recent.
Ficus sp.: Palaeocene, Nûgssuaq, W. Greenland.

Pl. 6.6.54. *Ranella* Lamarck, 1816
Spindle-shaped with well-developed siphonal canal; ornament of spiral cords and ribs crossed by growth lines, with periodic varices; maximum height about 6 cm.
Palaeocene–Recent.
Ranella sp.: Palaeocene, Nûgssuaq, W. Greenland.

SUPERFAMILY CYPRAEACEA

Body whorl usually involute, with early whorls covered by globose body whorl; aperture slit-like, with anterior and posterior notches; shell smooth and glossy, more rarely ribbed or pustulose; enveloped by mantle folds during life. U. Cretaceous–Recent. Mainly herbivores, some browse on coelenterates and ascideans.

Pl. 6.6.55. *Cypraea* Linné, 1758
Shell smooth, glossy; aperture commonly with denticles; maximum height about 10 cm, rarely 20 cm.
U. Cretaceous–Recent.
Cypraea sp.: Quaternary, E. Africa.

Pl. 6.6.56. *Cypraedia* Swainson, 1840
As *Cypraea* (Pl. 6.6.55), but ornament reticulate; maximum height 3 cm.
U. Cretaceous–Oligocene.
Cypraedia elegans (Sowerby): Eocene, Paris basin, France.

Plate 6.6.40 Plate 6.6.41 Plate 6.6.42 Plate 6.6.43 Plate 6.6.44 Plate 6.6.45 Plate 6.6.46 Plate 6.6.47 Plate 6.6.48 Plate 6.6.49 Plate 6.6.50 Plate 6.6.52 Plate 6.6.53 Plate 6.6.51 Plate 6.6.54 Plate 6.6.55 Plate 6.6.56 Plate 6.6.57 Plate 6.6.58 Plate 6.6.59

Order Neogastropoda

Prosobranchs with a single (left) monopectinate gill; heart with 1 auricle; sexes separate; mouth and radula at tip of a retractile proboscis; shells conispiral, with siphonal notch or canal. Cretaceous–Recent. Marine, active hunters or scavengers.

SUPERFAMILY MURICACEA

Commonly strongly ornamented with varices, spiral cords and spines; long siphonal canal. Cretaceous–Recent. Commonly shell borers.

Pl. 6.6.57. *Murex* Linné, 1758
Aperture subcircular, with long siphonal canal; periodic spinose varices; reticulate, tuberculate, ornament; maximum height about 10 cm.
Miocene–Recent.
Murex sp.: Quaternary, Mediterranean.

Pl. 6.6.58. *Hexaplex* Perry, 1811
Robust, with prominent lamellar, wrinkled varices; spiral ornament; maximum height about 10 cm.
Eocene–Recent.
Hexaplex sp.: Eocene, Paris basin, France.

SUPERFAMILY BUCCINACEA

Commonly spindle-shaped, or moderately high spired but with few whorls; spiral ornament dominating. U. Cretaceous–Recent. Scavengers or predators.

Pl. 6.6.59. *Neptunea* Röding, 1798.
Body whorl large, convex, with short siphonal canal; usually dextral, but some sinistral species; ornament spiral or reticulate; maximum height about 15 cm.
Eocene–Recent.
Neptunea contraria (Linné): Pliocene–Pleistocene, Essex, England.

Pl. 6.6.60. *Sycostoma* Cox, 1931
Body whorl large, with well-developed siphonal canal; whorls strongly adpressed to previous whorl, commonly producing concave upper whorl surface; smooth, but spiral ribs on base; maximum height about 7 cm.
U. Cretaceous–Oligocene.
Sycostoma pyrus (Solander): U. Eocene, Barton, England.

Pl. 6.6.61. *Clavilithes* Swainson, 1840
Spindle-shaped, with shouldered whorls and long siphonal canal; protoconch swollen; early whorls with varices and reticulate ornamentation; later whorls generally smooth; maximum height about 15 cm.
Palaeocene–Pliocene, Recent (?).
Clavilithes sp.: Eocene, Grignon, France.

Pl. 6.6.62. *Aquilofusus* Kautsky, 1925
Whorls convex; with robust siphonal canal; ornament generally of spiral ribs; maximum height about 8 cm.
Oligocene–Miocene.
Aquilofusus semiglaber (Beyrich): U. Miocene, Jutland, Denmark.

Pl. 6.6.63. *Fusinus* Rafinesque, 1815
Shell commonly slender; whorls convex, siphonal canal very long; ornament of varices crossed by spiral cords; maximum height about 15 cm.
U. Cretaceous–Recent.
Fusinus asper (Sowerby): U. Eocene, Barton, England.

SUPERFAMILY VOLUTACEA

Conispiral, robust, with large body whorl; commonly with elongate aperture with columellar folds and well-developed siphonal canal or notch; ornament generally of growth lines with nodes or varices on whorl shoulder; cancellate in some. U. Cretaceous–Recent.

Pl. 6.6.64. *Ancilla* Lamarck, 1799
Spindle-shaped with conical spire and large body whorl; aperture elongate with broad siphonal notch and narrow channel at suture; glossy with fine growth lines; maximum height about 5 cm.
U. Cretaceous–Recent.
Ancilla sp.: Miocene, Bordeaux, France.

Pl. 6.6.65. *Liopeplum* Dall, 1890
Step-like whorl profile, adpressed, with nodes at shoulder; aperture elongate, with siphonal notch; maximum height about 5 cm.
U. Cretaceous.
Liopeplum sp.: U. Cretaceous, Tennessee, USA.

Pl. 6.6.66. *Voluta* Linné, 1758
Robust with prominent pointed varices; thick inductura with 4 or 5 columellar folds; ornament of spiral cords crossed by growth lines; maximum height about 12 cm.
Eocene–Recent.
Voluta musicalis (Lamarck): M. Eocene, Grignon, France.

Pl. 6.6.67, 68. *Volutispina* Newton, 1906
Resembles *Voluta* (Pl. 6.6.66) but has 1 strong and several weak folds on the columellar; ornament of spiral cords with pointed varices at whorl shoulder and commonly subsutural nodes; maximum height about 12 cm.
U. Cretaceous–Recent.
Volutispina sp.: U. Eocene, Barton, England.

Pl. 6.6.69. *Volutocorbis* Dall, 1890
Whorls more rounded than *Voluta* (Pl. 6.6.66) or *Volutispina* (Pl. 6.6.67, 68); elongate aperture with numerous denticles inside outer lip and only a few columellar folds; ornament of spiral ridges and varices; maximum height about 5 cm.
U. Cretaceous–Recent.
Volutocorbis ambigua (Solander): U. Eocene, Barton, England.

Pl. 6.6.70. *Tudicla* Adams & Adams, 1863
Whorl profile equidimensional, with flattened upper whorl surface producing conical spire; siphonal canal long, narrow; 2 rows of nodes on outer whorl; obscure reticulate ornament; maximum height about 10 cm.
U. Cretaceous—Recent.
Tudicla rusticula (Basterot): Miocene, Hungary.

Pl. 6.6.71. *Cancellaria* Lamarck, 1799
Globose, with convex whorls and rounded aperture; siphonal notch short, but deep, producing a strong siphonal fold or fasciole; 3 columellar folds and numerous spiral folds inside outer lip; nodose, reticulate ornament; maximum height about 5 cm.
Eocene–Recent.
Cancellaria sp.: Tertiary, Italy.

SUPERFAMILY MITRACEA

Conispiral, spindle-shaped, slender, commonly high-spired with few whorls; well-developed siphonal notch; inner lip with columellar folds. Palaeocene–Recent.

Pl. 6.6.72. *Mitra* Martyn, 1784
Robust; nodose, reticulate ornament, or smooth and glossy; maximum height about 10 cm.
Eocene–Recent.
Mitra scrobiculata Brocchi: Miocene, Lapugy, Hungary.

SUPERFAMILY CONACEA

Conispiral, spindle-shaped, high-spired or biconical; aperture tear-shaped to elongate, with well-developed siphonal notch; columellar folds usually absent. U. Cretaceous–Recent. Active predators.

Pl. 6.6.73. *Terebra* Bruguière, 1789
High spired, robust, with curved siphonal notch producing siphonal fold; ornament of transverse cords or growth lines, with occasional spiral cords or grooves; maximum height about 15 cm.
U. Cretaceous–Recent. Active infaunal predator on annelids.
Terebra sp.: Tertiary, Hungary.

Pl. 6.6.74. *Conus* Linné, 1758
Biconical, with large body whorl; aperture narrow, with siphonal and subsutural notches; ornament of growth lines, but some

with spiral ribs or nodes at whorl shoulder; maximum height about 12 cm.
U. Cretaceous–Recent. Active predator, striking annelids, opisthobranchs or even small fish with poisoned radular tooth.
Conus edwardsi (Cossmann): Eocene, England.

Pl. 6.6.75. *Turris* Röding, 1798
Spindle-shaped, high-spired, with few whorls; robust siphonal canal; commonly with notch at peripheral angulation; ornament of spiral cords and ribs crossed by growth lines; maximum height about 10 cm.
Palaeocene–Recent.
Turris sp.: Palaeocene, Nûgssuaq, W. Greenland.

Pl. 6.6.76. *Clinura* Bellardi, 1875
Step-like profile, with tuberculate periphery; maximum length about 4 cm.
Palaeocene–Recent.
Clinura sp.: Palaeocene, Nûgssuaq, W. Greenland.

Subclass Opisthobranchia

Usually strongly detorted, shell often concealed in mantle or absent; mantle cavity commonly posterior or absent; 1 internal gill or, in shell-less forms, with external gills or gill-like outgrowths (= cerata). L. Carboniferous–Recent. Twelve orders of opisthobranchs are recognized; half of these lack a shell and have no fossil record. Mainly benthic carnivores or herbivores; some pelagic predators or ciliary feeders.

Order Entomotaeniata

High-spired, with many whorls; smooth to heavily ornamented; with or without siphonal notch. Jurassic–Recent. Recent representatives are ectoparasites.

SUPERFAMILY NERINEACEA

High- to very high-spired, with many whorls; often with concave upper whorl surface; smooth to strongly ornamented; shell interior with spiral folds which may considerably constrict living space. Jurassic–Cretaceous.

Pl. 6.6.77. *Nerinea* Deshayes, 1827
Robust, concave outer whorl face passing angularly on to flattened base; aperture with short siphonal canal and prominent folds on columellar, parietal and outer whorl regions; growth lines only; maximum height about 20 cm.
L. Jurassic–U. Cretaceous.
Nerinea tuberculosa Deshayes: Jurassic, France.

Pl. 6.6.78. *Trochalia* Sharpe, 1850
Many whorls, spire relatively wide with flat sides; umbilicus wide; aperture rhomboid, with a single spiral fold on parietal region protruding into whorl interior; ornament of spiral cords; maximum height about 20 cm.
M. Jurassic–U. Cretaceous.
Trochalia sp.: cross-section, Jurassic, France.

Order Cephalaspidea

Conispiral, with large body whorl, or involute. Carboniferous–Recent. Commonly infaunal carnivores.

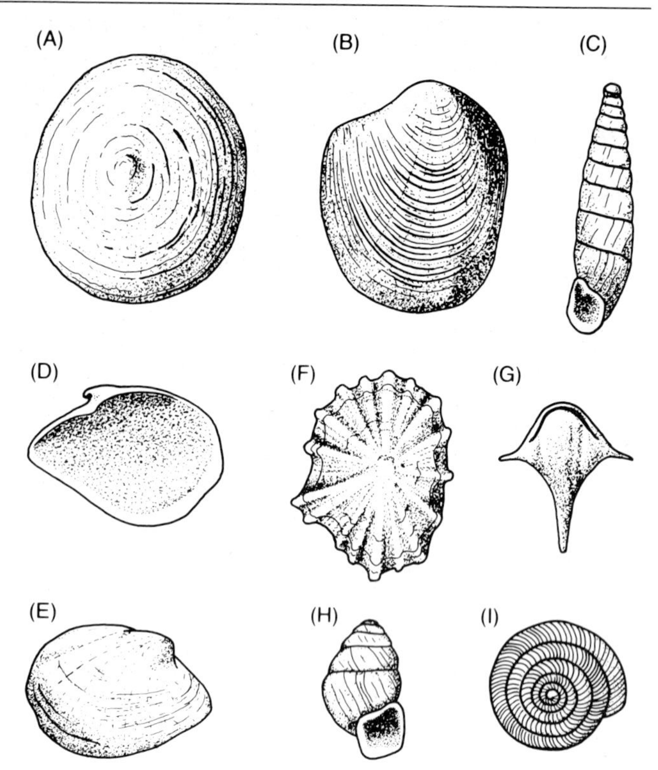

Fig. 6.6.3. Opisthobranch and pulmonate gastropod morphologies. (A) *Umbraculum* Schumacher, 1817 (Eocene–Recent); (B) *Aplysia* Linné, 1767 (Recent); (C) *Clausilia* Draparnaud, 1805 (Pliocene–Recent); (D, E) *Berthelinia* Crosse, 1875 (Miocene–Recent); (F) *Siphonaria* Sowerby, 1823 (U. Cretaceous–Recent); (G) *Diacria* Gray, 1842 (Miocene–Recent); (H) *Gonidomus* Swainson, 1840 (Pleistocene–Recent); (I) *Discus* Albers, 1850 (Pleistocene–Recent).

Pl. 6.6.79. *Bulla* Linné, 1758
Involute, globose, thin-shelled; glossy, with fine growth lines; maximum height about 4 cm.
U. Jurassic–Recent.
Bulla sp.: Palaeocene, Nûgssuaq, W. Greenland.

Pl. 6.6.80. *Cylichna* Lovén, 1846
As *Bulla* (Pl. 6.6.79), but slender with spiral ribs; maximum height about 2 cm.
U. Cretaceous–Recent.
Cylichna sp.: Palaeocene, Nûgssuaq, W. Greenland.

Order Notaspidea

Shell cap-shaped (Fig. 6.6.3A), redundant, but sometimes large (8 cm). Eocene–Recent. Browse on sponges or scavengers.

Order Anaspidea

Shell generally reduced to internal plate (Fig. 6.6.3B), or absent. Jurassic–Recent. Browsing herbivores.

Order Sacoglossa

Small, with or without shell; the latter may be bivalved (Fig. 6.6.3D, E). Eocene–Recent. Selective herbivores.

Plate 6.6.76

Plate 6.6.77

Plate 6.6.78

Plate 6.6.79

Plate 6.6.80

Plate 6.6.81

Plate 6.6.82

Plate 6.6.83

Order Thecosomata

Pelagic, shell small, coiled, cone-shaped or tubular (Fig. 6.6.3G). Eocene–Recent. Pelagic ciliary feeders.

Subclass Pulmonata

Detorted gastropods in which mantle cavity is converted to an air-breathing lung; shell commonly conispiral but reduced and internal in terrestrial slugs; internal fertilization, generally hermaphroditic. Carboniferous (?), Jurassic–Recent.

Order Basommatophora

Head with a single pair of tentacles with an eye at base of each; conispiral, rarely cap-shaped (Fig. 6.6.3F, p. 112); aquatic or marine. Carboniferous(?), Jurassic–Recent. Generally browsing or selective herbivores.

Pl. 6.6.81. *Galba* Schrank, 1803
Slender, thin-shelled with simple aperture and convex whorls; ornament of fine growth lines only; maximum height about 7 cm.
U. Jurassic–Recent, freshwater.
Galba longiscata (Brongniart): Eocene, Isle of White, England.

Pl. 6.6.82. *Planorbis* Müller, 1774
Sinistral, almost planispiral, with wide umbilicus; ornament of growth lines only; maximum width about 4 cm.
Oligocene–Recent, freshwater.
Planorbis sp.: Tertiary, France.

Order Stylommatophora

Head with 2 pairs of tentacles, with eyes located at the tips of the second pair; conispiral, high- to low-spired (Fig. 6.6.3C, H, I, p. 112), shell reduced and internal in slugs. Cretaceous–Recent. Terrestrial herbivores, scavengers, hunters.

Pl. 6.6.83. *Helix* Linné, 1758
Conispiral, with 4 or 5 globose whorls; shell thin, with growth lines only; maximum height about 5 cm.
Miocene–Recent.
Helix sp.: Quaternary, Austria.

6.7 Class Cephalopoda

Cephalopods first appear in the fossil record in the late Cambrian and thereafter they have formed an important element in marine waters to the present day. The novelty which gave the group their initial success was simply achieved from their ancestral benthonic molluscan ancestors. By partitioning the apex of the shell, and trapping gas linked to vascular tissue within it, the early forms became positively buoyant and then had the potential to join the active nekton as roaming scavengers and carnivores. They became free from the sea-bottom habit which still predominates among other groups of the Mollusca. The mantle cavity became modified to serve not only a respiratory but also a propulsive role with the development of a hyponome or funnel capable of directing exhalant water and giving jet propulsion.

Associated with the tactile and sensory needs of the new life style the ancestral 'foot' developed as a sensory head with tentacles and with the most highly developed nervous system known among invertebrates. Most remarkable was the development of paired simple eyes closely homoeomorphic with those of the vertebrates.

Early elaboration of the partitioned cone (phragmocone) and body chamber gave rise to the groups historically known as the 'nautiloids' and ammonoids. These retained the external shell of their ancestors and are hence grouped as the Ectocochlea, the earlier term Tetrabranchiata having fallen into disfavour since only *Nautilus* of this group survives and gill number is not known in fossil forms.

A second major novelty arose (certainly by the Carboniferous) when the shell became partly or wholly enclosed in soft tissue giving the group Endocochlea or Coleoidea, formerly Dibranchiata. The group includes the now extinct belemnitids and the common living groups, the sepiids, teuthids and octopodids. Figure 6.7.1 shows the range of the major cephalopod groups and indicates their chief characteristics.

How wide a range of life habit has been encompassed by the Cephalopoda will remain uncertain. They seem restricted to fully marine waters. Not all are actively nektonic and some are benthonic, but never sessile. In size the group ranges from minute orthocones and micromorphic ammonoids less than 1 cm to the giant living *Architeuthis*, 20 m in length, and actinoceratoids such as *Rayonnoceras* which, with soft tissue, may have exceeded that. Diet of modern forms is almost wholly carnivorous, but with the recognition of widespread radulae in fossil forms a herbivorous diet is possible, and bizarre constricted forms with minute aperture may have been microphagous.

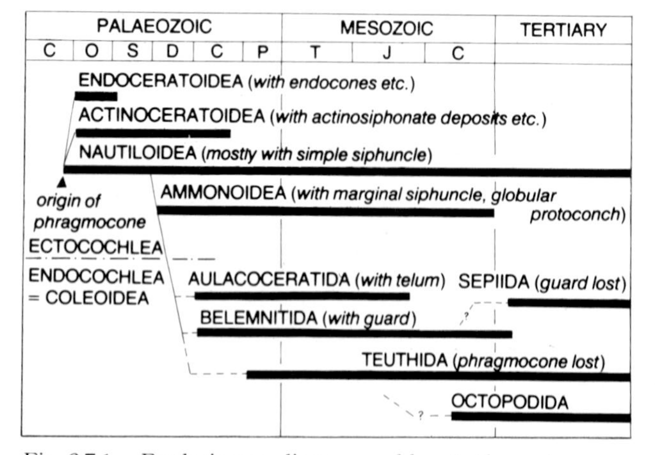

Fig. 6.7.1. Evolutionary diagram and key to the main groups of the Cephalopoda.

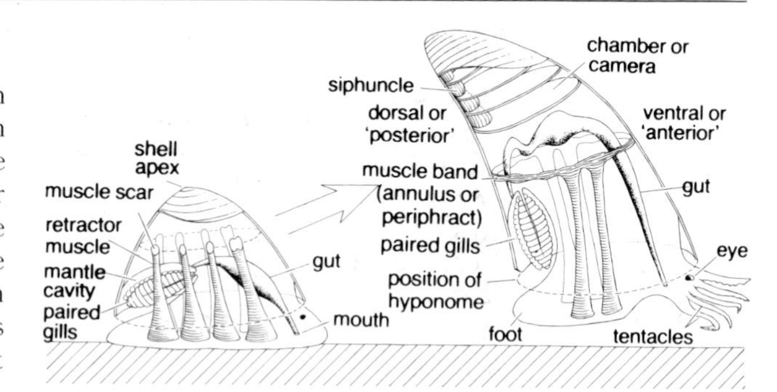

Fig. 6.7.2. Diagram illustrating the possible derivation of an early cephalopod mollusc from a benthonic monoplacophoran and illustrating the development of a chambered shell with a siphuncle, a reduction in retractor muscles, the adoption of a complex head region and the formation of a shell sinus associated with the hyponome, all features which characterize the cephalopods. (Modified from Yochelson and Holland.)

Some modern squids live at depths in excess of 2000 m, but they have lost the chambered shell. Tests have shown that the shell of *Nautilus* would implode by 800 m depth and that of *Spirula* by 2000 m. Unless chambers could become liquid-filled, implosion would give a limiting depth. But the teuthids and vampyromorphs have lost the phragmocone altogether. The ammoniacal squids have developed a quite different buoyancy mechanism using changes in body liquid density.

The young develop in an egg capsule from which they break free to commence active life and an adult-type feeding mode. Modern forms, on hatching, are provided with arms, large eyes and a functional ink sac. The immediate post-hatching habit is benthonic in living nautiloids and octopodids and nektobenthonic in *Sepia*, but in other groups is planktonic.

In shelled forms, the earliest stages are seen in the initial chamber or protoconch which may be cap-shaped or subglobular in most 'nautiloids' and egg-shaped in ammonoids and belemnitids. Growth continues in some cases for well over a whorl before hatching, but that event is often marked on the shell by a varix or nepionic constriction: this early stage is termed the ammonitella in ammonoids. Both the early and later shell is aragonitic, the adult shell is usually divisible into ostracum, hypostracum and thin resistant and camouflaged periostracum layers, but there are variants. Septa are laid down by the posterior part of the body chamber, a liquid-filled space being formed by forward movement of the body; the liquid is then readsorbed by the siphuncle vascular tissue. Both septa and siphuncular structures are hence secondary to the formation of the ostracum. In the endocochleate belemnitids the calcitic guard is formed on top of the phragmocone. Projecting sheet-like supports in teuthids and others are usually chitinophosphatic and are termed proostraca. The plate-like anaptychi and some aptychi are also chitinous but most aptychi are calcareous: these together with rhyncholite structures comprise the lower and upper jaws. Many adult shells are dimorphic, with microconch and macroconch forms. Dimorphism is most strongly developed in certain ammonoid and teuthid groups. In living teuthids the larger is the female.

Interesting reviews of modern cephalopods are given by Lane (1959) and Cousteau and Diolé (1973). The standard reviews for fossil forms are given in the *Treatise on Invertebrate Paleontology*, Part K for 'nautiloids' (Teichert *et al.* 1964) and Part L for ammonoids (Arkell *et al.* 1957). *The Ammonoidea* (House and Senior 1981) gives a modern review by many specialists of that group. The standard Russian treatises are Ruzhencev (1962a) and Lippov and Drushchitz (1958).

Origins of the Cephalopoda

Supposed cephalopods in the early Cambrian such as *Volborthella* and *Salterella* have now been shown not to have cephalopodan septa or siphuncles and are placed in a new enigmatic Phylum Agmata (Yochelson 1977). The earliest undoubted cephalopods are from the uppermost Cambrian (Holland 1979; Yochelson, Flower and Webers 1973) and are placed in the Ellesmerocerida. These will be commented on later. Ancestors for the cephalopods have been sought in the limpet-like monoplacophorans. A plausible intermediate is *Knightoconus* (Yochelson, Flower and Webers 1973) a septate monoplacophoran from the late Cambrian preceding the entry of the Ellesmerocerida. A possible transformation is indicated in Fig. 6.7.2. It is the development of the siphuncle, and extension of living tissue into the chambers which is the critical cephalopodan feature, and the corresponding hole in the septum is a clear morphological indication of this. In functional terms, the change in the role of the foot and mantle cavity and the assumption of jet propulsion are critical. Presumably the early forms would have had detritus feeding or herbivorous habits little different from their ancestors. More active life will have brought demands for a more efficient respiratory mechanism which would have been met by increased use of the gills and also in an enhanced circulatory system leading, in living coleoids, to branchial hearts and capillary circulation.

Primary radiation of the cephalopod chambered shell

Starting with stimulating essays by Flower (1955), Donovan (1964) and Tiechert (1967), it has been recognized that buoyancy achieved by gas in a chambered phragmocone would bring with it major problems of *poise*. Many of the diverse shell patterns used to give the older taxonomic divisions are now recognized as functional adaptations overcoming these problems in different ways. Many of these are illustrated in Fig. 6.7.3. Weighting to give convenient poise was achieved by several means: by enlarging the siphuncle and including cone-like calcareous structures within it (the Endoceratoidea, Fig. 6.7.3B); by elaborate beaded siphuncles and cameral tissue (the Actinoceratoidea, Fig. 6.7.3C); by close-set septa (many groups); by retaining liquid in chambers (Fig. 6.7.3D), probably shown in many groups); by cameral tissue (Actinoceratoidea, Orthocerida (Fig. 6.7.3E), Discosorida, some Belemnoidea); by changing the relative lengths of phragmocone and body chambers (many groups); by extending the phragmocone over the body chamber (Ascocerida, Fig. 6.7.3F, Sepiodea); by dehiscing the apical part of the phragmocone (some Ascocerida, rare Orthocerida, Fig. 6.7.3G); by very breviconic shells (many Oncoceratida, etc. (Fig. 6.7.3I); by endogastric coiling (many groups, Fig. 6.7.3H); by exogastric coiling (many groups, Fig. 6.7.3J, K, M, O); by torticonic coiling (many Nautilida and Ammonoidea, Fig. 6.7.3L, N) and by other methods. Some of the terminology related to calcareous deposits in the phragmocone is indicated in Fig. 6.7.4. In the belemnitids, among endocochleate forms, the guard is a calcitic weighting structure formed on top of the phragmocone.

Following fundamental work on buoyancy control methods in living cephalopods by Denton and Gilpin Brown (reviewed by Denton 1974) it is now appreciated that the ability to alter amounts of liquid in the phragmocone chambers provides a mechanism for altering density and hence equilibrium level in the water column without the use of propulsive energy. Such adaptations may be termed *hydrostatic* adaptations. Changes in osmotic pressure contrast between liquid in the chambers and in the siphuncular vessels is the means of effecting transfer.

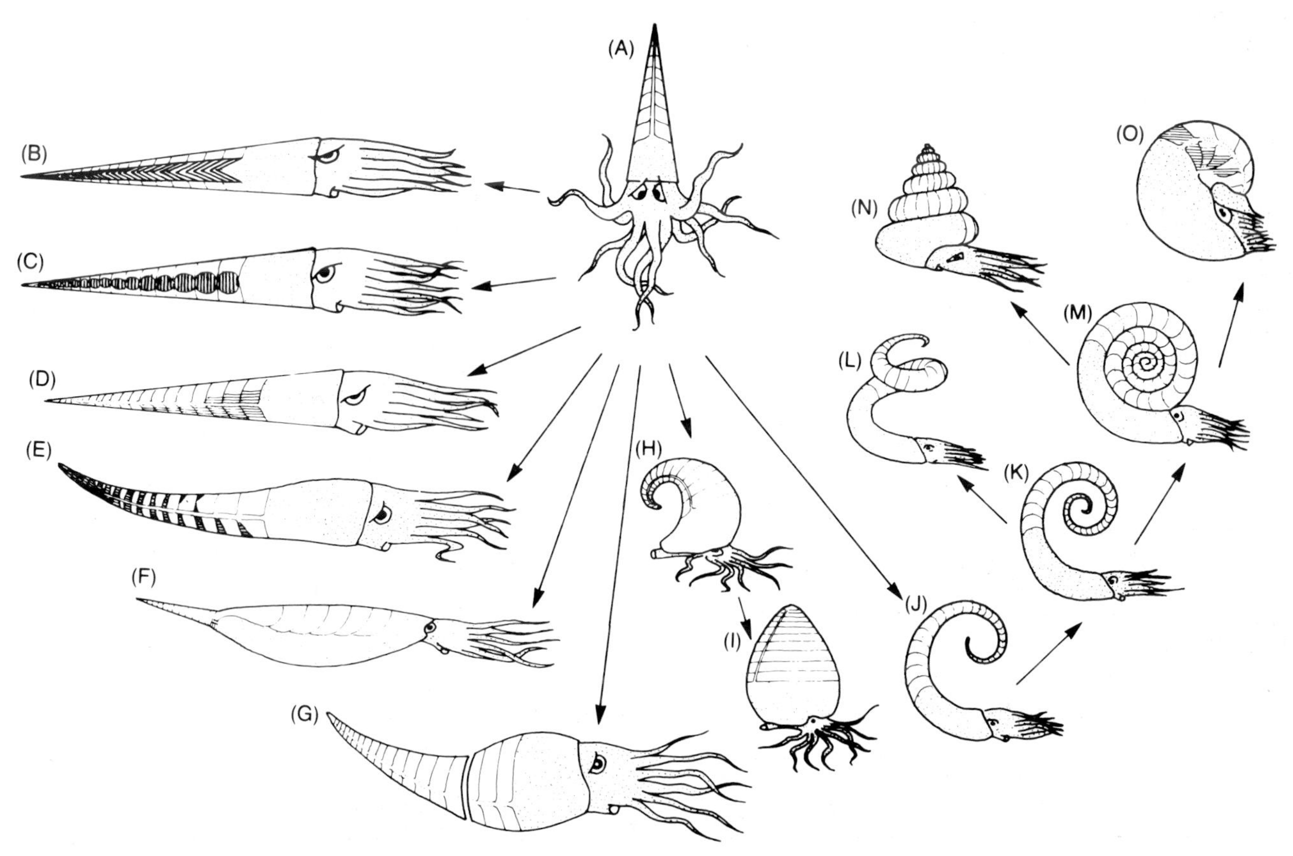

Fig. 6.7.3. A diagram illustrating some of the variety of shell form adopted by the Cephalopoda as a response to problems of buoyancy and poise. For details see text. (Modified from House.)

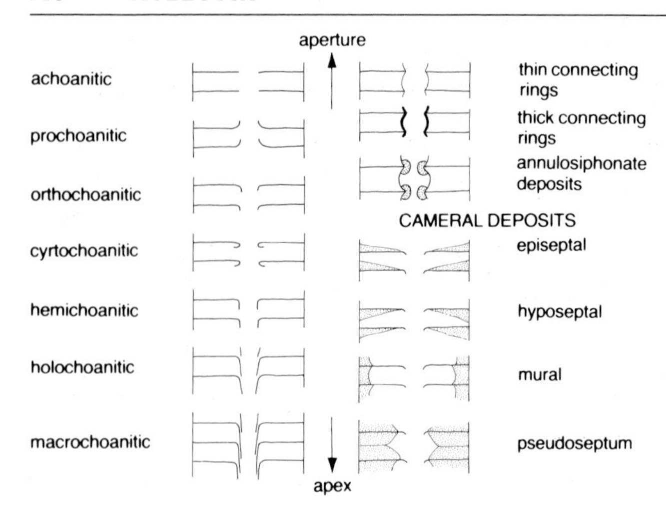

Fig. 6.7.4. Terminology for the siphuncle, septal necks and cameral deposits of early cephalopods. Siphuncle orientation vertical.

Recognition of this in fossil forms will always be somewhat speculative, but vertical migration is so important a feature of living cephalopods (except Octopodida) that it may have been equally important in the past.

Modern chambered cephalopods often show techniques to delay liquid transfer, facilitating short-term forays into other water levels without establishing longer-term equilibrium. These are *hysteresis* adaptations. Close-set septa (as in *Sepia*) or the development of extensive septal necks along the siphuncle (as in many nautiloids and in the Belemnitida) seem to be adaptations of this type (the morphological terminology relating to siphuncular necks is illustrated in Fig. 6.7.4). Septal folding, by isolating liquid in pockets in the chambers and limiting contact with the siphuncle may also be such an adaptation.

6.7.1 Subclass Nautiloidea

As now restricted, this subclass comprises ectocochleate cephalopods with a wide diversity of shell form, phragmocone and apertural type, but excluding forms with spectacular endosiphonate deposits (the Endoceratoidea and Actinoceratoidea) which were formerly included within it. The Ammonoidea, the remaining ectocochleate group, is exclusively exogastric and usually develops complex folded septa never seen to such extremes in the Nautiloidea.

The primary radiation of the Nautiloidea from its stock-group the Ellesmerocerida is shown in Fig. 6.7.5 which illustrates how most orders were established and became diversified in the early Ordovician, the orders then surviving for various lengths of time. As has already been indicated, the nautiloid orders may be seen as representing different structural ways in which the problems of buoyancy could be overcome, but much of the detailed diversity in shell type and ornament which cannot be well illustrated here must be related to the usual types of adaptations to a wide range of different ecological niches. Dzik (1984) has reviewed nautiloid phylogeny.

Nautilus pompilius (the Pearly Nautilus), and several other living species are the sole surviving members of the subclass. The major structural features and terminology of both shell and soft parts of *N. pompilius* are illustrated in Fig. 6.7.6.

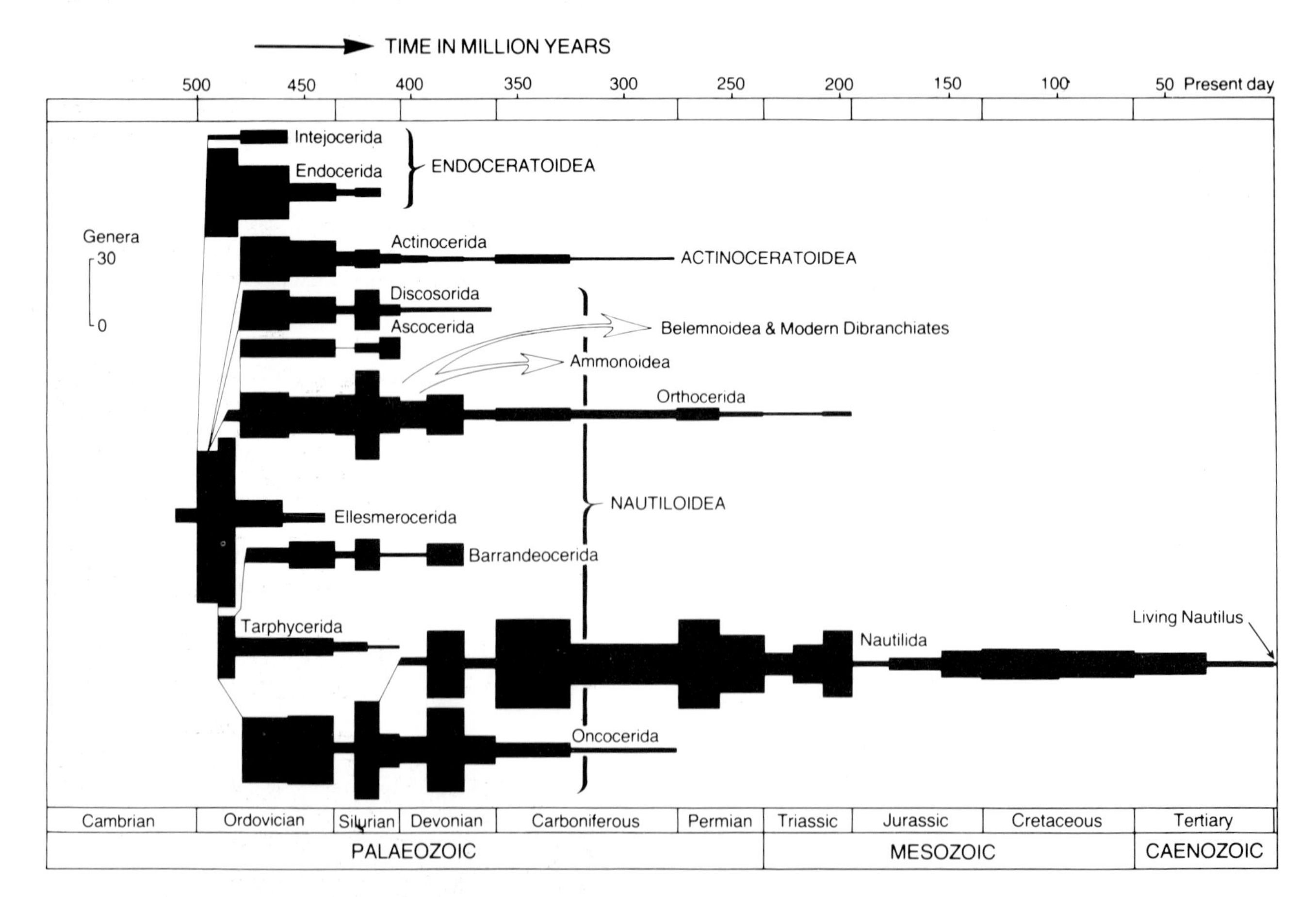

Fig. 6.7.5. A possible evolutionary tree for the endoceratoids, actinoceratoids and nautiloids. The width of the bars corresponds to the number of genera known at the particular time. (Modified from House.)

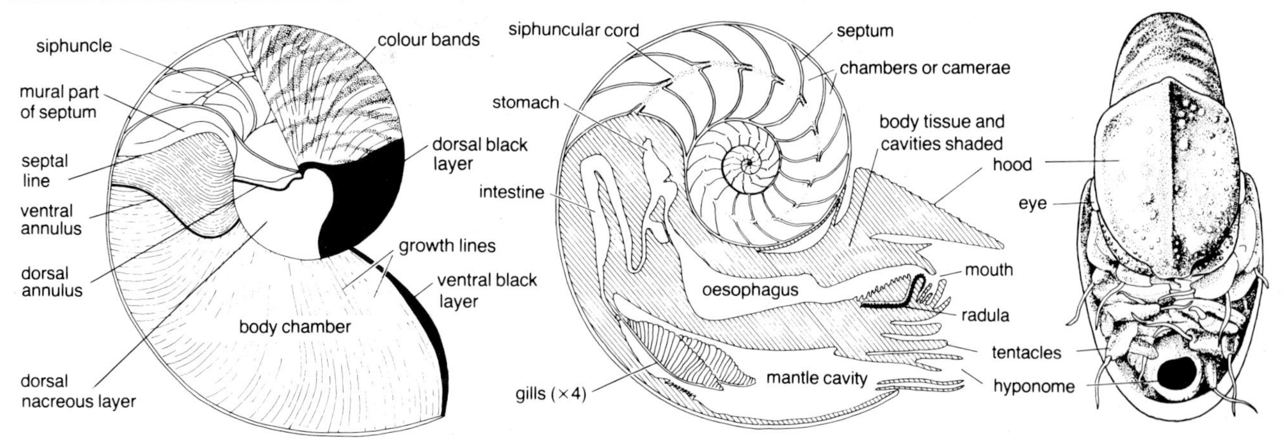

Fig. 6.7.6. The living nautilus, *Nautilus pompilius* Linné. Diagrams illustrating the form and terminology of the shell and the disposition of soft parts.

Order Ellesmerocerida

This basic group of chambered nautiloids occurs in the late Cambrian and Ordovician, possibly extending into the Silurian. It comprises minute to large forms, early members of which tend to be closely septate endogastric cyrtocones with marginal siphuncles; later members include orthocones and exogastric cyrtocones. The siphuncle is distinctive in showing transverse diaphragms, but these have not been recorded in all genera included.

Pl. 6.7.1A, B. *Ellesmeroceras* Foerste, 1921
Orthocones of circular cross-section with ventral siphuncle, thick connecting rings, and diaphragms crossing apical part of siphuncle. Phragmocone short. Suture with lateral lobe.
L. Ordovician. N. America and Asia.
A, B. *Ellesmeroceras* sp. Diagram illustrating shell form and showing diaphragms crossing siphuncle (length 15 cm). (After Flower 1964.)

Pl. 6.7.1C, D. *Plectronoceras* Ulrich & Foerste, 1933
Suborthoconic and endogastric cyrtocones moderately expanding with ventral siphuncle and orthochoanitic to cyrtochoanitic septal necks and tenuous connecting rings, sometimes bulb-like. Suture with lateral lobe. Diaphragms reported in related genera.
U. Cambrian. Asia and N. America.
C, D. *Plectronoceras cambria* (Walcott) showing phragmocone form and reconstruction of apex and aperture (at length *c.* 22 cm). (After Teichert *et al.* 1964.) Pl. 6.7.1F. A reconstruction of life poise showing endogastric coiling.

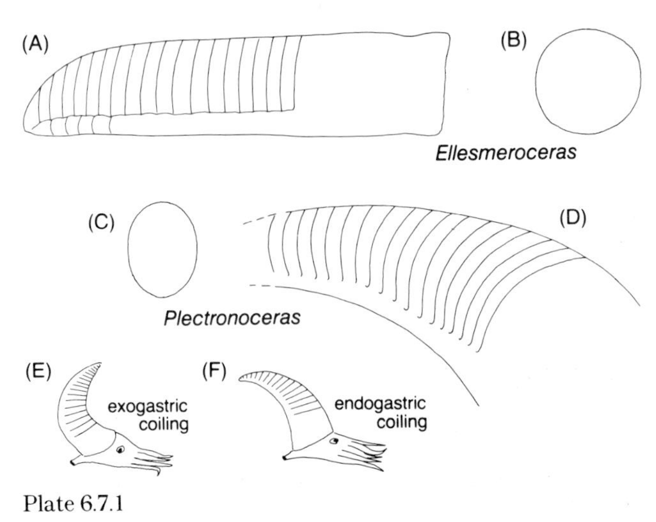

Plate 6.7.1

Order Orthocerida

Straight orthocones or very slightly curved with circular cross-section. Siphuncle central to marginal. Orthochoanitic to cyrtochoanitic with thick connecting rings. Chambers often with cameral tissue. Surface often elaborately ornamented. Thought to be derived from the Ellesmerocerida and surviving into the Trias. A bizarre member, the U. Carboniferous *Brachycycloceras*, with dehiscent early stages is illustrated in Fig. 6.7.3G.

Pl. 6.7.2A, B. *Orthoceras* Bruguière, 1789
Slightly expanding, subcylindrical orthocones. Subcentral siphuncle; orthochoanitic. Body chamber with transverse constriction. Surface ornamented with fine lirae. Reaching several metres in length.
L. Ordovician–U. Triassic. Cosmopolitan.
A, B. *Orthoceras* sp. Longitudinal section of incomplete specimen showing partial section of central siphuncle (length 3.2 cm) and an enlargement showing cameral deposits. (From Fischer and Teichert 1969.)

Pl. 6.7.2C, D. *Pseudorthoceras* Girty, 1911
Orthocones with slight exogastric curvature at apex with central or subcentral siphuncle. Suborthochoanitic to cyrtochoanitic progressively during growth. Siphuncle lined with

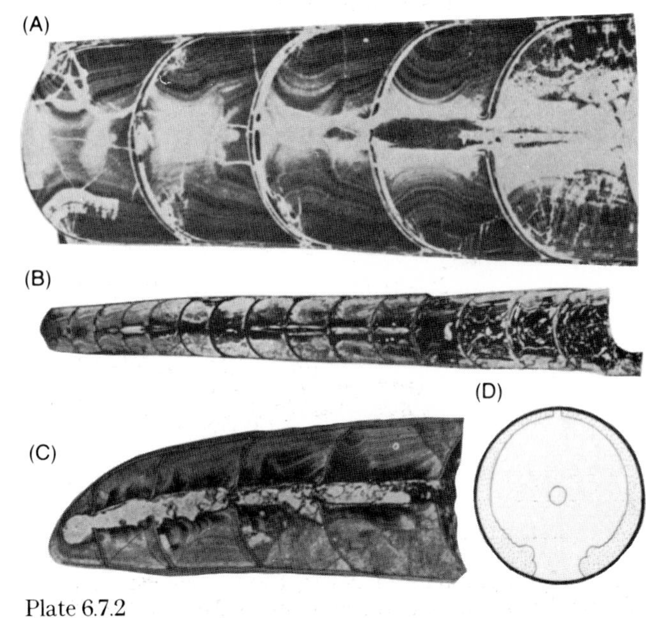

Plate 6.7.2

endosiphuncular tissue. Mural cameral tissue well developed to give ventral weighting and often with deposits around siphuncle (circuli).
U. Devonian–L. Permian. Cosmopolitan.
C, D. *Pseudorthoceras knoxense* (McChesney): U. Carboniferous, Oklahoma, USA. Longitudinal section showing exogastric apical tip and reconstruction showing deposits within a single chamber. (After Fischer and Teichert 1969.)

Order Ascocerida

A bizarre Ordovician and Silurian group in which mature phragmocone chambers may be dorsally placed over the body chamber and in which the apex is truncated, in some by dehiscence. The adult siphuncle segments may be button-shaped. The adult is often an expanded exogastric brevicone but the early stages are usually cyrtoconic.

Pl. 6.7.3A, B. *Parascoceras* Miller, 1932
Early orthoconic shell deciduous with ventrally placed siphuncle. Adult subcylindrical with ascoceroid chambers over body chamber.
U. Silurian. Europe.
A, B. *Parascoceras fistula* (Lindström): Sweden. Reconstruction of body chamber and mature phragmocone (length 5.5 cm). (After Teichert *et al.* 1964.) Fig. 6.7.3 F, poise reconstruction loosely based on species.

Pl. 6.7.3C, D. *Billingsites* Hyatt, 1884
Inflated, egg-shaped adult shell with extreme ascoceroid chamber over body chamber.
U. Ordovician, Europe and N. America.
C, D. *Billingsites canadensis* (Billings): U. Ordovician. Canada. Length 5.8 cm. Side view (after Teichert *et al.* 1964) and reconstruction of poise in life.

Order Oncocerida

A range of shell forms derived from primitive exogastric cyrtocones and brevicones leading to orthocones, gyrocones and nautiliconic shells, but especially distinctive brevicones with restricted apertures (Fig. 6.7.3I). Often with radial lamellae within the siphuncle. The group ranges from the M. Ordovician to Permian.

Pl. 6.7.4A, B. *Gomphoceras* Sowerby, 1839
Egg-shaped faintly endogastric brevicones. Aperture with ventral slit and smaller ovoid opening thought to be hyponomic sinus. Affinities uncertain.
Silurian, England, Europe.

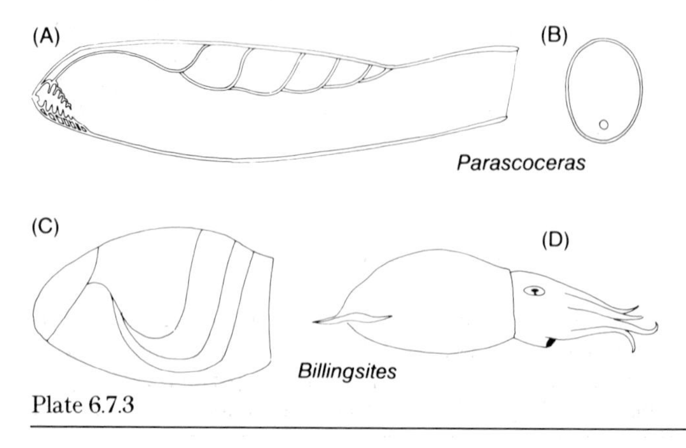

Plate 6.7.3

A, B. *Gomphoceras pyriforme* (Sowerby): Ludlovian, England. Side and apertural view. Length 9.2 cm. (After Teichert *et al.* 1964.)

Pl. 6.7.4C, D. *Tetrameroceras* Hyatt, 1884
Endogastric brevicones with inflated body chamber with visored aperture with a long, slit-like hyponomic sinus and 2 pairs of sinuses in the main aperture.
Silurian, Europe and N. America.
C, D. *Tetrameroceras bicinctum* (Barrande): Silurian. Czechoslovakia. Incomplete side view and apertural view. Length 5.5 cm. (After Teichert *et al.* 1964.)

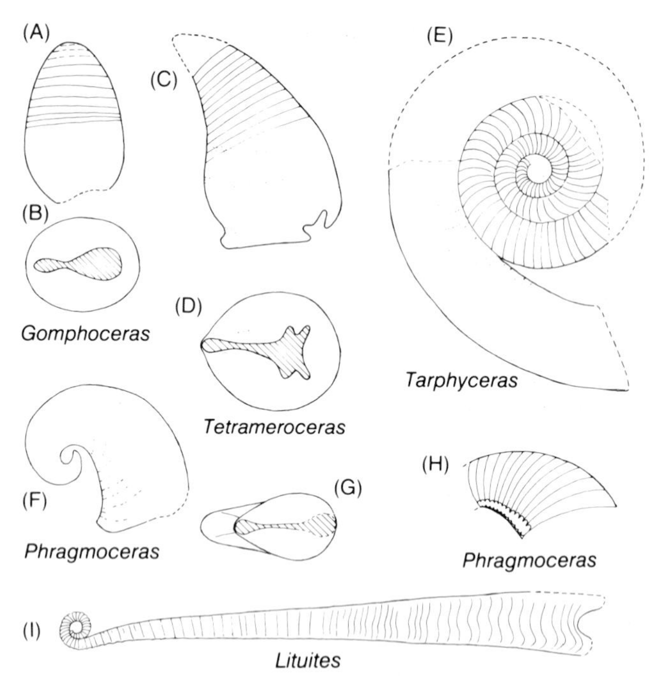

Plate 6.7.4

Order Discosorida

Mostly endogastric brevicones, breviconic cyrtocones or orthocones often with constricted aperture and often homoeomorphic with Oncoceratida. Siphuncle beaded with expanded segments and with thick connecting rings. Endosiphuncular deposits in some.

Pl. 6.7.4F–H. *Phragmoceras* Broderip, 1839
Endogastric rapidly expanding cyrtocone with constricted aperture with long slit leading to small ovate hyponomic sinus. Siphuncle ventral with broadly expanded segments.
Silurian. Europe and N. America.
F, G. *Phragmoceras lamellosum* Hedström: Silurian. Sweden. Length 12.2 cm. H. *P. farcimen* Hedström: Silurian. Sweden. Section showing siphuncle structure (after Teichert *et al.* 1964).

Order Tarphycerida

The main group of early coiled cephalopods. Generally with loosely evolute planispiral coiled shell from which the mature body chamber often diverges. Siphuncle position variable. Aperture with well-developed sinuses. A cosmopolitan Ordovician and Silurian group.

Pl. 6.7.4E. *Tarphyceras* Hyatt, 1894
Moderately expanding planispire with rounded whorls often

impressed dorsally. Orad part of adult body chamber uncoiling. Siphuncle central or subcentral.
L. Ordovician. America.
E. *Tarphyceras* sp.: Ordovician, Missouri, USA. Reconstruction based on *T. chadwickense*. Diameter 12.8 cm. (After Teichert *et al.* 1964.)

Pl. 6.7.4I. *Lituites* Bertrand, 1763
Loosely coiled spiral early part with elongated suborthoconic later phragmocone and body chamber. Aperture with lappets. Siphuncle subdorsal; chambers with cameral deposits.
M. Ordovician. Europe.
I. *Lituites lituus* (Modeer). Probably from Ordovician of Sweden. Length 35 cm. (After Teichert *et al.* 1964.)

Order Barrandeocerida

Early forms serpenticonic, later producing cyrtocones, gyrocones and torticones. Later forms often cyrtochoanitic with inflated segments. Often strongly ornamented, especially in early stages: aperture simple. Without cameral or endosiphonate deposits.

Pl. 6.7.5D. *Bickmorites* Foerste, 1925
Slender gyrocone with mature straightening in body chamber. Prominent oblique ribs following growth lines and forming a ventral hyponomic sinus.
U. Ordovician–M. Silurian. Europe and North America, USA.
D. *Bickmorites bickmoreanus* (Whitfield): Silurian. Indiana, USA. Diameter 18 cm. (From Teichert *et al.* 1964.)

Order Nautilida

Curved to coiled shells often with ribs, nodes, spines and spiral ornament. Siphuncle variable in position. Without cameral or endosiphonate deposits. Cosmopolitan, L. Devonian–Recent. *Nautilus* is the only living representative.

Pl. 6.7.5A–C. *Vestinautilus* Ryckolt, 1852
Evolute, whorls in contact in middle stages. Large perforate umbilicus. Shell with prominent spiral ridges often lost at maturity. Siphuncle subcentral. Suture often with ventral, lateral and dorsal lobes.
L. Carboniferous. Europe, N. America.
A–C. *Vestinautilus konincki* (d'Orbigny): L. Carboniferous. Belgium. Diameter 6.8 cm. (From Teichert *et al.* 1964.)

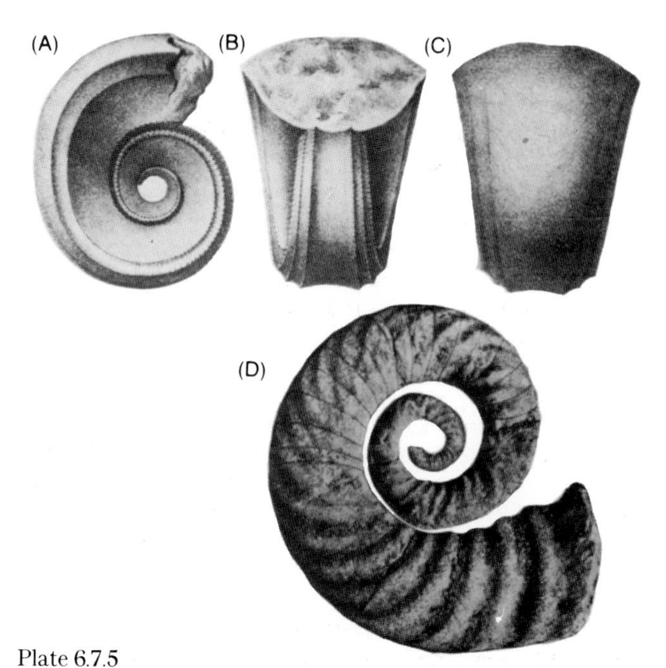

Plate 6.7.5

Tylonautilus Pringe & Jackson, 1928
Evolute with subquadrate whorl section and 3 nodes on the outer venter and 3 on the flanks arranged in radial rows. Central siphuncle. Suture with ventral and lateral nodes.
L. Carboniferous–Permian. Europe, Asia.

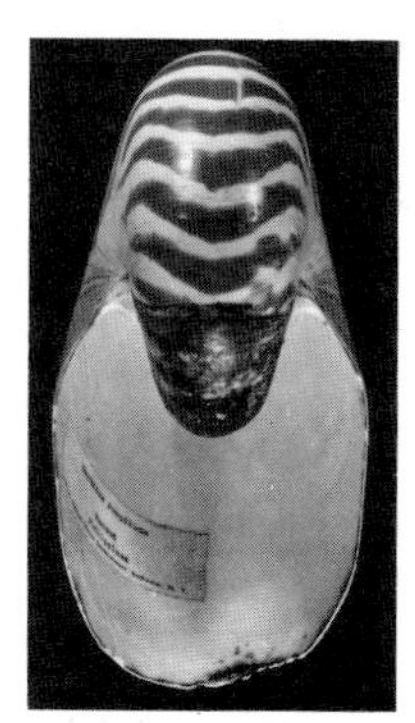
Plate 6.7.6A

Plate 6.7.6B

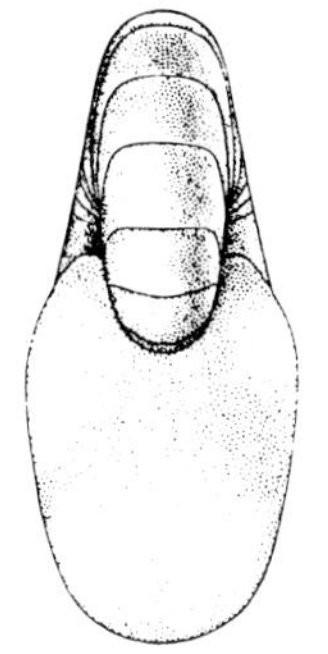
Plate 6.7.7A

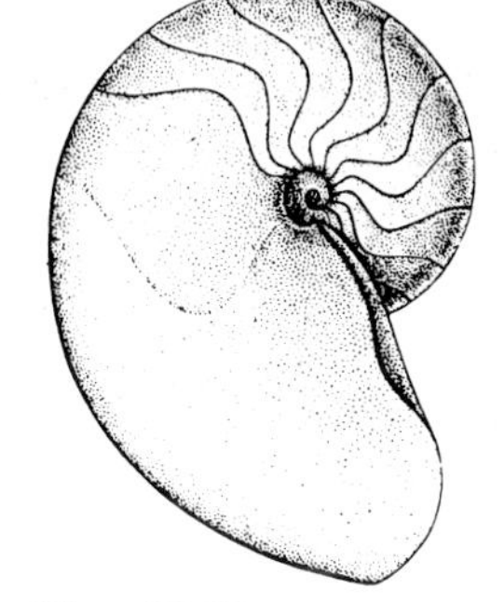
Plate 6.7.7B

Pl. 6.7.6, 7. *Nautilus* Linné, 1758
Smooth, involute nautilicones: umbilicus may be occluded with callus. Siphuncle subcentral. Suture with ventral saddle, lateral lobe, small subumbilical lobe and small saddle near seam and broad dorsal lobe. The present-day *Nautilus* includes several species (Saunders 1981) and lives around the Philippines and east to Samoa, and around Australia. Drift records, mostly of dead shells, are known throughout the Indian Ocean, north to Japan, and commonly in the eastern Pacific.
Oligocene–Recent. Widespread but localized at present time.
Pl. 6.7.6. *Nautilus pompilius* Linné. Recent shell from the Philippines. Pl. 6.7.7. Internal mould of filled recent shell after shell dissolution. Diameter about 18 cm. (After Teichert *et al.* 1964.) Figure 6.7.6, anatomical details.

Subclass Endoceratoidea

Medium to large mostly orthoconic shells with large siphuncles invariably filled with conical calcareous sheaths or endocones (Order Endocerida) especially in apical part, or with endosiphuncular longitudinal lamellae (order Interjocerida). Siphuncle deposits taken to be poise adaptations (Fig. 6.7.3B). Cosmopolitan in Ordovician, rare in Silurian.

Pl. 6.7.8A. *Cassinoceras* Ulrich & Foerste, 1936
Rapidly expanding brevicones. Ventral siphuncle, very large, filling apex; with simple endocones.
L. Ordovician. N. America.
A. *Cassinoceras explanator* (Whitfield): L. Ordovician. Vermont, USA. Side view and longitudinal section. Length 20 cm. (After Teichert *et al.* 1964.)

Pl. 6.7.8B. *Chazyoceras* Flower, 1958
Large orthocones with large ventral siphuncle filling apex as a bulb with faintly crescentic endocones.
M. Ordovician. Europe and N. America.
B. *Chazyoceras valcourense* Flower: M. Ordovician. New York, USA. Reconstruction without body chamber, length 0.37 m. (After Teichert *et al.* 1964.)

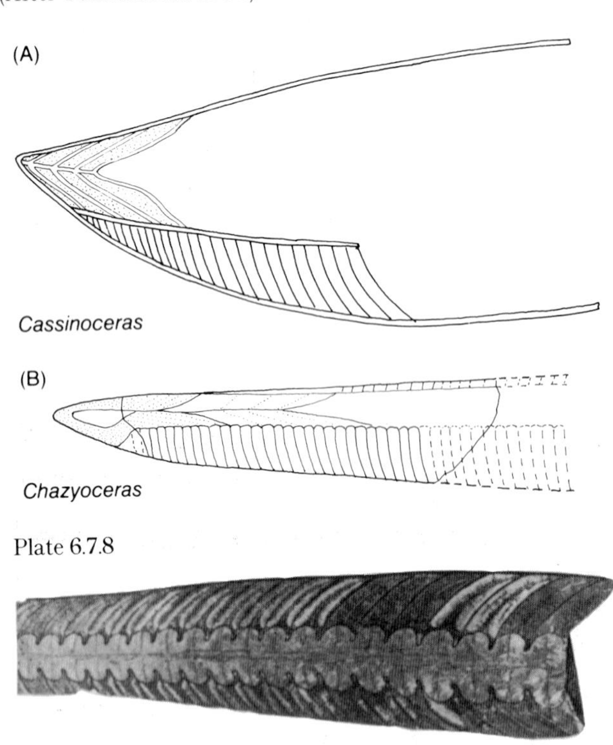

Plate 6.7.8

Plate 6.7.9

6.7.3 Subclass Actinoceratoidea

Generally orthocones of medium to very large size with siphuncle swollen bulbously between septa and with central canal in siphuncle and radiating canals (Fig. 6.7.7, after Teichert *et al.* 1964). Chambers with circulus deposits and cameral tissue well developed. Septal necks cyrtochoanitic with perispatial tissue on the siphuncular bulbs. Name refers to appearance of siphuncle in cross-section. Common in L. Ordovician–U. Carboniferous.

Pl. 6.7.9. *Rayonnoceras* Croneis, 1926
Large to very large orthocones with subcentral siphuncle and complex siphuncle with central canal and rectilinear radial canals. Cameral deposits mostly fill chambers.
Carboniferous. N. America, Europe, Asia.
Rayonnoceras bassleri Foerste and Teichert: L. Carboniferous. Arkansas, USA. Longitudinal section without body chamber. Length 8.2 cm. (From Fischer and Teichert 1969.)

Fig. 6.7.7. Diagram illustrating the complex siphuncular structure of an actinoceratoid. Siphuncle orientation horizontal. The siphuncle is swollen between septa (producing a bead-like siphuncle) and canal structures develop within the beads. (From Teichert.)

6.7.4 Subclass Ammonoidea

The earliest ammonoids known are from the late L. Devonian (Emsian) and a range of morphologies (Pl. 6.7.10) link straight bactritids with the typical tightly coiled and more complex-sutured ammonoids. The Bacritina are thought to be derived from the Orthocerida, the chief distinction being the egg-shaped protoconch and, presumably, a novel larval life style. Some regard the Bactritina as a distinct order (Bactritida) or even subclass (Bactritoidea), but the morphological distinction from their ancestors and successors is too trivial for such inflation; a case is made by Dzik (1981) that straight bactritines should be classed with the Orthoceratida and only the cyrtoconic and coiled forms retained in the Ammonoidea.

From the L. Devonian until they became extinct at the close of the Cretaceous, a wide range of diversity led to much homoeomorphy in shell shape, ornamentation and suture form. Nothing replaces long experience as the best aid to identification. Near the end of the M. Devonian, at the end of the Devonian, in the mid-Namurian, and at the ends of the Permian and Triassic the group (Fig. 6.7.8) suffered considerable extinctions. Spath's argument that ammonoids survived beyond the Cretaceous without a shell as the Octopodida is not accepted despite incredible similarities in radular structure.

Because of the diversity of evolution, simple diagnosis is not easy. As a whole most ammonoids differ from 'nautiloids' in their exclusive exogastric coiling, their egg-shaped protoconch and marginal siphuncules, their more complex sutures, their longer body chamber, and their thinner shells. More aptly they can be diagnosed as those groups thought to be descended from L. Devonian goniatites. A key to elucidating their phylogenetic relations is the ontogeny of the suture lines, and this basis for ordinal and subordinal division will be detailed later. Some terminology relating to ammonoid morphology is shown in Fig. 6.7.9.

Because of their great use for correlation of marine rocks from the Devonian to the end of the Cretaceous the Ammonoidea, comprising the goniatites, clymeniids and ammonites of popular parlance, form the standard for the subdivision of marine rocks, some 230 zonal time divisions being recognized. Together with finer subzonal subdivision time discrimination of the order of

0.25 to 1.0 million years is possible. For this reason much emphasis is laid here on genera which have international stratigraphic importance.

A general introduction to the group is given in the *Treatise on Invertebrate Paleontology* (Arkell *et al.* 1957) and there is an up-to-date review in *The Ammonoidea* (House and Senior 1981). More general accounts, especially relating to Mesozoic ammonites, are given in works by Lehmann (1981), Kennedy and Cobban (1976), Thomel (1980) and Mikaylova (1983).

Order Anarcestida

The basic stock group comprises orthoconic to tightly coiled forms with ventral siphuncle and egg-shaped protoconch and with perforate or imperforate umbilici. The first suture has up to three lobes (ventral or external, 'lateral' and dorsal or internal, given the symbols E (or V), L and I (or D) respectively) and the 'lateral' may remain lateral or be subumbilical and migrate laterally during ontogeny. Including the bactritines, they range at least from the Devonian to the Permian, but coiled members are exclusively Devonian, and cosmopolitan.

Suborder Bactritina

Shell orthoconic to cyrtoconic with short or long body chamber and apical angle up to 10°. Protoconch globular to egg-shaped. Siphuncle small, in contact with ventral wall; septal necks orthochoanitic to cyrtochoanitic. Suture with V-shaped ventral lobe and lateral suture straight or with a broad lateral lobe. Known from the U. Silurian to the Permian. Cosmopolitan, but especially in goniatite shales and pelagic limestones.

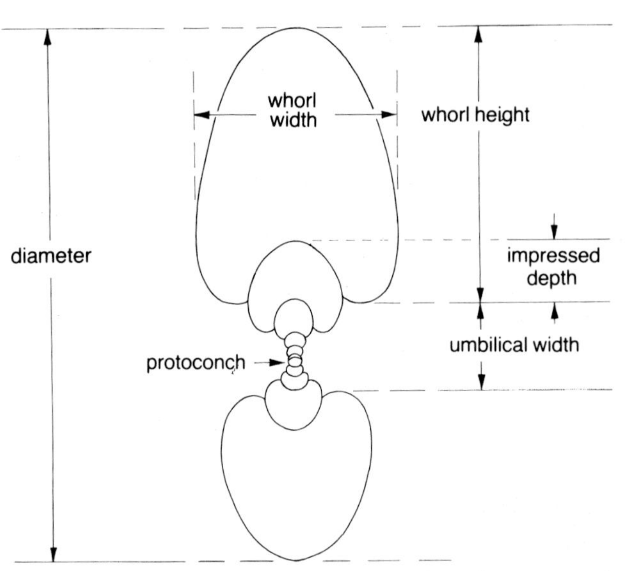

Fig. 6.7.9. Diagram showing a cross-section of an ammonite illustrating shell terminology.

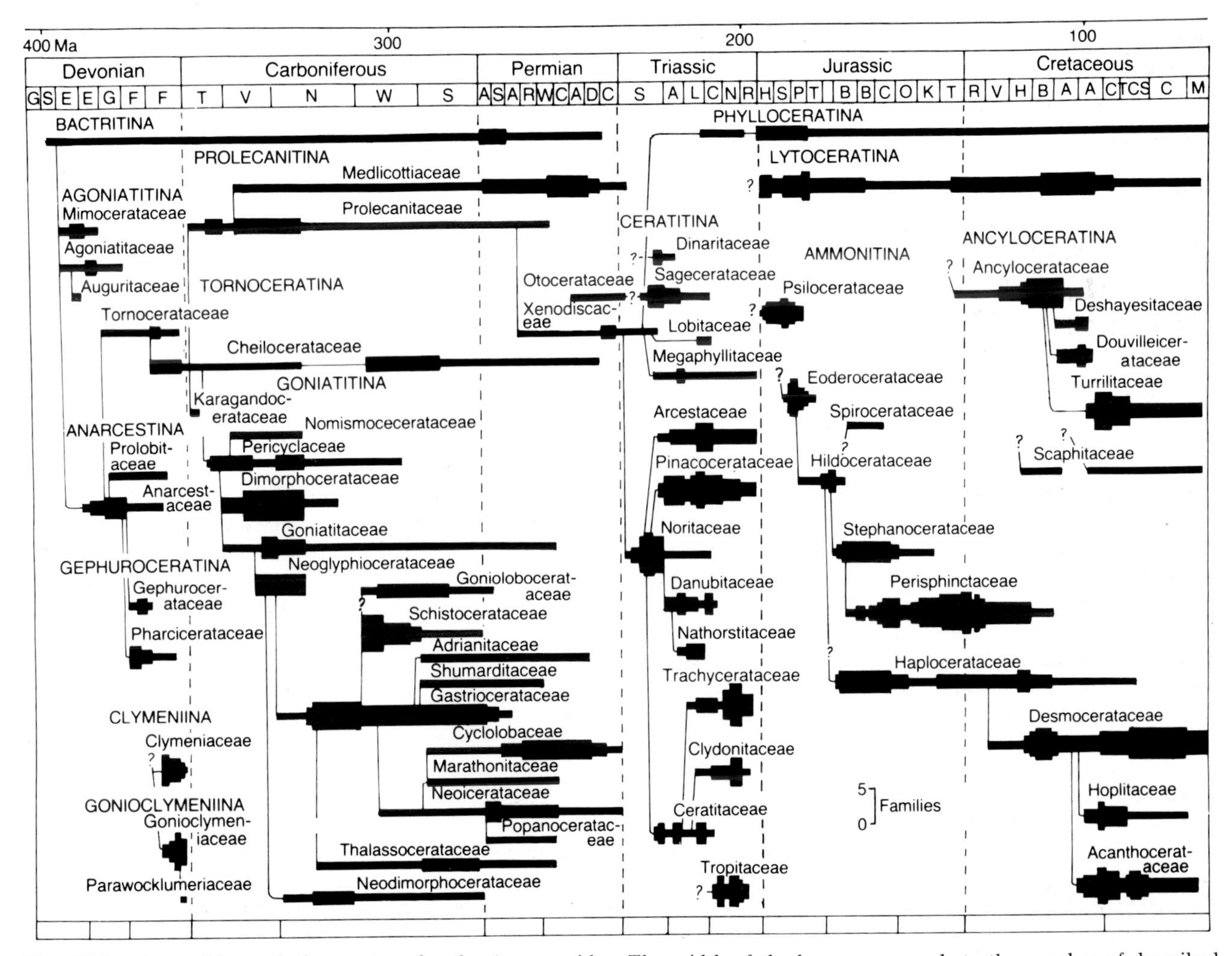

Fig. 6.7.8. A possible evolutionary tree for the Ammonoidea. The width of the bars corresponds to the number of described families within the groups at a particular time.

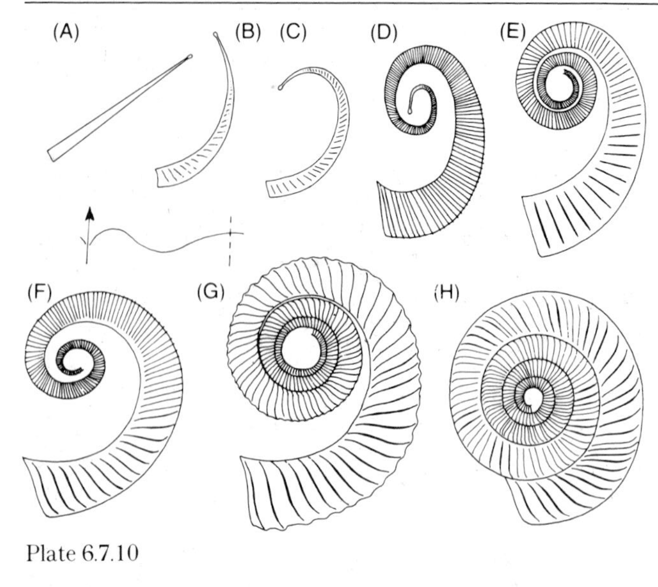

Plate 6.7.10

D–F. *Anetoceras hunsrueckianum* (Erben) group: Hunsrückschiefer, Emsian. Germany. Diameters about 3 cm. (After Erben 1964.) Fig. 6.7.10B *Anetoceras* sp. Adult suture.

Pl. 6.7.10G, H. *Erbenoceras* Bogoslovski, 1962
Like *Anetoceras* but with middle and sometimes outer whorls advolute. Ornament of lirae and ribs.
L. and M. Devonian (Emsian and Eifelian). Europe, Asia, N. America.
G. *Erbenoceras advolvens* (Erben): Emsian. N. France. (After Erben 1964.) H. *E. erbeni* House: Emsian. Nevada, USA. Diameters *c.* 10 cm. Fig. 6.7.10A. *Erbenoceras* sp. Adult suture.

Pl. 6.7.11. *Gyroceratites* von Meyer, 1831
Serpenticonic, advolute, never convolute. Umbilicus perforate. Whorl section oval. Ventral and lateral lobes (VL) only. With biconvex growth lines, not ribs. Ventrolateral furrows in adult body chamber.
L. Devonian (Emsian). Europe, Asia, N. America.
Gyroceratites gracilis (Bronn): Emsian. Wissenbach, Germany. Diameter 4.1 cm.

Pl. 6.7.10A. *Bactrites* Sandberger, 1843
Orthoconic, with circular to oval cross-section. Suture with ventral lobe small and lateral suture transverse (rectiradiate) or obliquely projecting dorsally towards aperture (V). *Lobobactrites* (Dev.) is similar but has a lateral lobe (VL).
?Silurian Devonian–U. Permian. Cosmopolitan.
A. *Bactrites* sp. Shell form. Length about 3 cm.

Pl. 6.7.10B. *Cyrtobactrites* Erben, 1960
Shell exogastric and cyrtoconic with oval cross-section. *Kokenia* (M. Devonian) is more tightly coiled (Pl. 6.7.10C).
L. Devonian (Emsian). Europe.
B. *Cyrtobactrites sinuatus* Erben, reconstruction based on Erben 1964. Emsian. Germany. Length about 3 cm.

Suborder Agoniatitina

Shell loosely gyroconic to tightly coiled and involute. First whorl with or without perforation. Septal necks orthochoanitic. Older genera with only a ventral and lateral lobe (EL), later genera with dorsal lobe (ELI) and, in some, with other lobes. The lateral lobe remains lateral in position from earliest stages. Growth lines convex to linear or biconvex. This group includes transitional forms between the Bactritina and typical early goniatites. Widely distributed except in S. America and Antarctica in L. and M. Devonian. Found in goniatite shales and common in pelagic limestones.

SUPERFAMILY MIMOCERATACEAE

Typically loosely coiled, in some with whorls advolute (touching) or rarely convolute (embracing previous whorl) for part of coil. Umbilicus always perforate. Ventral and lateral lobe, rarely with small dorsal lobe where convolute. L. (Emsian) and M. (Eifelian) Devonian.

Pl. 6.7.10D–F. *Anetoceras* Schindewolf, 1935
Expanding gyrocone with no whorls touching; whorls elliptical in cross-section. Suture with small ventral lobe, wide lateral lobe and broad dorsal saddle only (EL). Ribs and growth lines usually concave to rursiradiate but in some rectiradiate in adult. Thought to be derived from *Cyrtobactrites* or *Kokenia*.
L. and M. Devonian (Emsian and Eifelian). Europe and Asia. Best known from German Hunsrückschiefer.

SUPERFAMILY AGONIATITACEAE

Serpenticonic to involute, always substantially convolute apart from earliest whorls. With ventral, lateral and dorsal lobes (VLI), in some with additional lobes. Umbilici perforate or imperforate. With biconvex growth lines. Cosmopolitan apart from S. America and Antarctica. L. and M. Devonian.

Pl. 6.7.12. *Agoniatites* Meek, 1887
Tightly coiled with first and later whorls advolute to strongly convolute: always with imperforate umbilicus. Often ribbed and with ventrolateral furrows.
M. Devonian (Eifelian and Givetian), possibly L. Devonian (? Emsian). Distribution as for superfamily.
Agoniatites vanuxemi (Hall): M. Devonian. Manlius, New York, USA. Showing protoconch and early whorls. Fig. 6.7.10C. Adult suture of another specimen.

Suborder Anarcestina

Shell serpenticonic to subglobular and involute. Usually with an imperforate umbilicus. Suture with a ventral, subumbilical and dorsal lobe (ELI) in early stages, the subumbilical lobe remaining in that position or migrating to a lateral position

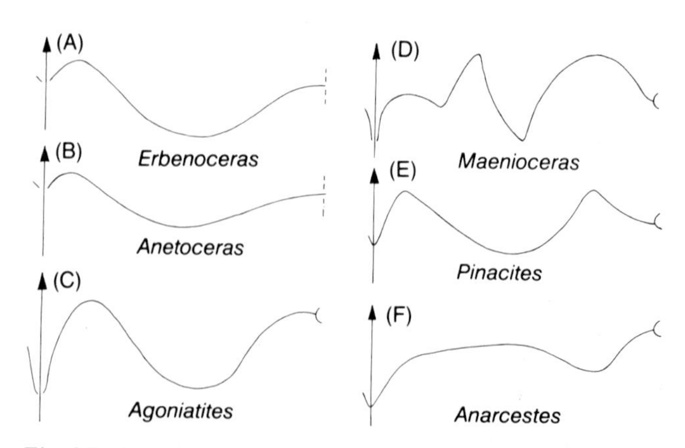

Fig. 6.7.10. Diagrams illustrating sutures of Devonian goniatites of the Agoniatitina and Anarcestina. In this and later suture diagrams the arrow marks the outer shell venter and points towards the aperture. The 'C' marks the position of the junction of the umbilicus with the earlier whorls.

during ontogeny. In some with additional lobes. Growth lines biconvex (typical) to convex (Prolobitaceae) and linear. L.–U. Devonian, but rare in U. Devonian. Cosmopolitan apart from S. America and Antarctica.

Pl. 6.7.13. *Anarcestes* Mojsisovics, 1882
Shell subinvolute to subevolute, open umbilicate. First whorl perforate. Suture with ventral lobe, rursiradiate lateral suture, subumbilical lobe and dorsal lobe (VLI). Growth lines biconvex. L. Devonian (Emsian) and M. Devonian (Eifelian). Europe, Asia, Africa, N. America.
Anarcestes lateseptatus (G. & F. Sandberger): probably M. Devonian (Eifelian), Wissenbacher Schiefer, Germany. Diameter 29.4 mm). Fig. 6.7.10F. *Anarcestes* sp. Adult suture.

Fig. 6.7.10E. *Pinacites* Mojsisovics, 1882
Shell oxyconic, involute, often with keeled venter. Suture with 3 primary lobes and additional umbilical lobe formed during ontogeny (ELUI). Ventrolateral and subumbilical saddles usually distinctively acute.
M. Devonian (Eifelian). Europe, Africa, N. America, ?Asia.
E. *Pinacites jugleri* (Roemer): M. Devonian (Eifelian), Germany. Adult suture.

Pl. 6.7.14. *Maenioceras* Schindewolf, 1933
Shell subevolute to involute, usually flat-sided, typically with ventrolateral furrows. Suture with ventral and an adventitious lobe on the venter; also lateral, umbilical, subumbilical and dorsal lobes (E_mE_1LUI). Growth lines biconvex.
M. Devonian. Typical of Givetian. Europe, N. America, Africa, Asia and ? Australia.
Maenioceras decheni (Kayser): Givetian. Germany. Diameter 1.7 cm. Fig. 6.7.10D. *M. terebratum* (G. & F. Sandberger): Givetian. Germany. Adult suture.

Suborder Gephuroceratina

Variable shell form from serpenticonic to involute; umbilicus imperforate. Suture with extra umbilical lobes added, and adventitious lobes between venter and primary ventrolateral saddle (which is always the largest saddle). Growth lines in most biconvex. Derived from the Anarcestaceae. Cosmopolitan except for S. America and Antarctica. M. Devonian occurrence results from 1982 definition of M./U. Devonian boundary above *Pharciceras* faunas.

SUPERFAMILY GEPHUROCERATACEAE

Up to 25 lobes between venter and umbilical seam. Lobes usually pointed at maturity, saddles rounded or pointed.

Pl. 6.7.15. *Manticoceras* Hyatt, 1884
Suture with 3 pointed or rounded lobes between small lobe in median saddle and deep dorsal lobe (E_mE_1LUI). Very rarely ribbed or noded.
U. Devonian (Frasnian only). Cosmopolitan.
Manticoceras cordatum (G. & F. Sandberger): Frasnian. Büdesheim, Germany. Diameter 18.7 mm. Fig. 6.7.11B. *Manticoceras.* sp. Adult suture.

Pl. 6.7.16. *Beloceras* Hyatt, 1884
Large oxycones with narrow rounded or tabular venter. Adult suture with up to 7 adventitious lobes between minute ventral lobe and large primary ventrolateral saddle and up to 18 umbilical lobes between it and the umbilical seam ($E_mE_{1-7}LU_{1-18}I$). Lobes and saddles pointed; rarely ceratitic frilling on 2 lobes.
U. Devonian (Frasnian). Cosmopolitan.
Beloceras sagittarium (G. & F. Sandberger): Frasnian. Martenberg, Germany. Diameter 4.9 cm. Fig. 6.7.11A. Adult suture.

Plate 6.7.11A

Plate 6.7.11B

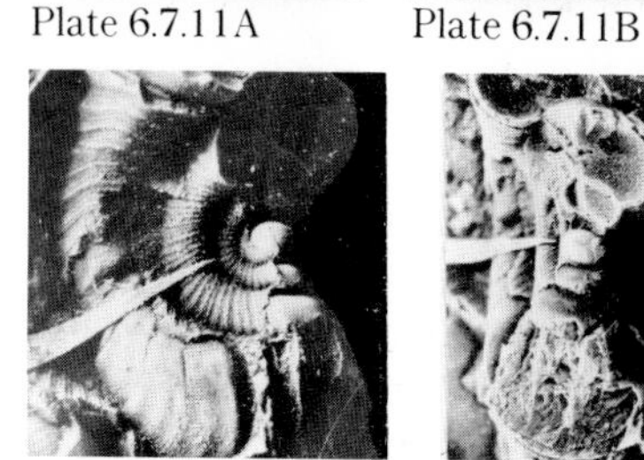

Plate 6.7.12A

Plate 6.7.12B

Plate 6.7.12C

Plate 6.7.13A

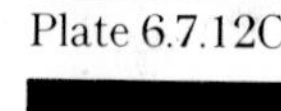

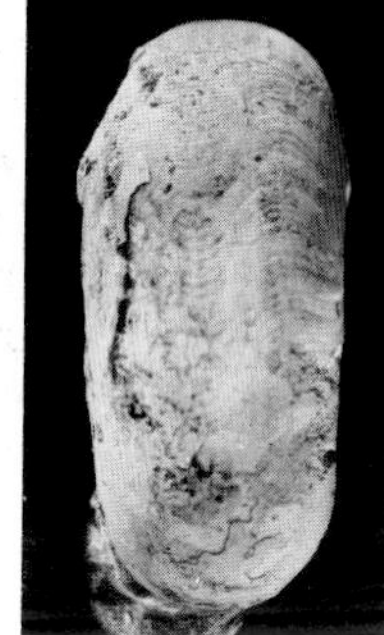

Plate 6.7.13B

Plate 6.7.14A

Plate 6.7.14B

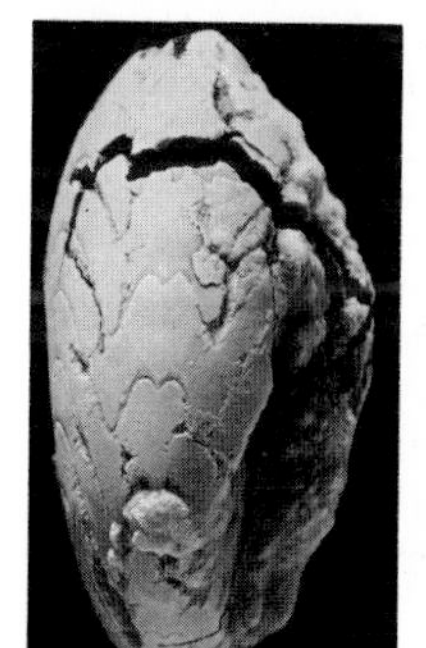

Plate 6.7.15A

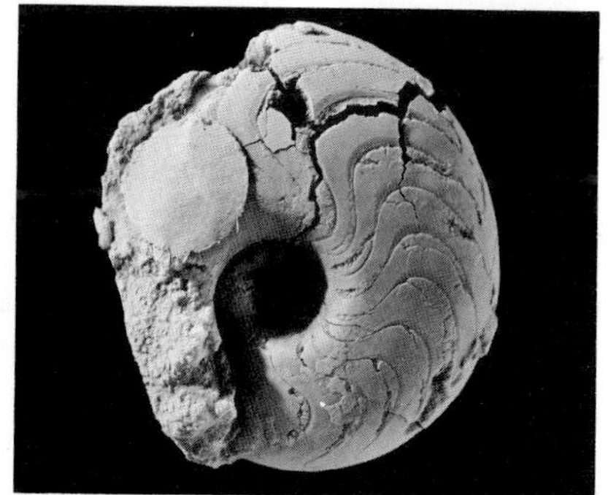

Plate 6.7.15B

SUPERFAMILY PHARCICERATACEAE
Up to 20 lobes between venter and umbilical seam. Lobes rounded or with pinched terminations. In one genus (*Devonopronorites*) with subceratitic frill on one lobe. *Pharciceras* (U. Givetian) with few lobes (Fig. 6.7.11E), *Neopharciceras* (U. Givetian) with many lobes (Fig. 6.7.11C).

Pl. 6.7.17. *Synpharciceras* Schindewolf, 1940
Involute and well rounded. Sometimes laterally compressed and with tabular venter in adult. Suture with up to 9 rounded lobes on flanks.
M. Devonian (late Givetian). Europe and Africa.
Synpharciceras clavilobum (G. & F. Sandberger): U. Givetian; Pharciceras level. Eibach, Germany. Diameter 29 mm. Fig. 6.7.11D. Adult suture.

Order Clymeniida

This group comprises the only ammonoids with dorsal siphuncles. The migration to the dorsum takes place during the first whorl. The group appears cryptically in the late U. Devonian (mid-Famennian), achieves wide distribution except in S. America and Antarctica, and suddenly becomes extinct near the end of the Famennian, that event helping to define the Devonian/Carboniferous boundary. They may have arisen from the Tornocerataceae by reduction of lobes to ELI and subsequent radiation (House 1970), or from the Anarcestaceae (Arkell *et al.* 1957). From a simple-sutured basic stock arise forms with complex sutures often homoeomorphic with ventrally siphuncled goniatites.

Suborder Gonioclymeniina

Characterized by the retention of a ventral and dorsal lobe. Adult suture often highly complex but always goniatitic, never ceratitic, in some groups with the loss of the ventral lobe and rarely the dorsal lobe in the adult.

Pl. 6.7.18. *Progonioclymenia* Schindewolf, 1937
Evolute shell, whorl section rectangular with flat or sulcate venter. Flanks with prorsiradiate ribs. Suture with rounded, broad, ventral, lateral and dorsal lobes only.
U. Devonian (Famennian; Clymenia Stufe). Europe, Asia.
Progonioclymenia aegoceras (Münster): Wildungen. Germany. Diameter 19 mm. (Photo J. D. Price.) Fig. 6.7.12G. Adult suture.

Pl. 6.7.19. *Gonioclymenia* Hyatt, 1884
Subdiscoidal shell with wide umbilicus with groove on venter (*Kalloclymenia* differs in having no groove). Faint prorsiradiate ribbing. Suture with ventral, small ventrolateral, 2 lateral and dorsal lobes. Lobes usually angular. *Sphenoclymenia* has more sutural elements (Fig. 6.7.12A).
U. Devonian (Famennian; Clymenia Stufe). Europe, N. Africa, Asia.
Gonioclymenia subcarinata (Münster): (Famennian; Clymenia Stufe). Schübelhammer, W. Germany. Diameter 11 cm. Fig. 6.7.12B. *Gonioclymenia* sp. Adult suture.

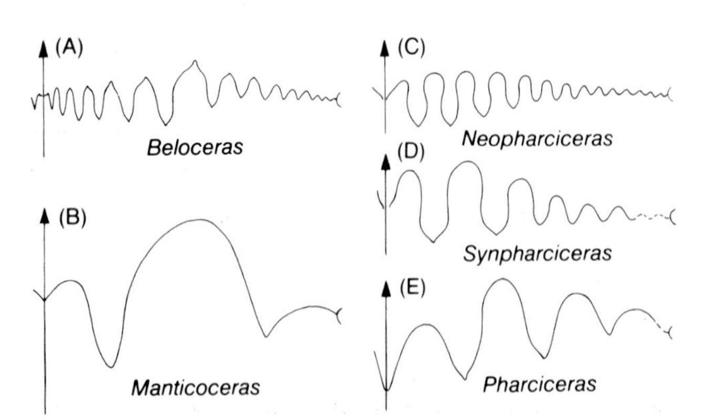

Fig. 6.7.11. Diagrams illustrating sutures of Devonian goniatites of the Gephuroceratina.

Pl. 6.7.20. *Wocklumeria* Wedekind, 1917
Subdiscoidal to subglobular with strong triradiate constrictions in early stages and trilobed form lost in adult. Suture with ventral 3 lateral (1 on dorsum) and dorsal lobe. Adult lobes deep.
U. Devonian (Famennian; Wocklumeria Stufe). Europe, Asia, N. Africa.
Wocklumeria sphaeroides (Richter): Oberrödinghausen, W. Germany. Famennian; Wocklumeria Stufe. Diameter 19.5 mm. (Photo J. D. Price.) Fig. 6.7.12C. *Wocklumeria* sp. Adult suture.

Pl. 6.7.21. *Soliclymenia* Schindewolf, 1937
Serpenticonic coiling, in some triangular. Whorl section reniform. Flanks densely ribbed. Suture as in *Progonioclymenia*.
U. Devonian (Famennian). Europe, Asia.
Soliclymenia solarioides (von Buch): Famennian; Wocklumeria Stufe. Dzikowiec (Ebersdorf), Poland. Largest specimen 14 mm max. diameter.

Pl. 6.7.22. *Parawocklumeria* Schindewolf, 1926
Ventral and dorsal lobes in early stages only. Shell involute, subglobular and trilobed. Adult suture with ventral saddle, lateral lobe, 2 umbilical lobes and a lobe and dorsal lobe on the dorsum.
U. Devonian (Famennian; Wocklumeria Stufe). Europe, Asia.
Parawocklumeria paradoxa (Wedekind): Famennian; Wocklumeria Stufe. Stourscombe, England. Diameter 11.5 mm.

Suborder Clymeniina (Platyclymeniina)

Characterized by retention of the ventral lobe only in the earliest stage and later forming a ventral saddle. Sutures generally simple.

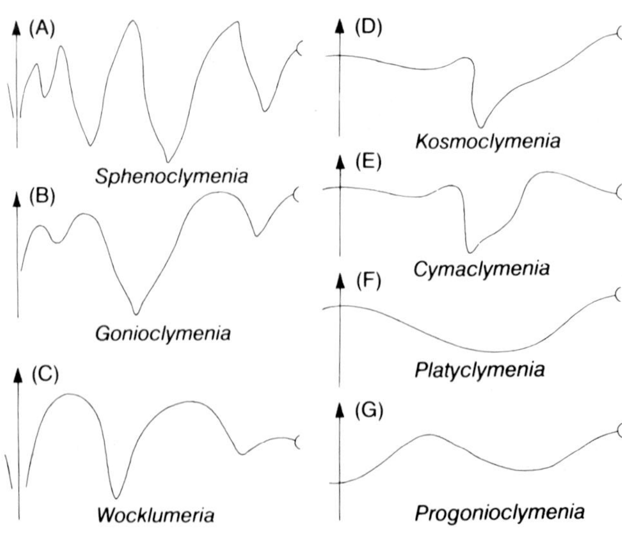

Fig. 6.7.12. Diagrams illustrating sutures of Devonian Clymeniida.

Plate 6.7.16A Plate 6.7.16B Plate 6.7.17A Plate 6.7.17B Plate 6.7.18A
Plate 6.7.18B Plate 6.7.19A Plate 6.7.19B Plate 6.7.20A Plate 6.7.20B
Plate 6.7.21 Plate 6.7.22A Plate 6.7.22B
Plate 6.7.23A Plate 6.7.23B Plate 6.7.24A Plate 6.7.24B Plate 6.7.25A Plate 6.7.25B

Pl. 6.7.23. *Platyclymenia* Hyatt, 1884
Widely umbilicate to serpenticonic shell. Often ribbed on flanks. Suture with broad ventral saddle, lateral lobe and broad dorsal lobe only.
U. Devonian (Famennian; Platyclymenia Stufe). Cosmopolitan except for S. America and Antarctica.
Platyclymenia richter Wedekind: Famennian. Ainkhausen, W. Germany. Diameter 3.9 cm. (Photo J. D. Price.) Fig. 6.7.12F. *Platyclymenia* sp. Adult suture.

Pl. 6.7.24. *Clymenia* Münster, 1832
Like *Platyclymenia* but compressed, and whorls with ovate section, not depressed, and not ribbed. Growth lines near rectiradiate. Lateral lobe broad and rounded, dorsal lobe very deep.
U. Devonian (Famennian; Clymenia and Wocklumeria Stufen). Europe, Asia and N. Africa.
Clymenia hoevelensis Wedekind: Famennian; Clymenia Stufe. Hoevel, W. Germany. Diameter 7.7 cm.

Pl. 6.7.25. *Kosmoclymenia* Schindewolf, 1949
Laterally compressed, subevolute to subinvolute. Without ribs but usually with marked biconvex growth lines. Suture with ventral saddle and well-rounded saddle ventrad of asymmetric

sharply V-shaped lateral lobe, sharp dorsal lobe.
U. Devonian (Famennian; Clymenia and Wocklumeria Stufen). Europe, Asia and N. Africa.
Kosmoclymenia undulata (Münster): Famennian; Clymenia Stufe. Dasberg, W. Germany. Diameter 9.1 cm. Fig. 6.7.12D. Adult suture.

Pl. 6.7.26. *Cymaclymenia* Hyatt, 1884
Shell form subinvolute to subevolute and with growth lines near rectiradiate to biconvex with prominent ventrolateral salient. Suture like *Kosmoclymenia*, but lateral lobe acuminate and only slightly asymmetric and a broad lobe centred on the umbilical seam in addition.
U. Devonian (U. Famennian). Cosmopolitan except for S. America and Antarctica.
Cymaclymenia cordata (Wedekind): Famennian; Wocklumeria Stufe. Chudleigh, England. Diameter 3.5 cm. Fig. 6.7.12E. *Cymaclymenia* sp. Adult suture.

Order Goniatitida

The major group of Palaeozoic goniatites. Characterized by a primary trilobed suture (ELI) in the earliest stages with the lateral lobe of the adult derived adventitiously (A) from an arched lateral saddle during early ontogeny (EALI as the basic form giving the 'A'-type ontogeny of Schindewolf in Arkell *et al.* 1957). Ranging from M. Devonian (Givetian) to the latest Permian (Changsinian). Cosmopolitan.

Suborder Tornoceratina

The basic stock with adult ventral, lateral (adventitious), umbilical and dorsal lobes (EALI) only or with additional adventitious or umbilical lobes but with the ventral lobe undivided.

SUPERFAMILY TORNOCERATACEAE

As for the suborder but with biconvex growth lines.

Pl. 6.7.27. *Tornoceras* Hyatt, 1884
Typically laterally compressed, involute, with closed umbilicus. Suture with small ventral lobe, asymmetrical lateral lobe, a lobe centred on the seam and a dorsal lobe (EALI).
M. Devonian–U. Devonian (Givetian–Famennian). Cosmopolitan except for Antarctica. The only Devonian ammonoid well represented in South America.
Tornoceras arcuatum House: Squaw Bay Limestone, Frasnian. Alpena, Michigan, USA. Diameter 2.6 cm. Fig. 6.7.13A. *Tornoceras* sp. Adult suture.

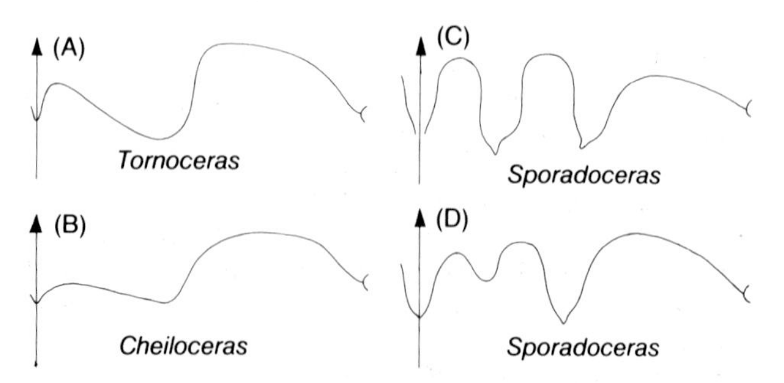

Fig. 6.7.13. Diagrams illustrating sutures of Devonian goniatites of the Tornoceratina.

SUPERFAMILY CHEILOCERATACEAE

As for the suborder but with convex growth lines in most members. In later members (Pseudohaloritidae) both lobes and saddles may be ceratitic or ammonitic.

Pl. 6.7.28. *Cheiloceras* Frech, 1897
Subglobular to stout lenticular with closed umbilicus. Form of lobes variable. Often with constrictions.
U. Devonian (L. Famennian). Cosmopolitan.
Cheiloceras amblylobum (G. & F. Sandberger): Gowanda Shale, U. Devonian. Corell's Point, Brocton, New York, USA. Diameter 3.0 cm. Fig. 6.7.13B. *Cheiloceras* sp. Adult suture.

Fig. 6.7.13C, D. *Sporadoceras* Hyatt, 1884
Shell form like *Cheiloceras* but usually larger. Suture with adventitious additional lobe(s) formed between ventral and lateral lobes (EA_2A_1LUI).
U. Devonian (M. and U. Famennian). Cosmopolitan.
C. *Sporadoceras muensteri* (von Buch): Famennian, Urals, USSR. Suture. D. *S. rotundum* (Wedekind): Famennian, Urals, USSR. Suture (sutures after Ruzhencev 1962b).

Pl. 6.7.29. *Imitoceras* Schindewolf, 1923
Shell globular to compressed rounded, with closed umbilicus. Growth lines of convex raised lirae. Suture with deep, narrow ventral lobe, often acute lateral lobe and umbilical lobe centred near seam.
U. Devonian–L. Carboniferous (Famennian–Viséan). Cosmopolitan.
Imitoceras (I.) infracarbonicum (Paeckelmann): Tournaisian. Barmen, W. Germany. Fig. 6.7.14A. *I. (Acutimitoceras) intermedium* Schindewolf: Famennian; Wocklumeria Stufe. Hof, W. Germany. Suture. (After Schindewolf 1923.) Fig. 6.7.14B. The same. Famennian; Wocklumeria Stufe. Stockum, W. Germany. Section. Diameter 1.6 cm. (After Weyer 1977.)

Fig. 6.7.14C, D. *Gattendorfia* Schindewolf, 1920
Like *Imitoceras* but open umbilicate and with umbilical lobe centred ventrad of the seam.
L. Carboniferous (L. and M. Tournaisian). Europe, N. Africa, Asia, N. America. The entry of this genus has been used to define the base of the Carboniferous.
C. *Gattendorfia crassa* Schmidt: L. Tournaisian. Germany. Suture. D. *G. costata* Vöhringer: L. Tournaisian. Schleiz, E. Germany. Section. (After Weyer 1977.)

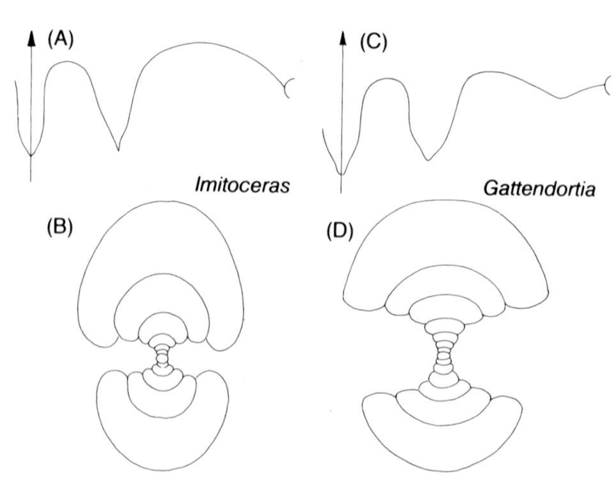

Fig. 6.7.14. Diagrams illustrating sutures and cross-sections of the late Devonian (*Imitoceras*) and early Carboniferous (*Gattendorfia*) members of the Tornoceratina.

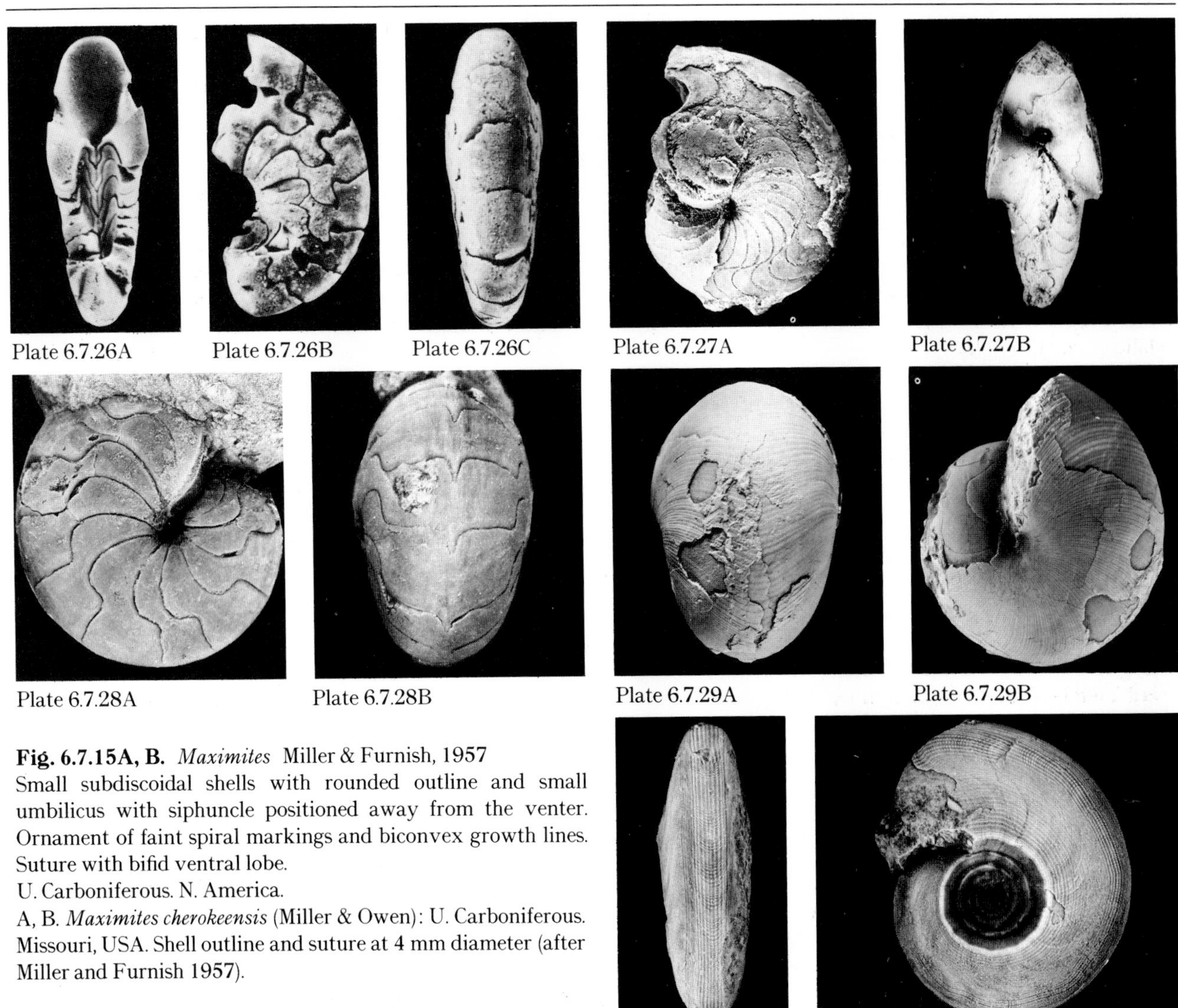

Plate 6.7.26A Plate 6.7.26B Plate 6.7.26C Plate 6.7.27A Plate 6.7.27B

Plate 6.7.28A Plate 6.7.28B Plate 6.7.29A Plate 6.7.29B

Plate 6.7.30A Plate 6.7.30B

Fig. 6.7.15A, B. *Maximites* Miller & Furnish, 1957
Small subdiscoidal shells with rounded outline and small umbilicus with siphuncle positioned away from the venter. Ornament of faint spiral markings and biconvex growth lines. Suture with bifid ventral lobe.
U. Carboniferous. N. America.
A, B. *Maximites cherokeensis* (Miller & Owen): U. Carboniferous. Missouri, USA. Shell outline and suture at 4 mm diameter (after Miller and Furnish 1957).

Fig. 6.7.15C, D. *Pseudohalorites* Yabe, 1928
Shell globular to subglobular with closed umbilicus and apertural constriction. Siphuncle almost dorsal. Ornament of convex ribs. Suture as in *Imitoceras*, but ventral, lateral and umbilical lobes may become digitate.
M. Permian. China, Urals, Saudi Arabia.
C, D. *Pseudohalorites subglobosus* Yabe: M. Permian. Hunan, China. Shell form at 19.5 mm diameter. Suture showing digitation (after Miller and Furnish 1957).

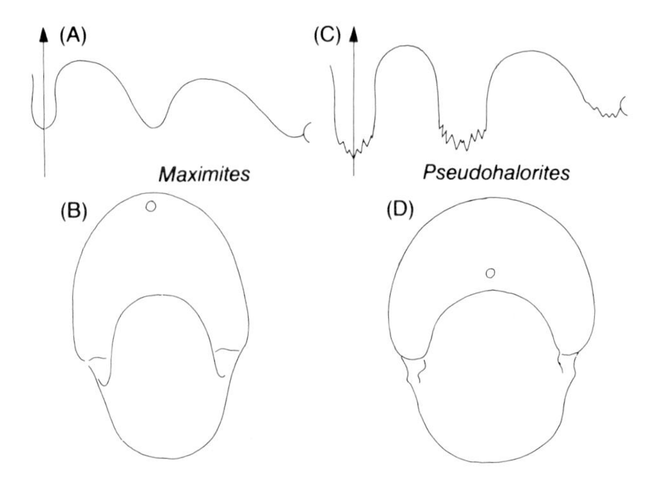

Fig. 6.7.15. Diagrams illustrating sutures and profiles of possible late Carboniferous (*Maximites*) and Permian (*Pseudohalorites*) members of the Tornoceratina.

Suborder Goniatitina

A major group arising from the cheiloceratacean *Imitoceras* and distinguished from its ancestors by the subdivision of the ventral lobe to give a median saddle ($E_m E_1 ALUI$), this feature appearing in several independent lineages. Later members show considerable complexity in lobation, including ceratitic and ammonititic frilling, and a wide range of ornament including spiral and transverse lirae, ribbing and nodation. Superfamily classification still fluid. Characteristic of the Carboniferous and becoming extinct by the close of the Permian. Abundant and widespread, especially in offshore and deeper-water facies.

SUPERFAMILY NOMISMOCERATACEAE

A small group of smooth-surfaced, laterally compressed, well-rounded shells. In some with ribs.

Pl. 6.7.30. *Hudsonoceras* Moore, 1946
Shell small, laterally compressed, moderately evolute with narrowly rounded deep umbilicus with steep walls. Transient ribs low on flanks. Both spiral and transverse (biconvex) ornament.
Carboniferous (Namurian; H). Europe.
Hudsonoceras proteus (Brown). Namurian; H_{2a}. Roadford, Ireland. Diameter 18 mm. (Photo N. J. Riley, IGS.)

SUPERFAMILY PERICYCLACEAE

The ancestral group for most of the suborder; appearing in the M. Tournaisian. Shell form mostly involute with globular to laterally compressed form. Ventral suture with bifid ventral lobe (and median saddle) but without subdivision of the lateral lobe or addition of other elements. The ventral lobe is typically still near parallel-sided. Some early forms smooth (such as *Muensteroceras*, Tournaisian, Fig. 6.7.16D), others strongly ribbed.

Pl. 6.7.31. *Fascipericyclus* Turner, 1948
Pericyclids are characterized by their strong ribbing, open umbilicus and frequently low median saddle (*Pericyclus*, Tournaisian, Fig. 6.7.16C) and are common in the U. Tournaisian and L. Viséan. *Fascipericyclus* is distinguished by the low median saddle, subangular first lateral saddle, and by the bifurcate ribbing.
Carboniferous (U. Tournaisian–L. Viséan). Europe.
Fascipericyclus fasciculatus (McCoy): L. Viséan; Chadian. Kniveton, England. Diameter 3.4 cm. (Photo N. J. Riley, IGS.)

Pl. 6.7.32. *Bollandoceras* Bisat, 1952
Beyrichoceratids are common in the Viséan and are characterized by near-globular shells, fine transverse growth striae, common constrictions and a suture with a high first lateral saddle (*Beyrichoceras*, Viséan, Fig. 6.7.16B). *Bollandoceras* is separated by a more compressed form and little or no umbilicus.
L. Carboniferous (Viséan). Europe.
Bollandoceras hodderense (Bisat): Viséan; B_1. Ashnott, England. Diameter 2.6 cm. (Photo N. J. Riley, IGS.)

SUPERFAMILY DIMORPHOCERATACAE

The chief distinction from the pericyclaceans is the more widely V-shaped (divided) ventral lobe and narrower prongs beside the median saddle, but the true dimorphoceratids are characterized by the irregular digitation of the external lateral and lateral lobes. In the *Dimorphoceras* group an evolutionary sequence is seen showing a sequential increase in complexity of this digitation: the functional explanation of this is not clear.

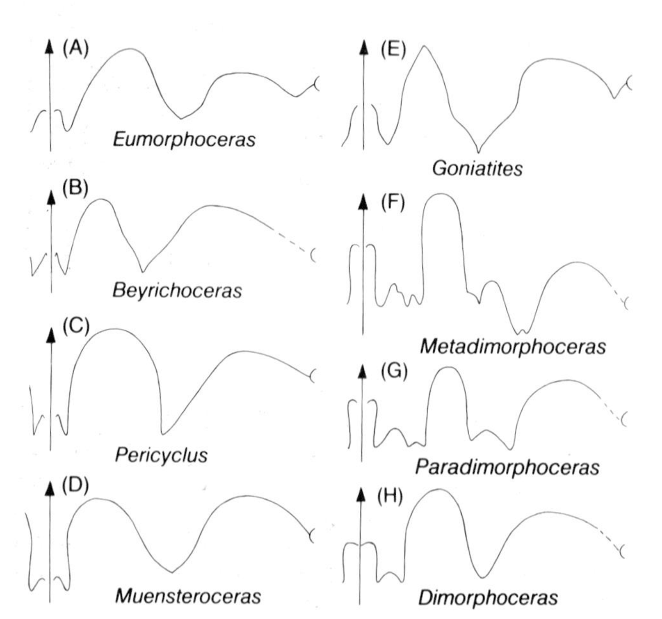

Fig. 6.7.16. Diagrams illustrating the sutures of a range of genera of early Carboniferous Goniatitina and all showing the characteristic subdivision of the ventral lobe distinguishing the suborder from earlier goniatites.

Pl. 6.7.33, 34. *Eumorphoceras* Girty, 1909
Laterally compressed, open umbilicate shell with pronounced ribbing in early stages and well-developed ventrolateral grooves which may persist to maturity; ribs and growth lines project into this groove. Suture with low median saddle and slightly asymmetric first lateral saddle.
Carboniferous (Namurian). Widespread in Europe, N. Africa, N. America and Asia.
Pl. 6.7.33. *Eumorphoceras pseudobilingue* (Bisat): Namurian; E_{1b}. Malham, England. Diameter 20 mm. (Photo N. J. Riley, IGS.) Fig. 6.7.16A. *E. bisulcatum* Girty: Namurian. Texas, USA. Suture (after Arkell *et al.* 1957). Pl. 6.7.34. The same. Namurian; E_{2a}. Saleswhell, England. Diameter 1.8 cm. (Photo N. J. Riley, IGS.)

Fig. 6.7.16F–H. *Dimorphoceras* Hyatt, 1884
Small goniatites, well rounded and laterally compressed with small or closed umbilicus. Ornament of biconvex growth lines with rare spiral lirae. Suture with a high median saddle and lobes subdivided, in *Dimorphoceras* only the external lateral (Fig. 6.7.16H), but in others the lateral lobe also (as in *Paradimorphoceras*, Fig. 6.7.16G, and *Metadimorphoceras*, Fig. 6.7.16F: both Namurian; R_1).
Carboniferous (Viséan and Namurian). Europe and N. Africa.
Fig. 6.7.16H. *Dimorphoceras gilbertsoni* (Phillips): Viséan; B_2. Dinckley, England. (All dimorphoceratid sutures after Ruzhencev 1962b.)

SUPERFAMILY GONIATITACEAE

Shell subspherical to discoidal, involute to evolute but typically rather involute. Growth lines simple to biconvex. Spiral lirae often well developed and may be dominant or may combine with growth lines to form crenistriate to reticulate pattern. Suture with widely diverging ventral lobe divided by median saddle and otherwise of simple ancestral type, but lobes and sometimes saddles often acuminate and elements angular to subangular. An abundant group.

Pl. 6.7.35, 36. *Goniatites* de Haan, 1825
Shell rotund and involute, usually with a very small umbilicus. Sutures with acuminate lateral lobe and with sigmoidal sides. Growth lines biconvex with subdued fine spiral ornament. Constrictions in some.
Carboniferous (Viséan). Europe, Asia, N. Africa and N. America.
Pl. 6.7.35. *Goniatites spirifer* Roemer: Viséan; P_{1b}. Dough Mountain, Ireland. Diameter 5.3 cm. Pl. 6.7.36. *G. moorei* Weyer. Viséan; B_2. Clitheroe, England. (Photos N. J. Riley, IGS.) Fig. 6.7.16E. *G. orientalis* Librovitch: Viséan. Kazakhstan, USSR. Suture (after Ruzhencev 1962b).

SUPERFAMILY NEOGLYPHIOCERATACEAE

Shell form with widely open to moderate umbilicus and laterally compressed to stout. Suture with a narrow ventral lobe with a low median saddle within it and the first lateral saddle broadly rounded.

Pl. 6.7.37. *Neoglyphioceras* Brüning, 1923
Shell laterally compressed with rounded venter: involute but with open umbilicus. Subdued growth lines and ornamented with strong, coarse spiral lirae. Often with constrictions. Lateral lobe weakly acuminate.
Carboniferous (U. Viséan and L. Namurian). Europe, Asia, N. Africa and N. America.
Neoglyphioceras spirale (Phillips): Viséan; P_{1d}. Co. Leitrim, Ireland. Diameter 2.04 cm. (Photo N. J. Riley, IGS.)

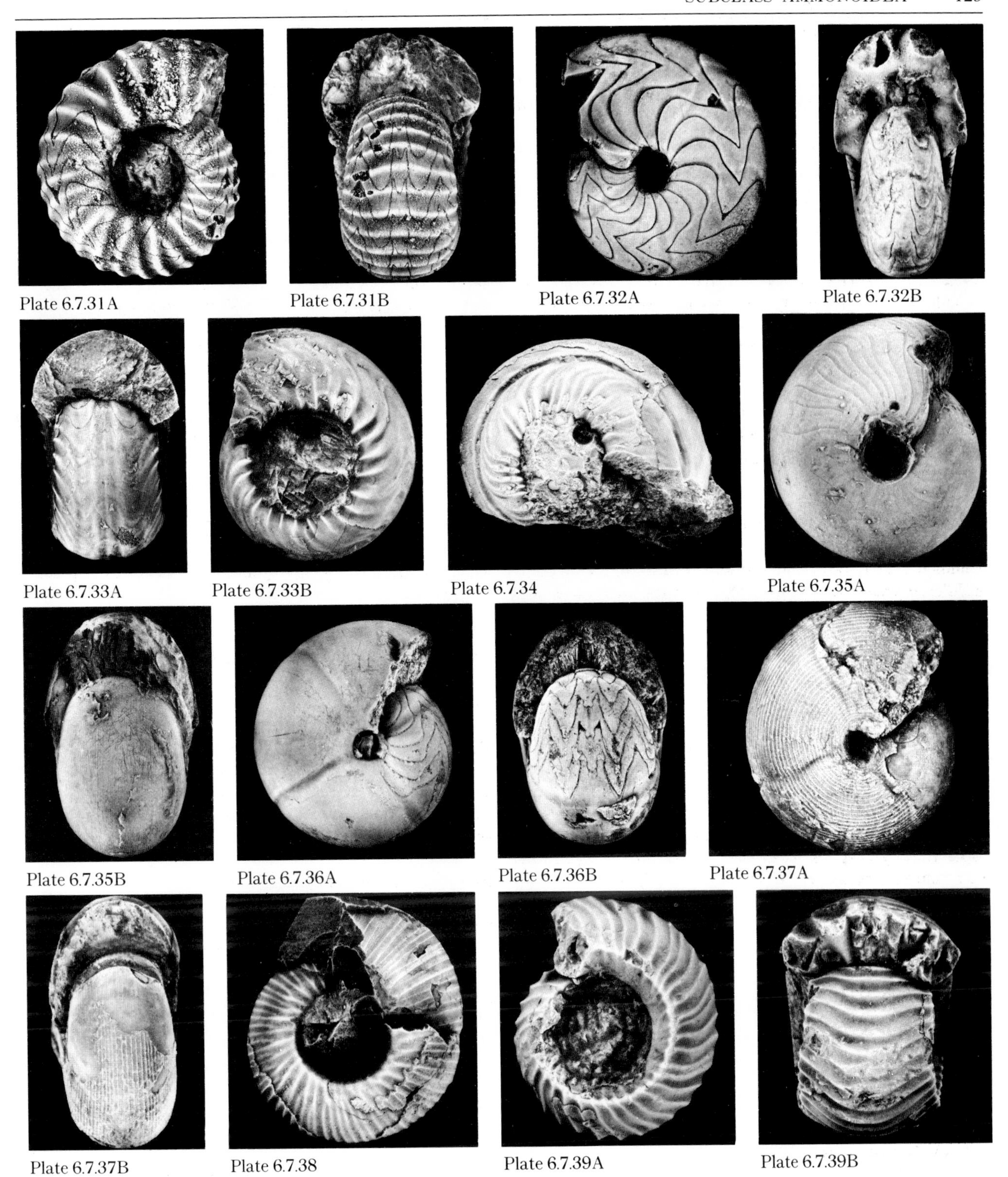

Pl. 6.7.38. *Cravenoceratoides* Bisat, 1928
Shell evolute in early stages, later with rotund to globular form and deep umbilicus. Spiral lirae if present limited to umbilical area only. Growth lines simple, with shallow ventral sinus. Radial striae divide low on the flanks. Umbilical lobe ventrad of seam.
Carboniferous (Namurian). Europe, Asia, N. Africa and N. America. The entry of the related *Cravenoceras leion* is used to define the base of the Namurian stage.
Cravenoceratoides edalensis (Bisat): Namurian; E_{2b}. Upper Hulme, England. Diameter 18 mm. (Photo N. J. Riley, IGS.)

SUPERFAMILY GASTRIOCERATACEAE
Group of generally globular to subglobular goniatites with an open umbilicus and nodes or tubercles usually well developed low on the flanks. Suture simple goniatitacean and thought to be derived from that family by a widening of the divided ventral lobe, heightening of the median saddle and the development of pouched and often divergent prongs beside it.

Pl. 6.7.39. *Homoceras* Hyatt, 1884
Subdiscoidal with rounded venter and often with wide open umbilicus with sharp umbilical shoulder; early whorls evolute.

Growth line ornament well developed approaching fine ribs, not usually dividing on flanks. Spiral ornament not shown.
Carboniferous (Namurian). Europe, Urals.
Homoceras beyrichianum (Haug): Namurian; H_{1b}. Cowling, England. Diameter 13 mm. (Photo N. J. Riley, IGS.)

Pl. 6.7.40, 41. *Reticuloceras* Bisat, 1924
Subdiscoidal with rounded venter; umbilicus nearly closed to open. Characterized by linear to biconvex growth lines crossed by spiral lirae forming a reticulate pattern. Some show weak nodes on the umbilical shoulder.
Carboniferous (Namurian). Europe, Asia and North America.
Pl. 6.7.40. *Reticuloceras stubblefieldi* Bisat & Hudson: Namurian; R_{1b}. Hope, England. Diameter 16 mm. (Photo N. J. Riley, IGS.)
Pl. 6.7.41. *R. circumplicatile* (Foord): Namurian; R_{1a}. Neheim, W. Germany. Diameter 14 mm. (From Hodson 1957.)

Pl. 6.7.42. *Gastrioceras* Hyatt, 1884
Shell laterally compressed to rotund, umbilicus open but width variable. Umbilical shoulder with well-developed, often bullate nodes.
Carboniferous (U. Namurian–M. Westphalian). Europe, Asia, N. Africa and N. America.
Gastrioceras listeri (J. Sowerby): Westphalian; G_1. Shore, England. Diameter 2.0 cm. (Photo N. J. Riley, IGS.) Fig. 6.7.18C. Adult suture.

Pl. 6.7.43. *Agathiceras* Gemmerello, 1887
Agathiceratids differ from earlier forms by the trifurcation of the lateral lobe. This may be weak, as in *Dombarites* (Namurian, Fig. 6.7.17C), or well developed, as in *Proshumardites* (Namurian to Bashkirian, Fig. 6.7.17B), or the lobes may be independent, as in *Agathiceras*, but the additional adult lobes arise from the trifurcation. The genus *Agathiceras* has a shell which is compressed, subglobular and involute and often with a closed umbilicus. Spiral ornament well developed. Suture with a very high median saddle and adult lateral lobes more or less U-shaped and equal: dorsal lobe V-shaped.
Carboniferous–Permian (Moscovian–Kazanian). Europe, Asia, Timor, Australia and N. America.
Fig. 6.7.17A. *Agathiceras uralicum* (Karpinski): Permian. USSR. Suture (after Ruzhencev 1962b). Pl. 6.7.43. *A. suessi* Gemmellaro: Permian. Sicily. Diameter 16 mm (after Arkell *et al.* 1957).

SUPERFAMILY SCHISTOCERATACEAE

A prolific U. Carboniferous group with variable shell form, in some with triangular inner whorls. Suture with a well-developed median saddle within a wide ventral lobe with additional sutural elements formed including up to 20 umbilical lobes and often lobe trifurcation.

Fig. 6.7.18A. *Schistoceras* Hyatt, 1884
Shell subglobular to subdiscoidal, subinvolute to subevolute. Ornament of biconvex growth lines and spiral striae. Suture with very high median saddle and spatulate lobes.
U. Carboniferous (Westphalian and Stephanian). N. America and USSR.
Schistoceras uralense Ruzhencev: U. Carboniferous. Urals, USSR. Suture (after Ruzhencev 1962b).

Fig. 6.7.18B. *Paralegoceras* Hyatt, 1884
Shell subdiscoidal with large umbilicus. Early stages triangular with ornament of ribs or nodes. Ventral lobe with high median saddle.
U. Carboniferous. N. America.
Paralegoceras iowense (Meek & Worthen): U. Carboniferous. Iowa, USA. Suture (after Miller and Furnish).

Fig. 6.7.18D. *Wellerites* Plummer & Scott, 1937
Subdiscoidal with rounded venter and wide umbilicus. Suture like *Schistoceras* but showing further adventitious ventrolateral lobes and additional umbilical lobes.
U. Carboniferous. N. America and USSR.
Wellerites russiensis Ruzhencev: Moskovian. Urals, USSR. Suture (after Ruzhencev 1962b).

SUPERFAMILY GONIOLOBOCERATACEAE

A small group of uncertain origin with distinctive angular sutures. U. Carboniferous and Permian.

Fig. 6.7.18F. *Gonioloboceras* Hyatt, 1900
Shell laterally compressed with venter narrowly rounded and umbilicus closed. Suture with moderately high median saddle and other lobes and saddles distinctively angular.
U. Carboniferous and rare in Permian (Westphalian–Asselian). N. America, Africa, USSR.
Gonioloboceras goniolobum (Meek): U. Carboniferous. Kansas, USA. Suture (after Ruzhencev).

SUPERFAMILY ADRIANITACEAE

A characteristic Permian group occurring rarely in the U. Carboniferous and showing basic external lobe but with up to

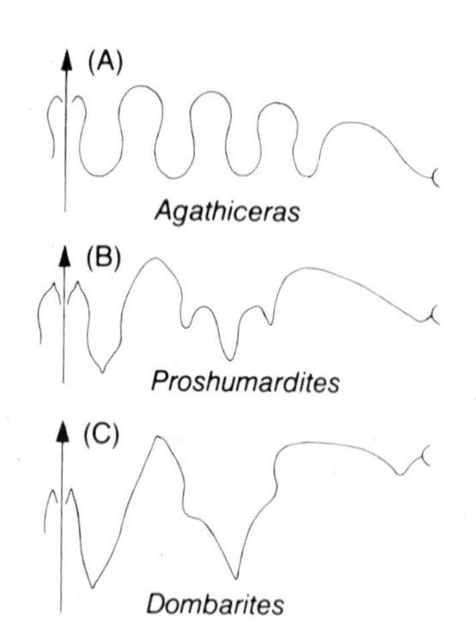

Fig. 6.7.17. Diagrams illustrating the sutures of some late Carboniferous and Permian Goniatitina.

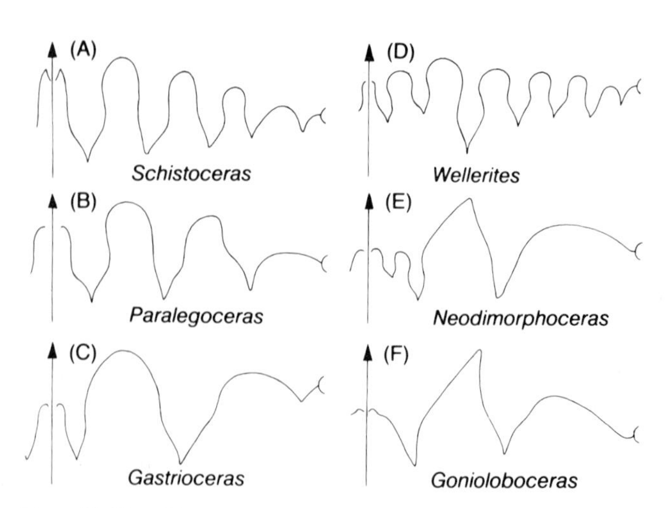

Fig. 6.7.18. Diagrams illustrating the sutures of some late Carboniferous and Permian Goniatitina.

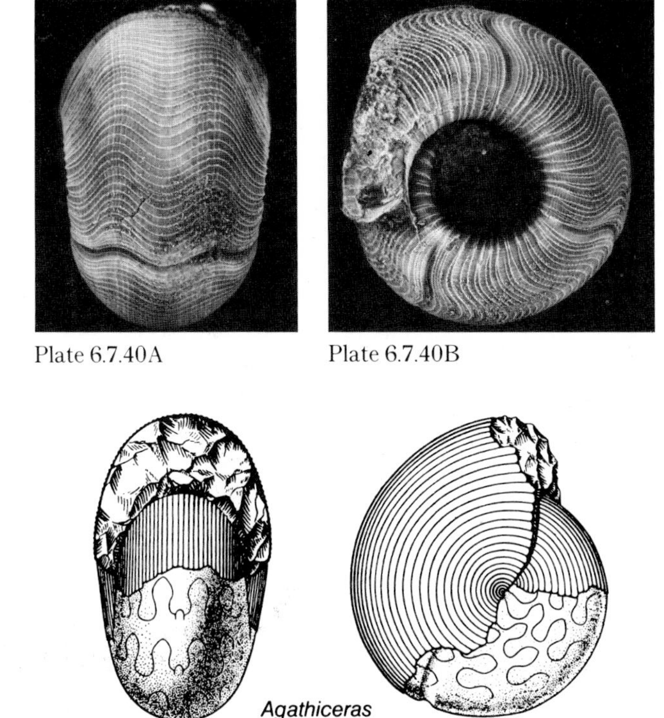

Plate 6.7.40A Plate 6.7.40B Plate 6.7.41 Plate 6.7.42

Plate 6.7.43A Plate 6.7.43B

30 unserrated lobes mostly arising from saddles in the umbilical region.

Fig. 6.7.19H. *Adrianites* Gemmellaro, 1887
Subglobular shell with small umbilicus and spiral ornament and weak growth lines. Six or 7 external lateral lobes in mature suture within a curved band across the flanks.
Permian. Sicily. Related forms widespread in Wordian.
Adrianites elegans Gemmellaro: Permian. Sicily. Suture (after Ruzhencev 1962b).

SUPERFAMILY SHUMARDITACEAE

Subglobular to globular shells with closed or open umbilicus with advanced goniatitic suture with ventral and dorsal lobes and lateral lobes distinctively trifid or bifid: in the perrinitids with 5 lateral lobes and ammonitic frilling. Widespread.

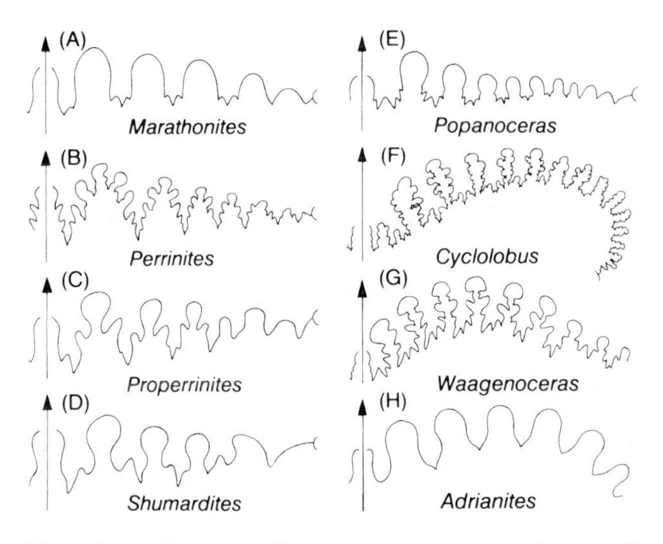

Fig. 6.7.19. Diagrams illustrating the sutures of some U. Carboniferous and Permian Goniatitina.

Fig. 6.7.19D. *Shumardites* Smith, 1903
Subglobular with large umbilicus. Suture with external lateral lobe, asymmetric bifid and lateral lobes differing but arising from trifid divisions of primary lateral lobe.
U. Carboniferous. N. America, USSR.
Shumardites confessus Ruzhencev: U. Carboniferous. Urals, USSR. Suture (after Ruzhencev 1962b).

Fig. 6.7.19B, C. *Perrinites* Böse, 1919
Involute, rounded and laterally compressed shell. Suture derived as in *Shumardites* with 5 lateral lobes and complex ammonitic frilling of lobes and saddles. *Properrinites* (L. Permian) differs in simpler lobes (Fig. 6.7.19C).
Permian (Asselian–Roadian). Typical of Artinskian.
Fig. 6.7.19B. *Perrinites hilli* (Smith): L. Permian. Texas, USA. Suture (after Ruzhencev 1962b).

SUPERFAMILY CYCLOLOBACEAE

Shell form diverse, smooth with open umbilicus. Many sutural elements characteristically within parallel-sided band with 20 to 60 lobes mainly arising from division of primary lateral lobe. Typical of Permian, especially of Sakmarian.

Fig. 6.7.19F. *Cyclolobus* Waagen, 1879
Subinvolute, laterally compressed rounded shells with suture of up to 15 lateral lobes within markedly arcuate band across the flanks: all elements frilled.
U. Permian (especially Dzhulfian). Asia, widespread along Tethyan belt, also Madagascar and Greenland.
Cyclolobus oldhami Waagen: U. Permian. Salt Range, Pakistan. Suture (after Arkell *et al.* 1957).

Fig. 6.7.19G. *Waagenoceras* Gemmellaro, 1887
Subglobular, subinvolute shell with suture like *Cyclolobus* but fewer elements and less frilled.
Permian (especially Wordian). Sicily, Timor and N. America.
Waagenoceras mojsisovicsi Gemmellaro: U. Permian. Sicily. Suture (after Ruzhencev 1962b).

SUPERFAMILY MARATHONITACEAE

Subglobular to globular shells with suture simple, with about 6 lobes laterally several with a characteristic pointedly trifid form. Advanced forms with lobes and saddles frilled.

Fig. 6.7.19A. *Marathonites* Böse, 1917
Subglobular shells with nearly closed umbilicus, often with constrictions. Lateral lobes with distinctive trifid lobes.
U. Carboniferous. N. America, Crimea, Urals, Asia, Timor.
Marathonites uralensis Ruzhencev: U. Carboniferous. Urals, USSR. Suture (after Ruzhencev 1962b).

SUPERFAMILY NEOICOCERATACEAE
A group descended from the Gastrioceratacea retaining essentially simple suture form with limited addition of elements.

Fig. 6.7.20A. *Pseudogastrioceras* Spath, 1930
Typically subdiscoidal with rounded outline and small to wide umbilicus. Ornament of spiral lirae and often marginal ribs. Biconvex growth lines. Suture similar to *Gastrioceras*.
Permian (especially Guadalupian). N. America, Sicily, Armenia, Pakistan, W. Australia.
A. *Pseudogastrioceras goochi* Teichert: U. Permian. W. Australia. Suture (after Glenister and Furnish 1961).

Fig. 6.7.20B. *Metalegoceras* Schindewolf, 1931
Shell subdiscoidal to subglobular. Ventral suture like *Pseudogastrioceras* but with extra umbilical lobes arising by tripartation of umbilical lobe.
Permian (especially Sakmarian). Urals, Oman, W. Australia, N. America.
B. *Metalegoceras clarkei* Miller: L. Permian. W. Australia. Suture (after Glenister and Furnish 1961).

SUPERFAMILY POPANOCERATACEAE
Generally small, laterally compressed, often discoidal and involute shells. Sutures with up to 38 lobes characterized by lobe denticulation, saddles rounded.

Fig. 6.7.19E. *Popanoceras* Hyatt, 1884
Thinly discoidal shells, subinvolute with rounded outline. Ornament of faint sinuous ribs generally with numerous constrictions. Lateral lobes typically with quadrifid digitation.
Permian (especially Guadalupian). Europe, Urals, N. Africa, Timor, Australia.
E. *Popanoceras bowmani* (Böse): Permian. Timor. Suture (after Arkell *et al.* 1957).

SUPERFAMILY THALASSOCERATACEAE
Characterized by basic sutural form with high median saddle dividing the ventral lobe and only the primary lateral and umbilical additional in the ventral suture but with first the lobes (*Eothalassoceras*, U. Carboniferous–L. Permian, Fig. 6.7.20E) then all ventral lobes and saddles (*Epithalassoceras*, U. Permian, Fig. 6.7.20C) becoming frilled.

Fig. 6.7.20D. *Thalassoceras* Gemmellaro, 1887
Subdiscoidal with small umbilicus and rounded outline. Ventral suture with simple lobe digitation.

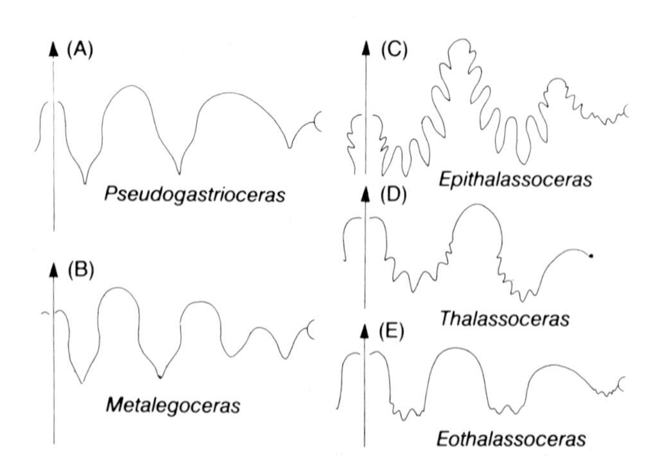

Fig. 6.7.20. Diagrams illustrating the sutures of some U. Carboniferous and Permian Goniatitina.

Permian. Europe, Asia, Australia, N. America.
D. *Thalassoceras welleri* (Böse): L. Permian. Texas, USA. Suture (after Arkell *et al.* 1957).

SUPERFAMILY NEODIMORPHOCERATACEAE
Group characterized by basic sutural form with simple lateral and umbilical lobes, but with the ventral lobe widening and additional lobes forming within it.

Fig. 6.7.18E. *Neodimorphoceras* Schmidt, 1925
Discoidal shell with closed umbilicus and tabular to grooved venter. Suture with 2 lobes between median and first lateral saddle, both arising from dorsal slope of median saddle.
L. Carboniferous–U. Carboniferous. N. America, Europe, Minorca, Urals, Novaya Zemlya, USSR.
E. *Neodimorphoceras texanum* (Smith): U. Carboniferous. Texas, USA. Suture. (After Arkell *et al.* 1957.)

Order Prolecanitida

This major and distinctive long-ranging group is characterized by an initially undivided ventral lobe, and by a progressive development of umbilical lobes which arise from near the umbilical seam ($ELU_{1-n}I$, the U-type ontogeny). The earliest members appear to arise from serpenticonic forms derived from *Imitoceras* and *Gattendorfia*, but differ from them in that no adventitious lobe arises in early ontogeny.

SUPERFAMILY PROLECANITACEAE
The primitive prolecanitids are restricted to the L. Carboniferous (up to E_2) and show a progressive increase in the number of umbilical lobes. Between the ventral lobe and the umbilical seam there are 2 lobes (ELU_2U_1I) in *Protocanites* (Tournaisian, Pl. 6.7.44 (from Ruzhencev), Fig. 6.7.21D), 3 lobes in *Merocanites* (Tournaisian, Fig. 6.7.21C), 4 lobes ($ELU_2U_3U_4U_1I$) in *Prolecanites* and on to 7 lobes in *Acrocanites* (M. Tournaisian, Fig. 6.7.21A). In the daraelitids (L. Carboniferous–U. Permian) there is a weak division of the ventral lobe and digitation of other lobes. *Prodromites* (Tournaisian, N. America, Fig. 6.7.21H) is a bizarre early form with digitation of lobes.

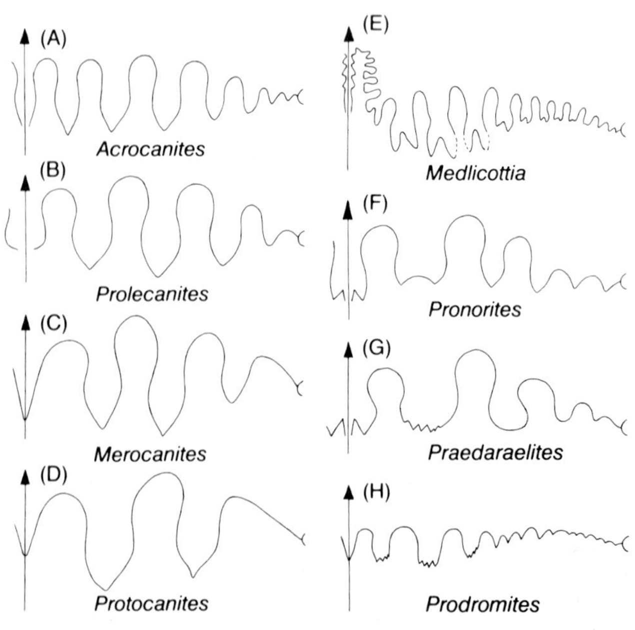

Fig. 6.7.21. Diagrams illustrating the sutures of some Carboniferous and Permian Prolecanitina.

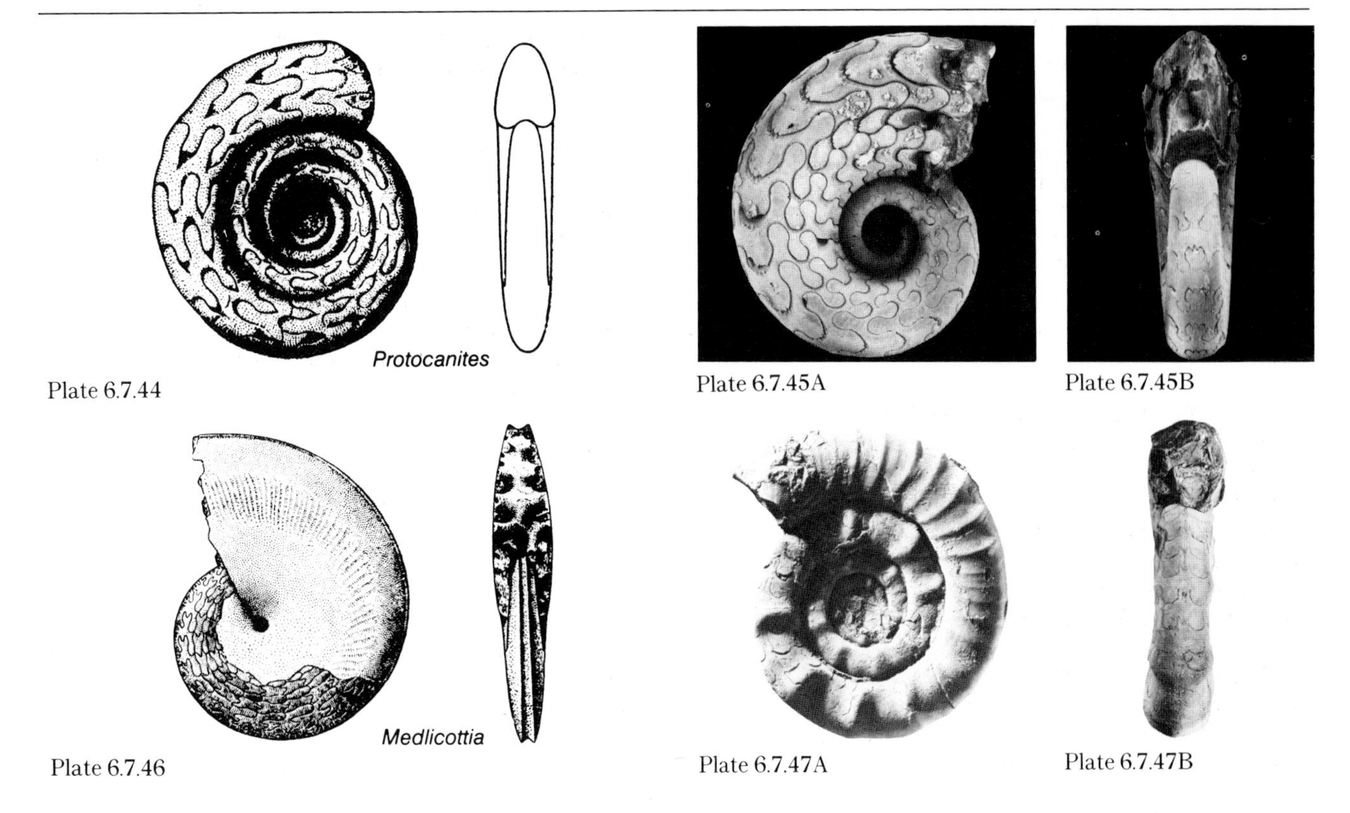

Plate 6.7.44 Plate 6.7.45A Plate 6.7.45B

Plate 6.7.46 Plate 6.7.47A Plate 6.7.47B

Fig. 6.7.21B *Prolecanites* Mojsisovics, 1882
Discoidal with wide open umbilicus, rounded venter and whorls with parallel sides. Undivided ventral lobe and deep dorsal lobe with 5 lobes between, 4 ventrad of the seam.
L. Carboniferous. Europe, Asia, N. America.
B. *Prolecanites americanus* Miller & Garner: Viséan. Indiana, USA. Suture (after Arkell *et al.* 1957).

Pl. 6.7.45. *Praedaraelites* Schindewolf, 1934
Shell discoidal with wide umbilicus and rounded venter. No ornament. Suture with bifid ventral lobe and fine digitation of the rounded lateral lobe(s).
L. Carboniferous (Viséan). Europe, Urals, Indochina.
Praedaraelites culmiensis (Kobold): Viséan; P_{1c}. Tawnyunshinagh, Ireland. Diameter 2.6 cm. (Photo N. J. Riley, IGS.) Fig. 6.7.21G. *P. aktubensis* Ruzhencev: Namurian. Urals, USSR. Suture (after Ruzhencev 1962b).

SUPERFAMILY MEDLICOTTIACEAE
Discoidal shells with narrow to closed umbilici. Suture in pronoritids (Viséan–U. Permian) with trifid ventral lobe, saddles rounded but lateral lobes often bifid (as in *Pronorites*, U. Carboniferous and Permian, Fig. 6.7.21F). In later medlicottids (U. Carboniferous–U. Permian), the first lateral saddle becomes increasingly digitate and a large number of bifurcate lateral lobes may be formed.

Pl. 6.7.46. *Medlicottia* Waagen, 1880
Compressed discoidal shell with closed umbilicus and often with a grooved venter. Suture with a high and digitate first lateral saddle and larger lobes typically bifid. *Artinskia* (U. Carboniferous–U. Permian) is similar but with ventrolateral lobes and a rather simpler suture.
Permian (Sakmarian–Kazanian). Sicily, Urals, Asia, Timor, N. America.
Medlicottia orbignyana (Verneuil): Artinskian. Urals, USSR. (From Ruzhencev 1962.) Fig. 6.7.21E. Suture (Ruzhencev 1962b).

Order Ceratitida

Derivatives of prolecanitacean daraelitids with continuance of U-type ontogeny and a spectacular evolutionary radiation in shell form, ornament and sutural type, the variety of which probably represents the acme of ammonoid evolution. Prosuture latisellate. Primary suture basically quadrilobate (ELUI) with ventral lobe divided by a median saddle. Adult sutures multilobed, mostly ceratitic or ammonitic, rarely secondarily goniatitic.

SUPERFAMILY XENODISCACEAE
Smooth or weakly ornamented subevolute to evolute shells with a mature suture with a divided ventral lobe, two lateral lobes and an umbilical lobe, these lobes with ceratitic frilling, and a deep bifid dorsal lobe and often added umbilical lobes.

Fig. 6.7.22A. *Xenodiscus* Waagen, 1879
Laterally compressed evolute shells with rounded venter and subparallel whorl sides. Usually ribbed. Suture ceratitic, simple.
U. Permian–L. Triassic. N. America, Arctic, Tethys and Pakistan.
A. *Xenodiscus carbonarius* Waagen: U. Permian. Salt Range. Suture including dorsum. (After Spinosa *et al.* 1975.)

Pl. 6.7.47. *Kashmirites* Diener, 1913
Subevolute to evolute shells with peripheral ribbing and often prominent periodic lateral ribs. Suture ceratitic.
Triassic (Scythian). Salt Range to Timor, N. America, Arctic.
Kashmirites borealis (Tozer): Nammalian. Ellesmere Island, Canada. Diameter 5.6 cm. (Photo E. T. Tozer and GSC.)

SUPERFAMILY OTOCERATACEAE
Group arising from Xenodiscaceae showing increasingly ceratitic lobation and up to five umbilical lobes.

Pl. 6.7.48. *Otoceras* Griesbach, 1880
Stout oxycones with triangular whorl section, small umbilici with rim flared in some.

Triassic (L. Scythian). N. America and Arctic, Asia, Siberia and Himalayas.
Otoceras boreale Spath: Griesbachian. Axel Heiberg Island, Canada. Diameter 11.2 cm. (Photo E. T. Tozer and GSC.) Fig. 6.7.22B. The same. Suture. (After Tozer 1981.)

SUPERFAMILY SAGECERATACEAE

Oxycones with multisellate suture with lobes ceratitic or bifid (as in *Sageceras*, U. Triassic, Fig. 6.7.22C). Referred by some to Prolecanitida. World-wide distribution.

SUPERFAMILY DINARITACEAE

Subevolute to evolute shells, laterally compressed, with a variety of ribbing or smooth or weakly ornamented. Suture elaborately ceratitic often with prominent first lateral lobe, rarely goniatitic.

Fig. 6.7.22D. *Tirolites* Mojsisovics, 1879
Laterally compressed shells with rectangular whorl section with tubercles on ventrolateral shoulder. With second lateral lobe on umbilical wall.
Triassic (Scythian). Alps to Himalayas, N. America.
D. *Tirolites idrianus* (Hauer): Yugoslavia. Suture. (After Arkell *et al.* 1957.)

SUPERFAMILY CHORISTOCERATACEAE

Ammoniticonic to heteromorphic shells, later forms being uncoiled or straight in outer whorls; some are helicoids. The only Triassic group retaining basic quadrilobate suture in adult.

Pl. 6.7.49. *Choristoceras* Hauer, 1865
Evolute to uncoiled planispiral shells with uncoiling especially in body chamber. Ornamented with strong unbranched ribs interrupted in some on venter. Suture goniatitic with weakly bifid ventral lobe and lateral lobes.
Triassic (U. Norian). Alps to Timor, N. America and Arctic.
Fig. 6.7.22E. *Choristoceras marshi* (Hauer): Tyrol, Austria. Suture based on Wiedmann and Kullmann (1981). Pl. 6.7.49. The same. Drawing based on Tozer (1980).

SUPERFAMILY MEGAPHYLLITACEAE

Small subglobular to compressed rounded, often involute, smooth shells. Suture simple ceratitic with many umbilical lobes.

Fig. 6.7.22F. *Megaphyllites* Mojsisovics, 1879
Moderately compressed involute shells. Smooth with sigmoidal growth lines and periodic constrictions.
Triassic (Anisian–Norian). Europe, Asia (widespread) and N. America.
F. *Megaphyllites immaturus* Kiparisova: Triassic. Caucasus. Suture. (After Kiparisova 1958.)

SUPERFAMILY LOBITACEAE

Shell globular with closed umbilicus, usually smooth with a contracting aperture. An aberrant group of uncertain origin. Suture goniatitic with lanceolate lobes and saddles.

Fig. 6.7.23A. *Lobites* Mojsisovics
Sphaerocones with faint radial ribs crossing flanks and venter. Suture goniatitic with lateral lobes produced by bifid division.
Triassic (Ladinian–?Carnian). Europe, Asia, E. Pacific, N. America.
A. *Lobites ellipticus* (Hauer): Ladinian. Alps, Europe. Suture. (After Arkell *et al.* 1957.)

SUPERFAMILY NORITACEAE

Probably the root-stock for the remaining ceratitids. Derived from xenodiscaceans. With goniatitic to ceratitic sutures and a wide range of shell form, smooth to ribbed.

Pl. 6.7.50. *Ophiceras* Griesbach, 1880
Compressed evolute shells with rounded venter and smooth surface, rarely with faint ribs. Growth line striae sigmoidal. Suture simple ceratitic.
Triassic (L. Scythian). Asia and Arctic.
Ophiceras commune Spath: Triassic (Griesbachian). Axel Heiberg Island, Canada. Diameter 7.4 cm. (From Tozer 1970.) Fig. 6.7.23B. *O. sakuntula* Diener: Scythian. Himalayas. Suture. (After Wiedmann and Kullmann 1981.)

Pl. 6.7.51. *Meekoceras* Hyatt, 1879
Discoidal, involute to subevolute shells with tabulate venters and smooth sides. Sutures simple ceratitic.
Triassic (Nammalian). N. America, Arctic, Timor, Madagascar.
Meekoceras gracililatum White: U. Scythian. Ellesmere Island, Canada. Diameter 7.8 cm. (Photo E. T. Tozer and GSC.) Fig. 6.7.23C. The same. Scythian. Idaho, USA. Suture. (After Spath 1934.)

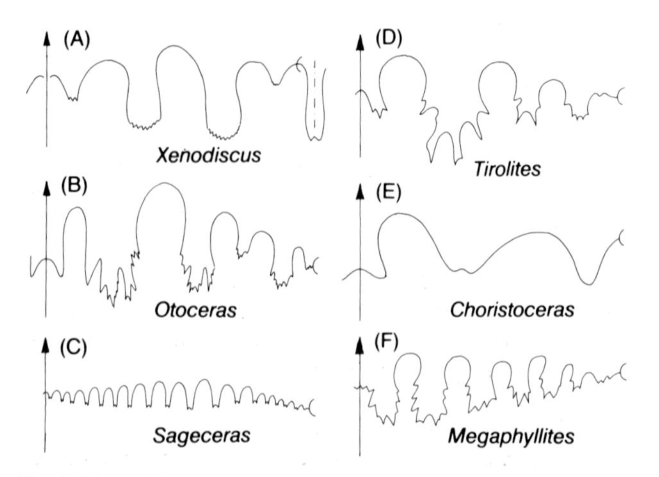

Fig. 6.7.22. Diagrams illustrating the sutures of some Triassic Ceratitina.

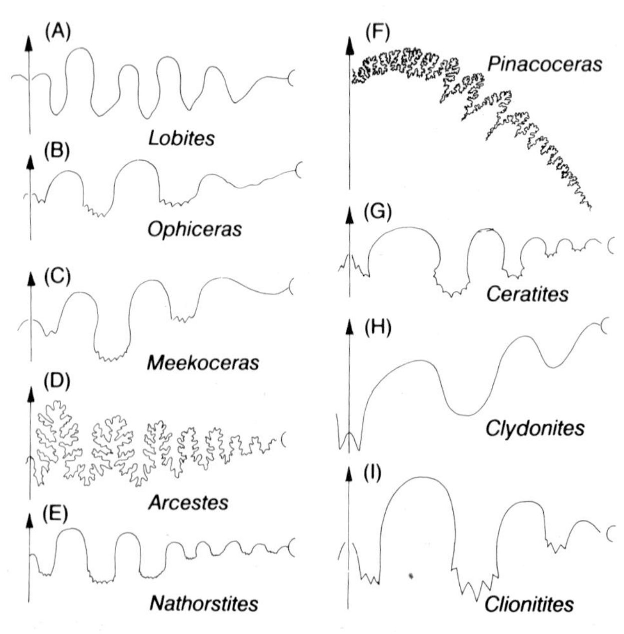

Fig. 6.7.23. Diagrams illustrating sutures of some Triassic Ceratitina.

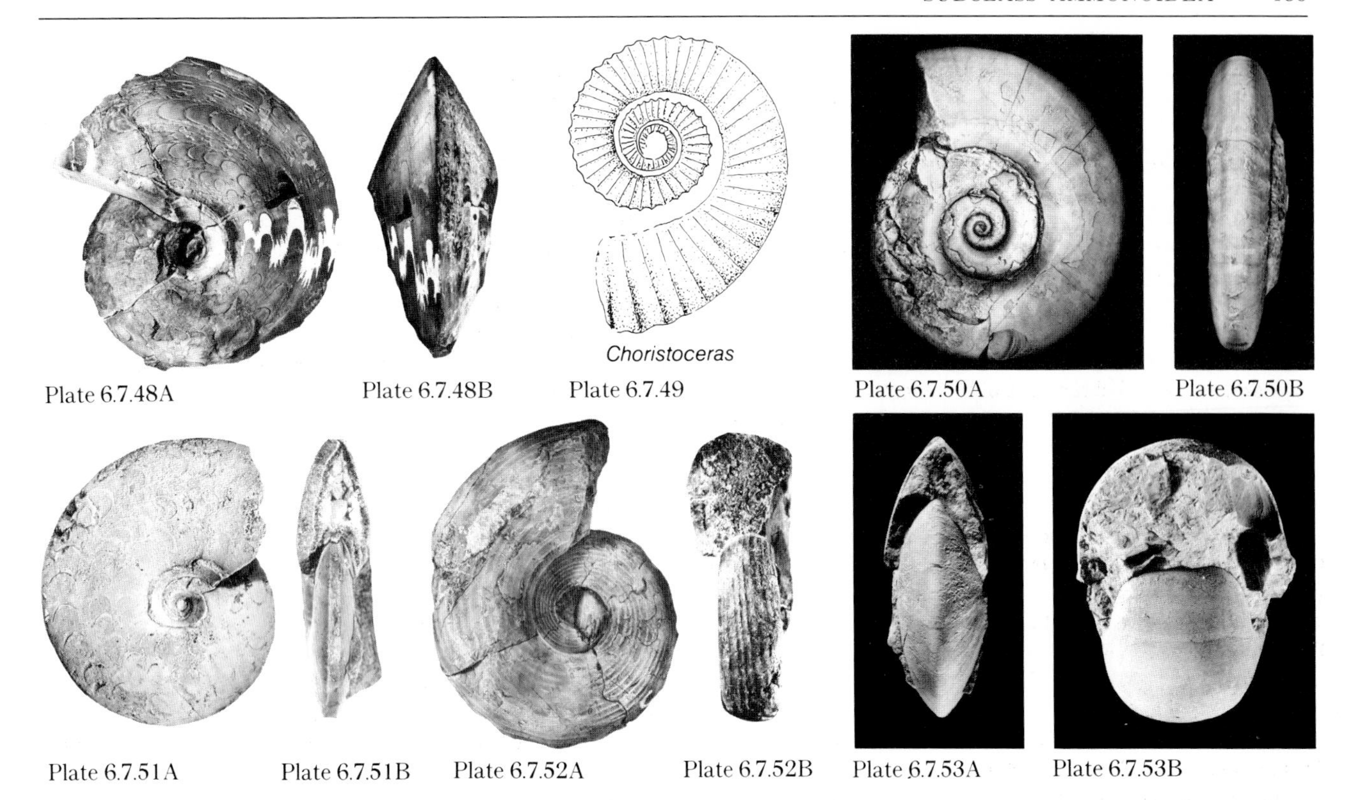

Plate 6.7.48A Plate 6.7.48B Plate 6.7.49 Plate 6.7.50A Plate 6.7.50B

Plate 6.7.51A Plate 6.7.51B Plate 6.7.52A Plate 6.7.52B Plate 6.7.53A Plate 6.7.53B

Pl. 6.7.52. *Euflemingites* Spath, 1934
Subevolute to subinvolute shells, slightly compressed, with strong strigate spiral ornament.
Triassic (Scythian). Himalayas to Timor, N. America, Arctic.
Euflemingites romunderi Tozer: Nammalian. Ellesmere Island, Canada. Diameter 19.6 cm. (Photo E. T. Tozer and GSC.)

Pl. 6.7.53A. *Owenites* Hyatt & Smith, 1905
Lenticular to oxyconic involute shells with smooth surface. Sutures ceratitic.
Triassic (Scythian). N. America, Timor, New Zealand, Japan, China, Afghanistan, Primor'ye.
A. *Owenites egrediens* Welter: Scythian. Timor. Diameter 4.6 cm.

SUPERFAMILY ARCESTACEAE

Involute, smooth-surfaced (leiostracous) subglobular shells with complex ammonitic sutures. An abundant group.

Pl. 6.7.53B. *Arcestes* Suess, 1865
Smooth, subglobular, many-whorled shells with long body chamber and constricted apertures and apertural modifications in many. Sutures ammonitic with saddles of triangular outline.
Triassic (Carnian–Norian).
Arcestes (Proarcestes) haueri (Welter): Anisian. Timor. Diameter 7.5 cm. Fig. 6.7.23D. *A. (A.) intuslobiatus* Mojsisovics. Suture. (After Arkell *et al.* 1957.)

SUPERFAMILY PINACOCERATACEAE

Smooth (leiostracous) involute to evolute laterally compressed shells with ammonitic sutures often very complex.

Fig. 6.7.23F. *Pinacoceras* Mojsisovics, 1873
Very compressed discoidal shells with acute venter and smooth surface. Sutures of extreme ammonitic complexity.
Triassic (Norian). Alps to Timor, N. America.
F. *Pinacoceras metternichi* (Hauer): Norian. Austria. Suture showing overall ventrad projection and moss-like fine frilling of the elements. (After Arkell *et al.* 1957.)

SUPERFAMILY DANUBITACEAE

Group characterized by simple ribbing, short body chamber and ceratitic suture but a wide range of shell forms.

SUPERFAMILY NATHORSTITACEAE

Smooth or ribbed shells with a long body chamber and variety of ceratitic suture patterns.

Fig. 6.7.23E. *Nathorstites* Böhm, 1903
Involute, often rotund, discoidal shells with smooth surface and sharp keel.
Triassic. (U. Ladinian, ?L. Carnian.)
E. *Nathorstites mcconnelli* (Whiteaves): ?Carnian. British Columbia, Canada. Suture. (After Arkell *et al.* 1957.)

SUPERFAMILY CERATITACEAE

Mostly subevolute to subinvolute highly ornamented (trachyostracous) shells with branched ribs. Basic groups with ceratitic suture, but derivatives both simpler and more complex.

Pl. 6.7.54. *Ceratites* de Haan, 1825
Moderately evolute shells with strong ornament, in outer whorls of coarse ribs usually terminating on ventrolateral shoulder with nodes.
Triassic (Ladinian). Europe.
Ceratites nodosus (Bruguière): Muschelkalk. Stuttgart, W. Germany. Diameter 10.4 cm. Fig. 6.7.23G. The same. Suture. (After Zittel 1884.)

SUPERFAMILY TRACHYCERATACEAE

Generally involute, highly ornamented (trachyostracous) shells with venter with two or three furrows, or keeled, with tubercles where ribs cross. Sutures mostly ammonitic.

Pl. 6.7.55. *Himavatites* Diener, 1906
Involute, compressed shells with flexuous primary and secondary ribs with nodes or spines on primaries and with furrowed venter.

Triassic (M. Norian). Himalayas, Timor, N. America.
Himavatites columianus McLearn: Norian. British Columbia, Canada. Diameter 7 cm. (Photo E. T. Tozer and GSC.)

SUPERFAMILY CLYDONITACEAE
Shells with sulcate venters and elaborate sculpture (trachyostracous). Sutures goniatitic (as in *Clydonites*, Norian, Fig. 6.7.23H) or weakly ceratitic (as in *Clionitites*, Ladinian–Norian, Fig. 6.7.23I).

SUPERFAMILY TROPITACEAE
Involute to evolute shells with ribs and nodes in some and development of a keel. Suture usually ammonitic but secondarily ceratitic or goniatitic in some.

Pl. 6.7.56. *Tropites* mojsisovics, 1875
Stout, open-umbilicate shells with arched venters and with keel and bordering furrows: aperture contracting. Flanks with prorsiradiate ribs and often umbilical nodes. Ammonitic suture.
Triassic. Carnian. Alps to Timor, N. America.
Tropites subbullatus (Hauer). Diameter 6 cm. (From Arkell *et al.* 1957.)

Pl. 6.7.57. *Juvavites* Mojsisovics, 1879
Involute, subglobular to subdiscoidal shells with rounded venter but without keel. Ribs branching and may be interrupted over venter.
Triassic. Norian. World-wide.
Juvavites magnus McLearn: Norian. British Columbia, Canada. Diameter 8.3 cm. (Photo E. T. Tozer and GSC.)

Order Phylloceratida

A very stable, long-ranging group the origins of which may lie in the early Triassic xenodiscaceans or otoceratacean. Usually smooth to weakly ornamented (leiostracous) involute to evolute shell. Early forms with primary suture quadrilobate (ELU_1I), later, and typically in the Jurassic and Cretaceous, quinquelobate (ELU_2U_1I). Adult suture with characteristic lituid double-pronged dorsal lobe (I) (as in *Sowerbyceras*, Valanginian, Fig. 6.7.24D), and usually with phylloid saddle terminations. Many small umbilical lobes may arise from an early umbilical lobe (U_4).

Pl. 6.7.58. *Phylloceras* Suess, 1865
Involute compressed shells with maximum whorl width near the mid flanks. Ornament of dense growth line lirae: inner shell surface smooth. Sutures with triphylloid saddle terminations.
Jurassic and Cretaceous (Sinemurian–Aptian). World-wide: in Old World more common in Tethyan area and reaching boreal regions only at times of significant sea-level rises.
Phylloceras heterophyllum (Sowerby): Toarcian. Whitby, England. Diameter 13.7 cm. (Photo M. K. Kowarth and BMNH.) Fig. 6.7.24C. *P. onoensis* (Stanton): Aptian. USA. Suture. (After Wiedmann 1962.)

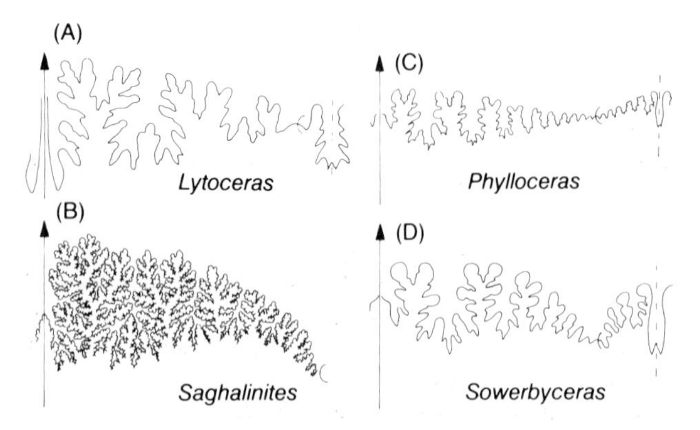

Fig. 6.7.24. Diagrams illustrating the sutures of some Jurassic and Cretaceous Phylloceratida and Lytoceratida.

Order Lytoceratida

A very long-ranging stock the origin of which is debated. Usually evolute and loosely coiled, in some gyroconic, with nearly circular whorl cross-section. Usually unornamented (leiostracous) apart from flares and in some constrictions and ribbing. Primary suture quinquelobate (ELU_2U_1I in Lytocerataceae) or sexilobate ($ELU_2U_3U_1I$ in Tetragoniatitaceae) but in the two-member superfamilies with the dorsal lobe simple or frilled and often laid down on the previous septum (septal lobe) in the Tetragoniatitaceae. Saddle terminations usually with bipolar frills and often complex and moss-like (as in the tetragoniatitacean *Saghalinites*, U. Cretaceous, Fig. 6.7.24B. (After Arkell *et al.* 1957.)

Pl. 6.7.59. *Lytoceras* Suess, 1865
Evolute shells with round to quadrate whorl section with little or no impressed depth. Ornament of crinkled radial lirae or riblets: in some with lamellar flares with corresponding constrictions on internal mould.
Jurassic. World-wide: in Old World more common in Tethyan areas and reaching boreal and Arctic regions at times of significant sea-level rises.
Lytoceras fimbriatus (Sowerby): U. Pliensbachian. Lyme Regis, Dorset, England. (Photo M. K. Howarth and BMNH.) Fig. 6.7.24A. *L. juilleti* (d'Orbigny): Valanginian. France. Suture (after Wiedmann 1968).

Order Ammonitida

Suborder Ammonitida

A major group of normally coiled ammonoids characteristic of the Jurassic and Cretaceous. Shell ornament usually well developed (trachyostracous) with ribs, tubercles, nodes and spines common. Shell usually thick. Primary suture basically quinquelobate (ELU_2U_1I) with dorsal lobe (I) simple and unfrilled. Prosuture angustisellate. Adult suture in some complex. Following Suess, the view was held for a long time that the various groups (families or superfamilies) of ammonitids were derived from the leiostracous Phylloceratina and Lytoceratina, probably in waves related to transgressive pulses leading to new colonization of boreal waters where the ammonitids predominate. Such a simple view is not now accepted, and whether the group was derived from the Lytoceratida or Ceratitida is debated. A common relationship of most stocks is currently accepted, as illustrated in Fig. 6.7.8. Many iterative evolutionary radiations are well documented, and several frequently repeated evolutionary trends are observed: to larger size; to smooth bands on the venter; to grooves on the venter; to smooth keels on the venter; to ribs swinging sharply over the venter; to these leading to corded keels. Within this plethora of form dimorphism is strong. Macroconchs (?♀) are often very large but simple-apertured; microconchs (?♂) are small but have distinctive apertures with constrictions, lappets, rostra and other variants. Found in a wide range of lithologies but commonest in offshore facies.

Plate 6.7.54A Plate 6.7.54B Plate 6.7.55A Plate 6.7.55B

Plate 6.7.56A Plate 6.7.56B Plate 6.7.57A Plate 6.7.57B Plate 6.7.57C

Plate 6.7.58A Plate 6.7.58B Plate 6.7.59A Plate 6.7.59B Plate 6.7.60

Plate 6.7.61A Plate 6.7.61B Plate 6.7.62A Plate 6.7.62B

SUPERFAMILY PSILOCERATACEAE

A group of diversely ornamented generally evolute to subevolute shells arising from smooth-ventered and unsculptured ancestors and progressively developing ribs, ventral chevrons or keels, often angular, or tricarinate venters. Usually with strong lateral ribs; some are involute oxycones (*Oxynoticeras*). Origin debated, either from Triassic Ceratitina or Phylloceratida.

Pl. 6.7.60. *Psiloceras* Hyatt, 1867

Smooth and evolute, laterally compressed shells developing weak simple lateral ribs but always with a smooth and rounded venter. Entry used to define basal Jurassic.

L. Jurassic (L. Hettangian). Eurasia, Americas.

Psiloceras planorbis (J. Sowerby): Hettangian. Doniford Bay, England. Diameter 6.3 cm. (Photo J. D. Price.)

Pl. 6.7.61. *Schlotheimia* Bayle, 1878

Laterally compressed shells with strong ribbing, simple or rarely bifurcating, producing distinctive chevrons crossing the venter or, more usually, interrupted by a ventral groove. Thought to be derived from *Psiloceras*.

L. Jurassic (U. Hettangian). Eurasia, Americas.

Schlotheimia oblonga (Quenstedt): Hettangian. Leicestershire, England. Diameter 3.8 cm.

Pl. 6.7.62. *Arietites* Waagen, 1869
Often very large evolute shells with subquadrate whorl section with tricarinate and bisulcate venter and strong, near-rectiradiate ribbing on flanks.
L. Jurassic (L. Sinemurian). Europe to S.E. Asia, Americas.
Arietites bucklandi macer (Quenstedt): Sinemurian. Stuttgart Vaihingen, W. Germany. Diameter 23.3 cm. (From Schlegelmilch 1976.)

Pl. 6.7.63. *Oxynoticeras* Hyatt, 1875
Subinvolute to involute, laterally compressed oxyconic shells with ribbing only strong on lower flanks.
L. Jurassic (Sinemurian). Europe and N. Africa to Indonesia and Japan. S. America.
Oxynoticeras oxynotum (Quenstedt): Sinemurian. Schömberg, Württemberg, W. Germany. Diameter 3.5 cm. (After Dean *et al.* 1961.)

SUPERFAMILY EODEROCERATACEAE

A group of cryptic origin derived from Psiloceratacea or Lytoceratida. Some early forms evolute and serpenticonic and ornamented with strong ribs and tubercles, then with fine to coarse ribbing, then perhaps tuberculate, and more involute. Later forms oxyconic or serpenticonic and tuberculate.

Pl. 6.7.64. *Microderoceras* Hyatt, 1871
Evolute, serpenticonic shells ornamented with coarse radial ribs on flanks with outer and inner spines and weak, fine ribs over venter.
L. Jurassic (Sinemurian). Europe, Central and S. America.
Microderoceras birchi (J. Sowerby): Sinemurian. Charmouth, England. Diameter 17.5 cm.

Pl. 6.7.65. *Liparoceras* Hyatt, 1867
Subinvolute to involute and sphaeroconic shells with whorl dimensions increasing rapidly and deep umbilicus. Ribbing fine to coarse, finer on arched venter and on flanks bituberculate. Spiral lirae in some.
L. Jurassic (Pliensbachian). Europe, N. Africa, Indonesia.
Liparoceras cheltiense (Murchison): Pliensbachian. Cheltenham, England. Diameter 7.2 cm. (From Spath 1938.)

Pl. 6.7.66. *Aegoceras* Waagen 1869
Serpenticones with close, strong ribbing, some forming ventral chevrons and may be weakly tuberculate. Possibly derived from liparoceratid ancestors by intermediates (such as *Androgynoceras*) which have inner whorls like *Aegoceras* and outer whorls like *Liparoceras* giving a paedomorphogenic phylogeny.
L. Jurassic (L. Pliensbachian). Europe.
Aegoceras aff. *figulinum* (Simpson): L. Pliensbachian. Lyme Regis, Dorset, England. Diameter 6.3 cm.

Pl. 6.7.67. *Amaltheus* de Montfort, 1808
Subevolute to involute, compressed to very compressed and oxyconic, with triangular to circular whorl section. Ribs bifurcate to trifurcate, passing forward to produce a prominent corded keel. Spiral ornament in some oxycones.
L. Jurassic (U. Pliensbachian). Europe, N. Africa, Asia, N. America.
Amaltheus margaritatus de Montford: Sandford, Dorset, England. Diameter 10.0 cm. (Photo M. K. Howarth and BMNH.)

Pl. 6.7.68. *Pleuroceras* Hyatt, 1867
Subevolute to evolute shells with whorl section quadrilateral with strong radial ribs and tubercles or spines often formed, venter flat with prominent keel bordered by flat areas or grooves: corded keel with strong chevrons to smooth keel.
L. Jurassic (U. Pliensbachian). Europe and N. Africa.
Pleuroceras spinatum (Bruguière): Pliensbachian. Quedlinburg, W. Germany. Diameter 6.5 cm. (Photo M. K. Howarth and BMNH.)

Pl. 6.7.69. *Dactylioceras* Hyatt, 1867
Evolute to serpenticonic, laterally compressed shells with subcircular or slightly compressed whorl section. Ribbing regular and near rectiradiate on flanks, bifurcating on the outer flanks. Early stages often tuberculate.
L. Jurassic (U. Pliensbachian–Toarcian). World-wide.
Dactylioceras commune (J. Sowerby): Toarcian. Whitby, England. Diameter 7.9 cm. (Photo M. K. Howarth and BMNH.)

Pl. 6.7.70. *Catacoeloceras* Buckman, 1923
Similar to *Dactylioceras* but shell subevolute and stouter with whorl section rather depressed and in some with flattened venter.
L. Jurassic (L. Toarcian). Europe to Indonesia, Arctic, S. America.
Catacoeloceras crassum (Young & Bird): Toarcian. Ravenscar, England. Diameter 6.7 cm. (Photo M. K. Howarth and BMNH.)

SUPERFAMILY HILDOCERATACEAE

Laterally compressed shells, often subevolute, with ventral keel and ornament of straight or, more typically, sigmoidal or falcate ribs. Derived from Eoderocerataceae. In some sutures secondarily ceratitic. Considered as root-stock for remaining Ammonitina. Dimorphism widespread and marked.

Pl. 6.7.71. *Harpoceras* Waagen, 1869
Subevolute, compressed shells with elliptical-compressed whorl section and flat flanks with a ventral keel and marked umbilical edge. Falcate ribbing strongest on outer flanks and projecting forward on to venter.
L. Jurassic (L. Toarcian). World-wide.
Harpoceras falciferum (J. Sowerby): Toarcian. Whitby, England. Diameter 12.5 cm. (Photo M. K. Howarth and BMNH.)

Pl. 6.7.72. *Hildoceras* Hyatt, 1867
Evolute, laterally compressed shells with quadrate whorl section and tricarinate and bisulcate venter with falcate ribs, stronger on outer flanks, interrupted usually by strong median lateral groove.
L. Jurassic (L. Toarcian). Europe, Asia Minor, Japan.
Hildoceras bifrons (Bruguière): Toarcian. Whitby, England. Diameter 9.5 cm. (Photo M. K. Howarth and BMNH.)

Pl. 6.7.73. *Dumortieria* Haug, 1885
Laterally compressed shells with subcircular to compressed elliptical to subquadrate whorl section and weak smooth keel. Frequent simple, almost radial straight ribs on flanks which curve abruptly forward towards venter.
L. Jurassic (U. Toarcian). Europe to S.E. Asia and Indonesia.
Dumortiera moorei (Lycett): Toarcian. Penn Wood, Stroud, England. Diameter 9.2 cm. (Photo M. K. Howarth and BMNH.)

Pl. 6.7.74. *Hammatoceras* Hyatt, 1867
Stout, subevolute to evolute shells with inflated-triangular whorl section and distinct keel. Primary ribs on umbilical wall lead to tubercles at umbilical edge, from which secondaries arise in bundles and cross whorl side to reach keel. Microconchs with lappets, macroconchs large with smooth outer whorl and simple aperture.
L. Jurassic (U. Toarcian). Europe, N. Africa, S.E. Asia and Indonesia, Americas.

Plate 6.7.63A 6.7.63B Plate 6.7.64A 6.7.64B

Plate 6.7.65A 6.7.65B Plate 6.7.66A 6.7.66B

Plate 6.7.67A 6.7.67B Plate 6.7.68A 6.7.68B Plate 6.7.69A 6.7.69B

Plate 6.7.70A 6.7.70B Plate 6.7.71A 6.7.71B Plate 6.7.72A 6.7.72B

Plate 6.7.73A 6.7.73B Plate 6.7.74A 6.7.74B Plate 6.7.75A 6.7.75B

Hammatoceras insigne (Schübler): Toarcian. France. Diameter 7.9 cm. (Photo M. K. Howarth and BMNH.)

Pl. 6.7.75. *Brasilia* Buckman, 1898
Subinvolute, laterally compressed shells with well-developed sharp keel and fine sigmoidal ribs developed especially on the outer flanks. Microconchs with lappets, macroconchs large with smooth outer whorl and simple aperture ornamented with only growth line lirae on body chamber.
M. Jurassic (Aalenian). Europe, N. Africa, Iran.
Brasilia similis (Buckman): Aalenian. Horn Park, Beaminster, England. Macroconch. Diameter 18.9 cm.

Pl. 6.7.76. *Sonninia* Douvillé, 1879
Stout subinvolute to subevolute shells with rounded whorl outline and prominent blunt keel. Ornament of strong irregular ribs with a median row of tubercles. Body chamber of macroconchs smooth.
M. Jurassic (Aalenian and L. Bajocian). World-wide.
Sonninia crassispinata (Buckman): Aalenian. Horn Park, Beaminster, England. Diameter 4.5 cm.

Pl. 6.7.77. *Haplopleuroceras* Buckman, 1892
Early whorls with keel and ribs with lateral nodes, later whorls with subquadrate whorl section and simple ribs on flanks and venter bisulcate and keeled.
M. Jurassic (L. Bajocian). Europe and N. Africa.
Haplopleuroceras subspinatum (Buckman): Bajocian. Horn Park, Beaminster, England. Diameter 6.3 cm.

Pl. 6.7.78. *Tmetoceras* Buckman, 1892
Laterally compressed subevolute to evolute shells with subquadrate to circular whorl section and strong, frequent radial ribs interrupted on venter by deep median groove.
M. Jurassic (Aalenian). World-wide.
Tmetoceras scissum Benecke: Bonscombe Hill, Dorset, England. Diameter 3.9 cm.

SUPERFAMILY SPIROCERATACEAE

A small group of Middle Jurassic uncoiled heteromorphic orthoconic to gyroconic ammonites of uncertain origin. The suture shows an ontogenetic reduction from primarily quinquelobate to trilobate in the adult (EU_2I) (Dietl 1978).

Pl. 6.7.79. *Spiroceras* Quenstedt, 1858
Shell cyrtoconic but with torticonic and helicoid variants. Ornament of ribs with lateral tubercles or spines and a smooth band on the venter.
M. Jurassic (Bajocian and Bathonian). Europe, USSR, Africa.
Spiroceras bifurcatum (Quenstedt): U. Bajocian. S. Germany. (After Arkell *et al.* 1957.)

SUPERFAMILY STEPHANOCERATACEAE

An abundant group showing a wide range of shell form from evolute serpenticones to globular sphaericones or extremely compressed oxycones but mostly ribbed with ribs passing over the venter, or forming corded keels, or interrupted. Dimorphism is well shown with significant apertural modification of the microconchs. Suture united by late appearance of umbilical lobes (U_n) in dorsal saddle (U_1I).

Pl. 6.7.80. *Sphaeroceras* Bayle, 1878
Tightly coiled subglobular shells with closed umbilicus and body chamber ending in constriction with flared collar. Ribbed, often smooth on internal mould. Ribs with primaries and secondaries, often weakly developed on umbilical edge.
M. Jurassic (Bajocian). Europe, N. Africa, Iran, Alaska.
Sphaeroceras brongniarti (Sowerby): L. Bajocian. Loders Cross, Dorset, England. Diameter 2.6 cm.

Pl. 6.7.81. *Morrisiceras* Buckman, 1920
Sphaerocones with deep umbilicus and rounded whorl outline. Branched ribbing on early whorls, later only with ventral ribbing which fades towards flanks.
M. Jurassic (M. Bathonian). Europe.
Morrisiceras comma (Buckman): M. Bathonian. Shepton Montague, Dorset, England. Macroconch. Diameter 6.7 cm.

Pl. 6.7.82. *Macrocephalites* Zittel, 1884
Large sphaerocones, slightly compressed, with ribbed inner whorls and smooth large body chamber with aperture slightly contracting in macroconch.
M. Jurassic (Callovian). World-wide.
Macrocephalites tumida (Reinecke): L. Callovian. Elat'ma, USSR. Diameter 6.4 cm. (From Lippov and Druishchitz 1958.)

Pl. 6.7.83. *Kosmoceras* Waagen, 1869
Compressed shells with rather flat venter and variously ribbed and noded. Probably derived from macrocephalitids. Shell with lateral and ventrolateral tubercles or spines and smooth ventral band. Dimorphism well developed, microconchs small and lappeted, macroconchs larger, less strongly ornamented in outer whorls, and with simple aperture.
M. Jurassic (Callovian). World-wide.
Kosmocercas spinatum (Sowerby): U. Callovian. Łuków, Poland. Diameter 4.4 cm. (From Makowski 1952.)

Pl. 6.7.84. *Quenstedtoceras* Hyatt, 1877
Derived from rotund early stephanocerataceans and generally laterally compressed in early whorls with well-developed sickle-shaped primary and intercalated secondary ribs forming chevrons on venter but not a keel. Macroconchs large, often approaching sphaerocones with smooth body chamber and simple contracted aperture. Microconchs small, strongly ribbed and with projecting rostrum.
M. and U. Jurassic (U. Callovian and L. Oxfordian). World-wide.
Quenstedtoceras mariae (d'Orbigny): L. Oxfordian. Łuków, Poland. A, B. Microconch, diameter 5.2 cm. C. Macroconch, diameter 15.5 cm. (From Makowski 1962.)

Pl. 6.7.85. *Cardioceras* Neumayr and Uhlig, 1881
Derivative of *Quenstedtoceras* by development of corded keel. Shell often compressed with ribs and bullate tubercles often well developed. Microconchs with rostra. Macroconchs larger, with body chamber smoother.
Jurassic (Oxfordian). World-wide.
Cardioceras cordatum (Sowerby): Oxfordian. Diameter 5.1 cm. (After Ruzhencev 1962b.)

SUPERFAMILY PERISPHINCTACEAE

Shell form variable but mostly rather serpenticonic and laterally compressed with regular, usually biplicate ribbing. Dimorphism gives large macroconchs with smoother or less frequently ribbed body chamber. Microconchs usually with apertural modifications. Suture very variable but with U_1 universally subdivided from which derivation from Stephanocerataceae is inferred. An abundant late Jurassic and early Cretaceous group.

Pl. 6.7.86. *Parkinsonia* Bayle, 1878
Compressed evolute shells and whorls with rectilinear flanks and venter with strong primary ribbing on flanks becoming biplicate on outer flanks and interrupted on the venter by a

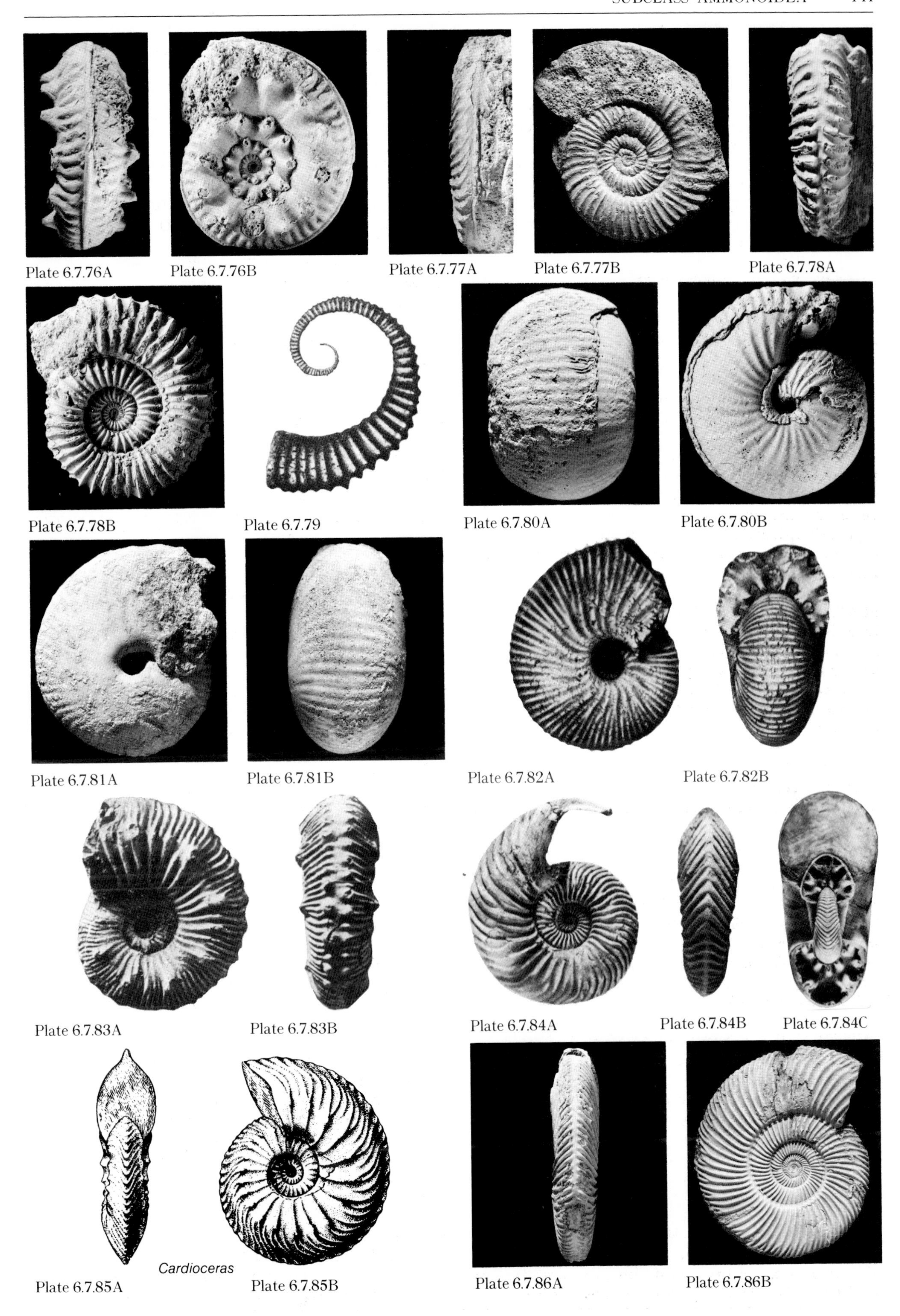

Plate 6.7.76A Plate 6.7.76B Plate 6.7.77A Plate 6.7.77B Plate 6.7.78A

Plate 6.7.78B Plate 6.7.79 Plate 6.7.80A Plate 6.7.80B

Plate 6.7.81A Plate 6.7.81B Plate 6.7.82A Plate 6.7.82B

Plate 6.7.83A Plate 6.7.83B Plate 6.7.84A Plate 6.7.84B Plate 6.7.84C

Plate 6.7.85A Plate 6.7.85B Plate 6.7.86A Plate 6.7.86B

Plate 6.7.87A

Plate 6.7.87B

Plate 6.7.88A

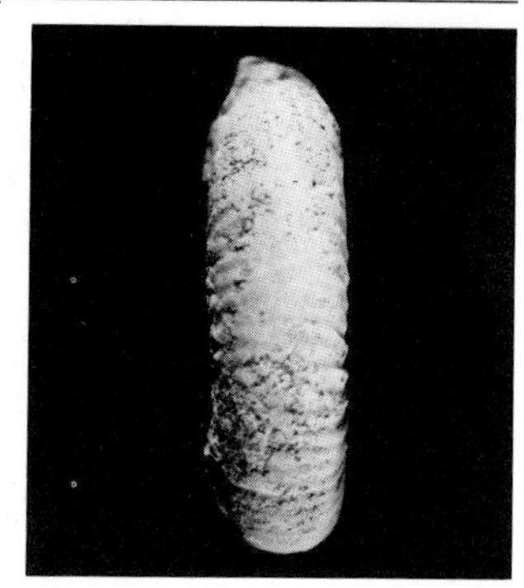

Plate 6.7.88B

smooth band.
M. Jurassic (Bajocian–L. Bathonian). Europe, N. Africa, USSR, Iran.
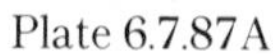
Parkinsonia parkinsoni (J. Sowerby): U. Bajocian. Burton Cliff, Dorset, England. Diameter 13.3 cm.

Pl. 6.7.87. *Tulites* Buckman, 1921
Rotund shells with rounded depressed whorl section and deep umbilicus with slowly contracting aperture to body chamber. Ribs with primaries and secondaries often weakly noded on umbilical edge. Formerly placed with Stephanoceratacea.
M. Jurassic (Bathonian). Europe, Saudi Arabia.
Tulites modiolaris (Smith): Thornford, England. Macroconch. Diameter 14.8 cm.

Pl. 6.7.88. *Cleistosphinctes* Arkell, 1953
Compressed evolute shells, ribbed with division from primaries giving secondaries on the mid flanks. With large, asymmetric spatulate lappets on aperture of macroconchs.
M. Jurassic (U. Bajocian). Europe, N. Africa, USSR.
Cleistosphinctes cleistus (Buckman): U. Bajocian. Burton Cliff, Dorset, England. Microconch. Diameter 3.2 cm.

Pl. 6.7.89. *Strenoceras* Hyatt, 1900
Subevolute shells with rounded whorl outline and ornamented with very strong and sharp ribs mostly simple and straight with ventral and lateral tubercles and a smooth band on the venter.
M. Jurassic (U. Bajocian). Europe, N. Africa, USSR.
Strenoceras (Garantiana) parkinsoni longidens (Quenstedt): U. Bajocian. Upton Farm, Dorset, England. Diameter 6.9 cm.

Pl. 6.7.90. *Peltoceras* Waagen, 1871
Evolute and serpenticonic shells with little or no impressed depth. Early whorls with strong ribs bifurcating or trifurcating on outer flanks. Outer whorls with coarse and massive lateral tubercles and quadrate section.
U. Jurassic (Callovian and Oxfordian). World-wide.
Peltoceras athleta (Phillips): U. Callovian. Chickerell, England. Length 14.1 cm.

Pl. 6.7.91. *Perisphinctes* Waagen, 1869
Large evolute shells with quadrate inner whorls strongly ribbed and usually regularly biplicate, changing in body chamber to coarse and distant ridged primary ribs. Macroconch with simple peristome.
U. Jurassic (Oxfordian). Europe to Pakistan, Africa, Japan, Cuba.
Perisphinctes (Arisphinctes) pickeringius (Young & Bird): U. Oxfordian. Headington, England. Diameter 9.8 cm.

Pl. 6.7.92. *Aulacostephanus* Tornquist, 1896
Laterally compressed subinvolute shells with fasciculate ribbing often produced from bullate tubercles on the umbilical shoulder. With prominent smooth ventral band. Microconch with lappets.
U. Jurassic (L. Kimmeridgian). Europe, USSR.
Aulacostephanus pseudomutabilis (de Loriol): L. Kimmeridgian. Near Moscow, USSR. Diameter 3.9 cm.

Pl. 6.7.93. *Pectinatites* Buckman, 1922
Subinvolute to subevolute, with inner whorls with biplicate ribbing. Microconch with ventral horns. Macroconchs larger, with variable outer whorl with up to 5 secondary ribs arising from primaries a distinctive style referred to as virgatome ribbing.
U. Jurassic (U. Kimmeridgian). Europe, Greenland, USSR.
Pectinatites encombensis Cope: U. Kimmeridgian. Kimmeridge, England. Microconch showing ventral horns. Diameter 10.3 cm. (From Cope 1967.)

Pl. 6.7.94. *Pavlovia* Ilovaisky, 1917
Subinvolute to subevolute shells with circular cross-section and slight impressed depth. Ornamented with very clear and strong usually biplicate ribs.
U. Jurassic (U. Kimmeridgian). N. Europe, Arctic, USSR. Usually boreal.
Pavlovia pallasioides (Neaverson): U. Kimmeridgian. Hartwell, England. Diameter 4.0 cm.

Pl. 6.7.95. *Titanites* Buckman, 1921
Often giant ammonites with inner whorls with regular mainly biplicate ribs and outer whorls with crowded ribbing with long secondaries: outermost parts almost smooth.
U. Jurassic (Portlandian). N. Europe. This or related forms widespread in Arctic area.
Titanites anguiformis Wimbledon & Cope: Portlandian. Portland, England. Diameter 62 cm. (From Wimbledon and Cope 1978.)

Pl. 6.7.96. *Craspedites* Pavlov, 1892
Generally compressed and involute shells with rounded whorl outline with fine ribbing on the inner whorls and smooth on outer whorls: with blunt and often prominent nodes low on flanks.
U. Jurassic (U. Volgian). USSR, Spitsbergen, Greenland, England.
Craspedites parakaschpuricus Gerassimov: Kaschput, Moscow, USSR. Diameter 5.1 cm. (From Casey 1973.)

Pl. 6.7.97. *Hectoroceras* Spath, 1947
Involute, discoidal to oxyconic shells with funnel-like umbilicus and sickle-shaped ribs branching irregularly on the outer flanks.
L. Cretaceous (Ryazanian). England, Greenland, Siberia and Russian Platform.
Hectoroceras kochi Spath: Ryazanian. West Dereham, England. Diameter 5.9 cm.

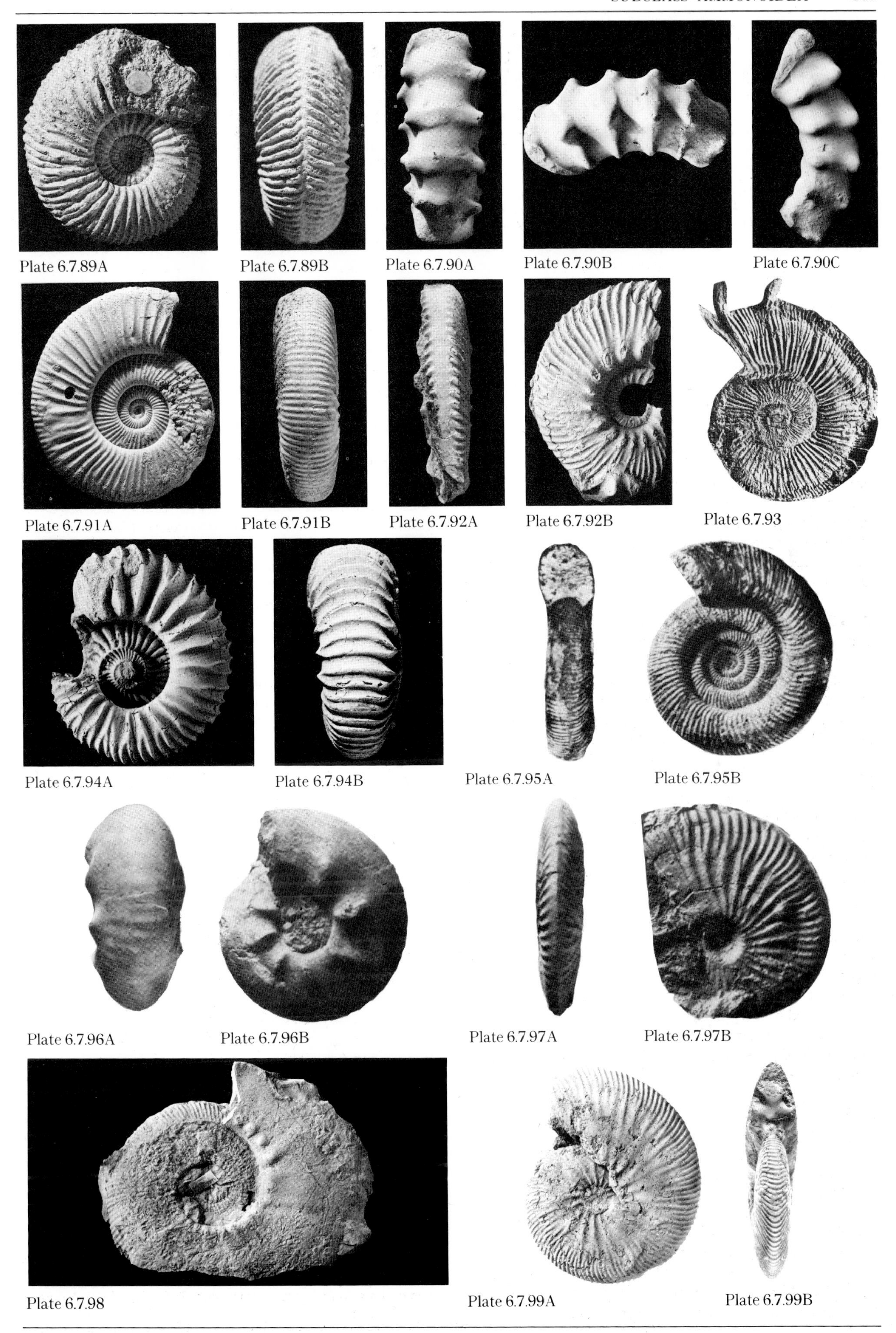

Plate 6.7.89A Plate 6.7.89B Plate 6.7.90A Plate 6.7.90B Plate 6.7.90C

Plate 6.7.91A Plate 6.7.91B Plate 6.7.92A Plate 6.7.92B Plate 6.7.93

Plate 6.7.94A Plate 6.7.94B Plate 6.7.95A Plate 6.7.95B

Plate 6.7.96A Plate 6.7.96B Plate 6.7.97A Plate 6.7.97B

Plate 6.7.98 Plate 6.7.99A Plate 6.7.99B

Pl. 6.7.98. *Berriasella* Uhlig, 1905
Laterally compressed subevolute shells with distinct sharp simple or biplicate ribbing dividing on outer flanks. Venter often with a smooth band. Microconch with lappets.
U. Jurassic–L. Cretaceous (Volgian–Berriasian). World-wide, except for Boreal areas.
Berriasella sp.: Berriasian. La Croix, France. Diameter 10.4 cm.

Pl. 6.7.99. *Craspedodiscus* Spath, 1924
Laterally compressed shells with fine and dense ribbing in early whorls, often becoming smooth later. Later whorls show increasingly compressed form and venter becomes narrowly arched to sharp. Ribs on outer flanks at first arising from tubercles low on flanks though tubercles disappear during growth.
L. Cretaceous (Hauterivian–Barremian). N.W. Europe, USSR, California, USA.
Craspedodiscus discofalcatus (Lahusen): L. Barremian. Normanby, England. Diameter 12.2 cm. (Photo P. F. Rawson.)

Pl. 6.7.100. *Polyptychites* Pavlov, 1892
Involute to evolute shells with depressed to high whorl section. Ornamented by groups of ribs which arise from umbilical bullae and branch once or twice on flanks and cross venter.
L. Cretaceous (Valanginian). Boreal.
Polyptychites beani (Pavlov): U. Valanginian. Speeton, England. Diameter 5.6 cm. (Photo P. F. Rawson.)

Pl. 6.7.101. *Lyticoceras* Hyatt, 1900
Evolute to involute, often very compressed shells, with sinous to falcoid ribs often branching low on flanks and again on mid-flanks. Ribs form chevrons often associated with tuberculation on rather flat venter.
L. Cretaceous (Hauterivian). S. and W. Europe.
Lyticoceras regale Pavlov: Hauterivian. Speeton, England. Diameter 4.7 cm.

SUPERFAMILY HAPLOCERATACEAE

Smooth (leiostracous) ammonites with ornament if present usually subdued: in some with ventral tubercles. Dimorphism well developed. Umbilical lobes arising usually from U_1, in some numerous.

Pl. 6.7.102. *Strigoceras* Quenstedt, 1886
Discoidal to oxyconic shells with closed umbilicus and hollow, floored keel. Ribs weak to coarse, in many spirally fluted and strigate.
M. Jurassic (U. Bajocian). Europe, N. Africa, USSR.
Strigoceras truellei (d'Orbigny): U. Bajocian. Burton Cliff, Dorset, England. Diameter 17.8 cm.

Pl. 6.7.103. *Oppelia* Waagen, 1869
Very compressed and involute shells with feeble keels and subdued fine falcoid primary ribbing with secondaries becoming more prominent on ventrolateral edge. Dimorphism marked, the microconchs often placed in other genera.
M. Jurassic (Bajocian and Bathonian). Europe, Africa, USSR, S.E. Asia, Alaska.
Oppelia aspidoides (Oppel): Bathonian. Niort, France. Larger macroconch with presumed microconch (*Oecotraustes serrigerus* Waagen). Diameters 12 cm and 3.5 cm respectively. (From Callomon 1963.)

Pl. 6.7.104. *Creniceras* Munier-Chalmas, 1892
Small, compressed, smooth shells with median ventral row of blunt coxcomb serrations or cogs in early whorls, the microconch terminating thus with lappets. Macroconch, named *Taramelliceras*, larger with smooth outer whorl but with up to 3 rows of ventral tubercles.
U. Jurassic (L. Oxfordian). Europe, Africa, Asia.
Creniceras rengerri (Oppel): L. Oxfordian. Woodham, England. Small microconch with macroconch (*T. richei* (de Loriol)). Diameters 2 cm and 4.8 cm respectively. (From Palframan 1966.)

Pl. 6.7.105. *Hecticoceras* Bonarelli, 1893
Evolute to subevolute compressed shells with carinate venters. Ribbing arising in pairs from umbilical edge and forming ventrolateral tubercles. Microconchs small with lappets: macroconchs larger, with smoother outer whorl and simple aperture.
M. and U. Jurassic (U. Bathonian–L. Oxfordian). Widespread.
Hecticoceras lonsdaleii (Pratt) and *Hecticoceras brightii* (Pratt): L. Oxfordian. Christian Malford, England. Probable dimorphic pair. Diameters 7.4 cm and 4.2 cm respectively. (From Callomon 1963.)

SUPERFAMILY DESMOCERATACEAE

A long-ranging group showing considerable variety in shell form and ornament, but usually with an oval whorl section and constrictions. Many have a smooth or weakly ribbed shell. Rarely weakly keeled. Many show periodic strengthened ribs and/or constrictions. Most show no more than four U lobes with further division arising within U_4. Dimorphism widespread.

Pl. 6.7.106. *Desmoceras* Zittel, 1884
Subinvolute to subevolute shells with subquadrate to oval whorl section and periodic sigmoidal constrictions and associated ribs with striae or weak ribs between, especially on outer parts of whorl.
L. and U. Cretaceous (U. Aptian–U. Cenomanian). World-wide.
Desmoceras latidorsatum (Michalski): Albian. France. Diameter 4.5 cm. (From Ruzhencev 1962b.)

Pl. 6.7.107. *Parapuzosia* Nowak, 1913
Giant shells including the largest ammonites known. Shell moderately evolute with rounded whorl section and flattened sides. Ribbed, with strengthened primaries and intercalaries on outer part of whorl.
U. Cretaceous (Cenomanian–Campanian). World-wide.
Parapuzosia seppenradensis (Landois): Senonian. Seppenrade, Münster, W. Germany. Diameter 1.7 m, estimated original diameter 2.5 m. (From Lehmann 1981.)

Pl. 6.7.108. *Pachydiscus* Zittel, 1884
Compressed to depressed, evolute to subinvolute shells with whorl section generally rounded. With short umbilical ribs or nodes and separate ventrolateral ribs tending to be absent on mid venter.
U. Cretaceous (Campanian–Maastrichtian). World-wide.
Pachydiscus gollevillensis (d'Orbigny): Maastrichtian. Fresville, France. Diameter 10.5 cm. (Photo W. J. Kennedy.)

SUPERFAMILY HOPLITACEAE

A group derived from desmocerataceans and showing a wide range of generally strong ornament and developing a variety of bands, grooves or smooth often high keels on the venter. Suture pattern as in Desmocerataceae; in some secondarily ceratitic.

Pl. 6.7.109. *Hoplites* Neumayr, 1875
Compressed subinvolute shells with rectangular compressed to depressed trapezoidal whorl section. Ornament of prominent ribs branching from strong bullate umbilical tubercles, and ribs

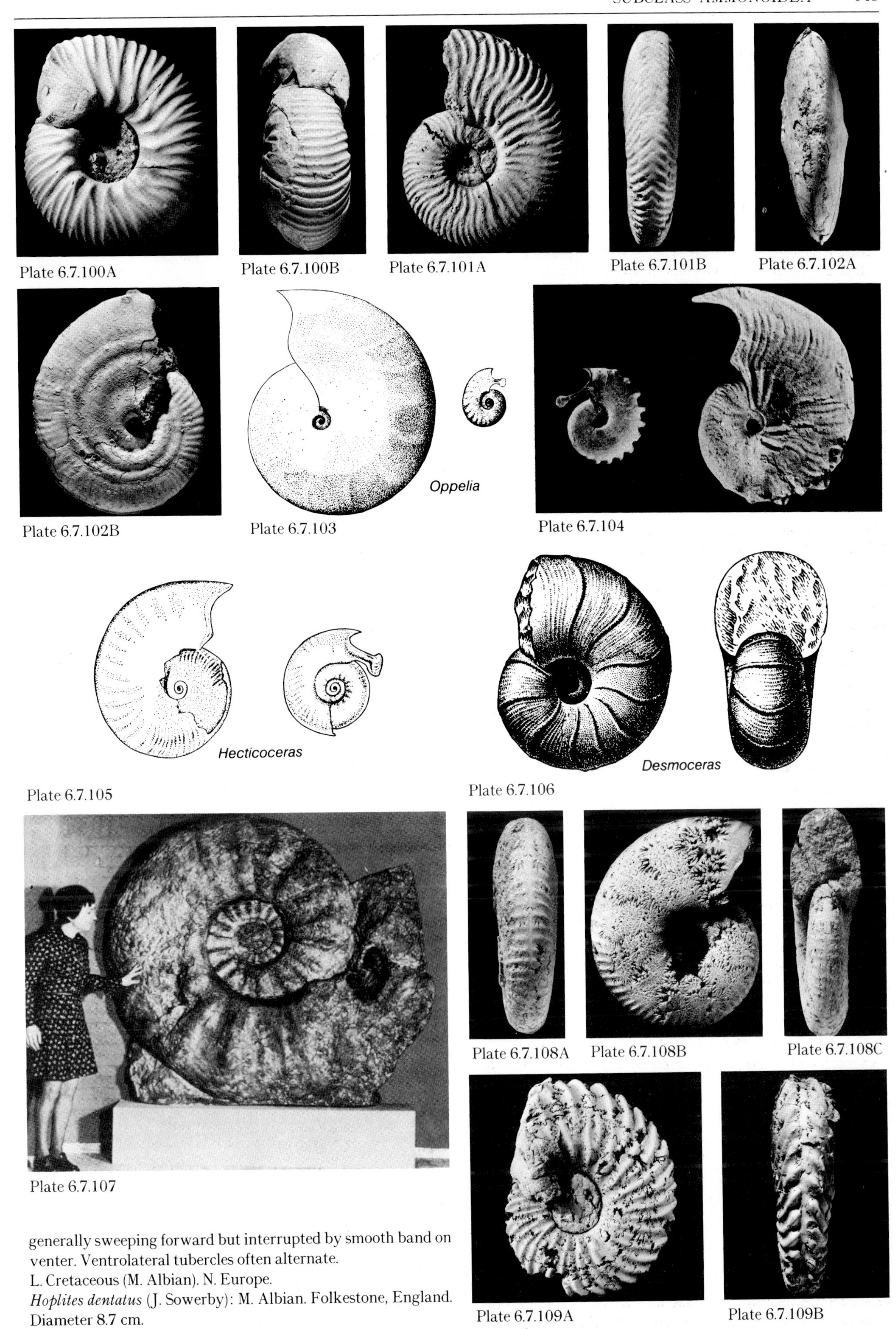

Plate 6.7.100A Plate 6.7.100B Plate 6.7.101A Plate 6.7.101B Plate 6.7.102A

Plate 6.7.102B Plate 6.7.103 Plate 6.7.104

Plate 6.7.105 Plate 6.7.106

Plate 6.7.107 Plate 6.7.108A Plate 6.7.108B Plate 6.7.108C

Plate 6.7.109A Plate 6.7.109B

generally sweeping forward but interrupted by smooth band on venter. Ventrolateral tubercles often alternate.
L. Cretaceous (M. Albian). N. Europe.
Hoplites dentatus (J. Sowerby): M. Albian. Folkestone, England. Diameter 8.7 cm.

Pl. 6.7.110. *Euhoplites* Spath, 1925
Subevolute or subinvolute, compressed to inflated shells with flat to deeply grooved venter. Strongly ribbed with secondaries arising from umbilical nodes and sweeping forward to periodic clavate subparallel nodes on ventrolateral shoulder. Some lose much ornament on outer whorls.
L. Cretaceous (M. and U. Albian). N. Europe, Greenland and Alaska.
Euhoplites lautus (d'Orbigny): Albian. Folkestone, England. Diameter 3.9 cm.

Pl. 6.7.111. *Schloenbachia* Neumayr, 1875
Subinvolute compressed to inflated shells and venter smooth with flat or arched keel. Ornament variable from strong ribs with umbilical, lateral and ventrolateral tubercles to virtually smooth tubercles with long umbilical bullae and ventral clavi, or none.
L. and U. Cretaceous (U. Albian–Cenomanian). Europe, Greenland, S.W. Asia.
Schloenbachia varians (J. Sowerby): Cenomanian. Pyrton, Watlington, England. Diameter 6.5 cm.

Fig. 6.7.25C. *Engonoceras* Neumayr & Uhlig, 1887
Compressed and involute shells with narrow flat sulcate venter in early whorls, later with weak ribs and ventrolateral clavi alternate on either side of venter. Sutures irregularly ceratitic.
L. and U. Cretaceous (Albian–Cenomanian). World-wide.
C. *Engonoceras serpentinum* (Cragin): Albian. Texas. Suture. (After Arkell *et al.* 1957.)

SUPERFAMILY ACANTHOCERATACEAE
Generally strongly tuberculate and ribbed shells but of a variety of forms. A major component of U. Cretaceous ammonite faunas.

Pl. 6.7.112. *Mortoniceras* Meek, 1876
Subevolute shells with quadrate to trapezoidal whorl section and a ventral high or low keel. Ribs strongly developed with prominent umbilical and ventrolateral tubercles and often others.
L. Cretaceous (U. Albian). World-wide.
Mortoniceras inflatum (J. Sowerby): U. Albian. Isle of Wight, England. Partially crushed specimen. Diameter 8.9 cm. (Photo W. J. Kennedy.)

Pl. 6.7.113. *Texanites* Spath, 1925
Compressed subevolute to evolute shells with flat sides in early whorls converging in later whorls to a narrow-keeled venter. Ornamented with strong straight ribs with 3 or more tubercles and indications on keel. Known with aptychus termed *Spinaptychus.*

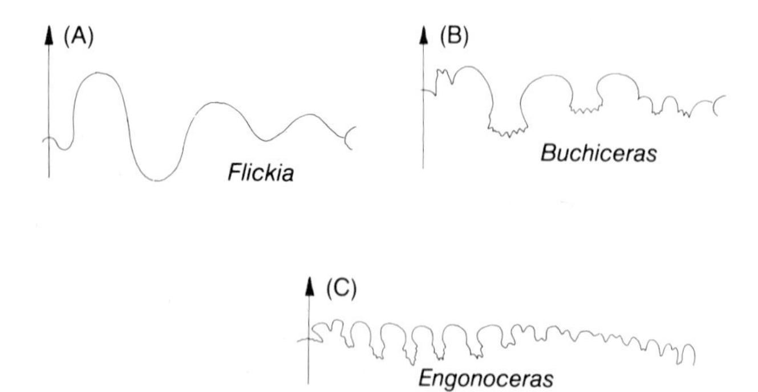

Fig. 6.7.25. Diagrams illustrating reversion to ancestral-type sutural patterns in some Cretaceous Ammonitida.

U. Cretaceous (Santonian–L. Campanian). World-wide.
Texanites texanus (Roemer): Santonian. Umzamba Cliff, Transkei, Africa. Diameter 14.6 cm. (From Klinger and Kennedy 1980.)

Pl. 6.7.114. *Acanthoceras* Neumayr, 1875
Subinvolute to subevolute inflated shells, often with polygonal whorl outlines owing to placing of strong tubercles on prominent radial ribs. Ventrolateral tubercles may be horn-shaped.
U. Cretaceous (M.–U. Cenomanian). World-wide.
Acanthoceras rhotomagense (Brongniart): Cenomanian. Chard, England. Diameter 13.2 cm. (Photo W. J. Kennedy.)

Fig. 6.7.25A. *Flickia* Pervinquière, 1907
Small or dwarf ammonites with subevolute to subinvolute compressed shells with rounded venter. Generally with smooth surface. Suture very simple, goniatitic, with entire, rounded, lobes and saddles.
L. Cretaceous (U. Albian). Widespread in Africa, Madagascar, Texas, New Mexico, USA.
A. *Flickia simplex* Pervinquière: Albian. Tunisia. Suture. (After Wright and Kennedy 1979.)

Pl. 6.7.115. *Buchiceras* Hyatt, 1875
Subinvolute shell with subquadrate whorl section and broad, flat keel. Bulging ribs branch from umbilical tubercles and end at blunt or sharp ventrolateral tubercles. Suture ceratitic. Genus homoeomorphic with Triassic *Ceratites.*
U. Cretaceous (Senonian). N. Africa, Israel, Peru.
Buchiceras bilobatum Hyatt: Senonian. Peru. Specimen encrusted with oysters suggesting life poise as indicated. (From Seilacher 1960.) Fig. 6.7.25B. *Buchiceras bilobatum* Hyatt: Suture. (After Arkell *et al.* 1957.)

Suborder Ancyloceratina

A bizarre and possibly polyphyletic group including most Cretaceous heteromorphs with unusual coiling patterns which are probably indicative of specialized location and feeding niches rather than racial senescence as formerly speculated by some. Primary suture variable, often quadrilobate (ELUI), internal lobe simple and unfrilled: these characters have been taken to imply monophyletic origin. Dimorphism widespread. A world-wide group in the Cretaceous.

SUPERFAMILY ANCYLOCERATACEAE
The typical heteromorphs with a basic loose coiling and with variously straight to hooked apertures. Primary unstable quinquelobate suture little changed in the adult apart from frilling; lobes often trifid. Giant size, some almost reaching 1 m across.

Pl. 6.7.116. *Ancyloceras* d'Orbigny, 1842
An open spiral in early whorls with a moderately long shaft and final hook, the aperture facing early whorls. Growth lines radial to prorsiradiate with associated ribs, tubercles and spines.
L. Cretaceous (U. Barremian–L. Aptian). Perhaps world-wide. Especially common in Mediterranean area.
Ancyloceras matheronianum (d'Orbigny): L. Aptian. Bédoule, France. Restoration. Length *c.* 0.6 m. (After Casey 1959.)

Pl. 6.7.117. *Tropaeum* J. de C. Sowerby, 1837
Early whorls irregularly coiled, then advolute and body chamber slightly coiled and perhaps hooked. Early ornament of dense tuberculate ribs, later finer ribs, and on the body chamber an

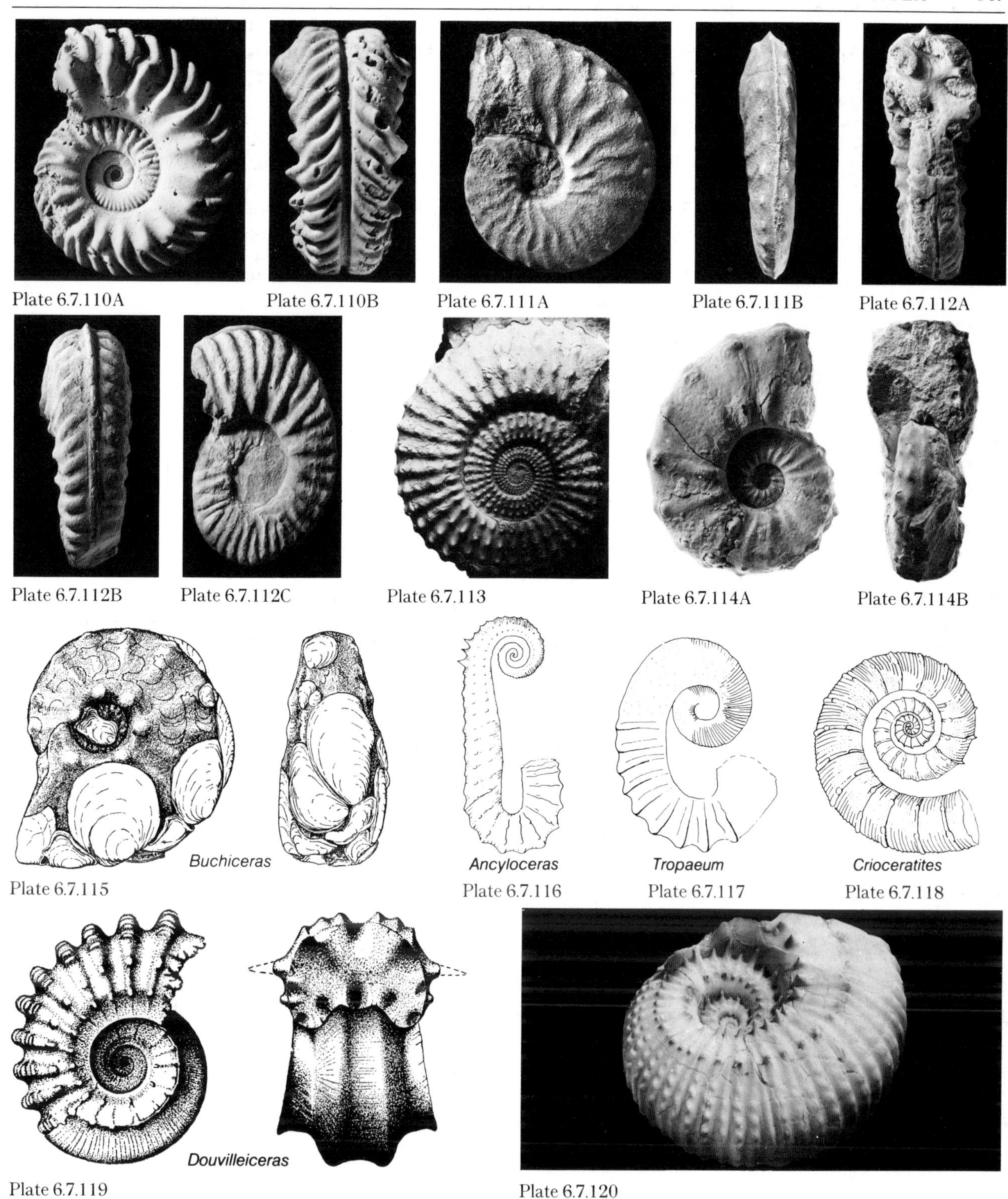

Plate 6.7.110A Plate 6.7.110B Plate 6.7.111A Plate 6.7.111B Plate 6.7.112A

Plate 6.7.112B Plate 6.7.112C Plate 6.7.113 Plate 6.7.114A Plate 6.7.114B

Plate 6.7.115 Plate 6.7.116 Plate 6.7.117 Plate 6.7.118

Plate 6.7.119 Plate 6.7.120

abrupt change to coarse, distinct ribs.
L. Cretaceous (Aptian).
Tropaeum hilli (J. de C. Sowerby): Aptian. Maidstone?, England. Diameter *c.* 36 cm. (After Casey 1959.)

Pl. 6.7.118. *Crioceratites* Leveillé, 1837
Open spiral shell with whorl section ovoid to quadrate. Ornamented with dense ribs, usually without tubercles, and distinct strong ribs often with spines.
L. Cretaceous (Hauterivian to Barremian). World-wide.
Crioceratites nolani (Kilian): Hauterivian, France. (After Arkell *et al.* 1957.)

SUPERFAMILY DOUVILLEICERATACEAE
Ammoniticonic generally coarsely ribbed shells derived by secondary recoiling from loosely coiled early Cretaceous ancestors. Primary quadrilobate suture leading to frilling and subdivision of the lobes in the adult. Dimorphism widespread.

Pl. 6.7.119, 120. *Douvilleiceras* de Grossouvre, 1894
Subinvolute rounded shells with polygonal or depressed whorl section. Ornamented with prominent unbranched ribs with prominent nodes developing along them: outer whorls with untuberculated ribbing or rarely smooth. With dorsal body chamber deposits forming dorsal shield.

L. Cretaceous (Albian). World-wide.
Pl. 6.7.119. *Douvilleiceras* sp. Diagram showing shell form and dorsal shield. (After Casey 1962.) Pl. 6.7.120. *D. clementianum* (d'Orbigny): M. Albian. Aube, France. Oblique view. Diameter 11.5 cm. (Photo W. J. Kennedy.)

SUPERFAMILY DESHAYESITACEAE
Typically ammoniticone recoiled derivatives of loosely coiled ancestors. Shell laterally compressed with strong branching ribs crossing the venter or with flat or smooth venter. Primary quadrilobate suture leading to subdivision of saddles and frilling in adult.

Pl. 6.7.121. *Deshayesites* Kazansky, 1914
Subevolute, discoidal shells with venter flattened or convex. Ribbing well developed with intercalaries and arching over the venter but all untuberculated.
L. Cretaceous (L. Aptian). N.W. Europe, USSR and Greenland, but related forms world-wide.
Deshayesites forbesi (Casey): L. Aptian. Atherfield, England. Diameter 58 mm. (From Casey 1963.)

SUPERFAMILY TURRILITACEAE
Dextral or sinistral helicoids varying from regular and tightly coiled to loosely coiled and irregular. In some, body chamber loops over helix. Frilled quadrilobate suture, with stable bifid lateral lobe. Siphuncle often migrates apicad and suture becomes asymmetric, presumably a buoyancy control modification. Dimorphism widespread.

Pl. 6.7.122A. *Turrilites* Lamarck, 1801
Tightly helical shell with acute apical angle and ornamented with weak to strong ribs with up to 4 tubercles or none.
U. Cretaceous (Cenomanian). World-wide.
A. *Turrilites costatus* Lamarck: Cenomanian. France. Length *c.* 15 cm. (After Arkell *et al.* 1957.)

Pl. 6.7.122B, 123. *Nipponites* Yabe, 1904
Coiling in a series of U's forming a variously shaped, tight to loose tangle.
U. Cretaceous (Turonian–Senonian). Madagascar, Japan, Kamchatka and Oregon, USA.
Pl. 6.7.122B. *Nipponites* sp.: Turonian. S. Oregon, USA. Reconstruction based on Klinger (1981). Pl. 6.7.123. *N. mirabilis* Yabe: Saku, Japan. 7.5 cm across.

Pl. 6.7.122D. *Anaklinoceras* Stephenson, 1941
Early part a regular helicoid, but with body chamber hooked up one side of spire and down the other.
Cretaceous (Senonian). N. America.
D. *Anaklinoceras reflexum* Stephenson: Campanian. Texas, USA. Length 3.8 cm. (After Arkell *et al.* 1957.)

Pl. 6.7.122C. *Anisoceras* Pictet, 1854
Loose, rather helicoid early spire changing to body chamber of 2 parallel shafts. With rather coarse ribbing, tubercles and often spines.
L. and U. Cretaceous (Albian–Turonian). World-wide.
C. *Anisoceras raynaudi* Boule, Lemoine & Thévenin: U. Cretaceous. (After Klinger 1981.)

Pl. 6.7.122G. *Baculites* Lamarck, 1799
With minute early helicoid then a straight or slightly curved shell with section often pyriform with venter narrowly rounded to acute. Ornament of growth lines or sinuous striae varies from sinuous prorsiradiate to strong ribs to strong ventrolateral tubercles on the venter and with nodes following the same course. Aperture with long dorsal rostrum. With rugaptychi. Dimorphic. Reaching up to 2 m in length.
U. Cretaceous (Turonian to Maastrichtian). World-wide.
G. *Baculites* sp. Illustration of shell form and one possible life poise. (After Klinger 1981.)

Pl. 6.7.122F. *Labeceras* Spath, 1925
An early scaphitacean with open early whorls, curved shaft and terminal hook.
L. Cretaceous (Albian). S. Africa, Madagascar and Australia.
F. *Labeceras plasticum* Spath. Drawn in probable life position. Length 4.2 cm. (After Arkell *et al.* 1957.)

SUPERFAMILY SCAPHITACEAE
Early whorls planispiral, often very involute, with a body chamber with a terminal hook on a short or moderately long shaft. Primary quadrilobate suture leading to frilling and lengthening of saddles in adult. Strongly dimorphic; some lappeted. Derived from loosely coiled turrilitacean ancestors. With synaptychi.

Pl. 6.7.122E, 124. *Scaphites* Parkinson, 1811
Involute, early whorls tightly coiled: body chamber with a short shaft and constricted hooked aperture facing early whorls. Ribbed, with tubercles in many.
L. and U. Cretaceous (Albian–Maastrichtian). Most strongly dimorphic. Common in Northern hemisphere; also Madagascar and Australia.
Pl. 6.7.122E. *Scaphites equalis* (Parkinson): Cenomanian. France. Length 3.4 cm. (After Arkell *et al.* 1957.) Pl. 6.7.124. *S. obliquus* (J. Sowerby): M. Cenomanian. Rouen, France. Length 2.9 cm. (Photo W. J. Kennedy.)

Subclass Coleoidea

The belemnitids, aulacoceratids, sepiids, teuthids and octopids have been grouped together under several names: Endocochlea, Dibranchiata or Coleoidea (Fig. 6.7.1). The endocochleate condition, the soft parts enclosing the phragmocone, is first seen in Devonian or Carboniferous belemnitids. It is recognizable by the calcitic guard or rostrum laid down on top of the phragmocone. The similar telum of aulacoceratids is a guard with more organic material. In some belemnitids vascular markings occur on the outside of the guard and there are often flattenings thought to correspond to stabilizing fins. In some Coleoidea parts of the shell protrude (as in *Spirula*); in others, especially the teuthids and octopods, the calcareous shell is mostly or wholly lost and the remaining support, if present, is chitinoid. A classic review of the Coleoidea is by Naef (1922), and fossil forms have been reviewed by Jeletzky (1966). Good popular accounts are by Lane (1959) and Cousteau and Diolé (1975).

Order Aulacoceratida

A group of early 'belemnites' but without a proostracum and probably with a tubular body chamber. Septal necks generally prochoanitic. The telum (guard) consists of coarse organic and calcareous lamellae usually longitudinally ridged and furrowed. Certainly from U. Carboniferous (for example, *Hematites* Flower & Gordon, 1959) and continuing to U. Jurassic (Oxfordian). Common only in Triassic.

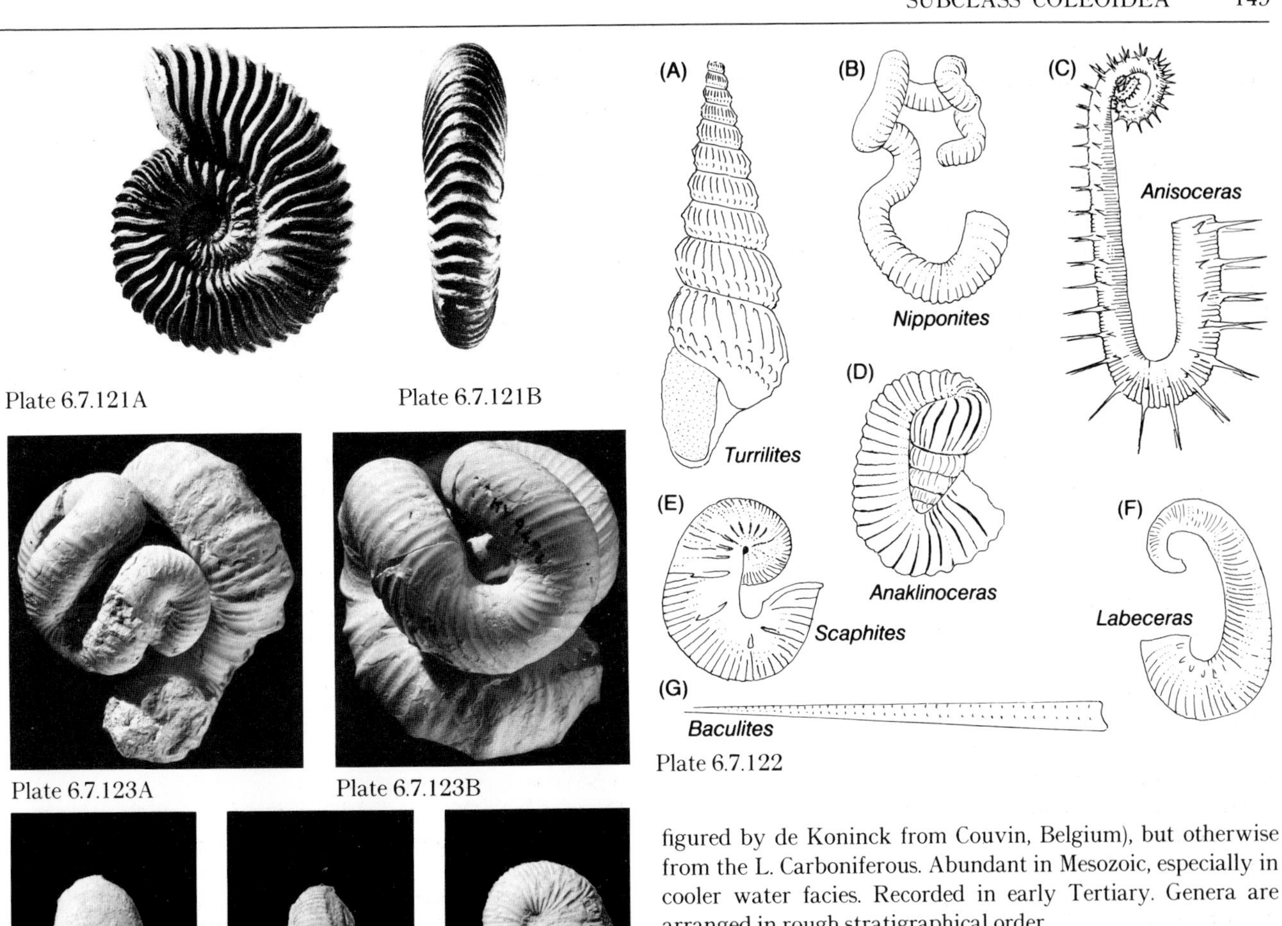

Plate 6.7.121A

Plate 6.7.121B

Plate 6.7.122

Plate 6.7.123A

Plate 6.7.123B

Plate 6.7.124A

Plate 6.7.124B

Plate 6.7.124C

Pl. 6.7.125B–E. *Aulacoceras* von Hauer, 1860
Telum long with longitudinal ribs and lateral furrows. Phragmocone very long, apical angle 5 to 12°. Septa well spaced.
Triassic. Europe, Indonesia, N. America. Restricted distribution.
B–E. *Aulacoceras sulcatum* Hauer: Triassic. Timor. Lateral view showing furrow, transverse sections, and longitudinal section showing phragmocone. (After Naef 1922.)

Order Belemnitida

Known from the L. Carboniferous and possible Devonian, this group is thought to be derived from the Bactritina. The traditional view has been that it formed the root-stock for other coleoid groups, but Jeletzky considers them a specialized offshoot of phragmoteuthids which he takes to be the root stock. The order is characterized by a solid calcitic guard and by a dorsally extended proostracum (Pl. 6.7.128A). The phragmocone is often weakly calcified or absent in fossils and the corresponding cavity is referred to as the alveolus, and alveolar angle replaces apical angle. The phragmocone has a ventral siphuncle and septal necks are orthochoanitic to macrochoanitic. Some have cameral tissue. Some are preserved with ink sacs and tentacular impressions. Possibly first recorded in the Devonian (a specimen figured by de Koninck from Couvin, Belgium), but otherwise from the L. Carboniferous. Abundant in Mesozoic, especially in cooler water facies. Recorded in early Tertiary. Genera are arranged in rough stratigraphical order.

Pl. 6.7.125A. *Eobelemnites* Flower, 1945
Large phragmocone with septa closely spaced and oblique, sloping orad from venter to dorsum. Guard radially fibrous, compressed in section. Very rare.
L. Carboniferous (Viséan). N. America.
A. *Eobelemnites caneyense* Flower: L. Carboniferous, Caney Shale. Oklahoma. Incomplete specimen. Length 12 cm. (After Flower 1964.)

Pl. 6.7.126A, B. *Coeloteuthis* Lissajous, 1906
Guard forming a thin sheath, with radial crystal structure, covering convexly expanding phragmocone giving very deep and large alveolar cavity.
L. Jurassic (Lias). Europe and Asia. Rare.
A, B. *Coeloteuthis excavatum* (Phillips): Lias, Lyme Regis, Dorset, England. Length 3.8 cm. (After Phillips 1866.)

Pl. 6.7.126F. *Hastites* Mayer, 1883
Dagger-shaped form with guard extended and expanding

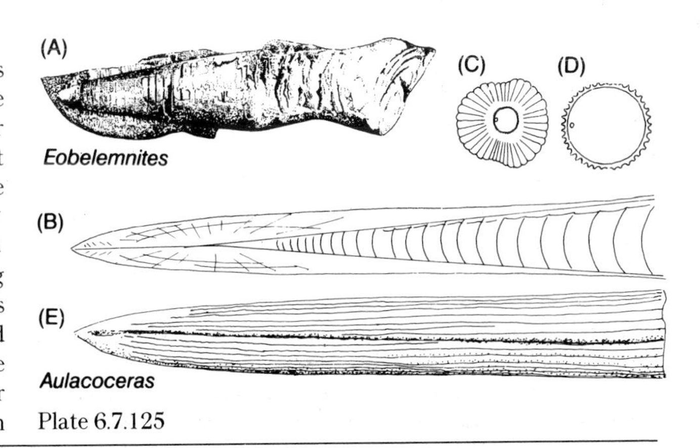

Plate 6.7.125

apically from phragmocone. Alveolar angle up to 20°.
L. and M. Jurassic (Pliensbachian–Bajocian). Widespread in Europe and Asia.
F. *Hastites semihastatus* Quenstedt: Bajocian. Württemberg, W. Germany. Length *c.* 22 cm. (After Pivetau 1952.)

Pl. 6.7.126D. *Megateuthis* Bayle, 1878
Large and long subcylindrical guard with conical termination. Often with elliptical cross-section and apex tip with several short grooves.
M. Jurassic (Bajocian). Europe and Asia.
D. *Megateuthis ellipticus* (Miller): Bajocian. Dundry, England. Length 0.28 m. (After Phillips 1868.)

Pl. 6.7.126G, H. *Belemnopsis* Bayle, 1879
Guard more or less cylindrical with acute apex; slightly hastate in young. With a long ventral furrow. Section at alveolus circular with a furrow notch and the furrow may give a reniform section towards the apex.
L. and M. Jurassic. Europe, Asia, Australasia.
G, H. *Belemnopsis anomala* (Phillips): Bajocian. Scarborough, England. Length 7 cm. (After Phillips 1868.)

Pl. 6.7.126E. *Cylindroteuthis* Bayle, 1878
Very long cylindrical guard with pointed apex. With subdued ventral furrow from apex weakening towards alveolar region. Cross-section laterally flattened near apex, circular in the restricted alveolar region.
M. and U. Jurassic. Europe, Greenland, N. America.
E. *Cylindroteuthis puzosi* (d'Orbigny): Callovian or Oxfordian. St Neots, England. Length 18 cm. (After Phillips 1869.)

Pl. 6.7.126C. *Pachyteuthis* Bayle, 1878
Robust guard with alveolar region 30 to 50% of guard. Apex hooked ventrally in some. Section with dorsoventral diameter less than lateral diameter.
M. and U. Jurassic (especially Callovian and Oxfordian). Europe, Asia, Greenland, N. America.
C. *Pachyteuthis excentralis* (Young & Bird): Oxfordian. Calvados, France. Length 10 cm. (After Pivetau 1952.)

Pl. 6.7.127A. *Hibolites* Montfort, 1808
Dagger-shaped like *Hastites* but with ventral groove dying out from alveolar region towards apex. With lateral lines well developed.
M. Jurassic–L. Cretaceous (Bathonian–Neocomian). Widespread in Europe, N. America, N. Africa, Asia and Indonesia.
A. *Hibolites jaculoides* Swinnerton: Neocomian, Speeton Clay. Speeton, England. Length 17 cm. (After Swinnerton 1952.)

Pl. 6.7.127B, C. *Duvalia* Bayle, 1878
Bizarre-shaped guards, short and asymmetrical, often flattened laterally. Without ventral furrow but with short, dorsal alveolar groove.
U. Jurassic and L. Cretaceous (Tithonian and Neocomian). Widespread in carbonates of Tethyan belt of Europe, N. Africa, Pakistan and Indonesia, also Madagascar.
B, C. *Duvalia lata* (Blainville): Neocomian. France. Lateral and dorsal views. Length 6 cm. (After Pivetau 1952.)

Pl. 6.7.127F, G. *Neohibolites* Stolley, 1911
Small guard with well-developed lateral lines. Ventral furrow confined to alveolar region.
L. and U. Cretaceous (Aptian–Cenomanian). Europe, Asia, N. and S. America.
F. *Neohibolites ewaldi* (Strombeck): Sutterby Marl, Aptian. Sutterby, England. Length 6.4 cm. G. *N. minimus:* Red Chalk, Albian. Speeton, England. Length 3.4 cm. (All after Swinnerton 1955.)

Pl. 6.7.127D. *Acroteuthis* Stolley, 1919
Large stout guard rather like *Pachyteuthis*, but with lateral diameter exceeding dorsoventral diameter. With lateral lines. Alveolus depth up to 50 per cent of guard; alveolus often excentric.
L. Cretaceous. Europe and Arctic.
D. *Acroteuthis lateralis.* (Phillips): Speeton Clay, L. Neocomian. Ventral view. Speeton, England. Length 15.7 cm. (After Swinnerton 1937.)

Pl. 6.7.127E. *Oxyteuthis* Stolley, 1911
Guard subcylindrical, maximum diameter in alveolar region, apex acute to obtuse. Alveolar length about 30%. Ventral surface slightly flattened, without ventral furrow. With paired lateral lines.
L. Cretaceous (Hauterivian–Aptian). Europe.
E. *Oxyteuthis brunsvicensis* (Strombeck): Speeton Clay, Neocomian. Speeton, England. Length 8.4 cm. (After Swinnerton 1948.)

Pl. 6.7.127H, I. *Actinocamax* Miller, 1826
Guard lanceolate. Alveolar region either not calcified or lost, guard terminating bluntly with faceted end pyriform in section or quadrate (*A. quadratus*). Short ventral groove orad. With dorsolateral lines seen on dorsal surface diverging apicad. Guard surface often granular and with vascular impressions.
U. Cretaceous (Cenomanian–Santonian). Europe, Asia, Greenland.
H, I. *Actinocamax primus* Arkhangelski: Cenomanian. Bornholm. Length 9.8 cm. (After Birkelund 1957.)

Pl. 6.7.127K, L. *Belemnitella* d'Orbigny, 1840
Guard cylindrical, apex often mucronate, section circular with well-developed groove in alveolar region. Dorsolateral lines seen on dorsal surface which diverge towards the apex. Often with vascular impressions.
U. Cretaceous (Santonian–Maastrichtian). Europe, Asia, Greenland, N. America.
K, L. *Belemnitella mucronata* (Schlotheim): Campanian. Norwich, England. Length 12.9 cm. (After Cox 1962.)

Order Teuthida

This group includes the modern squids and sea-pens and is known fossil from the Permian (Fig. 6.7.1). It embraces coleoids in which the conus and septa (which comprise the phragmocone) are lost or are rudimentary and in which a guard is not formed. The proostracum is often extensive and forms a variously shaped chitinoid support, in some giving 'sea-pens'. In a primitive member such as *Phragmoteuthis* (Triassic, Pl. 6.7.128B) there is a phragmocone, but no guard (compare with the belemnitid, Pl. 6.7.128A) and the proostracum consists of median and lateral areas. Septa may then be lost and only the conus remains, as in *Plesioteuthis* (U. Jurassic, Pl. 6.7.128C, reconstruction Pl. 6.7.129A). In others the phragmocone may be modified as a variously arched sheet, either blunt posteriorly (apicad) as in *Teudopsis* (L. Jurassic, Pl. 6.7.128E) or blunt anteriorly as in *Necroteuthis* (Tertiary, Pl. 6.7.128D), or even sharply pointed anteriorly as in *Palaeololigo* (U. Jurassic, Pl. 6.7.128F).

It is now thought unlikely that all these forms are descended from belemnitids. It may be that the primitive forms still with a phragmocone formed a basic stock derived from orthocerids,

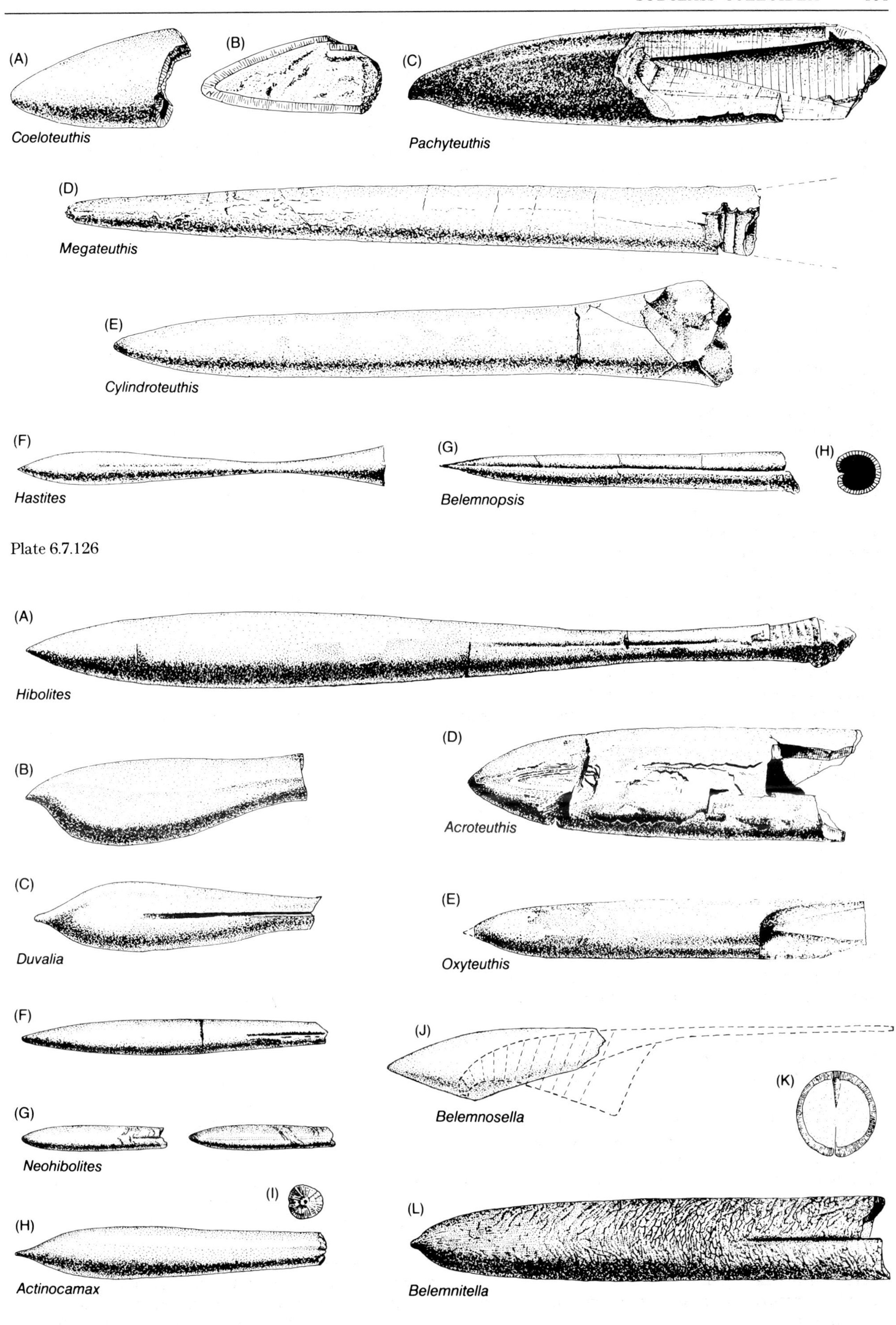
(A)
Coeloteuthis
(B)
(C)
Pachyteuthis
(D)
Megateuthis
(E)
Cylindroteuthis
(F)
Hastites
(G)
Belemnopsis
(H)
Plate 6.7.126
(A)
Hibolites
(B)
(D)
Acroteuthis
(C)
Duvalia
(E)
Oxyteuthis
(F)
(J)
Belemnosella
(K)
(G)
Neohibolites
(I)
(H)
Actinocamax
(L)
Belemnitella

Plate 6.7.127

and for these Jeletzky has erected an order Phragmoteuthida, with *Phragmoteuthis* (Pl. 6.7.128B) as a typical member. This is not followed here. It is clear that much has still to be learnt about Palaeozoic teuthids. For example, a genus *Jeletzkyia* has been described from the U. Carboniferous of Mazon Creek, Illinois, USA, which lacks the median field and wings of teuthids and does not have the differentiation of two arms as grasping tentacles as is usual in the teuthids and sepiids. There is probably a wide range of variety of which we are as yet quite unaware.

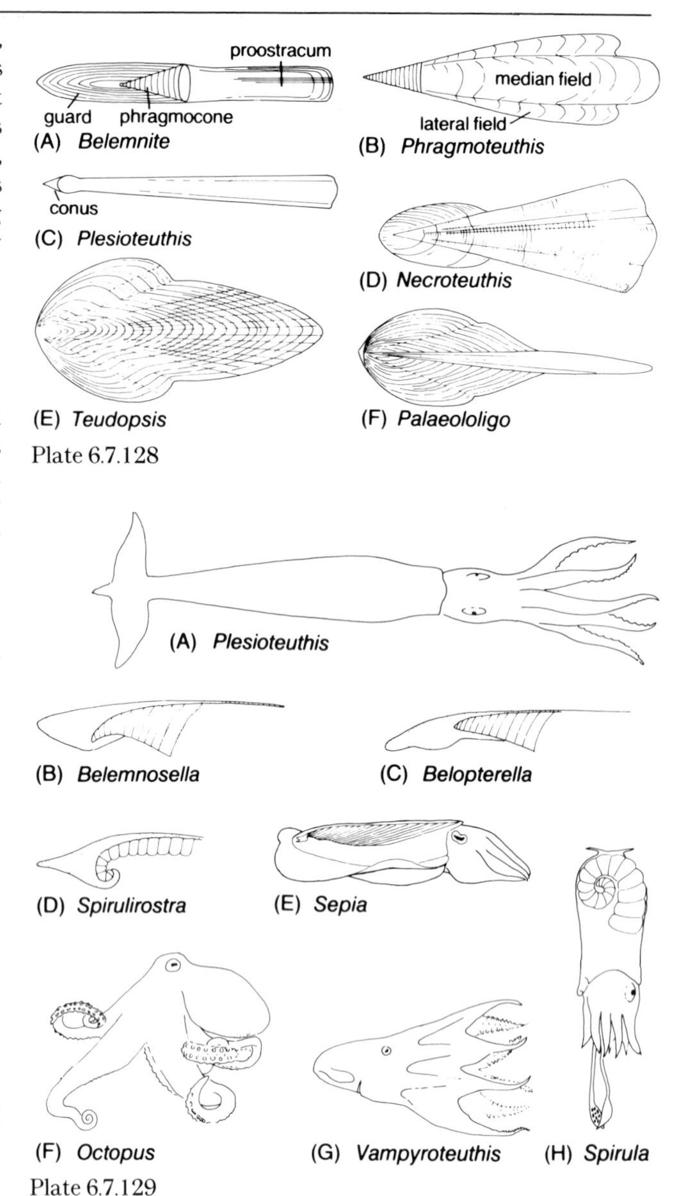

Plate 6.7.128

Plate 6.7.129

Order Sepiida

This group includes the living cuttlefish, *Sepia* (Pl. 6.7.129E) and the distinctive living *Spirula* (Pl. 6.7.129H). It comprises coleoids with a well-calcified shell consisting of a conus and septa and a more belemnitid-like proostracum than in teuthids. Living forms have 10 tentacles. Some early forms have a guard-like calcareous sheath, usually lacking the typical radial symmetry of belemnitids. There is a morphological sequence from *Belemnosella* (Tertiary (Eocene), Pl. 6.7.127J and Pl. 6.7.129B) through *Belopterella* (Tertiary (Montian), Pl. 6.7.129C) and *Spirulirostra* (Tertiary (Miocene), Pl. 6.7.129D) to *Spirula* (Recent, Pl. 6.7.129H). Also it is possible to derive *Sepia* from part of such a sequence by the dorsal expansion of the phragmocone (Pl. 6.7.129E).

Such a morphological series has been the traditional argument for deriving sepiids from belemnitids by a progressive reduction and modification of the guard. However, a wide range of ecological niches is occupied by the group and Jeletzky (1964) has argued that all may have been derived from late Cretaceous forms with head-down poise (as *Spirula*, Pl. 6.7.129H) and guardless. On this interpretation the guard-like phragmocone sheaths of the sepiids may be unrelated to the belemnitid guard and the development of them would be associated with the adoption of a horizontal poise by early Tertiary sepiids, perhaps only *Spirula* retaining the head-down poise. Thus, after the extinction of the belemnitids, the sepiids modified to occupy a similar range of ecological niches.

Order Octopodida

Octopus (Pl. 6.7.129F) is the typical living form of this group. The group has eight tentacles and shows a reduction and often complete loss of a calcareous shell apart from in embryonic stages. The earliest known octopodid is from the Jurassic, but they are rare as fossils. Modern forms generally live at less than 100 m and most are benthonic. *Argonauta* is an unusual shell, known fossil in the Tertiary, which simulates an ammonitic shell such as *Hoplites* with ribs and tubercles but it lacks septa. It is a brood pouch produced by the female from two enlarged dorsal tentacles.

Quite a remarkable change of habit is indicated by the living *Vampyroteuthis* (Pl. 6.7.129G) in which webs for enveloping prey occur between the tentacles. Some have thought the distinct habit change sufficient to coin the Order Vampyromorpha for the group; this, again, is not followed here.

The general loss of shell and associated buoyancy techniques in the Octopodida is thought to be related to the usual adoption of a benthonic mode of life. Thus, in this, they revert to the life mode of the late Cambrian progenitors of the Cephalopoda.

CHAPTER 7

Echinodermata

Echinoderms and carpoids

Echinoderms are common and conspicuous marine organisms at the present time and have been an important and diverse element of marine communities in the geological past. They first appeared in the L. Cambrian and the major lines of evolution were established within this group by the end of the Ordovician. Echinoderms are coelomate deuterostomes with a multiplated calcite endoskeleton and a coelomic hydrostatic system of canals and tube-feet, called the water vascular system. The skeletal plating and the water vascular system are arranged with radial symmetry. It has recently been suggested that chordates and echinoderms are closely related. Both apparently show evidence of having passed through a stage in their evolution when the right-hand-side organs in an originally bilaterally symmetrical organism were suppressed while the left-hand-side organs were expanded. In echinoderms, this is clearly shown in the development of the water vascular system, which is almost entirely developed from the left anterior coelom of the larva. This similarity has led Jefferies (1979) to propose the superphylum **Dexiothetica** for the group chordates plus echinoderms.

Within the Dexiothetica there is a small group of asymmetrical, calcite-plated organisms called carpoids, whose phylogenetic position has been much disputed. Traditionally, carpoids have been classified as echinoderms, but it has been suggested by several workers, notably Gislén and Jefferies, that they might be ancestral to many of the chordates. Whether or not they were ancestral to chordates or were simply a bizarre early offshoot from the dexiothete or echinoderm line, it is quite clear that they are fundamentally different from radiate echinoderms. They have therefore been removed from the phylum Echinodermata by Paul and Smith (1984) and are treated as a separate group here.

Stratigraphical ranges for the principal groups dealt with in this chapter are shown in Fig. 7.1.

Diagnostic features Apart from the fundamental asymmetry in development, which we can only infer in fossil groups, the unifying characteristic linking carpoids and echinoderms is their distinctive skeleton. This is a multiplated calcite endoskeleton with plates that are single crystals formed as a three-dimensional porous meshwork termed 'stereom'. This makes even isolated plates easily recognizable as belonging to this group and consequently their fossil record is moderately good.

Basis for subdivision Carpoids and echinoderms differ fundamentally in their body plan. Whereas echinoderms show some evidence of radial symmetry and have multiple ambulacra which form an integral part of the body wall for at least part of their length, carpoids are asymmetrical and either lack ambulacra or have a single free appendage that may be homologous with ambulacra. Radiate echinoderms can be divided into those that show a clear dorsoventral differentiation and those that do not.

ARTIFICIAL KEY

1. Theca asymmetrical, lacking ambulacra or with a single ambulacrum projecting from the theca .... carpoids
   Theca with radial symmetry and multiple ambulacra (primitively 3 and incorporated into the thecal wall) 2
2. Theca spindle-shaped with 3 ambulacra, a laterally positioned mouth and no dorsoventral differentiation .... Helicoplacoidea (stem group echinoderms)
   Theca basically pentaradiate with clear dorsoventral differentiation and the mouth opening centrally on the ventral surface .... crown group echinoderms

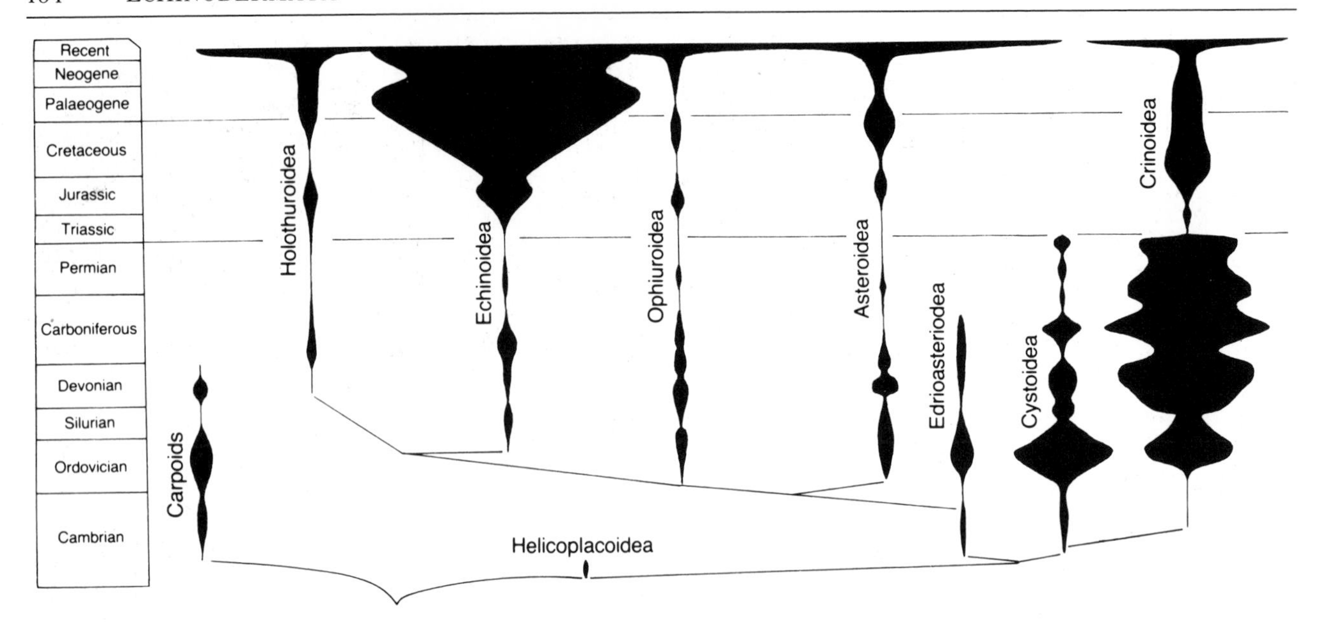

Fig. 7.1. Balloon diagram to show the diversity and stratigraphic range of the echinoderms and carpoids.

7.1 CARPOIDS (L. Cambrian–M. Devonian)

Diagnostic features Free-living Dexiothetica with an endoskeleton of calcite plates made of stereom but without a trace of radial symmetry.

Basis for subdivision Carpoids are a small but morphologically diverse group, consisting of all calcite-plated Dexiothetica that lack the radial symmetry characteristic of echinoderm groups. As their status as echinoderms or chordates is still under dispute and as they are most unlikely to be a monophyletic group, they have been left without a formally designated rank. Regardless of their phylogenetic position, carpoids can be divided into a number of easily identified groups according to their overall body plan. There are four principal groups but the relationship between these groups is far from clear. Most carpoids have a sac-like theca or head and a posterior appendage, the stele or tail. Of the four groups, only the ctenocystoids lack a posterior appendage. Solutes have, in addition to the stele, a single biserial ambulacrum which extends free from the anterior of the theca. The only appendage in the Stylophora and the Cincta is the stele. In Stylophora the stele is complex and clearly differentiated along its length, whereas, in Cincta, the stele is relatively simple and undifferentiated. Strikingly different interpretations of carpoid morphology can be found in Ubaghs (1967), Ubaghs and Caster (1967), Philip (1979) and Jefferies (1981).

ARTIFICIAL KEY

1. With no stele .... ORDER Ctenocystoida
   Stele present 2
2. Stele simple, undifferentiated; marginal ossicles with external grooves leading to the peristome .... ORDER Cincta
   Stele complex, differentiated into at least 2 distinct regions; marginal frame, if present, without external groove 3
3. Theca sac-like with single erect biserial ambulacrum and no marginal frame .... ORDER Soluta
   Theca without ambulacral appendage; marginal frame usually present............... 4 (SUPERORDER Stylophora)
4. Theca strongly asymmetrical, with obvious gill slits on the left-hand side of the theca .... ORDER Cornuta
   Theca only weakly asymmetrical, tending to become almost bilaterally symmetrical; gill slits, if present, not visible externally .... ORDER Mitrata

Order Soluta

Pl. 7.1.1. *Dendrocystoides* Jaekel, 1918
Theca sac-like with anterior horn and 2 posterior lobes; thecal plating irregular; periproct situated near the tip of one of the posterior lobes; short biserial ambulacrum extending forwards and attached to the theca off centre; stele differentiated into proximal and distal regions. Theca up to 8 cm long.
U. Ordovician.
Dendrocystoides scoticus (Bather): Ashgillian, Girvan, Scotland.

Order Cincta

Pl. 7.1.2. *Trochocystites* Barrande, 1887
Theca with superficial appearance of bilateral symmetry; marginal frame distinct, composed of a single series of ossicles; stele small and undifferentiated; large exhalent orifice near the mid anterior, with a large opercular plate; peristome opens through marginal frame ossicles and is offset to one side; inside marginal frame the dorsal surface has tesselate plating, the ventral surface has sutural pores; periproct ventral, near anterior on opposite side to the peristome. Theca up to 2 cm long.
M. Cambrian.
Trochocystites bohemicus Barrande: M. Cambrian, Bohemia, Czechoslovakia. (A) ventral; (B) dorsal.

Superorder Stylophora

Order Cornuta

Pl. 7.1.3. *Cothurnocystis* Bather, 1913
Theca boot-shaped with distinct marginal frame enclosing dorsal and ventral membranes of tiny plates; stele differentiated into 3 zones; peristome at most anterior point of 'boot', with an articulated spine-like process on one side; gill slits large, forming a single row inside the marginal frame. Theca up to 6 cm wide.

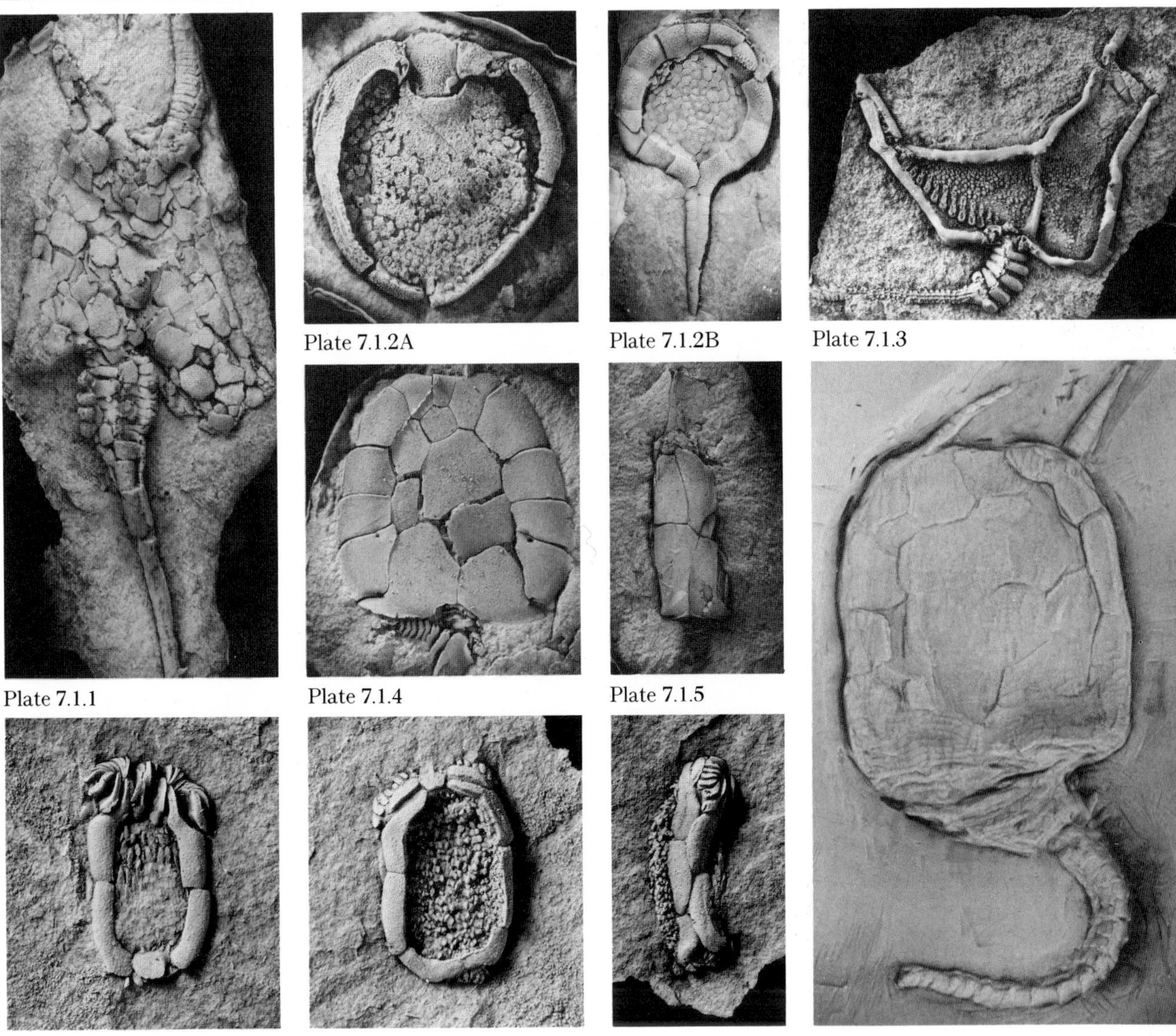
Plate 7.1.1 Plate 7.1.2A Plate 7.1.2B Plate 7.1.3 Plate 7.1.4 Plate 7.1.5 Plate 7.1.6 Plate 7.1.7A Plate 7.1.7B Plate 7.1.7C

U. Ordovician.
Cothurnocystis elizae Bather, 1913: Ashgill, Girvan, Scotland.

Order Mitrata

Pl. 7.1.4. *Mitrocystites* Barrande, 1887
Theca almost bilaterally symmetrical externally; marginal frame feebly developed, hardly distinguished from other plates; peristome submarginal, at mid-anterior; stele short, differentiated into 3 regions, the middle including a large hook-shaped ossicle; no articulating spines at anterior. Theca up to 4 cm long.
M.–U. Ordovician.
Mitrocystites mitra Barrande: M. Ordovician, Bohemia, Czechoslovakia.

Pl. 7.1.5. *Lagynocystis* Jaekel, 1918
Theca elongately conical with a single short articulated process extending anteriorly; anterior end obliquely truncated; one face composed of just 7 marginal plates, the other with numerous small plates; stele relatively broad, differentiated into 3 regions. Theca up to 3 cm long.
M. Ordovician.
Lagynocystis pyramidalis (Barrande): M. Ordovician, Bohemia, Czechoslovakia.

Pl. 7.1.6. *Rhenocystis* Dehm, 1932
Theca subrectangular; superficially bilaterally symmetrical, with 2 anterior articulated spines, one on either side of the broad submarginal peristome; 11 marginal plates, hardly differentiated from the rest, typically with fine, cuesta-shaped ribbing; remainder of dorsal and ventral surfaces composed of a small number of large polygonal plates; stele differentiated into 3 regions. Theca up to 4 cm long.
L. Devonian.
Rhenocystis latipedunculata Dehm: Hünsrück Shale, Bundesbach, Germany.

Order Ctenocystoida

Pl. 7.1.7. *Ctenocystoides* Robison & Sprinkle, 1969
Theca small, flattened, with a distinct marginal frame; not quite bilaterally symmetrical; marginal frame composed of a double series of ossicles; no appendages; peristome submarginal at anterior with distinctive ctenoid organ of curved wedge-shaped plates; periproct marginal at mid-posterior. Theca up to 1 cm long.
M. Cambrian.
Ctenocystoides utahensis Robison & Sprinkle: M. Cambrian, Utah, USA. (A) ventral; (B) dorsal; (C) lateral.

7.2 Class Helicoplacoidea (L. Cambrian)

Diagnostic features Spindle-shaped echinoderms with three ambulacra, two of which spiral up and one spirals down, forming an integral part of the theca; peristome positioned laterally; no dorsoventral differentiation.

The ambulacral structure of helicoplacoids is identical with that of other early echinoderms, but their triradial ambulacra, laterally positioned mouth and lack of any discernible differentiation into dorsal and ventral surfaces set them clearly apart from other echinoderms. They were probably attached low-level suspension feeders. A review of helicoplacoid morphology is given by Paul and Smith (1984). Only three genera are known (two of which are probably synonymous), all from the L. Cambrian.

Pl. 7.2.1. *Helicoplacus* Durham & Caster, 1963
Spindle-shaped theca with spirally arranged plating; ambulacra narrow, with biserial flooring plates and cover-plate sheets; oral area not enlarged. Theca up to 8 cm long.
L. Cambrian.
Helicoplacus curtisi Durham & Caster: California, USA.

CROWN GROUP ECHINODERMS (L. Cambrian–Recent)

Diagnostic features Theca with radial symmetry, usually pentaradiate; dorsal and ventral surfaces well differentiated, the ventral surface composed of ambulacral and interambulacral zones; the peristome opens centrally on the ventral surface.

Basis for subdivision The term 'crown group echinoderms' was used by Paul and Smith (1984) for the monophyletic group which consists of the latest common ancestor of all living echinoderms and all its descendants. All the remaining echinoderms belong to this group. Crown group echinoderms are divided into two subphyla and a number of classes. This is done on the basis of their general body plan. Features that are thought to be important include whether the dorsal surface is expanded as a stalk, whether the ambulacra extend free of the theca distally and the structure of the ambulacra, particularly the adoralmost few ossicles.

ARTIFICIAL KEY

1. Dorsal surface expanded into a stalk (secondarily lost in some); free appendages arising from the theca, carrying extensions of the water vascular system . . . . 2 (SUBPHYLUM Pelmatozoa)
   Dorsal and ventral surfaces of similar size or dorsal surface reduced; generally free living; ambulacra never extending free of the theca . . . . 3 (SUBPHYLUM Eleutherozoa)
2. Appendages originating as evaginations of the theca, carrying major body coelomic systems and homologous with ambulacra; no internal gonads or gonopore . . SUPERCLASS Crinozoa
   Terminal appendages originating as serially aligned cover-plate series, carrying only the radial water vessel and associated nerve; ambulacra, if present, incorporated into the theca or, occasionally, erect and free; gonads intrathecal, opening through a gonopore . . . . SUPERCLASS Cystoidea
3. Ambulacra roofed by cover-plate series; mouth frame of firmly sutured ambulacral ossicles; periproct opening through ventral surface . . . . CLASS Edrioasteroidea
   Ambulacra with modified cover-plates or cover-plates lost; adoralmost ambulacral ossicles not firmly united into a mouth frame; periproct absent or opening through dorsal surface 4
4. Radial water vessel not enclosed by ambulacral plates; body form stellate . . . . CLASS Asteroidea
   Radial water vessel enclosed by ambulacral ossicles or internal; body form stellate or globular 5
5. Dorsal and ventral surfaces equal in size; body form stellate with arms clearly differentiated from a central disc . . . . CLASS Ophiuroidea
   Dorsal surface greatly reduced compared to ventral surface; body form basically globular 6
6. Skeleton well developed; ambulacral plates perforated for tube-feet; adoralmost ambulacral ossicles modified as dental apparatus or secondarily lost . . . . CLASS Echinoidea
   Skeleton generally reduced to microscopic spicules; ambulacral plates, if present, not perforate; adoralmost ambulacral ossicles modified to form calcareous ring . . . . CLASS Holothuroidea

Subphylum Pelmatozoa (L. Cambrian–Recent)

Diagnostic features In Pelmatozoans the dorsal surface is expanded to form a functional stalk (although this may be secondarily lost) and there are elongate appendages to the theca that project into the surrounding medium carrying extensions of the water vascular system.

Basis for subdivision Several rival classification schemes are available for this group and I have opted for the scheme proposed by Breimer and Ubaghs (1974) with the exception that the name Crinozoa has been substituted for their group Brachiatoidea as recommended in Paul and Smith (1984). Pelmatozoans fall clearly into two groups, namely cystoids (superclass Cystoidea) and crinoids (superclass Crinozoa). Cystoids and crinoids differ from one another in several important features. In cystoids, the free appendages projecting from the theca are relatively small and generally, though not always, biserial. They almost never branch and are originally derived from outgrowth of cover-plate series. These appendages are called brachioles and apparently carried extensions of the water vascular system and associated adoral nerve but of no other coelomic systems. Brachiole facets on the theca are typically very small and ambulacra, where they occur, are usually an integral part of the thecal wall. In crinoids, the free appendages are called arms and these originated as evaginations of the theca carrying the ambulacra outwards. They are therefore generally large and carry a variety of coelomic systems including the gonads. Cystoids had internal gonads since they have a gonopore that opens close to the mouth whereas crinoids lack internal gonads and have no gonopore. Finally, whereas most cystoids have some sort of pore or fold structure for gaseous exchange, crinoids almost never have.

7.3 Superclass Cystoidea

Diagnostic features Pelmatozoans with free appendages that are brachioles, internal gonads and, in the great majority, a theca with specialized respiratory structures.

Basis for subdivision Cystoids have been divided into five classes primarily on the basis of the type of respiratory structure

Plate 7.2.1

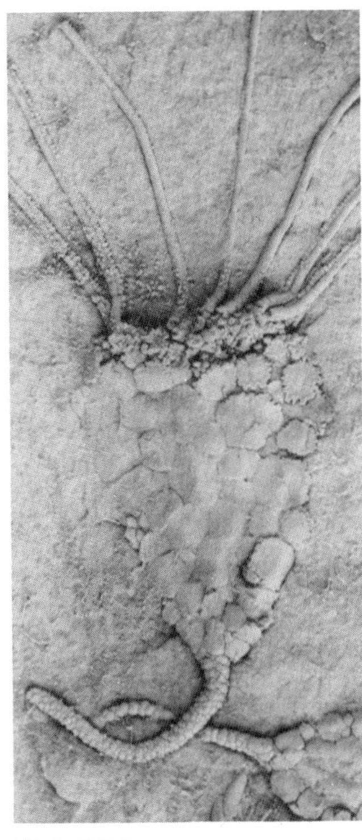
Plate 7.3.1

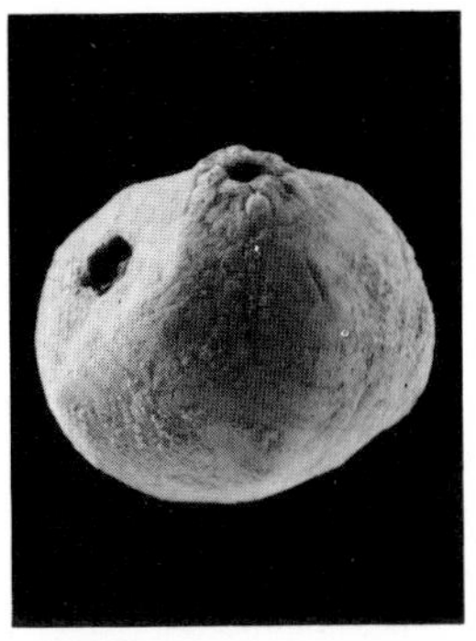
Plate 7.3.2A

Plate 7.3.2B

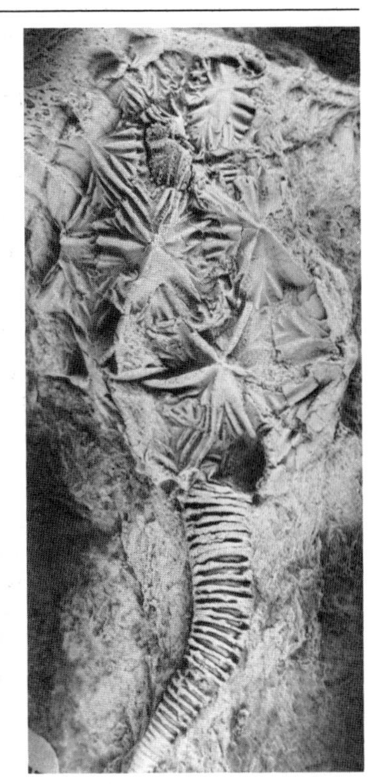
Plate 7.3.3

that is developed and on the structure and arrangement of the appendages. The Diploporita have paired pore structures, Rhombifera have tubular canal systems arranged in a rhombic pattern, Blastoidea generally have regions of the theca that are very thin and tightly folded, and eocrinoids either have simple sutural pores, termed 'epispires', or lack respiratory structures altogether. The Paracrinoidea may also lack respiratory structures or have simple internal pits, but are readily distinguished from other cystoids on account of their appendages, which are uniserial, not biserial, and arise from only one side of each ambulacral tract.

ARTIFICIAL KEY

1. Brachioles uniserial, arising from only 1 (generally the left-hand) side of each ambulacrum/arm .. CLASS Paracrinoidea
   Brachioles generally biserial and always arising from both sides of ambulacral tracts 2
2. Respiratory structures present 3
   Respiratory structures absent 6
3. Respiratory structures pore pairs which perforate thecal plates and were capped by soft tissue structures or by a thin stereom layer externally .... CLASS Diploporita
   Respiratory structures not as above 4
4. Respiratory structures thecal canals arranged in a rhombic pattern shared equally between adjacent plates and opening externally or internally .... CLASS Rhombifera
   Respiratory structures not as above 5
5. Respiratory structures thin-walled folds shared between adjacent plates on either side of the ambulacra; often hidden externally and opening to the exterior via narrow slits or pores close to the mouth ... CLASS Blastoidea (Eublastoidea)
   Respiratory structures simple pores at plate sutures (epispires) .... Eocrinoids (part)
6. Thecal plating generally irregular, without adoral processes .... Eocrinoids (part)
   Thecal plating highly organized, with prominent adoral processes.................. CLASS Blastoidea (Coronata)

Eocrinoids (L. Cambrian–Silurian)

Diagnostic features. Cystoids with biserial appendages and either lacking specialized respiratory structures or with simple sutural pores.

The class Eocrinoidea is a most unsatisfactory, artificial group of primitive cystoids that do not have any of the advanced characteristics which distinguish the other cystoid classes. It almost certainly contains ancestors to the other cystoid classes and possibly even to the crinoids. Paul and Smith (1984) informally split eocrinoids among various pelmatozoan groups, but for the purposes of this book eocrinoids have been treated as a paraphyletic group. The best review of eocrinoids remains that of Ubaghs (1967), but both Sprinkle (1973) and Bockelie (1981) have added a great deal of information. No satisfactory classification above family level has been proposed and the following illustrations may give some idea of the range in diversity that exists.

Pl. 7.3.1. *Gogia* Walcott, 1917
Theca more or less conical or subglobular, and generally clearly differentiated from the stem, which is a polyplated holdfast with a large lumen; theca composed of a large number of polygonal plates without regular arrangement, those towards the upper part with sutural pores (epispires); oral surface flat or domed with variable number of brachioles arising from it. Theca up to 3 cm in length.
L.–M. Cambrian.
Gogia aff. *kitchnerensis* Sprinkle: M. Cambrian, Idaho, USA.

Pl. 7.3.2. *Cryptocrinites* von Buch, 1840
Theca globular, composed of relatively few plates arranged in regular cycles (3 in the lowest circlet, and 5 each in the next two); peristome small, slightly elevated, surrounded by miniscule brachiole facets; small stem facet at aboral pole; no sutural pores; periproct lateral, hexagonal in outline. Theca up to 1 cm in diameter.

M. Ordovician.
Cryptocrinites laevis (Pander): M. Ordovician, Papovka, Leningrad, USSR.

Pl. 7.3.3. *Macrocystella* Callaway, 1877
Theca roughly ovoid, composed of 5 circlets of plates all with prominent ridged ornament; oral surface rather flat, bearing brachioles around its outer edge; stem enlarged proximally, composed of alternating large and small columnals; stem with large lumen. Theca up to 4 cm in length.
L.–M. Ordovician. (Best considered as a rhombiferan cystoid).
Macrocystella azaisi (Thoral): Arenig, Herault, France.

Pl. 7.3.4. *Lichenoides* Barrande, 1846
Stemless; theca ovoid, composed of relatively few plates, with small irregular infrabasals at the aboral pole followed by 3 circlets of plates with prominent slit-like epispires; all plates notably swollen and thickened centrally; brachioles attaching directly on to the second and third circlets of plates; no tegmen. Theca up to 2 cm in length.
M. Cambrian.
Lichenoides priscus Barrande: M. Cambrian, Jince, Czechoslovakia.

Pl. 7.3.5. *Lingulocystis* Thoral, 1935
Theca highly flattened, paddle-shaped, with a prominent marginal frame of elongate ossicles; oral surface long and narrow with brachioles at either end connected to the central mouth by covered food grooves; within the frame plating irregular with a large number of tiny ovoid plates; stem long, undifferentiated. Theca up to 2 cm in length.
L. Ordovician.
Lingulocystis elongata Thoral: Arenig, Herault, France.

Class Paracrinoidea (M.–U. Ordovician)

Diagnostic features Cystoids with an irregularly plated theca and a stem of thin columnals; respiratory structures present in some groups, consisting of internal pits that do not quite pierce the thecal plates; brachioles uniserial, arising from only one side of each ambulacrum.

Basis for subdivision Paracrinoids have been divided into two distinct groups, those with endothecal respiratory structures and those without (Parsley and Mintz 1975). Whether the ambulacra are recumbent or extend as free arms is of less consequence as both conditions occur in otherwise very similar and closely related groups.

ARTIFICIAL KEY

Endothecal pits present: thecal plates numerous, in some concave: ambulacra as free arms or recumbent .... ORDER Comarocystitida
Theca without endothecal pits or other respiratory structures: thecal plates relatively few in number: ambulacra always recumbent .... ORDER Platycystitida

Order Comarocystitida

Pl. 7.3.6. *Comarocystites* Billings, 1854
Theca ovoid, composed of a large number of polygonal plates, all concave and with multiple cycles of internal pits; peristome and stem at opposite poles; 2 short, diametrically opposed ambulacral grooves run from the peristome to 3 or 4 large facets for the erect appendages; stem large, circular in cross-section.
M. Ordovician.
Thecal length up to 10 cm.
Comarocystites punctatus Billings: M. Ordovician, Ottawa, Canada.

Order Platycystitida

Pl. 7.3.7. *Canadocystis* Jaekel, 1900
Theca globular, composed of 20 to 40 plates lacking endothecal pits: peristome and stem not at opposite poles; 2 recumbent ambulacra forming raised S-shaped ridge with a central peristome; brachiole facets on outer curve of each; periproct small, more or less opposite stem. Thecal length up to 15 mm.
M. Ordovician.
Canadocystis emmonsi (Hudson): M. Ordovician, New York, USA.

Class Diploporita (L. Ordovician–M. Devonian)

Diagnostic features Cystoids with thecal plates that are pierced by double pores which are either visible externally and were covered in life by soft tissue (diplopores) or are covered by a thin external layer of stereom, in which case pore pairs are connected by short subsurface canals (humatipores).

Basis for subdivision The best studies of this group are those of Paul (1971, 1973) and his classification is followed here. Diploporite cystoids are subdivided on the basis of their pore morphology and the arrangement of thecal plating. Features considered to be important include whether they have diplopores or humatipores, whether thecal plating is complex and irregular or is arranged in cycles, each composed of relatively few plates, whether there are distinct ambulacral zones, and whether ambulacral grooves and brachiole facets are confined to the area around the mouth or extend over much of the theca.

ARTIFICIAL KEY

1. Ambulacral grooves extending over many thecal plates, usually with discrete ambulacral plating 2
   Ambulacral grooves confined to the region immediately adjacent to the peristome, without discrete ambulacral zones 3
2. Diplopores on all thecal plates; ambulacral zones poorly differentiated .... SUPERFAMILY Glyptosphaeritida
   Diplopores on interambulacral plates only; ambulacral zones clearly differentiated .... SUPERFAMILY Asteroblastida
3. Thecal plates relatively few, often arranged in regular cycles; palate of 6 plates covering peristome; brachiole facets single or arranged in bundles radiating from the corners of the peristome .... 4 (SUPERFAMILY Sphaeronitida)
   Thecal plates many, generally arranged irregularly; stemless; diplopores partially or completely sealed; brachioles few, connected to the peristome by 2 short, wide ambulacra .... SUPERFAMILY Aristocystida
4. Respiratory structures diplopores... FAMILY Sphaeronitidae
   Respiratory structures humatipores.. FAMILY Holocystitidae

SUPERFAMILY SPHAERONITIDA

Pl. 7.3.8. *Haplosphaeronis* Jaekel, 1926 (FAMILY Sphaeronitidae)
Stemless; theca of 2 cycles of plates, 7 plates in each, plus 6

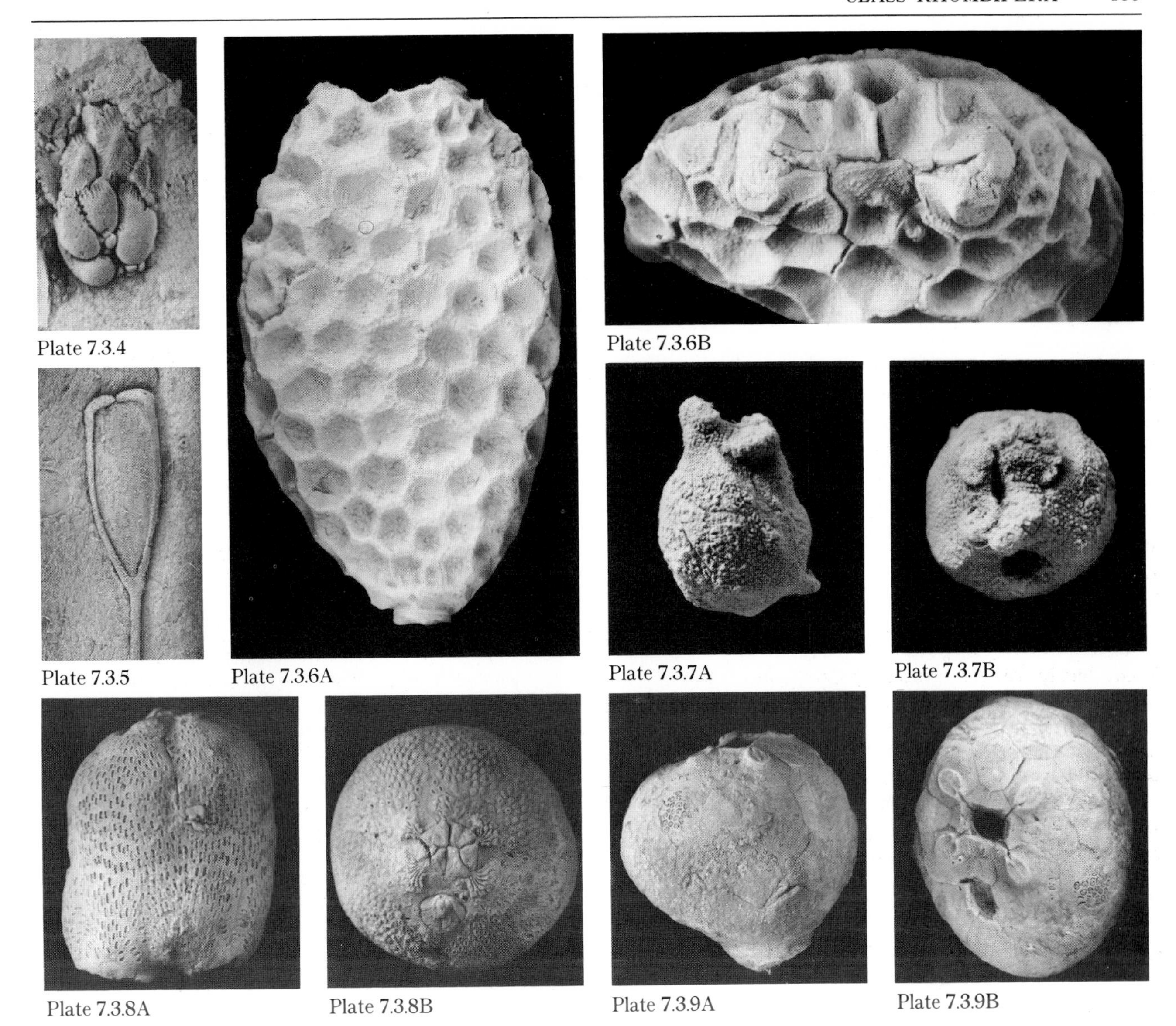

Plate 7.3.4 Plate 7.3.5 Plate 7.3.6A Plate 7.3.6B Plate 7.3.7A Plate 7.3.7B Plate 7.3.8A Plate 7.3.8B Plate 7.3.9A Plate 7.3.9B

palatal plates covering the peristome; ambulacral grooves spread fan-wise from the corners of the mouth, 3–10 in each bundle, leading to brachiole facets at the outer edge of the oral plates; anal pyramid close to peristome; gonopore small, offset between the peristome and periproct. Theca up to 25 mm in diameter.
Ordovician.
Haplosphaeronis oblonga (Angelin): Caradoc, Dalarna, Sweden.

Pl. 7.3.9. *Trematocystis* Jaekel, 1899 (FAMILY Holocystitidae)
Stemless; theca irregularly globular; peristome oval, surrounded by a cycle of 6 plates and an outer cycle of 8 plates; 4 large brachiole facets lie close to the peristome; thecal plates with humatipores, visible only on worn surfaces. Theca up to 4 cm in diameter.
M. Silurian.
Trematocystis globosus (Miller): Osgood Formation, Indiana, USA. (A) lateral; (B) oral.

SUPERFAMILY ARISTOCYSTIDA

Pl. 7.3.10. *Aristocystites* Barrande, 1887
Theca ovoid, rounded aborally and stemless; plates numerous, in semiregular cycles often in 2 or more discrete sizes; peristome small, at junction of 2 short, wide ambulacral grooves, each ending in a single large brachiole facet; thecal plates with covered diplopores, only visible on worn surfaces. Theca up to 7 cm in length.
M. Ordovician.
Aristocystites bohemicus Barrande: Caradoc, Bohemia, Czechoslovakia.

SUPERFAMILY GLYPTOSPHAERITIDA

Pl. 7.3.11. *Glyptosphaeronites* Müller, 1854
Theca large, apple-shaped, composed of many polygonal plates; peristome covered by 5 oral plates; ambulacral grooves narrow, extending over thecal plates without following plate sutures to below ambitus; alternating side branches lead to small brachiole facets; all plates with diplopores. Theca up to 6 cm in diameter.
Ordovician.
Glyptosphaeronites leuchtenbergi (Volborth): L. Ordovician, Leningrad, USSR.

Class Rhombifera (L. Ordovician–U. Devonian)

Diagnostic features Cystoids with external or internal pore structures that consist of rhombic sets of thecal canals shared equally between two adjacent plates.

Basis for subdivision The classification scheme adopted here is that of Paul (1972). Rhombifera are divided into two groups according to whether their pore structures open externally (dichopores) or internally (fistulipores). Other important features for taxonomy include the structure of the stem and the overall plating arrangement. A fairly good account of this group can be found in Fay (1967).

ARTIFICIAL KEY

1. Pore structures endothecal, opening externally as pores or slits and connected internally .... 2(ORDER Dichoporita)
   Pore structures exothecal, opening internally with subsurface canals visible externally only in worn specimens .... ORDER Fistuliporita (SUPERFAMILY Caryocystitida)
2. Pore structures open externally as slits (pectinirhombs); stem with expanded proximal zone .... SUPERFAMILY Glyptocystitida
   Pore structures open externally as pores (cryptorhombs); stem thin and undifferentiated .... SUPERFAMILY Hemicosmitida

Order Dichoporita (SUPERFAMILY Glyptocystitida)

Pl. 7.3.12. *Pleurocystites* Billings, 1854
Theca flattened, one side composed of a mosaic of small, polygonal plates (the periproctal system) within a frame of marginal ossicles, the other with relatively few, large plates and 3 or fewer pectinirhombs; 2 large arms extend anteriorly from either side of the small peristome. Theca up to 5 cm long.
Ordovician.
(A) *Pleurocystites quadratus* Bather: Ashgill, Girvan, Scotland; anal view. (B) *P. elegans* Billings: M. Ordovician, Ontario, Canada; antanal view.

Pl. 7.3.13. *Homocystites* Barrande, 1887
Theca box-like, plates large, ornamented with ridges radiating from centre; ambulacra confined to flat oral surface; brachioles small, relatively few; base indented where column inserts; periproct fairly large, containing many small plates. Theca up to 3 cm long.
Ordovician.
Homocystites constrictus (Bather): Ashgill, Girvan, Scotland.

Pl. 7.3.14. *Apiocystites* Forbes, 1848
Theca ovate, elongate with 3 small disjunct pectinirhombs; 4 ambulacra extending almost to the column, never branched; anal pyramid of 6 plates surrounded by a ring of squarish plates. Theca up to 3 cm long.
M. Silurian–L. Devonian.
Apiocystites pentrematoides Forbes: Wenlock, Dudley, England.

Pl. 7.3.15. *Pseudocrinites* Pearce, 1842
Theca biconvex with 2 ambulacra forming a heavy rim, reaching almost to the column; ambulacral plates thick, giving rise to numerous short brachioles; theca of relatively few, large plates; 3 large, disjunct pectinirhombs, 2 on one face, 1 on the other; anal pyramid with wide border of small plates. Theca up to 4 cm broad.
U. Silurian–L. Devonian.
Pseudocrinites bifasciatus Pearce: Wenlock, Dudley, England.

Pl. 7.3.16. *Echinoencrinites* von Meyer, 1826
Theca roughly globular; oral area produced, small, with relatively few brachioles arising from around the mouth; plates ridged, typically highly ornamented; rhombs few, opening as narrow slits; base indented for column; periproct large, slightly produced, facing laterally. Theca up to 3 cm broad.
L. Ordovician.
Echinoencrinites senckenbergii von Meyer: Kunda, Leningrad, USSR.

(SUPERFAMILY Hemicosmitida)

Pl. 7.3.17. *Hemicosmites* von Buch, 1840
Theca ovate, composed of large plates arranged in cycles with 4 basals, 6 infralaterals, 9 laterals and a circle of radials; peristome at apex with 3 large brachiole facets immediately adjacent; short ambulacral grooves lead from the mouth to each facet; cryptorhombs numerous, pores opening through tubercles. Theca up to 4 cm long.
M. Ordovician–L. Silurian.
Hemicosmites extraneus Eichwald: M. Ordovician, Wesenberg, Baltic USSR.

Order Fistuliporita (SUPERFAMILY Caryocystitida)

Pl. 7.3.18. *Caryocystites* von Buch, 1846
Theca elongate, tapering adorally, broadest part below mid-height; thecal plating irregular, without strong sculpture; all plates with narrow, straight fistulipore canals, visible on weathered surfaces; peristome small, apical, without ambulacral grooves or prominent brachiole facets; periproct angular, about mid-height; gonopore circular, near peristome; column small, pentameric. Theca up to 9 cm in length.
Ordovician.
Caryocystites lagenalis Regnéll: Caradoc, Dalarna, Sweden.

Pl. 7.3.19. *Echinosphaerites* Wahlenberg, 1818
Theca spherical, composed of a great number of small polygonal plates without ornament; all plates with fistulipores; small oral projection with tiny brachiole facets and miniscule pentameric stem at opposite pole; anal pyramid and gonopore in upper half of theca. Theca up to 10 cm in diameter.
Ordovician.
Echinosphaerites aurantium (Gyllenhall): M. Ordovician, Leningrad, USSR.

Pl. 7.3.20. *Stichocystis* Jaekel, 1899
Theca ovoid, composed of many plates but sutures difficult to distinguish; parallel series of straight ridges cross plate sutures, each pierced by a series of pores; peristome large, raised, with 4 surrounding brachiole facets. Theca up to 5 cm in diameter.
M. Ordovician.
Stichocystis geometrica (Angelin): Caradoc, Radbandet, Sweden.

Class Blastoidea (L. Ordovician–Permian)

Diagnostic features Bud-shaped cystoids with highly organized thecal plating, in three circlets, arranged pentamerally; ambulacra either erect and free or, more commonly, recumbent and incorporated into the theca; giving rise to biserial brachioles; thin-walled fold structures generally present.

Basis for subdivision The Blastoidea are a distinct and easily recognizable group of cystoids with simple thecal plating arranged pentamerally. It contains three fairly distinct groups which nevertheless appear to be more closely related to one another than to any other cystoid. The Eublastoidea is the largest of these groups and the only one of any importance. Eublastoids have recumbent ambulacra, a theca composed of three basals, five radials and five deltoids, and fold structures (termed hydrospires) which are shared between the deltoid and

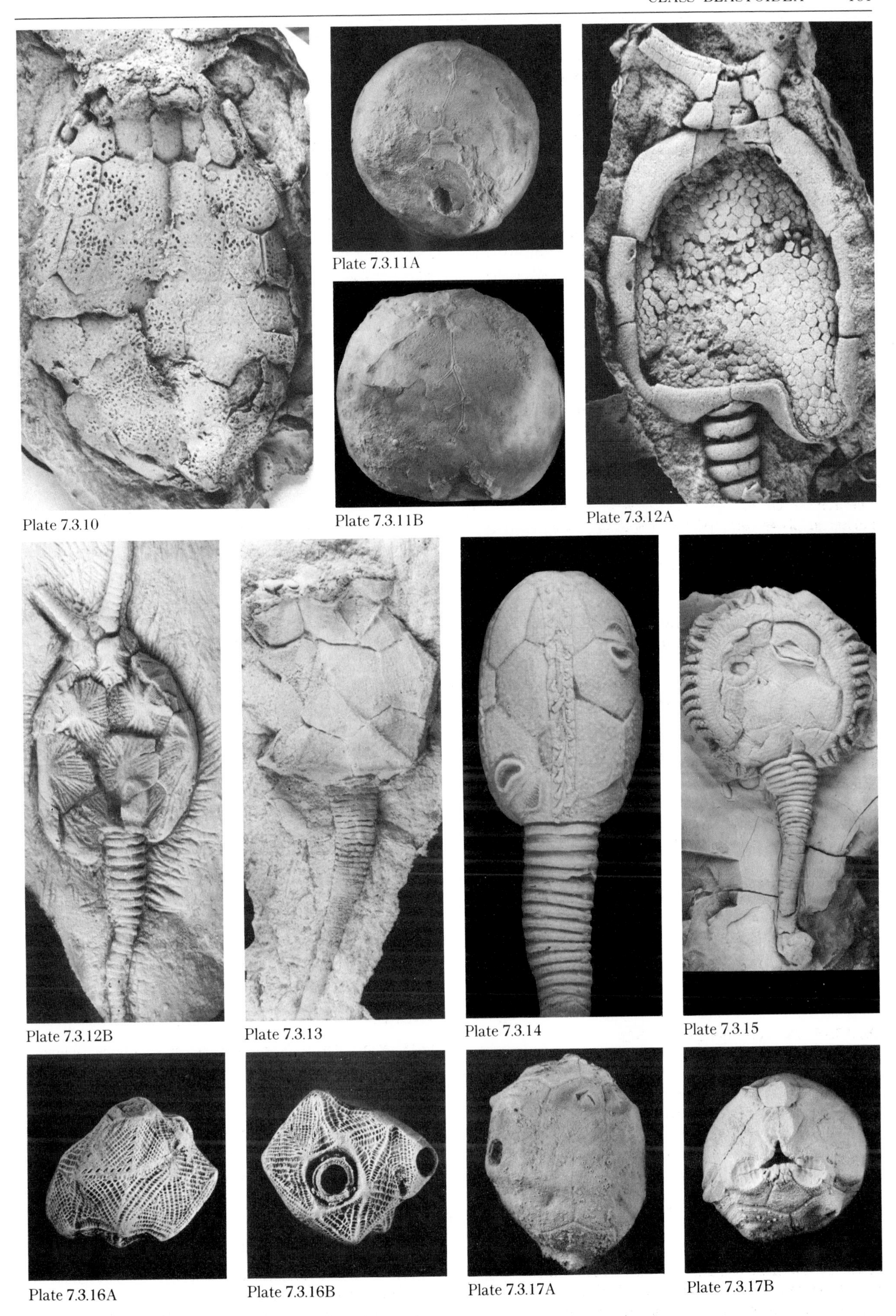

Plate 7.3.10

Plate 7.3.11A

Plate 7.3.11B

Plate 7.3.12A

Plate 7.3.12B

Plate 7.3.13

Plate 7.3.14

Plate 7.3.15

Plate 7.3.16A

Plate 7.3.16B

Plate 7.3.17A

Plate 7.3.17B

radial plates. The coronates have basically the same thecal plating, but lack hydrospires and have erect ambulacra that extend free of the theca and give rise to alternating brachioles. They almost certainly include the ancestors of the eublastoids. Parablastoids, the third group, have less regular thecal plating and their fold structures are confined to the deltoid plates. They are extremely rare and none is illustrated here.

Eublastoids are divided into two orders, the Fissiculata and the Spiraculata. In fissiculates, the hydrospire folds are generally exposed, but may be partially or more or less completely hidden by the ambulacra. They always open to the exterior by adradial slits running parallel to the ambulacra. In spiraculates, the hydrospires are completely internal and have tiny inhalant pores along the margins of ambulacra and large exhalant pores (termed 'spiracles') adjacent to the peristome. The arrangement of hydrospire fields and spiracles, the arrangement of accessory plates around the anus and the general thecal shape are all important characteristics at the family level.

A general account of blastoids is given in the *Treatise on Invertebrate Paleontology* (Moore 1967) and a superb review of fissiculate eublastoids can be found in Breimer and Macurda (1972).

ARTIFICIAL KEY

1. Theca composed of 5 basals, 5 radials and 5 deltoids and sometimes additional plates; deltoids large, with slit-like fold structures .... SUBCLASS Parablastoidea
   Theca composed of 3 basals, 5 radials and 5 deltoids arranged in cycles 2
2. Theca without recumbent ambulacra or fold structures ... . SUPERORDER Coronata
   Theca incorporating ambulacral zones; fold structures present, shared between deltoids and radials .... 3 (SUPERORDER Eublastoidea)
3. Hydrospires exposed, or partially to completely hidden and opening via adradial slits .... 4 (ORDER Fissiculata)
   Hydrospires internal, opening via large adoral spiracles and tiny adradial pores .... 9 (ORDER Spiraculata)
4. Ambulacra more or less flush with theca 5
   Ambulacra in sinuses between interambulacral crests .. 8
5. Oral surface vaulted 6
   Oral surface more or less flat 7
6. Theca clavate, ambulacra not extending below ambitus .. .. FAMILY Orophocrinidae
   Theca globular, ambulacra extending far down the theca .... FAMILY Nymphaeoblastidae
7. Theca cup-shaped; 10 hydrospire fields, all clearly visible, those in the posterior interradius are much reduced .... FAMILY Codasteridae
   Theca highly elongate and horn-shaped; hydrospire fields concealed .... FAMILY Ceratoblastidae
8. Ambulacral sinuses broad and shallow; theca cup-shaped or cylindrical; deltoid crests usually present, sloping outwards adorally .... FAMILY Neoschismatidae
   Ambulacral sinuses feeble to pronounced; theca conical or biconical; deltoid crests sloping inwards adorally .... FAMILY Phaenoschismatidae
9. 10 spiracles 10
   8 spiracles and an anispiracle .... FAMILY Granatocrinidae
   5 V-shaped spiracles or 4 and an anispiracle 11
   4 spiracles and an anispiracle 12
10. Anal area with 2 elongate plates (cryptodeltoids) exposed and forming sides of anal opening .... FAMILY Nucleocrinidae
    Anal area without visible cryptodeltoids .... FAMILY Schizoblastidae
11. Theca conical or biconical, elongate .... FAMILY Troosticrinidae
    Theca globular.................. FAMILY Diploblastidae
12. Theca subglobular, ambulacra linear .... FAMILY Orbitremitidae
    Theca subconical to clavate, ambulacra generally lanceolate .... FAMILY Pentremitidae

Superorder Coronata (M. Ordovician–U. Silurian)

Pl. 7.3.21. *Stephanocrinus* Conrad, 1842
Theca conical, composed of 3 circlets of ridged plates; 3 basals, 5 radials and 5 deltoids; radials and deltoids prolonged into large processes but lack hydrospires; a single arm (ambulacrum) giving rise to biserial brachioles attached to a basal plate between each process and connected to central peristome by covered grooves. Theca up to 25 mm in height.
M. Silurian.
Stephanocrinus angulatus Conrad: M. Silurian, New York, USA. (A) lateral; (B) oral.

Superorder Eublastoidea

Order Fissiculata

Pl. 7.3.22. *Pleuroschisma* Reimann, 1945 (FAMILY Phaenoschismatidae)
Theca biconical with distinct ambulacral sinuses and interambulacral processes sloping inwards adorally; ambulacra straight, narrow; lancet concealed; hydrospire folds well developed and clearly exposed. Theca up to 25 mm in length.
L.–M. Devonian.
Pleuroschisma verneuili (Etheridge & Carpenter): L. Devonian, Sabero, Spain. (A) lateral; (B) oral.

Pl. 7.3.23. *Pentremitidea* d'Orbigny, 1850 (FAMILY Phaenoschismatidae)
Theca elongate, conical with relatively flat top and feeble interambulacral processes, sloping inwards adorally; ambulacra lanceolate, confined to apical region; hydrospire fields almost completely concealed. Theca up to 20 mm long.
L. Devonian.
Pentremitidea archiaci (Etheridge & Carpenter): L. Devonian, Sabero, Spain.

Pl. 7.3.24. *Cryptoschisma* Etheridge & Carpenter, 1886 (FAMILY Phaenoschismatidae)
Theca conical with flat top, interambulacral processes feeble; ambulacra petaloid, lancet exposed along mid-line; hydrospires concealed by ambulacra, absent in posterior interambulacrum. Theca up to 8 mm in diameter.
L. Devonian.
Cryptoschisma schultzii (de Verneuil & d'Archiac): L. Devonian, Sabero, Spain.

Pl. 7.3.25. *Timoroblastus* Wanner, 1924 (FAMILY Neoschismatidae)
Theca box-like, stellate in plan view; base slightly concave; ambulacra small, petaloid, confined to flat upper surface; hydrospires concealed; ambulacral sinuses broad and shallow; deltoid crest small, outward sloping. Theca up to 30 mm in diameter.
Permian.
Timoroblastus coronatus Wanner: Permian, Timor, Indonesia. (A) lateral; (B) oral.

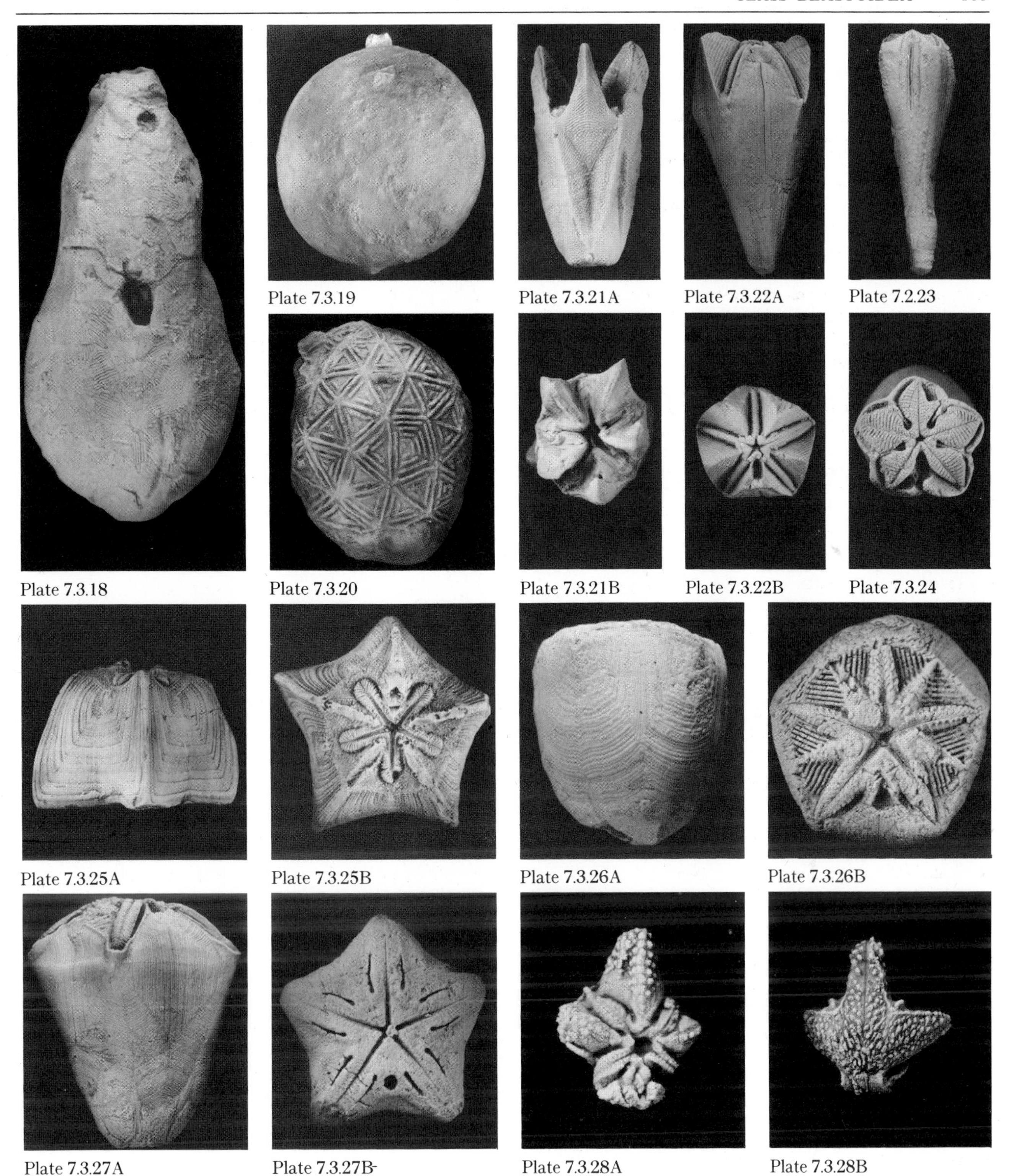

Pl. 7.3.26. *Codaster* McCoy, 1849 (FAMILY Codasteridae)
Theca cup-shaped with flat summit and rounded base; ambulacra confined to summit, lanceolate; hydrospire fields well exposed, greatly reduced in posterior interambulacrum; lancet exposed at mid-line of ambulacra. Theca up to 20 mm in diameter.
L. Carboniferous.
Codaster acutus McCoy: L. Carboniferous, Settle, England. (A) lateral; (B) oral.

Pl. 7.3.27. *Orophocrinus* von Seebach, 1865 (FAMILY Orophocrinidae)
Theca clavate, with conical pelvis and convex vault; pentagonal in plan view; ambulacra linear, narrow, with exposed lancet; hydrospire fields concealed, with well-defined adradial slits. Theca up to 50 mm in length.
L. Carboniferous.
(A) *Orophocrinus orbygniana* (de Koninck): Tournaisian, Tournai, Belgium; lateral. (B) *O. stelliformis* Owen & Schumard: Burlington Limestone, Iowa, USA; oral.

Pl. 7.3.28. *Astrocrinus* Morris, 1843 (FAMILY Astrocrinidae)
Stemless, tetralobate theca with external bilateral symmetry; 4 of the 5 ambulacra well developed, linear, curving around theca;

D ambulacrum short and petalloid; hydrospire folds concealed. Theca up to 5 mm in length.
L. Carboniferous.
Astrocrinus tetragonus (Austin & Austin): L. Carboniferous, Kidlaw, Scotland. (A) oral; (B) aboral.

Order Spiraculata

Pl. 7.3.29. *Pentremites* Say, 1820 (FAMILY Pentremitidae)
Theca clavate to subpyriform with 4 spiracles and a large anispiracle located in an undivided deltoid plate; ambulacra long, petaloid, with exposed lancet; 1 hydrospire pore to each ambulacral side plate. Theca up to 30 mm long.
Carboniferous.
Pentremites symmetricus Hall: Paint Creek Formation, L. Carboniferous, Illinois, USA. (A) lateral; (B) oral.

Pl. 7.3.30. *Eleutherocrinus* Shumard & Yandell, 1856 (FAMILY Pentremitidae)
Stemless, flattened ellipsoidal theca with bilateral symmetry through the A/B–D plane; 4 ambulacra long, lanceolate; ambulacrum D short; petaloid; lancet plate concealed; 4 spiracles and an anispiracle. Theca up to 25 mm long.
Devonian.
Eleutherocrinus cassedayi Shumard & Yandell: M. Devonian, Ontario, Canada. (A) lateral; (B) oral.

Pl. 7.3.31. *Cordyloblastus* Fay, 1961 (FAMILY Pentremitidae)
Theca clavate with concavo-conical pelvis and convex vault; deltoids small; ambulacra linear, with concealed lancet; 4 spiracles and an anispiracle; anispiracle bounded by 3 anal plates. Theca up to 20 mm tall.
Devonian.
Cordyloblastus clavatus (Schultze): M. Devonian, Eifel, W. Germany.

Pl. 7.3.32. *Cryptoblastus* Etheridge & Carpenter, 1886 (FAMILY Granatocrinidae)
Theca ellipsoidal, with long, narrow ambulacra and partially exposed lancet; 8 spiracles plus an anispiracle with complex anal plating; 2 hydrospire pores per side plate; interradial sutures strongly depressed. Theca up to 20 mm.
L. Carboniferous.
Cryptoblastus melo Owen & Shumard: Burlington Limestone, Iowa, USA. (A) lateral; (B) oral.

Pl. 7.3.33. *Elaeacrinus* Roemer, 1851 (FAMILY Nucleocrinidae)
Theca elongate, ellipsoidal with 10 spiracles and a separate anal opening set between 2 lateral elongate cryptodeltoid plates; deltoids long, overlapping radials; ambulacra long and narrow, with concealed lancet plates; 1 hydrospire pore per side plate; oral area with many small cover plates. Theca up to 25 mm.
Devonian.
Elaeacrinus verneuili (Troost): M. Devonian, Montana, USA. (A) lateral; (B) oral.

Pl. 7.3.34. *Deltoblastus* Fay, 1961 (FAMILY Schizoblastidae)
Theca subpyriform to ellipsoidal with 10 very small spiracles at apex and a separate anal opening at suture between epideltoid and hypodeltoid; ambulacra long, lanceolate, slightly sunken; lancet partially exposed; 1 hydrospire pore per side plate. Theca up to 30 mm tall.
Permian.
Deltoblastus jonkeri (Wanner): Permian, Timor, Indonesia. (A) lateral; (B) oral.

Pl. 7.3.35. *Diploblastus* Fay, 1961 (FAMILY Diploblastidae)
Theca globular with 4 paired, V-shaped spiracles and a separate anispiracle; ambulacra long, lanceolate, with concealed lancet at distal end only. Theca up to 5 mm in length.
L. Carboniferous.
Diploblastus glaber (Meek & Worthen): Renault Formation, Illinois, USA. (A) lateral; (B) oral.

Pl. 7.3.36. *Ellipticoblastus* Fay, 1961 (FAMILY Orbitremitidae)
Theca ellipsoidal with 4 spiracles and an anispiracle; ambulacra long, narrow; lancet concealed; deltoids large; 2 hydrospire pores to each side plate. Theca up to 25 mm in length.
L. Carboniferous.
Ellipticoblastus orbicularis (Sowerby): Viséan, Clitheroe, England.

Pl. 7.3.37. *Globoblastus* Hambach, 1903 (FAMILY Orbitremitidae)
Like *Ellipticoblastus* but with greatly reduced deltoid plates. Theca up to 20 mm in length.
L. Carboniferous.
Globoblastus norwoodi (Owen & Shumard) 1850: Burlington Limestone, Iowa, USA.

Pl. 7.3.38. *Metablastus* Etheridge & Carpenter, 1886 (FAMILY Troosticrinidae)
Theca biconical with 5 paired, slit-like spiracles and a large anal opening; ambulacra narrow, relatively short, sunken between interambulacral crests; deltoids very small. Theca up to 20 mm in length.
L. Carboniferous.
Metablastus bipyramidalis (Hall): Salem Limestone, Montana, USA. (A) lateral; (B) oral.

Superclass Crinozoa (M. Cambrian–Recent)

7.4 Class Crinoidea (M. Cambrian–Recent)

Diagnostic features Pelmatozoans with arms that carry extensions of the major body coeloms; calyx differentiated into a ventral tegmen and a dorsal cup composed of two or three cycles of plates with or without additional anal plates and fixed arm plates; gonads extending into the arms, no gonopore.

Basis for subdivision With the exception of the M. Cambrian genus *Echmatocrinus*, which has been put in a subclass of its own by some workers because of its lack of regular thecal plating, crinoids can be divided into four subclasses. The Flexibilia have cup plates that are not rigidly sutured to one another and arms which characteristically curve inwards distally and always lack pinnules. The Camerata have a tegmen of tesselate plates which forms a rigid vaulted roof to the cup, creating a fairly solid calyx that is often preserved without arms or stem. This calyx generally incorporates some of the lowest arm plates (called fixed brachials) together with plates between the arms (interbrachials). The Inadunata and the Articulata have relatively small calices that lack a firm tegmen and rarely incorporate fixed brachials and interbrachials. The inadunate cup generally includes one or more anal plates whereas the cup of articulates never does. Furthermore, the mouth lies hidden beneath the flexible plated tegmen in inadunates whereas, in articulates, the mouth opens through the tegmen. Ubaghs *et al.* (1978) give the most authoritative and up-to-date account of this group. Crinoids are suspension feeders, using their arms to form a filtration net, and mostly live anchored to the sea-floor by their stem.

Plate 7.3.29A Plate 7.3.29B Plate 7.3.30A Plate 7.3.30B Plate 7.3.31

Plate 7.3.32A Plate 7.3.32B Plate 7.3.33A Plate 7.3.33B

Plate 7.3.34A Plate 7.3.34B Plate 7.3.35A Plate 7.3.35B

Plate 7.3.36 Plate 7.3.37 Plate 7.3.38A Plate 7.3.38B

ARTIFICIAL KEY

1. Cup plates firmly sutured together 2
   Cup plates typically rather weakly bound together; arms curve inwards distally, always without pinnules .... SUBCLASS Flexibilia
2. Tegmen stout, forming a solid calyx which generally includes the lowest arm plates .... SUBCLASS Camerata
   Tegmen flexible, never rigid; arms rarely incorporated into the calyx 3
3. Cup usually includes anal plates; mouth subtegminal .... SUBCLASS Inadunata
   Cup never includes anal plates; mouth opens through tegmen .... SUBCLASS Articulata

Subclass Camerata (L. Ordovician–Permian)

Diagnostic features Crinoids with a rigidly sutured calyx generally including fixed brachials, interbrachials and anal plates and with a stout tesselate tegmen concealing the mouth; arms pinnate, uniserial or biserial; stem holomeric.

Basis for subdivision Camerates can be divided into two groups, those with just radial and basal plate cycles (monocyclic forms) and those with an additional cycle of infrabasal plates (dicyclic forms). Camerate superfamilies are distinguished principally on the basis of calyx plating. Important characteristics include the number of basals that are present, the extent to which fixed brachials are incorporated into the cup and whether radial plates form an uninterrupted circlet or are separated by anal plates posteriorly or by interbrachial plates all round.

ARTIFICIAL KEY

1. Cup monocyclic; no infrabasals . 2 (ORDER Monobathrida)
   Cup dicyclic; infrabasals present .... 10 (ORDER Diplobathrida)
2. Circlet of radial plates separated in the posterior interray by an anal plate .... 3 (SUBORDER Compsocrinina)
   Circlet of radial plates uninterrupted .... 6 (SUBORDER Glyptocrinina)
3. Fixed brachials greatly reduced or absent .... SUPERFAMILY Hexacrinitacea
   Cup with prominent fixed brachials and interbrachials . . 4
4. Interbrachial zones depressed, composed of many small plates; 4 basals in cup ...... SUPERFAMILY Xenocrinacea
   Interbrachial zones more or less flush, with relatively few plates; 3 basals in cup 5
5. Primibrachs (first arm plates) typically tall and hexagonal .... SUPERFAMILY Periechocrinacea
   Primibrachs typically broad and quadrangular .... SUPERFAMILY Carpocrinacea
6. Arm plates free of calyx above primibrachs .... SUPERFAMILY Platycrinitacea
   Calyx includes arm plates above the primibrachs 7
7. Fixed brachials relatively few in number .... SUPERFAMILY Patelliocrinacea
   Calyx with many fixed brachials and interbrachials ... 8
8. 5 basals in cup .... SUPERFAMILY Glyptocrinacea
   3 or 4 basals in cup 9
9. Calyx conical, tapering towards stem .... SUPERFAMILY Melocrinitacea
   Calyx typically broad with basal concavity .... SUPERFAMILY Eucalyptocrinacea
10. Radials and basals alternating, forming a single circlet .... SUBORDER Zygodiplobathrina
    Radials and basals forming two discrete circlets .... 11 (SUBORDER Eudiplobathrina)
11. Circlet of radial plates uninterrupted .... SUPERFAMILY Nyctocrinacea
    Circlet of radial plates interrupted by anal or interbrachial plates 12
12. Radial plate circlet interrupted in the posterior interray by the insertion of an anal plate .... SUPERFAMILY Dimetrocrinitacea
    All radial plates separated from one another by interbrachial plates .... SUPERFAMILY Rhodocrinitacea

Order Monobathrida (L. Ordovician–Permian)

Suborder Compsocrinina (Ordovician–Permian)

Pl. 7.4.1. *Periechocrinus* Morris, 1843 (SUPERFAMILY Periechocrinacea)
Cup conical, with 3 basals, 5 radials and numerous fixed brachials and interbrachials; radial circlet interrupted posteriorly by heptagonal primanal plate; radials and fixed brachials with median ridge; primanal followed by 3 plates in next highest row; free arms biserial, branched. Theca up to 6 cm in diameter.
M. Silurian.
Periechocrinus costatus Austin & Austin: Wenlock, Dudley, England.

Pl. 7.4.2. *Xenocrinus* S. A. Miller, 1881 (SUPERFAMILY Xenocrinacea)
Calyx with prominent fixed brachials and depressed interbrachial zones composed of a tesselate pavement of tiny plates; tegmen without anal tube; 10 pinnulate arms, uniserial near calyx, becoming biserial distally; basals small, sutures between radial plates covered by small supplementary plates. Calyx up to 15 mm in diameter.
U. Ordovician.
Xenocrinus baeri S. A. Miller: U. Ordovician (Richmondian), Ohio, USA.

Pl. 7.4.3. *Carpocrinus* Müller, 1840 (SUPERFAMILY Carpocrinacea)
Cup conical, with 3 basals, 5 radials and relatively few fixed brachials and interbrachials; radial circlet interrupted posteriorly by heptagonal anal plate; primibrachs quadrangular, broader than tall; posterior interray with median series of anal plates; arms stout, uniserial, pinnulate, 2 to 4 in each ray. Calyx up to 20 mm in diameter.
M. Silurian.
Carpocrinus ornatus (Angelin): Slite Beds, Gotland, Sweden.

Pl. 7.4.4. *Hexacrinites* Austin & Austin, 1843 (SUPERFAMILY Hexacrinitacea)
Calyx conical with relatively flat tegmen; cup with 2 circlets of large plates, the lower composed of 5 basals, the upper of 5 radials plus a large anal plate of similar size and shape; primibrachs and secundibrachs greatly reduced in size and incorporated into the calyx, but arms otherwise free; tegmen stout, composed of numerous small plates; anus opening directly through tegmen. Calyx up to 5 cm in diameter.
U. Silurian–U. Devonian.
Hexacrinites anaglypticus (Goldfuss): M. Devonian, Gerolstein, W. Germany. (A) lateral; (B) oral.

Suborder Glyptocrinina (M. Ordovician–Permian)

Pl. 7.4.5. *Pleurocrinus* (Miller) 1821 (SUPERFAMILY Platycrinitacea)
Calyx with 2 circlets of plates, 3 basals in lower circlet, 5 abutting radials in the upper; primibrach firmly fixed into calyx but standing out proud from it; tegmen stout, flat, with relatively few plates; anus opening at edge of tegmen; posterior cup plating undifferentiated. Calyx up to 3 cm in diameter.
L. Carboniferous–U. Permian.
Pleurocrinus tuberculatus (Miller): L. Carboniferous, Bolland, England. (A) lateral; (B) oral.

Pl. 7.4.6. *Melocrinites* Goldfuss, 1831 (SUPERFAMILY Melocrinitacea)
Calyx taller than broad, clavate; tegmen domed; cup including fixed brachials (primibrachs and secundibrachs); 4 basals; radial circlet uninterrupted; primanal followed by 3 plates in next highest row; anus opening subcentrally through tegmen. Calyx up to 3 cm in diameter.
M.–U. Devonian.
Melocrinites gibbosus Goldfuss: M. Devonian, Gerolstein, W. Germany. (A) lateral; (B) oral.

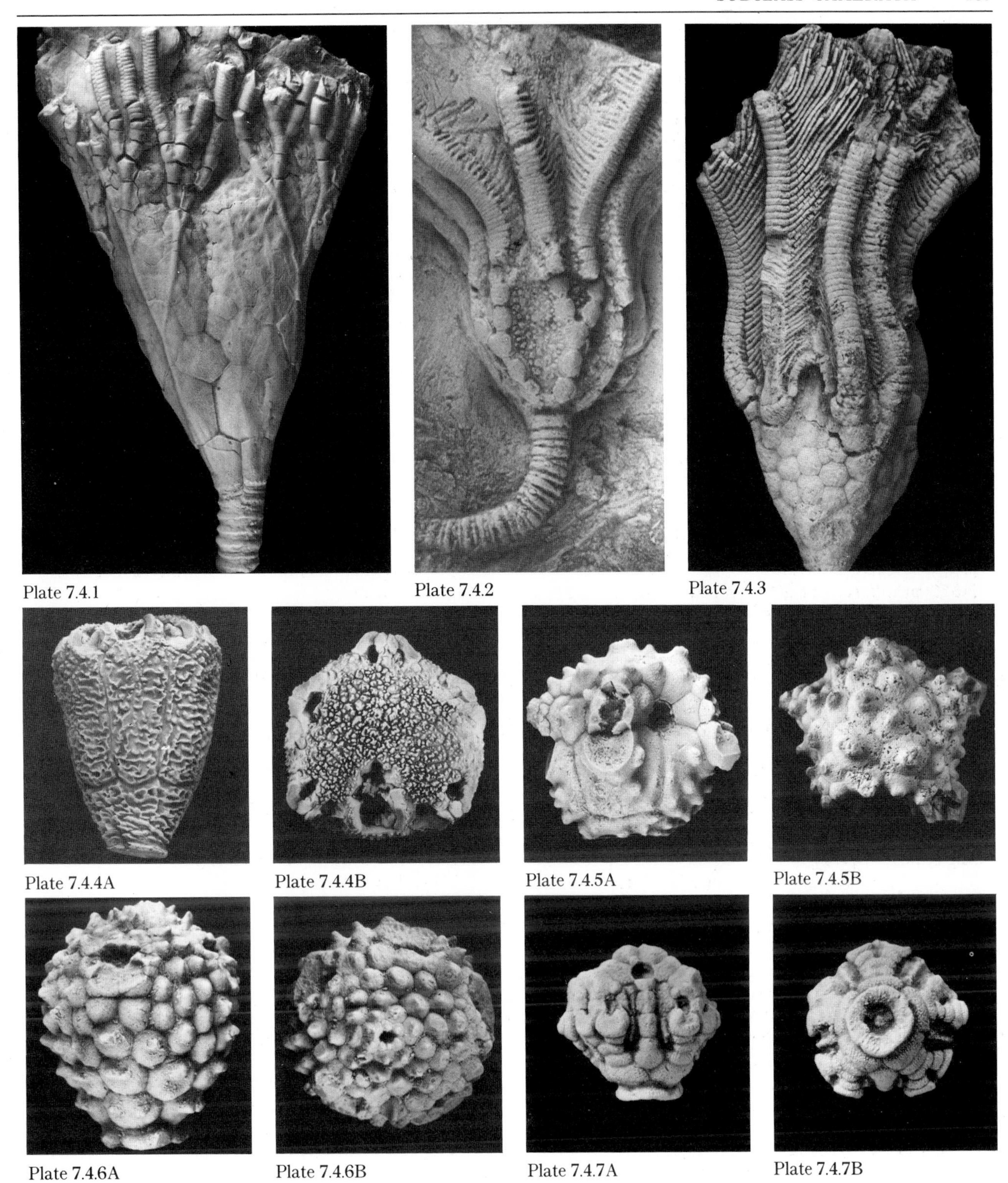

Pl. 7.4.7. *Stelidocrinus* Angelin, 1878 (SUPERFAMILY Patelliocrinacea)
Calyx globular, with 5 basals and 5 abutting radials; 2 interbrachs only between rays; fixed arms of 2 primibrachs and 2 secundibrachs only; primibrachs small, quadrangular, broader than tall; primanal followed by 3 plates; tegmen low, with 14 plates; periproct opening laterally through tegmen; 10 free biserial arms. Theca up to 1 cm in diameter.
U. Silurian.
Stelidocrinus capitulum Angelin: U. Silurian, Gotland, Sweden. (A) lateral; (B) aboral.

Pl. 7.4.8. *Glyptocrinus* Hall 1847 (SUPERFAMILY Glyptocrinacea)
Calyx conical, plates with strong stellate ornamentation obscuring sutures; fixed brachials numerous, including tertibrachs, arms 20, becoming free a little above the third branch, uniserial, pinnate; basal circle pentagonal; radial circlet uninterrupted; median anal ridge present above primanal; stem heterotomous, cylindrical, with pentagonal axial canal. Theca up to 5 cm in diameter.
M. Ordovician–U. Silurian.
Glyptocrinus decadactylus Hall: M. Ordovician, Ohio, USA.

Pl. 7.4.9. *Calliocrinus* d'Orbigny, 1850 (SUPERFAMILY Eucalyptocrinacea)
Calyx vase-shaped with basal concavity; cup wider than tall; basals 4, confined to basal concavity and not visible in side view; radial circlet uninterrupted, posterior interray hardly differentiated; plates with strong stellate ornament; primibrachs, secundibrachs and tertibrachs included in cup; tegmen stout, elevated into a spout-like projection; arm facets separated by small spinose processes. Theca up to 2 cm in diameter.
U. Silurian–L. Devonian.
Calliocrinus costatus (Hisinger): U. Silurian, Gotland, Sweden.

Order Diplobathrida (M. Ordovician–L. Carboniferous)

Suborder Eudiplobathrina (M. Ordovician–L. Carboniferous)

Pl. 7.4.10. *Reteocrinus* Billings, 1859 (SUPERFAMILY Rhodocrinitacea)
Cup conical; basals and infrabasals with stellate ornament; radials unornamented, separated from one another by interbrachs; interbrachial zones depressed, composed of many small plates; fixed primibrachs and secundibrachs prominent; calyx weakly bound together. Theca up to 25 mm.
M.–U. Ordovician.
Reteocrinus stellaris Billings: M. Ordovician, Ohio, USA.

Pl. 7.4.11. *Gilbertsocrinus* Phillips, 1836 (SUPERFAMILY Rhodocrinitacea)
Calyx short, subcylindrical; basal concavity with 5 infrabasals; tegmen flat, composed of many plates; anus opening subcentrally through tegmen; radials separated from one another by interbrachs; fixed primibrachs and secundibrachs included in the cup; posterior interray hardly differentiated from the others. Theca up to 3 cm in diameter.
M. Devonian–L. Carboniferous.
Gilbertsocrinus bursa Phillips: L. Carboniferous, Bolland, England.

Pl. 7.4.12. *Dimerocrinites* Phillips, 1839 (SUPERFAMILY Dimerocrinitacea)
Calyx low conical; infrabasals small, largely hidden by column and not visible in side view; radial circlet interrupted in posterior interray by anal plate; primanal rests directly on basal; interbrachs relatively few; free arms biserial. Theca up to 3 cm in diameter.
M. Silurian–M. Devonian.
Dimerocrinites speciosus (Angelin): M. Silurian, Dudley, England.

Class Inadunata (L. Ordovician–M. Triassic)

Diagnostic features Crinoids with a calyx of firmly sutured cup plates and a flexible plated tegmen; the tegmen has a periproctal opening but no opening for the mouth; the calyx typically includes anal plates but never has fixed brachials or interbrachials.

Basis for subdivision The inadunates are the least satisfactory of all crinoid groups and contains a heterogeneous assemblage of forms which may not be monophyletic. There seems little doubt that both the Flexibilia and the Articulata evolved from inadunates, but there is no current classification that reflects this. There are three orders of inadunate crinoids, one of which is very small and unimportant. The two principal orders are easily distinguished on their cup plating, monocyclic inadunates (those with radial and basal plate circlets) are placed in the order Disparida while dicyclic inadunates (those with a circlet of infrabasal plates in addition to radial and basal plate circlets) are placed in the order Cladida. A special feature of disparid inadunates is that their calyx usually shows a certain degree of bilateral symmetry. The third order, Hybocrinida, contains pseudomonocyclic inadunates with rather globular cups and which usually have some recumbent arms that form an integral part of the calyx. In some inadunates, the radial plates are compound and this is considered an important taxonomic feature. Other features that are useful in subdividing inadunates include the structure of the stem, the style and extent of arm branching, the presence or absence of pinnules, the size of the arm facets on radial plates relative to the width of the plate and whether these facets are muscular (facets with a transverse ridge) or fixed (smooth, planar facets), and whether there is an anal sac. Although disparids have been keyed down to the superfamily level, the cladids are only subdivided to suborder level, as some of the superfamilies currently accepted are rather ambiguously defined.

ARTIFICIAL KEY

1. Cup dicyclic .... 3 (ORDER Cladida)
   Cup monocyclic 2
2. Cup globular; 3 to 5 unbranched non-pinnulate arms, typically some or all recumbent ...... ORDER Hybocrinida
   Cup conical to bowl-shaped; arms 5 to many, never recumbent .... 5 (ORDER Disparida)
3. Arms narrow, rounded, arm facets on radial plates relatively narrow; tegmen low or with short anal sac............. .... SUBORDER Cyathocrinina
   Arms relatively broad, arm facets occupying most or all of radial plate width; tegmen usually with large, porous anal sac 4
4. Arms typically pinnulate and often biserial; radial arm facets muscular with transverse articulation ridge .... SUBORDER Poteriocrinina
   Arms rarely pinnulate and never biserial; radial arm facets smooth and non-muscular ..... SUBORDER Dendrocrinina
5. Calyx hinge-jointed and folded acutely back against the stem .... SUPERFAMILY Calceocrinacea
   Calyx sutured to stem and held perpendicular 6
6. Radial plates simple 7
   Radial plates compound in some rays 10
7. Some radial plates with multiple arm facets .... SUPERFAMILY Allagecrinacea
   Radial plates with single arm facets 8
8. Anal plates arm-like, arising from 1st primibrach .... SUPERFAMILY Myelodactylacea (FAMILY Iocrinidae)
   Anal plates forming part of the cup 9
9. Cup conical; arms simple or with a single isotomous branch .... SUPERFAMILY Belemnocrinacea
   Cup bowl-shaped; arms branching many times unequally .... SUPERFAMILY Anomalocrinacea
10. Arms unbranched; cup with prominent interradial processes .... SUPERFAMILY Pisocrinacea
    Arms branched; cup without prominent interradial processes 11
11. All 5 radials compound.............................. ..SUPERFAMILY Myelodactylacea (FAMILY Myelodactylidae)
    Some radials simple, others compound 12
12. 3 of the 5 radials compound ..SUPERFAMILY Homocrinacea
    2 of the 5 radials compound .... SUPERFAMILY Heterocrinacea

Plate 7.4.8 Plate 7.4.9 Plate 7.4.10 Plate 7.4.11A

Plate 7.4.11B

Plate 7.4.11C Plate 7.4.12 Plate 7.4.13 Plate 7.4.15

Plate 7.4.14 Plate 7.4.16A Plate 7.4.16B

Order Disparida (L. Ordovician–U. Permian)

Pl. 7.4.13. *Iocrinus* Hall, 1866 (SUPERFAMILY Myelodactylacea)
Cup conical, monocyclic; 5 small basals; radials with sutural pits; primibrachs numerous; arms branching isotomously many times; anal plates a vertical arm-like series arising from one side of the first C ray primibrach; stem pentastellate. Theca up to 6 mm in diameter.
Ordovician.
Iocrinus crassus (Meek & Worthen): M. Ordovician, Ohio, USA.

Pl. 7.4.14. *Synchirocrinus* Jaekel, 1918 (SUPERFAMILY Calceocrinacea)
Crown bent back on stem; almost perfectly bilaterally symmetrical; calyx hinged; arms with very distinctive axil arms branching from main axil series on each side; stem circular. Theca up to 1 cm in width.
Silurian.
Synchirocrinus serialis Salter: Wenlock, Dudley, England.

Pl. 7.4.15. *Ectenocrinus* Miller, 1889 (SUPERFAMILY Homocrinacea)
Cup small, almost cylindrical; 5 short basals and 5 radials of which 3, in rays B, C and E, are compound; radial facets as broad as radials; anal plates small, forming a single series not interrupting radial circlet; arms uniserial, branched once at

primibrach; stem round in cross-section, heteromorphic. Theca up to 5 mm in diameter.
Ordovician.
Ectenocrinus simplex (Hall): M. Ordovician, Cincinnati, USA.

Pl. 7.4.16. *Pisocrinus* de Koninck, 1858 (SUPERFAMILY Pisocrinacea)
Calyx cup-shaped with flat base; crown slender with long unbranched uniserial arms; 5 unequal basals; 5 radials, in C and E rays radials small and not in contact with basals, in A and D rays large and simple, while B ray has a compound radial; anal plates small, above main cup plates; radial facets narrower than radials, sunken, separated by clear ridges. Theca up to 5 mm in diameter.
M. Silurian–L. Devonian.
Pisocrinus pilula de Koninck: Wenlock, Dudley, England.

Pl. 7.4.17. *Calycanthocrinus* Follman, 1887 (SUPERFAMILY Pisocrinacea)
Cup cone-shaped; 3 basals; A and D radials large and simple, C and E radials small, not in contact with basals, B radial compound; 4 additional arm bearing plates are incorporated into the cup; arms 9, long and straight. Cup up to 4 mm in diameter.
Devonian.
Calycanthocrinus decadactylus Follman: L. Devonian, Bundenbach, W. Germany.

Pl. 7.4.18. *Heterocrinus* Hall, 1847 (SUPERFAMILY Heterocrinacea)
Cup steeply conical; 5 basals; 5 radials of which C and E are compound; anal plates arm-like, forming elongate series; arm facets occupying full width of radials; arms uniserial, branched isotomously; stem heterotomous, pentagonal. Theca up to 2 mm in diameter.
Ordovician.
Heterocrinus heterodactylus Hall: Ordovician (Edenian), Cincinnati, USA.

Pl. 7.4.19. *Synbathocrinus* Phillips, 1836 (SUPERFAMILY Belemnocrinacea)
Crown cylindrical; cup small, conical, with 3 small basals; radials large, simple, with articulation facets occupying full width of plate; facets with transverse ridge; anal plate notching posterior radials; arms uniserial, unbranched. Theca up to 1 cm in diameter.
M. Devonian–U. Carboniferous.
Synbathocrinus dentatus Owen & Shumard: L. Carboniferous, Ohio, USA. (A) Cup, lateral; (B) cup, oral; (C) part of crown and column.

Pl. 7.4.20. *Paracatillocrinus* Wanner, 1916 (SUPERFAMILY Allagecrinacea)
Cup flattened, discoidal; basals small, visible in side view; radials flaring outwards; A and D radials greatly expanded and bearing multiple arm facets, other radials narrow; cup with pronounced bilateral symmetry; arms uniserial, unbranched. Theca up to 15 mm in diameter.
Permian.
Paracatillocrinus granulatus Wanner: U. Permian, Timor, Indonesia. (A) lateral; (B) oral.

Pl. 7.4.21. *Isoallagecrinus* Strimple, 1966 (SUPERFAMILY Allagecrinacea)
Crown small, cylindrical; bowl-shaped cup; 3 small basals; 5 bulbous radials of unequal size; single arm facets on C and E radials, rest with variable number; anal plates arm-like; arms simple, uniserial; stem circular in cross-section. Calyx up to 3 mm in diameter.
U. Carboniferous–L. Permian.
Isoallagecrinus strimplei Kirk: U. Carboniferous, Oklahoma, USA.

Order Hybocrinida (Ordovician)

Pl. 7.4.22. *Hybocystis* Wetherby, 1880
Cup pear-shaped, monocyclic; 3 erect arms attaching to narrow radial facets and 2 recumbent arms in rays B and E running towards the base of the cup; C radial compound; 1 anal plate incorporated into cup; arms uniserial unbranched; stem meric, transversely circular; no anal tube. Calyx up to 1 cm in diameter.
M. Ordovician.
Hybocystis eldonensis (Parks): M. Ordovician (Trentonian), Ontario, Canada.

Order Cladida (L. Ordovician–M. Triassic)

Suborder Dendrocrinina (L. Ordovician–L. Carboniferous)

Pl. 7.4.23. *Cupulocrinus* d'Orbigny, 1850
Cup conical; infrabasals visible in side view; basals and radials large; C radial compound; radial arm facets occupying full width of plate; anals arranged in a vertical series within cup; arms branching mostly isotomously. Calyx up to 15 mm in diameter.
Ordovician.
Cupulocrinus polydactylus Shumard: M. Ordovician, Ohio, USA.

Pl. 7.4.24. *Dendrocrinus* Hall, 1852
Cup conical; crown very tall, cylindrical; 5 infrabasals visible in side view; radial circlet interrupted by a large anal plate; radial arm facets relatively small and rounded; anal sac tall, composed of numerous small plates; arms rounded, branching isotomously. Cup up to 8 mm in diameter.
M. Ordovician–U. Silurian.
Dendrocrinus granditubus Ramsbottom: U. Ordovician, Girvan, Scotland.

Pl. 7.4.25. *Mastigocrinites* Bather, 1892
Crown elongate, cylindrical; cup broadly conical; infrabasals relatively large; cup plating unornamented; radial arm facets wide, almost as wide as radial plate, with curved outer edge; slight interradial notches present; large anal plate in cup; tall anal sac of plicate plates; arms numerous, branching isotomously. Cup up to 1 cm in diameter.
M. Silurian.
Mastigocrinites loreus Bather: Wenlock, Dudley, England.

Suborder Poteriocrinina (L. Devonian–M. Triassic)

Pl. 7.4.26. *Holcocrinus* Kirk, 1945
Crown steeply conical; cup bowl-shaped; 5 small infrabasals, not visible in side view; radial arm facets occupying full width of plates; 1 anal plate in cup, interrupting radial circlet; arms 10, branching once above first primibrach; arms pinnulate, composed of wedge-shaped plates arranged alternately. Cup up to 15 mm in diameter.
L. Carboniferous.
Holcocrinus longicirrifer (Wachsmuth & Springer): L. Carboniferous (Kinderhookian), Ohio, USA.

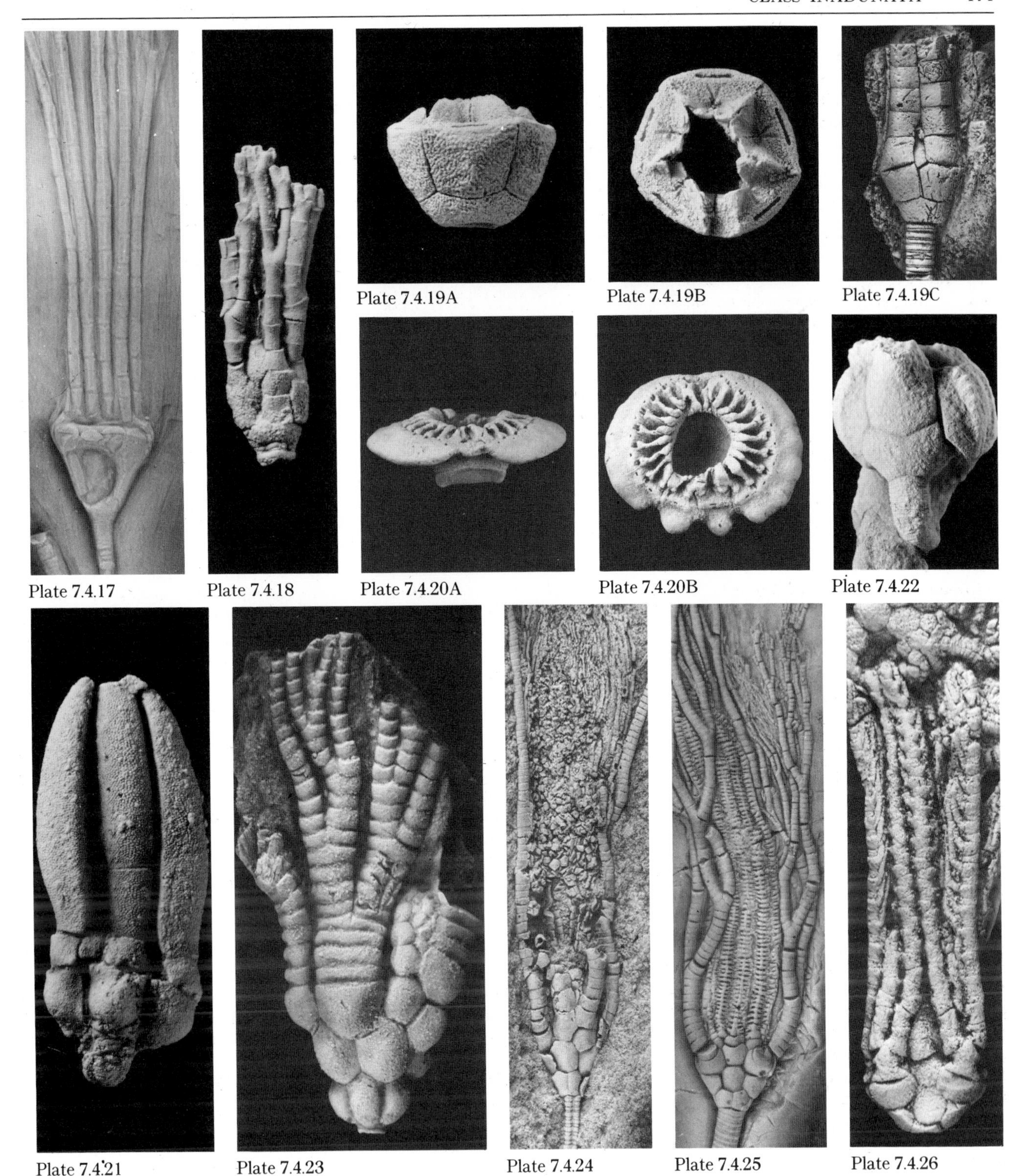

Plate 7.4.17 Plate 7.4.18 Plate 7.4.19A Plate 7.4.19B Plate 7.4.19C Plate 7.4.20A Plate 7.4.20B Plate 7.4.22 Plate 7.4.21 Plate 7.4.23 Plate 7.4.24 Plate 7.4.25 Plate 7.4.26

Pl. 7.4.27. *Decadocrinus* Wachsmuth & Springer, 1880
Crown cylindrical; cup bowl-shaped; infrabasals more or less hidden, situated in basal concavity; radial arm facets occupying full width of plate, straight-edged; anal plates numerous, interrupting radial circlet posteriorly; arms 10, pinnulate, composed of alternating wedge-shaped plates and zigzag in appearance, branching isotomously on primibrach 2. Cup up to 15 mm in diameter.
M. Devonian–L. Carboniferous.
Decadocrinus depressus (Meek & Worthen): L. Carboniferous, Indiana, USA.

Pl. 7.4.28. *Agassizocrinus* Owen & Shumard, 1852
Cup stout, bowl-shaped, with convexly rounded base; stemless; infrabasals fused into a thick solid piece with sutures partially or completely obliterated; basals large; radial circlet interrupted by 4 anal plates posteriorly which project above the radials; arm facets occupying most of the radial plate width; arms 10, uniserial, pinnulate, branching isotomously on the first primibrach. Cup up to 15 mm in diameter.
Carboniferous.
Agassizocrinus conicus Owen & Shumard: Carboniferous (Chesterian), Illinois, USA.

Pl. 7.4.29. *Zeacrinites* Troost, in Hall, 1858
Cup broad, saucer-shaped with concave base; infrabasals totally hidden by stem; basals small, spear-shaped; 3 anal plates in cup, interrupting radial circlet; arm facets occupying full width of radial plates; arms uniserial, branching several times. Cup up to 2 cm in diameter.
Carboniferous.
Zeacrinites wortheni (Hall): L. Carboniferous, Kentucky, USA.

Pl. 7.4.30. *Cromyocrinus* Trautschold, 1867
Cup subglobular; infrabasals just visible in side view; 3 anal plates interrupting radial circlet; radial arm facets occupying full width of plate; 5 uniserial arms composed of broad stout brachials; stem transversely circular. Cup up to 1 cm in diameter.
Carboniferous.
Cromyocrinus simplex Trautschold: L. Carboniferous, Mjatschkowa, USSR.

Pl. 7.4.31. *Poteriocrinites* Miller, 1821
Cup steeply conical; infrabasals clearly visible in side view; arm facets occupying less than full width of radial plates, horseshoe shaped; 3 anal plates in cup, interrupting radial circlet; stem relatively large, circular in cross-section; arms uniserial, branching many times. Cup up to 3 cm in diameter.
L. Devonian–L. Carboniferous.
Poteriocrinites spissus (de Koninck & Le Hon): L. Carboniferous, Visé, Belgium.

Pl. 7.4.32. *Cupressocrinites* Goldfuss, 1831
Crown cylindrical; cup bowl-shaped; infrabasals small, not visible in side view; basals and radials large; radial circlet not interrupted; no anal plates in cup; arm facets straight-edged, occupying full width of radial plates; arms 5, massive, unbranched, brachials stout. Cup up to 3 cm in diameter.
Devonian.
Cupressocrinites elongatus Goldfuss: M. Devonian, Gerolstein, W. Germany.

Pl. 7.4.33. *Abrotocrinus* Miller & Gurley, 1890
Crown tall and slender; cup bowl-shaped, with basal concavity; infrabasals not visible in side view; radials larger than basals; 3 anal plates in cup, interrupting radial circlet; arm facets occupying full width of radial plates; arms uniserial, branching many times. Cup up to 2 cm in diameter.
L. Carboniferous.
Abrotocrinus unicus (Hall): L. Carboniferous, Indiana, USA.

Pl. 7.4.34. *Moscovicrinus* Jaekel, 1918
Cup conical, 5 infrabasals clearly visible in side view; arm facets occupying full width of radial plate, with prominent transverse articulation ridge; 3 anal plates; interrupting radial circlet; arms branching isotomously 2 or 3 times, uniserial. Cup up to 15 mm in diameter.
U. Carboniferous–L. Permian.
Moscovicrinus multiplex (Trautschold): U. Carboniferous, Moscow, USSR.

Pl. 7.4.35. *Histocrinus* Kirk, 1940
Cup conical, 5 infrabasals clearly visible in side view; basals large; arm facets not quite as broad as radial plates, with transverse articulation ridge; arms uniserial, not abutting, branching isotomously on primibrach 2; stem transversely circular, heteromorphic. Cup up to 2 cm in diameter.
L. Carboniferous.
Histocrinus coreyi (Meek & Worthen): L. Carboniferous (Osagian), Indiana, USA.

Pl. 7.4.36. *Paragraphiocrinus* Wanner, 1937
Cup bowl-shaped with small basal concavity and incurved sides; infrabasals small, not visible in side view; 1 anal plate incorporated into the cup; radial arm facets occupying full width of radial plates; 5 arms. Cup up to 1.5 cm in diameter.
U. Permian.
Paragraphiocrinus exornatus (Wanner): Basleo Beds, Timor, Indonesia.

Suborder Cyathocrinina (M. Ordovician–Permian)

Pl. 7.4.37. *Nanocrinus* Müller, 1856
Cup conical bowl-shaped with low tegmen; 3 infrabasals, fused, just visible in side view; 4 radials with arm facets, radial A without arm facet; facets prominent, horseshoe shaped, relatively narrow; large oral plates of tegmen; anus opening through tegmen, no anal sac. Cup up to 2 cm in diameter.
Devonian.
Nanocrinus paradoxus Müller: Givetian, Gerolstein, W. Germany. (A) lateral; (B) oral.

Pl. 7.4.38. *Monobrachiocrinus* Wanner, 1916
Cup pear-shaped; 3 large infrabasals and 5 tall basals form most of the cup; D radial plate large, with single small facet, other radials absent; tegmen composed of 5 oral plates only, with anus offset to one side; tegmen plates often lost leaving keyhole-shaped opening. Cup up to 3 cm tall.
Permian.
Monobrachiocrinus ficiformis Wanner: Basleo Beds, Timor, Indonesia.

Pl. 7.4.39. *Embryocrinus* Wanner, 1916
Calyx globular; cup of 3 infrabasals, 5 basals and 5 tiny trigonal radials inset between basals; upper half of calyx formed of 5 large orals resting on basals and radials; anus opening between posterior oral and basal; no arms. Calyx up to 1 cm tall.
Permian.
Embryocrinus hanieli Wanner: Basleo Beds, Timor, Indonesia.

Pl. 7.4.40. *Cyathocrinites* Miller, 1821
Crown ovoid; cup bowl-shaped with flat base; infrabasals visible in side view; radial plates with narrow, horseshoe-shaped facets; 1 large anal plate in cup; narrow anal sac; arms branching 2 or 3 times isotomously. Cup up to 1 cm in diameter.
M. Silurian–L. Carboniferous.
Cyathocrinites actinotubus Angelin: M. Silurian, Dudley, England.

Subclass Flexibilia (M. Ordovician – U. Permian)

Diagnostic features Crinoids whose cup plates are not rigidly sutured and which generally incorporate fixed brachials and interbrachials into the calyx. Arms are uniserial and non-pinnulate and characteristically curve inwards distally to hide the tegmen. The cup consists of three cycles of plates, infrabasals, basals and radials and may also include anal plates.

Basis for subdivision The Flexibilia are divided into two orders and four superfamilies. Features that have been used to distinguish these groups include: (a) whether anal plates are incorporated into the cup; (b) whether there are fixed brachials in the calyx; and (c) whether fixed brachials are separated by interbrachial plates.

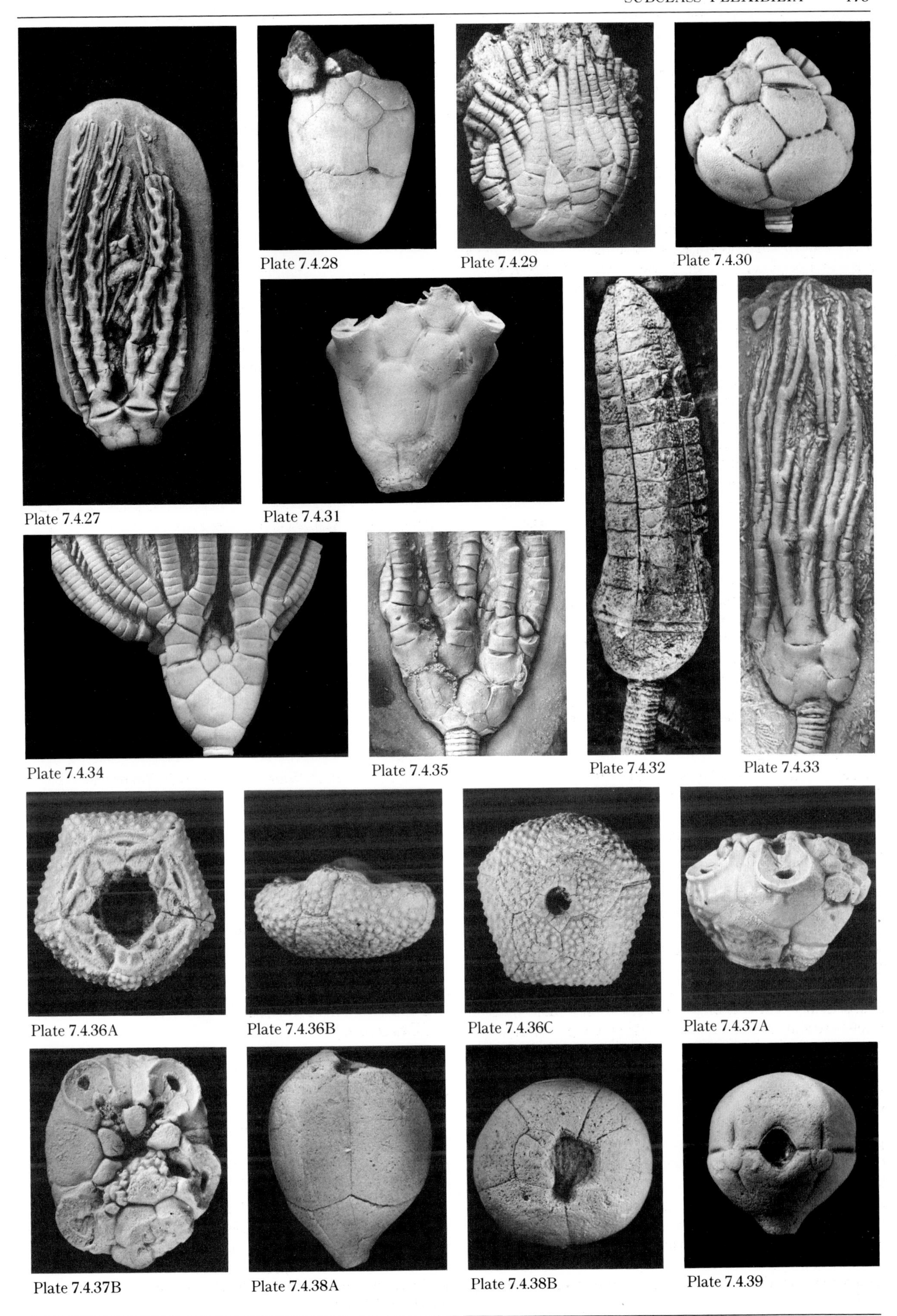

Plate 7.4.27
Plate 7.4.28
Plate 7.4.29
Plate 7.4.30
Plate 7.4.31
Plate 7.4.32
Plate 7.4.33
Plate 7.4.34
Plate 7.4.35
Plate 7.4.36A
Plate 7.4.36B
Plate 7.4.36C
Plate 7.4.37A
Plate 7.4.37B
Plate 7.4.38A
Plate 7.4.38B
Plate 7.4.39

ARTIFICIAL KEY

1. Anal plates not incorporated into the cup but forming a vertical row in the tegmen separated by weakly plated zones from adjacent arms; cup not clearly differentiated . . . . ORDER Taxocrinida (SUPERFAMILY Taxocrinacea)
   Anal plates incorporated into the cup; cup clearly differentiated from arms . . . . 2 (ORDER Sagenocrinida)
2. Arms moderately long and repeatedly branched; lower parts incorporated into calyx 3
   Arms short and stout, branching 1 to 3 times only, not incorporated into calyx . . . . . SUPERFAMILY Lecanocrinacea
3. Fixed brachials in calyx separated by interbrachials . . . . SUPERFAMILY Sagenocrinitacea
   Fixed brachials in calyx abut, interbrachials absent . . . . SUPERFAMILY Ichthyocrinacea

Order Taxocrinida (M. Ordovician–U. Carboniferous)

Pl. 7.4.41. *Protaxocrinus* Springer, 1906 (SUPERFAMILY Taxocrinacea)
Cup and crown conical; arms curving inwards distally; 5 low infrabasals; basals and radials broad; calyx not sharply differentiated from free arms; interbrachial zones of tiny plates; 2 primibrachs above radial plate; arms not abutting; anal plates separated from adjacent arm plates; arms branching isotomously several times. Cup up to 1 cm in diameter.
M. Ordovician–L. Devonian.
Protaxocrinus tuberculatus Miller: M. Silurian, Dudley, England.

Order Sagenocrinida (L. Silurian–U. Permian)

Pl. 7.4.42. *Sagenocrinites* Austin & Austin, 1842 (SUPERFAMILY Sagenocrinitacea)
Crown ovoid; cup elongate conical, forming about half the height of the crown; infrabasals visible in side view; basal and radial circlets interrupted by anal plates; calyx with numerous fixed brachials and well-developed interbrachial zones; free arms well differentiated from calyx, uniserial, branching isotomously several times. Cup up to 3 cm in diameter.
M. Silurian.
Sagenocrinites expansus (Phillips): Wenlock, Dudley, England.

Pl. 7.4.43. *Ichthyocrinus* Conrad, 1842 (SUPERFAMILY Ichthyocrinacea)
Crown elongate, ovoid, tapering towards stem; cup with reduced infrabasals, hidden by stem; fixed brachials numerous, forming most of calyx, abutting, without interbrachial zones; no anal plates; arms branching isotomously several times. Calyx up to 2 cm in width.
M. Silurian–L. Devonian.
Ichthyocrinus pyriformis (Phillips): M. Silurian, Dudley, England.

Pl. 7.4.44. *Hormocrinus* Springer, 1920 (SUPERFAMILY Lecanocrinacea)
Crown short, subglobular, with bowl-shaped cup clearly differentiated from free arms, forming about half the height of the crown; infrabasals small, largely hidden; basals smaller than radials, posterior one noticeably elongate; radials large, radial circlet interrupted by anal plate; 2 fixed brachials per ray and only a few interbrachials in calyx; arms broad, uniserial, branching several times. Cup up to 2 cm in diameter.
M. Silurian.
Hormocrinus anglicus Springer: Wenlock, Dudley, England.

Pl. 7.4.45. *Mespilocrinus* de Koninck & Le Hon, 1854 (SUPERFAMILY Lecanocrinacea)
Cup stout, composed of interlocking plates; crown globular with short, broad arms curving inwards distally; anal plates in cup; radial circlet interrupted by elongate posterior basal; infrabasals largely hidden by stem. Calyx up to 2 cm in diameter.
L. Carboniferous.
Mespilocrinus forbesianus de Koninck & Le Hon: Tournaisian, Tournai, Belgium.

Pl. 7.4.46. *Prophyllocrinus* Wanner, 1916 (SUPERFAMILY Lecanocrinacea)
Calyx and crown globular, with flat base; basals and radials massive, strongly curved; arm facets on radial plates narrow, deeply sunken between interradial processes; most species lacking anal plates; arms short, composed of broad, stout brachials, branching 3 times isotomously and curving inwards distally to cover tegmen. Crown up to 2.5 cm in diameter.
U. Permian.
Prophyllocrinus dentatus Wanner: Basleo Beds, Timor, Indonesia.

Subclass Articulata (L. Triassic–Recent)

Diagnostic features Stemmed or stemless crinoids with simple cups without anal plates and a flexible tegmen with a central peristome and exposed food grooves; arms uniserial, pinnulate; radial arm facets muscular with transverse articulation ridge; some or all of the facets between arm plates are also muscular.

Basis for subdivision There are seven clearly differentiated orders of articulate crinoid. Details of calyx plating are less important for subdividing the articulates than they are for the other three crinoid subclasses, although they are still useful. The various orders are distinguished on the basis of stem structure (if present), whether or not cirri are present; whether fixed brachials are incorporated into the calyx, and whether basals and infrabasals are present. Some articulates retained a flexible stem throughout their lives while others became secondarily cemented to hard substrata. The largest and today the most successful group, comatulids, have lost their stem altogether as adults and are free living. Only the comatulids have been subdivided into superfamilies, but as it is often difficult to assign fossil comatulids to these superfamilies with certainty, I have not included them in the key.

ARTIFICIAL KEY

1. Stemmed 2
   Stemless 5
2. Stem with cirri . . . . ORDER Isocrinida
   Stem without cirri 3
3. Cup composed of radials only, typically set obliquely to the stem; proximal columnals typically thickened and often semi-fused . . . ORDER Cyrtocrinida (SUBORDER Cyrtocrinina)
   Cup composed of radials and basals with or without infrabasals, never set obliquely to the stem 4
4. Columnal facets with articulation ridge (synarthrial articulation facets) . . . . ORDER Bourgueticrinida
   Columnal facets with radial crennulae (symplectial articulation facets) . . . . ORDER Millericrinida
5. Cup cemented directly on to substratum; plating fused . . . . ORDER Cyrtocrinida (SUBORDER Holopodina)
   Cup unattached; radials and basals distinct 6
6. Centrodorsal structure with cirri . . . . ORDER Comatulida

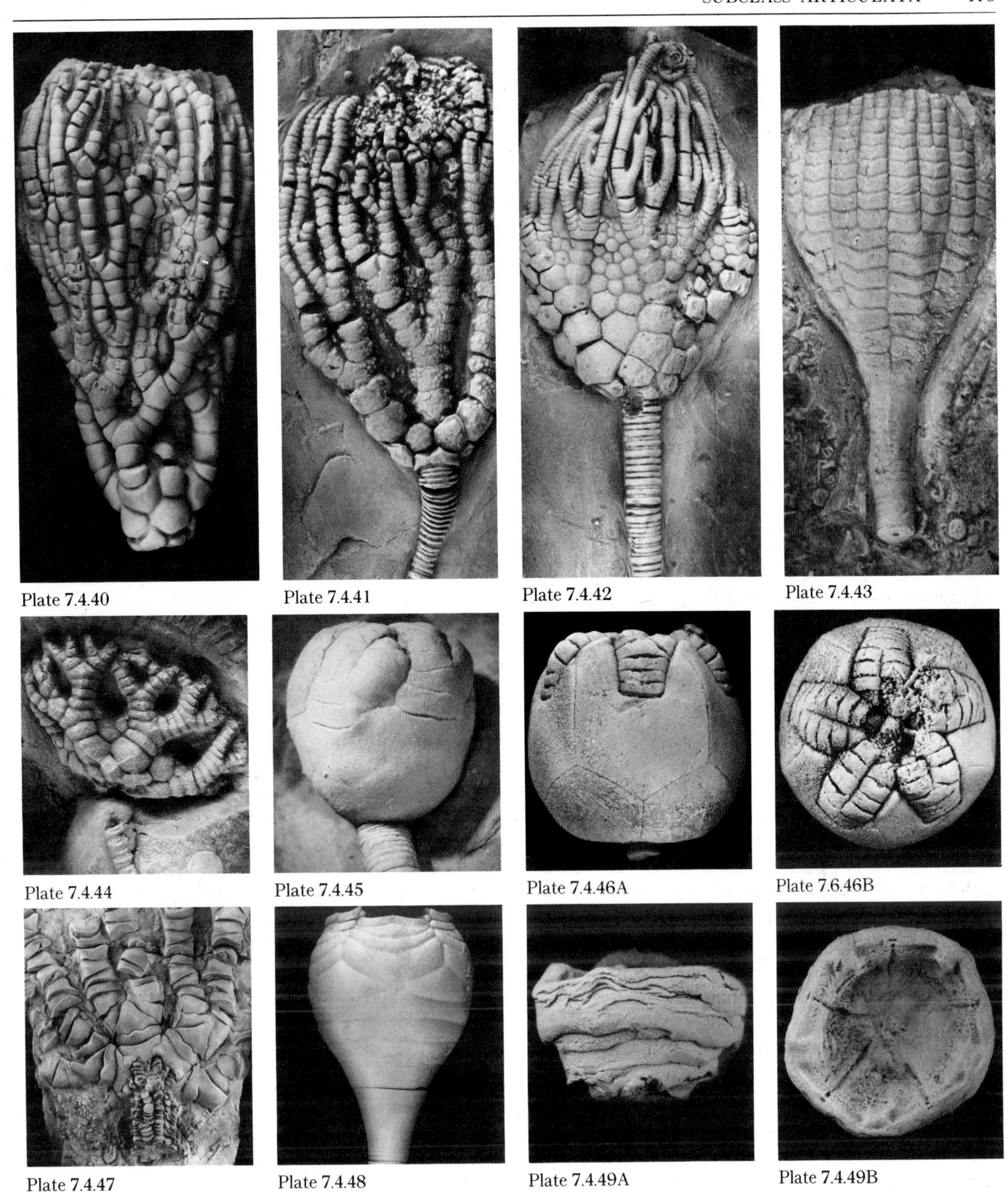

Plate 7.4.40 Plate 7.4.41 Plate 7.4.42 Plate 7.4.43

Plate 7.4.44 Plate 7.4.45 Plate 7.4.46A Plate 7.6.46B

Plate 7.4.47 Plate 7.4.48 Plate 7.4.49A Plate 7.4.49B

No cirri present 7

7. Cup plates large; infrabasals, basals and radials all similar in size .... ORDER Uintacrinida

Cup minute, with delicate plating; largely composed of radials .... ORDER Roveacrinida

Order Isocrinida (L. Triassic–Recent)

Pl. 7.4.47. *Chladocrinus* Agassiz, 1836

Cup broad, low; no visible infrabasals; basals small, triangular, separated from one another by large radials; arms long, branching isotomously on primibrach 2 and up to 4 more times higher up; articulations between primibrachs 1 and 2 and secundibrachs 1 and 2 noticeably undulose (embayed synarthrial), no symmorphial articulations; stem pentastellate to pentagonal with cirri on nodals; columnals with petalloid arrangement of crenulae; internodals with up to 20 columnals. Cup up to 2 cm in diameter.

Triassic–Recent.

Chladocrinus robustus (Wright): L. Jurassic, Chipping Campden, England.

Order Millericrinida (M. Triassic–Recent)

Pl. 7.4.48. *Apiocrinites* Miller, 1821
Cup bulbous, thick-walled; transition from stem to cup gradational, stem enlarged proximally, columnals discoidal, without cirri or articulation ridge; infrabasals absent; basals and radials low and broad; arms branching on primibrach 2 and sometimes again higher up; proximal brachials fixed. Cup up to 5 cm in diameter.
L. Jurassic–L. Cretaceous.
Apiocrinites elegans (Defrance): M. Jurassic, Bradford, England.

Order Cyrtocrinida (L. Jurassic–Recent)

Suborder Holopodina (L. Jurassic–Recent)

Pl. 7.4.49. *Cyathidium* Steenstrup, in Michaelis & Scherk, 1847
Stemless; cup bowl-shaped, cemented directly on to substratum; cup plating completely obscured; externally smooth or with growth lines; radial arm facets narrow, filling most of plate width, with transverse ridge; central cavity large, deep, with mid-radial furrows; arms short, stout, rarely preserved. Cup up to 2 cm in diameter.
U. Jurassic–Recent.
Cyathidium holopus Michaelis & Scherk: Danian, Faxe, Denmark. (A) lateral; (B) oral.

Suborder Cyrtocrinina (L. Jurassic–U. Cretaceous)

Pl. 7.4.50. *Phyllocrinus* Remeš, 1912
Cup conical, composed of fused radials only; arm facets small, separated by large interradial projections from the radial plates; stem more or less rigid and fused to cup; columnals long and cylindrical, becoming stouter towards the cup; arms very small, rarely preserved. Cup up to 8 mm in diameter.
M. Jurassic–L. Cretaceous.
Phyllocrinus colloti de Loriol: M. Jurassic, Rians, France.

Pl. 7.4.51. *Hemicrinus* d'Orbigny, 1841
Cup low and wide, set obliquely to column; cup composed of 5 variably sized radials fused together; radial arm facets broad, outward facing; arms short, stout, rarely preserved; proximal columnal elongate, cylindrical, fused to cup; distal columnals unknown, possibly attaching to radix directly. Cup up to 1 cm in diameter.
U. Jurassic–L. Cretaceous.
Hemicrinus canon (Seeley): Albian, Leighton Buzzard, England.

Pl. 7.4.52. *Gammarocrinites* Quenstedt, 1857
Cup barrel-shaped, composed of 5 radials set obliquely to the stem; radial plate sutures visible externally; radial cavity small; arm facets large, more or less flat; first columnal with oblique upper face, other columnals elongate and cylindrical. Cup up to 5 mm in diameter.
U. Jurassic–L. Cretaceous.
Gammarocrinites compressus (Goldfuss): Oxfordian, Streitberg, W. Germany.

Order Bourgueticrinida (U. Cretaceous–Recent)

Pl. 7.4.53. *Bourgueticrinus* d'Orbigny, 1841
Cup small, generally fusiform, composed of 5 basals, 5 radials and a large proximal columnal; sutures visible externally but faint; radial arm facets wide, with prominent muscle areas; column composed of elongate, cylindrical ossicles with synarthrial articulation facets, transverse ridges generally in different orientations on upper and lower faces of 1 columnal. Cup up to 1 cm in diameter.
U. Cretaceous–Eocene.
Bourgueticrinus ellipticus Miller: U. Cretaceous. (A) Cup and proximal stem, side view; (B) oral view; Swindon, England; (C) articulation facet of columnal; Thanet, England.

Order Comatulida (L. Jurassic–Recent)

Pl. 7.4.54. *Paracomatula* Hess, 1951 (SUPERFAMILY Paracomatulacea)
Cup broad, flat, largely covered by centrodorsal structure; radials broad, slightly overhanging centrodorsal area; arms branching at primibrach 2 and several times more higher up; centrodorsal stellate, composed of a small number of firmly sutured columnals with numerous cirri. Cup up to 6 mm in diameter.
M. Jurassic.
Paracomatula helvetica Hess: U. Bajocian, Aargau, Switzerland.

Pl. 7.4.55. *Solanocrinites* Goldfuss, 1829 (SUPERFAMILY Solanocrinitacea)
Centrodorsal a truncated pentameral cone with a flat dorsal surface; cirral sockets large, with axial canal and transverse articulation ridge, arranged into 10 columns of 1 to 3 cirri; dorsal surface with large cirrus-free area, generally roughly pitted; tiny basals exposed between large radials; radial articulation facets broad and relatively steeply inclined outwards; radial cavity large. Cup up to 1 cm in diameter.
Jurassic.
Solanocrinites ooliticus Gislén: M. Jurassic, England. (A) Lateral; (B) dorsal.

Pl. 7.4.56. *Glenotremites* Goldfuss, 1829 (SUPERFAMILY Notocrinacea)
Centrodorsal a truncated cone with a flat base; dorsal surface depressed and cirrus-free, with prominent depressed stellate scar; cirral scars irregularly crowded laterally, with large axial canal and marginal crenulae but no transverse ridge; upper surface of centrodorsal with rod-shaped depressions for basals; small centrodorsal cavity, less than 30 per cent of diameter, surrounded by 5 single or double radial pits. Up to 8 mm in diameter.
Cretaceous.
Glenotremites paradoxus Goldfuss: L. Senonian, Dover, England. Centrodorsal plate: (A) dorsal; (B) ventral.

Pl. 7.4.57. *Hertha* von Hagenow, 1840 (SUPERFAMILY Antedonacea)
Centrodorsal low with slightly pointed base and flat top; cirral scars small, with small axial canal and without distinct ornament, covering more or less the entire surface; ventral surface with relatively large cavity, about 30 per cent of diameter, without surrounding pits; rod-shaped grooves for basals tapering to a point marginally and basals not exposed externally. Up to 5 mm in diameter.
U. Cretaceous–Miocene.
Hertha mystica von Hagenow: U. Senonian, Isle of Rugen, Baltic. Centrodorsal. (A) Dorsal; (B) ventral.

Pl. 7.4.58. *Amphorometra* Gislén, 1924 (SUPERFAMILY Tropiometracea)
Centrodorsal steeply conical, taller than wide and with 10

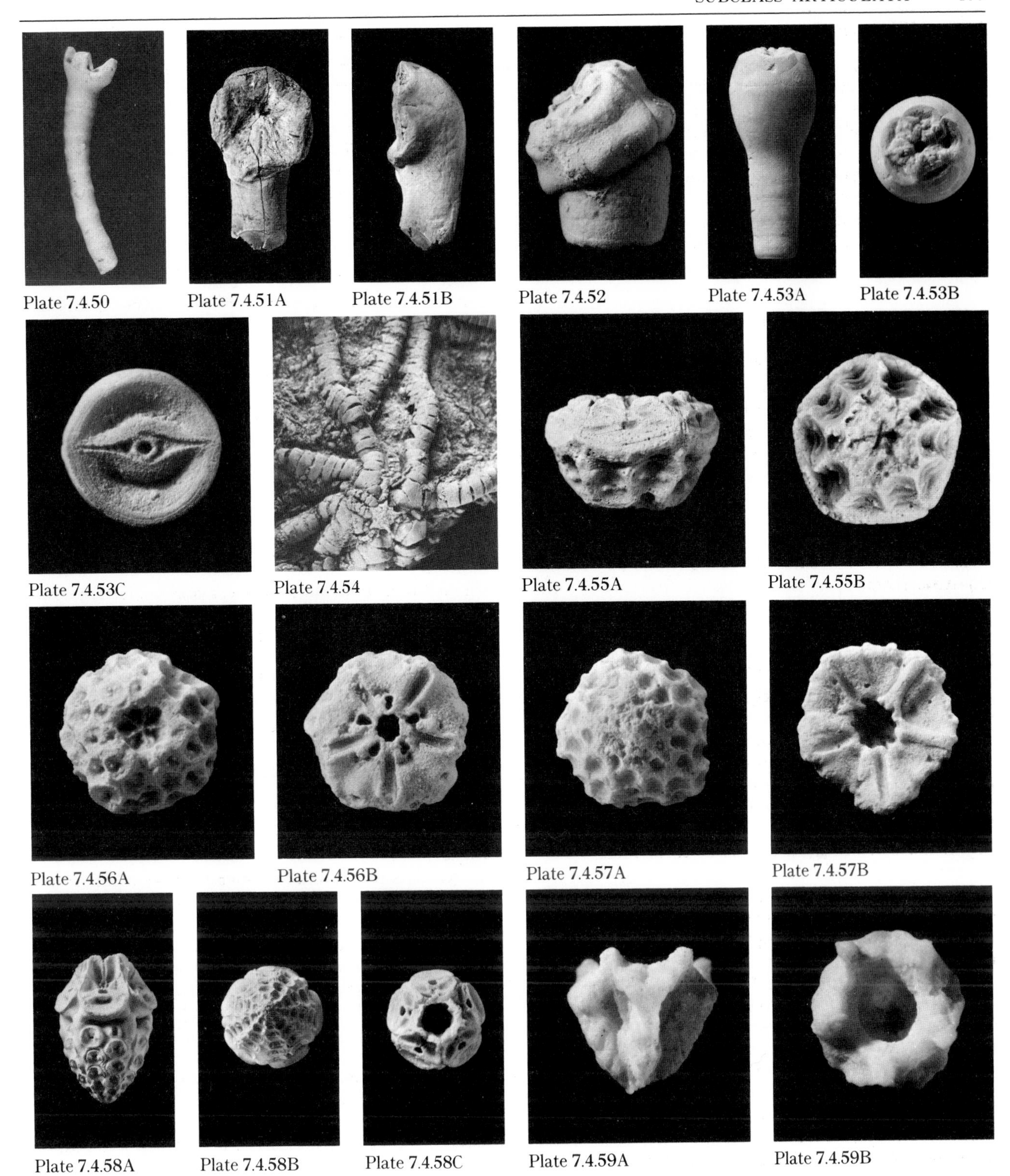

Plate 7.4.50 Plate 7.4.51A Plate 7.4.51B Plate 7.4.52 Plate 7.4.53A Plate 7.4.53B

Plate 7.4.53C Plate 7.4.54 Plate 7.4.55A Plate 7.4.55B

Plate 7.4.56A Plate 7.4.56B Plate 7.4.57A Plate 7.4.57B

Plate 7.4.58A Plate 7.4.58B Plate 7.4.58C Plate 7.4.59A Plate 7.4.59B

vertical rows of cirral scars, extending more or less to the dorsal point; cirral scars with axial canal and faint transverse ridge but lacking marginal crenullae; ventral surface of centrodorsal without radial pits and with narrow central cavity; tiny rod-shaped basals just visible externally in most species; radials with prominent steeply inclined arm facets with large muscle fossae and prominent, oblique fulcral ridge; radials enclosing a deep, narrow radial cavity. Up to 5 mm in diameter.

U. Cretaceous–Palaeocene.

Amphorometra brydoni Gislén: Senonian, Seaford, England. (A) Lateral; (B) dorsal; (C) ventral.

Order Roveacrinida (M. Triassic–U. Cretaceous)

Pl. 7.4.59. *Roveacrinus* Douglas, 1908

Stemless; cup conical, composed largely of radial plates; basals small, overgrown by radials; no centrodorsal or cirral scars; arms 10, attaching to round and discrete radial arm facets; radial cavity broad, separated from dorsal cavity by internal basals; exterior of radials with median ridge or flange. Cup up to 2 mm in diameter.

Cretaceous (pelagic).

Roveacrinus rugosus Douglas: Coniacian, Surrey, England. (A) Lateral; (B) oral.

Order Uintacrinida (U. Cretaceous)

Pl. 7.4.60. *Marsupites* Miller, 1821
Stemless; cup large, bowl-shaped; composed of 16 thin polygonal plates (a large centrodorsal, 5 infrabasals, 5 basals and 5 radials) of similar size; lightly ornamented; arm facets narrow, curved; no cirri; cup may incorporate some interbrachials loosely connected; arms uniserial, branching on primibrach 2. Cup up to 6 cm in diameter.
U. Cretaceous.
Marsupites testudinarius (von Schlotheim): Santonian, Kent, England.

Subphylum Eleutherozoa (L. Cambrian–Recent)

Diagnostic features Echinoderms with a globular, discoidal or stellate theca; dorsal surface as large or smaller than ventral surface, almost never elongate into a stalk; ambulacra forming an integral part of the theca, never extending free.

Although in recent years the subphylum Eleutherozoa has fallen into disfavour, the traditional view that echinoids, ophiuroids, asteroids and holothuroids are more closely related to one another than they are to crinoids has the support of a great deal of evidence from embryology and comparative morphology which no rival hypothesis can match. There are five classes within the Eleutherozoa of which only one, the Echinoidea, is of any importance to palaeontologists (see section 7.9). All but one of these classes are extant. An artificial key to the five classes has been given earlier.

7.5 Class Edrioasteroidea (L. Cambrian–U. Carboniferous)

Diagnostic features Eleutherozoans that have ambulacral grooves protected by cover-plate series, a fixed mouth frame formed from the most adoral ambulacral flooring plates, and a periproct that opens ventrally through the CD interray. They generally lived attached by their dorsal surface.

Basis for subdivision Edrioasteroids are a small group of extinct echinoderms which, apart from some of the earliest forms, attached themselves to hard substrata. They were low-level suspension feeders living with their oral surface facing upwards away from the sea-floor. The group probably includes ancestors to the other eleutherozoan groups among its earliest members. Four orders of edrioasteroid are distinguished, based on whether ambulacral flooring plates are uniserial or biserial, the extent to which the dorsal surface is developed, the arrangement of cover-plates both above the mouth and along the ambulacra, and whether interambulacral zones have sutural pores (epispires). The Cyclocystoida are also included here, although this problematic group is far from well understood. An authoritative review of the most important edrioasteroid groups is given by Bell (1976).

ARTIFICIAL KEY

1. Dorsal surface partially or completely plated 2
   Dorsal surface uncalcified . . . . 6 (ORDER Isorophida)
2. Ambulacra branched; marginal ring of stout perforate ossicles always developed . . . . ORDER Cyclocystoida
   Ambulacra simple; marginal ossicles rarely developed and, if present, never perforate 3
3. Interambulacra with epispires (sutural pores) . . . . ORDER Stromatocystitoida
   Interambulacra without epispires 4
4. Theca globular . . . . ORDER Edrioasterida
   Theca turret-shaped 5
5. Dorsal surface formed of a single conical element . . . . ORDER Cyathocystida
   Dorsal surface formed of imbricate plates . . . . FAMILY Pyrgocystidae
6. Ambulacral cover-plates multiserial, without sutural pores; anal opening a cone of triangular plates . . . . SUBORDER Lebetodiscina
   Ambulacral cover-plates a simple series, with sutural pores; anal opening a periproct . . . . SUBORDER Isorophina

(Family Pyrgocystidae is a highly distinctive group of uncertain affinities.)

Order Stromatocystitoida (Cambrian)

Pl. 7.5.1. *Stromatocystites* Pompeckj, 1896
Theca pentagonal to ovoid; dorsal surface fully plated, with polygonal, tesselate plates irregularly arranged; ventral surface with 5 straight ambulacra forming ridges on the theca and meeting centrally in a 2–1–2 pattern; flooring plates biserial, exposed at adradial edge; cover-plates a multiserial sheet; oral cover-plates undifferentiated interambulacral plates with epispires; no peripheral skirt. Theca up to 4 cm in diameter.
L.–M. Cambrian.
Stromatocystites pentangularis Pompeckj: M. Cambrian, Jince, Czechoslovakia.

Order Cyclocystoida (M. Ordovician–L. Carboniferous)

Pl. 7.5.2. *Apycnodiscus* Smith & Paul, 1982
Theca circular with dichotomously branched ambulacra and a prominent ring of marginal ossicles, perforated by radial canals leading from the interior to external cupules; cupule zone with a flexible peripheral skirt of small plates; ventral surface with large spaces left between plates; uniserial, unbranched rows of interambulacral plates between ambulacra; flooring plates uniserial, cover-plates small and irregular; dorsal surface covered in polygonal annular plates. Theca up to 3 cm in diameter.
M. Ordovician–M. Silurian.
Apycnodiscus salteri (Hall): M. Ordovician (Trentonian), Ottawa, Canada.

Order Edrioasterida (M. Cambrian–M. Ordovician)

Pl. 7.5.3. *Edriophus* Bell, 1976
Theca subglobular with dorsal surface much reduced in size and only partially plated; ambulacra extending below ambitus, all curved anticlockwise; with biserial flooring plates, exposed adradially and large primary plus small secondary cover-plates; oral cover-plates undifferentiated; interambulacral plates polygonal, tesselate, without epispires; dorsal surface with marginal zone of lath-like plates and central uncalcified zone. Theca up to 5 cm in diameter.
M. Ordovician.
Edriophus levis (Bather): M. Ordovician (Trentonian), Kirkfield, Canada.

Plate 7.4.60 Plate 7.5.1 Plate 7.5.2 Plate 7.5.3

Plate 7.5.4 Plate 7.5.5 Plate 7.5.6 Plate 7.5.7

Order Isorophida (M. Ordovician–U. Carboniferous)

Suborder Lebetodiscina (M. Ordovician–U. Silurian)

Pl. 7.5.4. *Lebetodiscus* Bather, 1908
Theca with domed ventral surface and uncalcified dorsal surface; ambulacra curved anticlockwise with uniserial flooring plates and simple cover-plate series with distinctive sutural passageways; oral area with 3 slightly larger cover-plates; interambulacral plates imbricate; peripheral rim of imbricate plates narrow. Theca up to 3 cm in diameter.
M. Ordovician.
Lebetodiscus dicksoni (Billings): Trenton Limestone, Ottawa, Canada.

Pl. 7.5.5. *Cystaster* Hall, 1871
Theca discoidal to clavate with uncalcified dorsal surface; ambulacra straight, broad, with uniserial flooring plates and simple cover-plate series; cover-plates wedge-shaped with slit-like sutural pores; oral area with 3 larger cover-plates; interambulacra composed of many tiny plates and granular in appearance; peripheral rim narrow, overhung. Theca up to 1 cm in diameter.
M.–U. Ordovician.
Cystaster stellatus (Hall): Maysvillian, Forestville, Ohio, USA.

Pl. 7.5.6. *Cryptogoleus* Bell, 1976
Theca discoidal with uncalcified dorsal surface; ambulacra with uniserial flooring plates and simple cover-plate series; ambulacra straight, reaching peripheral rim; cover-plate passageways slit-like; oral area with 3 large cover-plates; interambulacral plates imbricate; anal opening a periproct; peripheral rim stout. Theca up to 1.5 cm in diameter.
M.–U. Ordovician.
Cryptogoleus youngi (Raymond): Trenton Limestone, Ottawa, Canada.

Pl. 7.5.7. *Carneyella* Foerste, 1917
Theca discoidal, with uncalcified dorsal surface; ambulacra curved, I to IV anticlockwise, V clockwise, not reaching peripheral rim, composed of uniserial flooring plates and simple cover-plate series with slit-like sutural pores; oral area covered by 3 large cover-plates; anal opening a periproct; interambulacra narrow, plates imbricate; peripheral rim prominent. Theca up to 2 cm in diameter.
M.–U. Ordovician.
Carneyella pilea (Hall): M. Ordovician (Cincinnatian), Ohio, USA.

Suborder Isorophina (M. Ordovician–U. Carboniferous)

Pl. 7.5.8. *Isorophusella* Bassler, 1935
Theca discoidal with uncalcified dorsal surface; ambulacra straight or slightly curved; ambulacra I to III curving anticlockwise, IV to V clockwise; ambulacral flooring plates uniserial; cover-plates of two sizes regularly alternating; oral area without differentiated cover-plates; interambulacral plates squamose, imbricate; anal opening a cone of plates; peripheral rim prominent. Theca up to 2 cm in diameter.
M.–U. Ordovician.
Isorophusella incondita (Raymond): Ordovician (Mohawkian), Ottawa, Canada.

Pl. 7.5.9. *Stalticodiscus* Smith, 1983
Theca with relatively small uncalcified dorsal surface and large clavate ventral surface; ambulacra I to IV curved anticlockwise, V clockwise; flooring plates uniserial; cover-plates arranged in cycles of 3; oral cover-plates not differentiated from the rest; interambulacral plates subtesselate adorally, imbricate laterally; anal opening a cone of plates. Theca up to 2 cm in diameter.
L. Carboniferous.
Staltodiscus milleri (Sharman & Newton): L. Carboniferous (Asbian), Penrith, England.

FAMILY PYRGOCYSTIDAE (M. ORDOVICIAN–L. DEVONIAN)

Pl. 7.5.10. *Pyrgocystis* Bather, 1915
Theca turret-shaped; dorsal surface a ferrule of miniscule membrane-embedded plates; lateral zone highly elongate, composed of imbricate plates; small domed ventral surface with broad, short ambulacra with simple cover-plates; interambulacral zones with a couple of large plates only. Theca up to 3 cm in length.
M. Ordovician–M. Silurian.
Pyrgocystis grayae Bather: Ashgill, Girvan, Scotland.

7.6 Class Asteroidea (L. Ordovician–Recent)

Diagnostic features Stellate eleutherozoans with dorsal and ventral surfaces more or less equally developed; ambulacra biserial; arms with large body cavity containing branches of main internal organs and not sharply separated from the central disc; radial water vessels external to ambulacral plates; anus absent or opening dorsally; no fixed mouth frame.

Although asteroids are a relatively diverse group, they have not been treated in the same depth as other groups because of the space available. Although the taxonomy of Recent asteroids is now fairly well established, using soft tissue data as well as ossicle morphology to establish a number of orders and suborders, it can only be applied successfully to post-Palaeozoic asteroid groups. Various schemes have been proposed for the higher classification of Palaeozoic asteroids, but there has been little published recently and I have chosen not to commit myself to any of these until further information becomes available.

Pl. 7.6.1. *Archegonaster* Jaekel, 1923
Body pentagonal with stout marginal frame of single ossicles; ambulacral plates alternate and are slightly imbricate; adambulacral ossicles articulate upon the adradial edge of ambulacral ossicles and give rise to a series of rod-shaped ossicles which extend to the marginal frame; disc with madreporite, adoralmost ambulacral ossicles only slightly modified into mouth angle plates. (The specimen shows 1 ambulacrum and associated marginal ossicles.) Disc up to 5 cm in diameter.
L. Ordovician.
Archegonaster pentagonus Spencer: Llanvirn, Osek, Czechoslovakia.

Pl. 7.6.2. *Cnemidactis* Spencer, 1918
Arms long, narrow, parallel-sided; stout marginal ossicles together with squarish adambulacral ossicles form the sides of the arm; dorsal surface covered by numerous small ossicles; mouth with well-differentiated mouth angle plates and large spade-shaped tooth plates; ambulacral ossicles broad and stout. Arm tip to centre of disc up to 6 cm.
Ordovician.
Cnemidactis girvanensis (Schuchert): U. Ordovician, Girvan, Scotland.

Pl. 7.6.3. *Metopaster* Sladen, 1893
Pentagonal body without produced arms; marginal ring consisting of an upper and lower series of stout ossicles set one above the other; relatively few marginal ossicles to each side, each ornamented by pitting except for a smooth narrow rim; disc plating tesselate; many small plates form both dorsal and ventral surfaces; ambulacra narrow. Up to 6 cm in diameter.
U. Cretaceous–Miocene.
Metopaster parkinsoni Forbes: U. Cretaceous, Kent, England.

7.7 Class Ophiuroidea (L. Ordovician–Recent)

Diagnostic features Stellate eleutherozoans with arms clearly differentiated from a central disc; arms without large body space into which lobes from the digestive system extend; no anal opening; radial water vessel enclosed; adoralmost ambulacral ossicles modified into a jaw apparatus.

Basis for subdivision The current classification of ophiuroids is based on grades of organisation rather than on phylogenetic relationship. Ophiuroids are separated into four orders on the basis of their arm structure and disc plating. The order Ophiurida contains all those with arms in which the ambulacral ossicles are arranged opposite one another and fused into vertebrae. These vertebrae are more or less completely concealed by the two lateral arm plates, a large dorsal plate and a slightly smaller ventral plate. Larger plates are also differentiated from among the disc plating, and radial shields, buccal shields and genital plates are all present. The Phrynophiurida also have ambulacral plating that is fused into vertebrae, but instead of having a single large dorsal plate the arms are covered by a thick skin with tiny membrane-embedded plates. The remaining two orders contain only Palaeozoic groups and are defined on the absence of advanced character states. The Oegophiurida have neither dorsal nor ventral arm plates and the lateral arm plates do not curve round to cover the ambulacral tube-foot basins as they do in the previous two orders. Some oegophiurids have the two columns of ambulacral ossicles in each ambulacrum arranged alternately, others have them opposite. The fourth order, Stenurida, is the least satisfactory and houses a mixture of primitive groups which do not belong to any of the other three orders. They generally have ambulacral plating arranged as an alternating series and the podial basin which houses the tube-foot is shared between two adjacent ossicles rather than being restricted to one, as it is in the other three groups. In the most primitive, the radial water vessel lies externally, as in asteroids.

ARTIFICIAL KEY

1. Ambulacra with basins for tube-feet shared between 2 ossicles .... ORDER Stenurida
   Ambulacra with basins for tube-feet contained in 1 plate and not shared 2
2. Ambulacral ossicles clearly exposed ventrally .... ORDER Oegophiurida
   Ambulacral ossicles largely or completely covered by arm plates 3
3. Arm with dorsal and ventral arm plates . . ORDER Ophiurida
   Arm without dorsal and ventral arm plates, covered dorsally by a thick skin with tiny ossicles . . . ORDER Phrynophiurida

Order Oegophiurida (L. Ordovician–L. Carboniferous)

Pl. 7.7.1. *Euzonosoma* Spencer, 1930
Central disc relatively large with stout marginal frame enclosing a lightly plated disc; ambulacra slightly petaloid, broadest at mid-length; ambulacral ossicles arranged alternately; radial water vessel enclosed by ambulacral ossicles; lateral arm plates stout, largely ventral in position, not covering podial basins of ambulacral ossicles; no dorsal skeleton on arms. Disc up to 5 cm in diameter.
U. Ordovician–L. Devonian.
Euzonosoma tischbeinianum (Roemer): L. Devonian, Bundenbach, W. Germany.

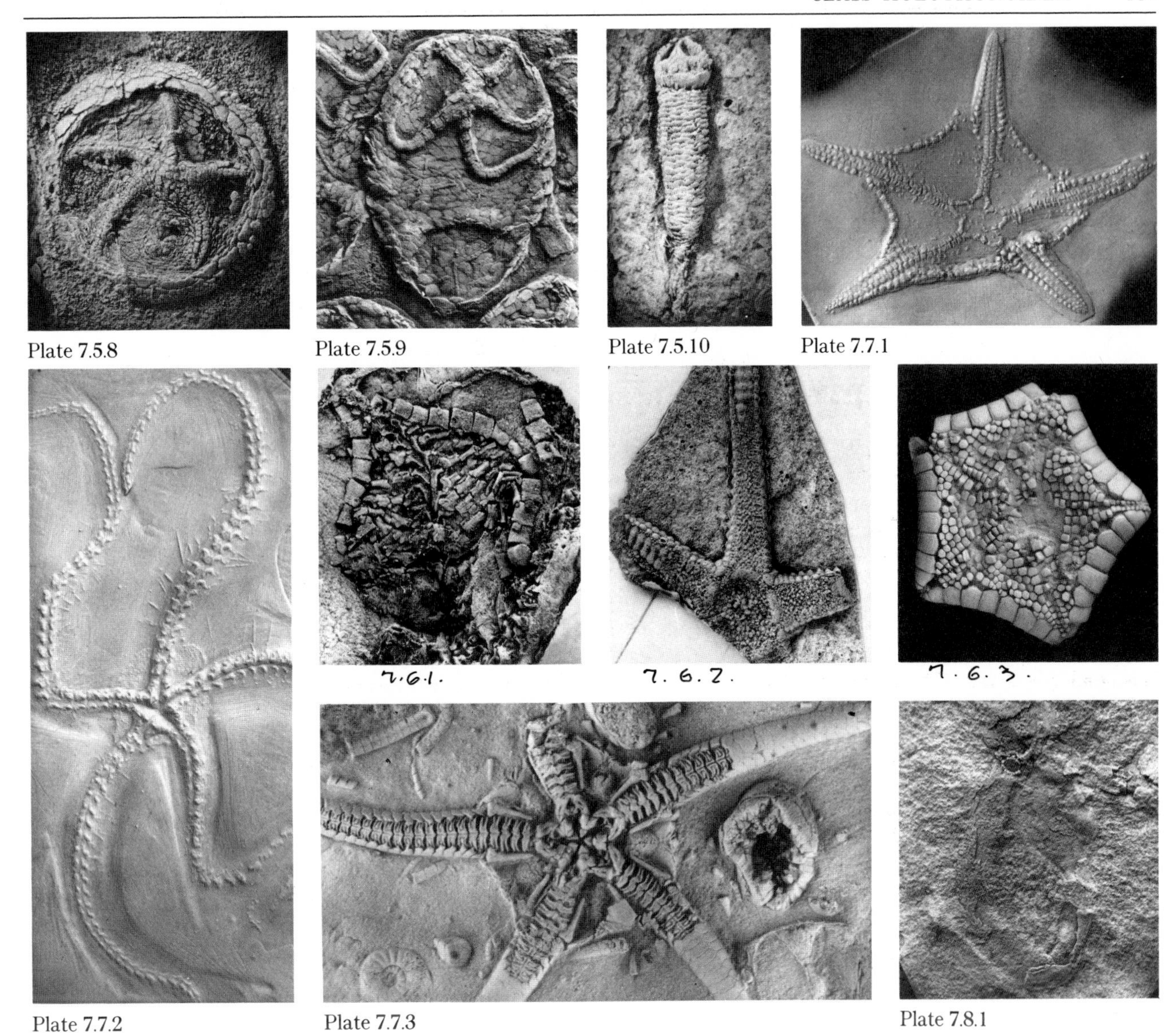

Plate 7.5.8 Plate 7.5.9 Plate 7.5.10 Plate 7.7.1

Plate 7.7.2 Plate 7.7.3 Plate 7.8.1

Order Phrynophiurida (L. Devonian–Recent)

Pl. 7.7.2. *Eospondylus* Gregory, 1897
Arms long and central disc relatively small; disc composed of numerous tiny undifferentiated plates plus small side shields; ambulacral ossicles opposite one another and fused into vertebrae, largely covered by the prominent lateral arm plates, which are sickle-shaped and wrapped around the arms; no ventral or dorsal arm plates differentiated; lateral arm spines long. Disc up to 2 cm in diameter.
L. Devonian.
Eospondylus primigenius Sturtz: L. Devonian, Bundenbach, W. Germany.

Order Ophiurida (Silurian–Recent)

Pl. 7.7.3. *Palaeocoma* d'Orbigny, 1850
Disc with differentiated radial shields, buccal shields and genital plates; arms with ambulacral ossicles opposite and fused into vertebrae, completely hidden by arm plates; diamond-shaped dorsal and ventral arm plates; lateral arm plates with rudimentary spines. Disc up to 2.5 cm in diameter.
L. Jurassic.
Palaeocoma milleri (Phillips): Pliensbachian, England.

7.8 Class Holothuroidea (?Ordovician, Silurian–Recent)

Diagnostic features Dorsal surface greatly reduced relative to ventral surface; anus opening through dorsal surface; mouth surrounded by large tentacular tube-feet in most; adoralmost ambulacral ossicles modified forming an internal calcareous ring; body wall skeleton generally reduced to microscopical spicules; radial water vessel wholly internal.

Although holothuroid spicules are not uncommon as microfossils, whole body fossils are extremely rare. Today holothuroids are a successful and diverse group adapted for suspension or deposit feeding. Some have even become free-swimming. However, we know very little about their fossil record. The earliest members appear to be the ophiocistioids, a peculiar L. Palaeozoic group with a plated skeleton and an echinoid-type jaw apparatus. As holothuroid orders are based almost entirely on soft tissue anatomy, no key is given here and only one specimen is illustrated.

Pl. 7.8.1. Undescribed holothuroid
This specimen shows the impression of a looped gut, the outer body wall and, most characteristically, the small calcite ring of 10 plates which surrounds the pharynx.
U. Carboniferous, Mazon Creek Formation, Illinois, USA.

7.9 Class Echinoidea (Ordovician–Recent)

Diagnostic features Eleutherozoans that have a well-developed skeleton of interlocking calcareous plates. The ambulacral plates are perforated for tube-feet. The adoralmost ambulacral ossicles are modified as a dental apparatus or are secondarily lost.

Basis for subdivision The number of rows of plates in the ambulacral and interambulacral columns are used to distinguish between the more primitive Perischoechinoidea (number variable) and the more advanced Euechinoidea (two rows in each column). The position of the periproct either within (endocyclic) or outside (exocyclic) the apical system, presence or absence of a lantern and the shape of the teeth, and the pattern of the apical system plates are some of the many morphological features used to define the superorders and orders.

The classification used is essentially that of the *Treatise on Invertebrate Paleontology* (Durham *et al.* 1966) because those seeking further details of the Echinoidea will certainly refer to that work. However, that classification is not universally accepted and, recently, Smith (1981) has suggested some taxonomic regrouping to produce a phylogenetic classification (see Fig. 7.9.1).

Major taxonomic units There are two subclasses: the **Perischoechinoidea** which are regular (endocyclic) echinoids with a variable number of columns of plates in both the ambulacra and interambulacra, no compound plates and a lantern with simple grooved teeth – it includes all the Palaeozoic echinoids and the cidaroids which continue to the present day; and the **Euechinoidea** with two columns of plates in both the ambulacra and the interambulacra. This includes all non-cidaroid Mesozoic to Recent echinoids.

The Euechinoidea is divided into two major groups: Regular echinoids characterized by having the periproct within the apical system (endocyclic), and Irregular echinoids, characterized by having the periproct outside the apical system (exocyclic).

The Regular echinoids include the superorders Diadematacea (minus the order Pygasteroida) and Echinacea. The Diadematacea is made up of the orders Echinothurioida (not discussed here), Diadematoida (has perforate crenulate tubercles) and Pedinoida (perforate non-crenulate tubercles). The Echinacea is divided into seven orders. Four have a stirodont lantern (Salenioida, Hemicidaroida, Phymosomatoida, Arbacioida), two have a camarodont lantern (Temnopleuroida, Echinoida), and the details of the seventh are not known (Plesiocidaroida).

The Irregular echinoids include the order Pygasteroida (placed in the Diadematacea in the *Treatise*), and the superorders Gnathostomata and Atelostomata (in the sense of the *Treatise* classification). The orders Holectypoida and Clypeasteroida have a lantern ('Gnathostomata'), whereas the Cassiduloida, Holasteroida and Spatangoida do not ('Atelostomata').

ARTIFICIAL KEY TO THE ORDERS OF ECHINOIDEA DISCUSSED

1. Periproct within apical system at apex. . . . . Regular echinoids 2
   Periproct clearly separated from the apical system or within a deep sulcus to the posterior of the apex . . . . Irregular echinoids 9
2. Ambulacra compound; gill slits present 3
   Ambulacra simple; no gill slits . . . . Cidaroids
3. Apical system large and ornate with suranal plate (Fig. 7.9.2) . . . . Salenioids
   Apical system relatively small, without suranal plate . . . 4
4. Tubercles perforate 5
   Tubercles imperforate 7

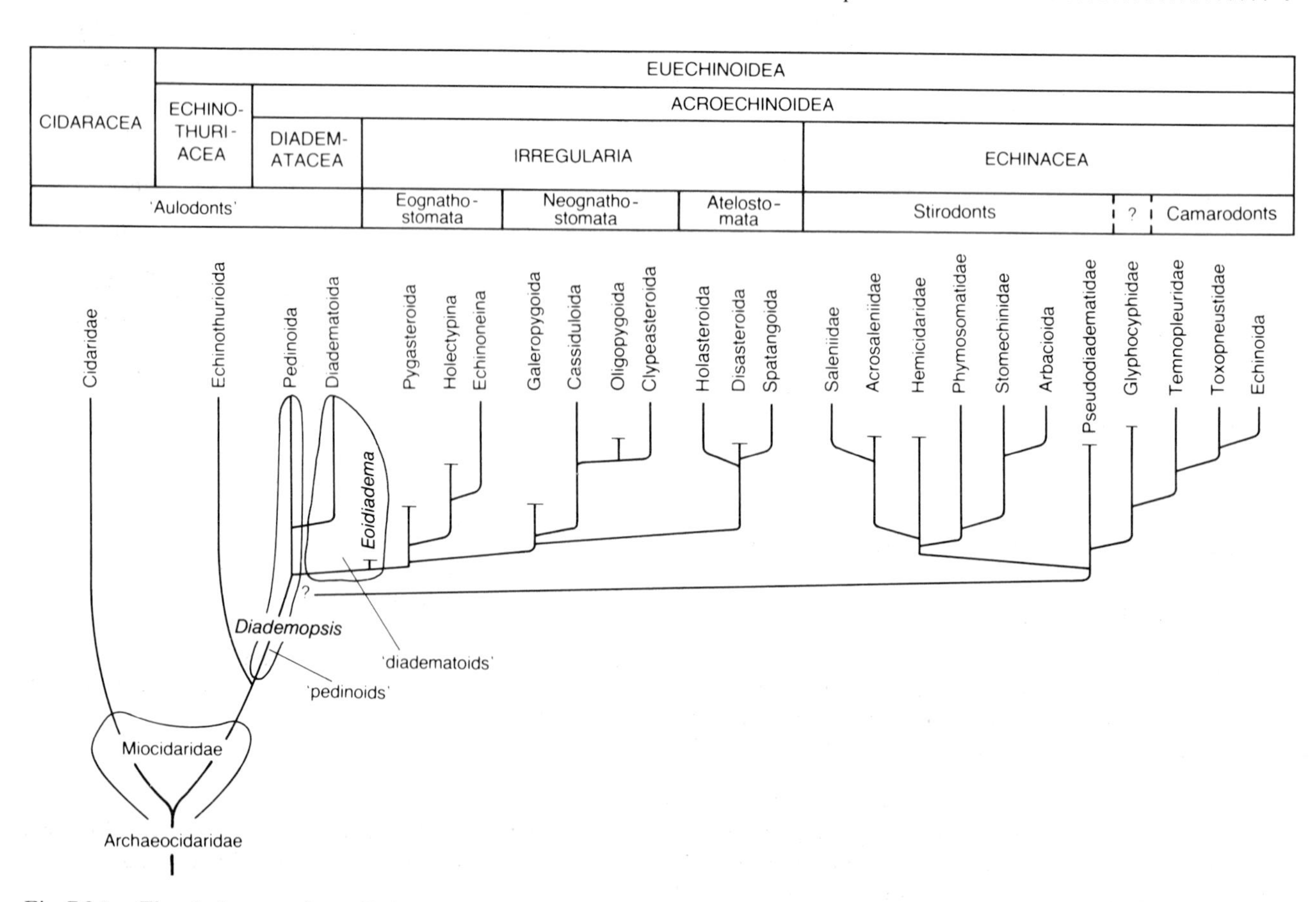

Fig. 7.9.1. The phylogeny of post-Palaeozoic echinoids. (From Smith 1981.)

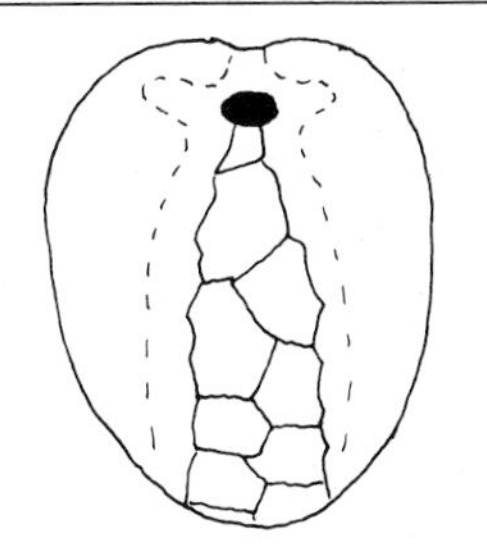

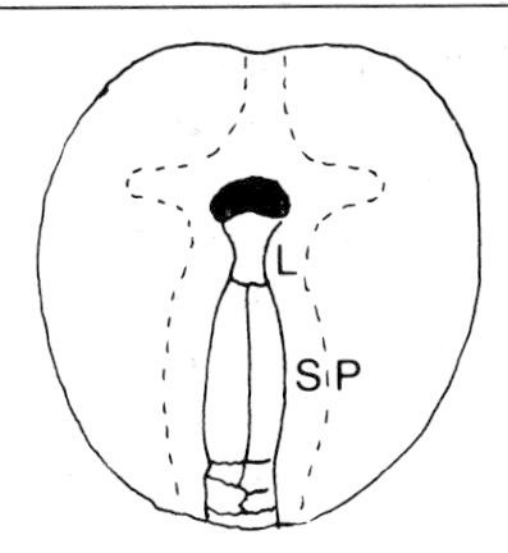

Fig. 7.9.2. Essential differences between holasteroids (left) with plastron and spatangoids (right) with labrum (L) and sternal plates (SP).

5. Tubercles crenulate 6
   Tubercles non-crenulate . . . . Pedinoids
6. Spines hollow, lantern aulodont . . . . Diadematoids
   Spines solid, lantern stirodont . . . . Hemicidaroids
7. Test with sutural pits and crenulate tubercles . . . . Temnopleuroida (except Taxopneustidae)
   Test without sutural pits; tubercles non-crenulate 8
8. Gill slits deep . . . . Temnopleuroida (Taxopneustidae only)
   Gill slits feeble . . . . Echinoida
9. Some or all ambulacra petalloid or subpetalloid adapically 11
   Ambulacral pores non-petalloid, uniform from peristome to apex 10
10. Periproct opens on apical surface, in contact with apical system . . . . Pygasteroids
    Periproct opens ambitally or adorally separated from apical system . . . . Holectypoids
11. All 5 ambulacra petalloid 12
    Anterior ambulacrum differentiated, non-petalloid 13
12. Phyllodes surround the mouth; 1 ambulacral pore per plate . . . . Cassiduloids
    Phyllodes never present; pores below the petals minute perforations, many to each ambulacral plate . . . . Clypeasteroids
13. Interambulacrum posterior to peristome on oral surface with a labrum + pair of sternal plates (Fig. 7.9.2) . . . . Spatangoids
    Interambulacrum posterior to peristome on oral surface, an alternating biseries of plates or a uniserial row of plates . . . . Holasteroids

Key to plates In this section each genus is illustrated with three plates: (A) aboral view; (B) oral view; (C) lateral view.

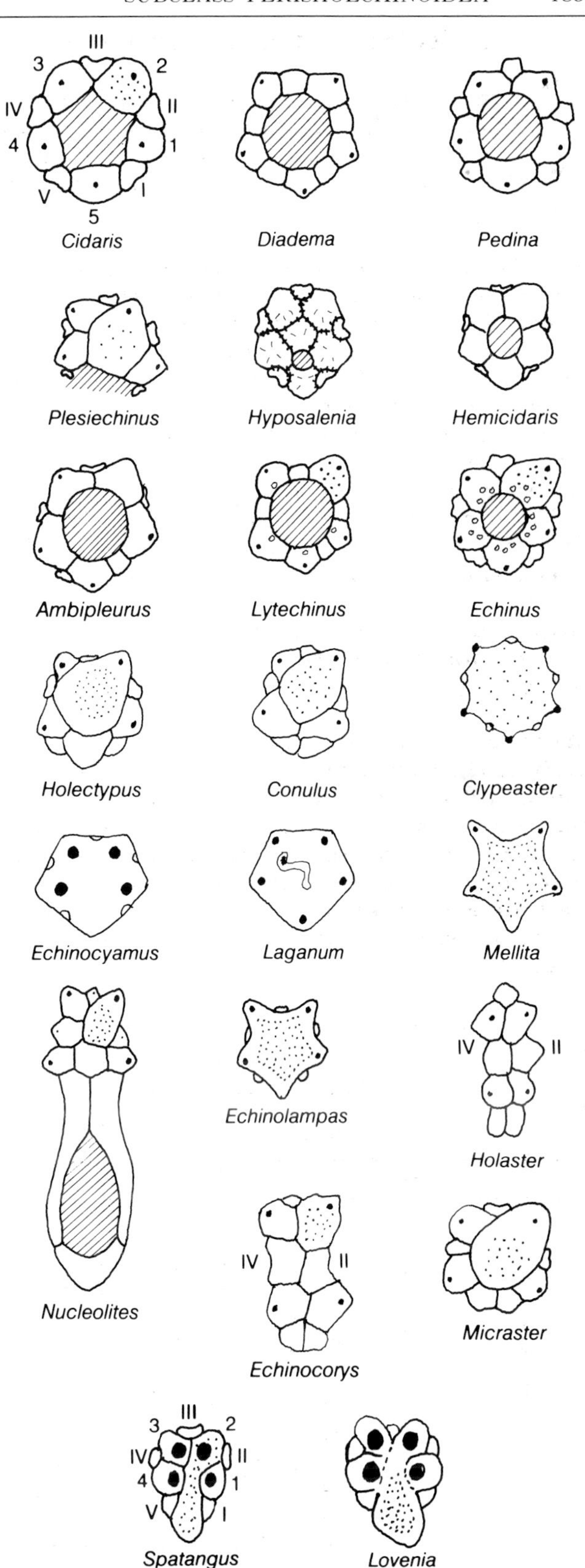

Fig. 7.9.3. Sketches of the apical systems of the illustrated genera. The numbers refer to the Loven scheme of plate nomenclature.

Subclass Perischoechinoidea (Ordovician–Recent)

Order Cidaroida (U. Silurian–Recent).

Pl. 7.9.1. *Cidaris* Leske, 1778, *sensu lato*
Test medium, subspherical, rigid, pentaradially symmetrical. Endocyclic. Apical system monocyclic or dicyclic (Fig. 7.9.3). Ambulacra narrow, composed of simple plates, each with a single pore pair. Interambulacra wide, each plate bearing 1 large, perforate, primary tubercle with a well-developed scrobicular ring (Fig. 7.9.4). Spines long, with lengthwise ornament of spinules or ridges. Peristome covered with imbricating plates. Lantern without V-shaped notch (cidaroid), teeth grooved. Gills absent.

U. Triassic–Recent (Recent only for *Cidaris s. str.*). Epifaunal slow-moving or inactive. Tropics to poles, especially around Antarctica.
Cidaris s. l.: Recent, locality unknown.

Subclass Euechinoidea (U. Triassic–Recent)

REGULAR ECHINOIDS

Superorder Diadematacea (U. Triassic–Recent)

Order Diadematoida (U. Triassic–Recent)

Pl. 7.9.2. *Diadema* Gray, 1825
Test medium or large, subhemispherical, flattened, pentaradially symmetrical. Endocyclic, monocyclic (Fig. 7.9.3). Ambulacral plates compound by fusion; a large primary tubercle on every third plate forming 2 conspicuous regular series. Interambulacral plates each bearing several perforate and crenulate primary tubercles (Fig. 7.9.4). Gill slits present around peristomial margin. Lantern aulodont, teeth grooved.
?U. Cretaceous, Recent. Epifaunal, shallow water, tropical, often on reefs. Has ability to detect light and shadow.
Diadema savigni Michelin: Recent, locality unknown.

Order Pedinoida (U. Triassic–Recent)

Pl. 7.9.3. *Pedina* L. Agassiz, 1838
Test medium to large, subspherical, depressed, pentaradially symmetrical. Endocyclic, dicyclic, with 5 genital pores (Fig. 7.9.3). Ambulacral plates compound, pore pairs arranged in arcs of 3 about a primary tubercle. Interambulacra wider than ambulacra, each plate with 1 central perforate but non-crenulate tubercle and 1 or more smaller tubercles adjacent to the ambulacral margin (adradial suture Fig. 7.9.4). Gill notches around the peristomial margin. Lantern aulodont.
Jurassic–Miocene. Epifaunal, continental shelf down to *c.* 2000 m in extant pedinoids.
Pedina rotata Wright: M. Jurassic, England.

IRREGULAR ECHINOIDS

Order Pygasteroida (L. Jurassic–U. Cretaceous)

Pl. 7.9.4. *Plesiechinus* Pomel, 1883
Test medium to large, plano-convex, secondarily bilaterally symmetrical. Exocyclic. Periproct adjacent to apical system which has only 4 genital plates (Fig. 7.9.3), forming keyhole-like slit. Ambulacral plates compound, with small tubercles spanning 2 out of every 3 plates. Interambulacra broad, with small tubercles arranged in horizontal and vertical series (Fig. 7.9.4). Lantern present, teeth trapezoidal in cross-section.
M. Jurassic (Bajocian)–U. Cretaceous (Cenomanian). ?Epifaunal.
Plesiechinus ornatus (Buckman): M. Jurassic (Bajocian), Gloucester, England.

Superorder Echinacea (U. Triassic–Recent)

Order Salenioida (L. Jurassic–Recent)

Pl. 7.9.5. *Hyposalenia* Desor, 1856
Test small, subspherical, compressed, pentaradially symmetrical. Endocyclic, periproct displaced posteriorly towards genital 5. Apical system large, dicyclic, with sutural depressions and ornament on the plates (Fig. 7.9.3), and a prominent central plate (suranal plate). Ambulacra with 2 pore pairs and 1 tubercle on each plate. Interambulacral plates each bear 1 large tubercle as in cidaroids (Fig. 7.9.4). Peristome with gill notches. Lantern stirodont (open foramen magnum and keeled teeth).
U. Jurassic (Kimmeridgian)–U. Cretaceous (Senonian).
Hyposalenia sp.: Cretaceous, Texas.

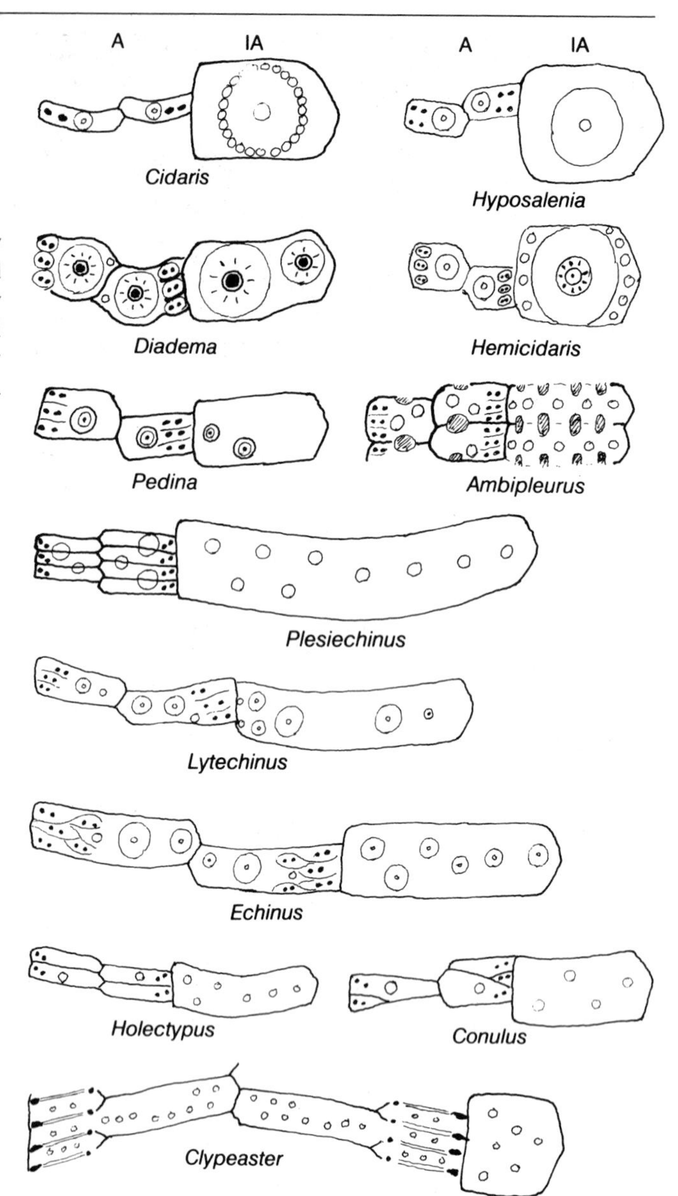

Fig. 7.9.4. Sketches of coronal plates. Left two plates – ambulacral; right plate – interambulacral.

Order Hemicidaroida (U. Triassic–U. Cretaceous)

Pl. 7.9.6. *Hemicidaris* Wright, 1857
Test medium, subspherical, pentaradially symmetrical. Endocyclic, periproct centrally placed. Apical system dicyclic (Fig. 7.9.3). Ambulacra compound adorally with larger tubercles confined to the lower third of the corona. Interambulacral plates each bearing 1 large perforate tubercle of cidaroid type (Fig. 7.9.4). Peristome large with gill notches. Lantern stirodont (open foramen magnum and keeled teeth).
L. Jurassic–U. Cretaceous (Cenomanian).
Hemicidaris crenularis Lamarck: U. Jurassic, England.

Order Temnopleuroida (L. Jurassic–Recent)

Pl. 7.9.7. *Ambipleurus* Lambert, 1932
Test small, hemispherical, pentaradially symmetrical. Endocyclic, with ocular I insert (Fig. 7.9.3). Ambulacra having 3 pore pairs on each plate. Primary tubercles in regular series in each ambulacral and interambulacral column. Deep depressions in

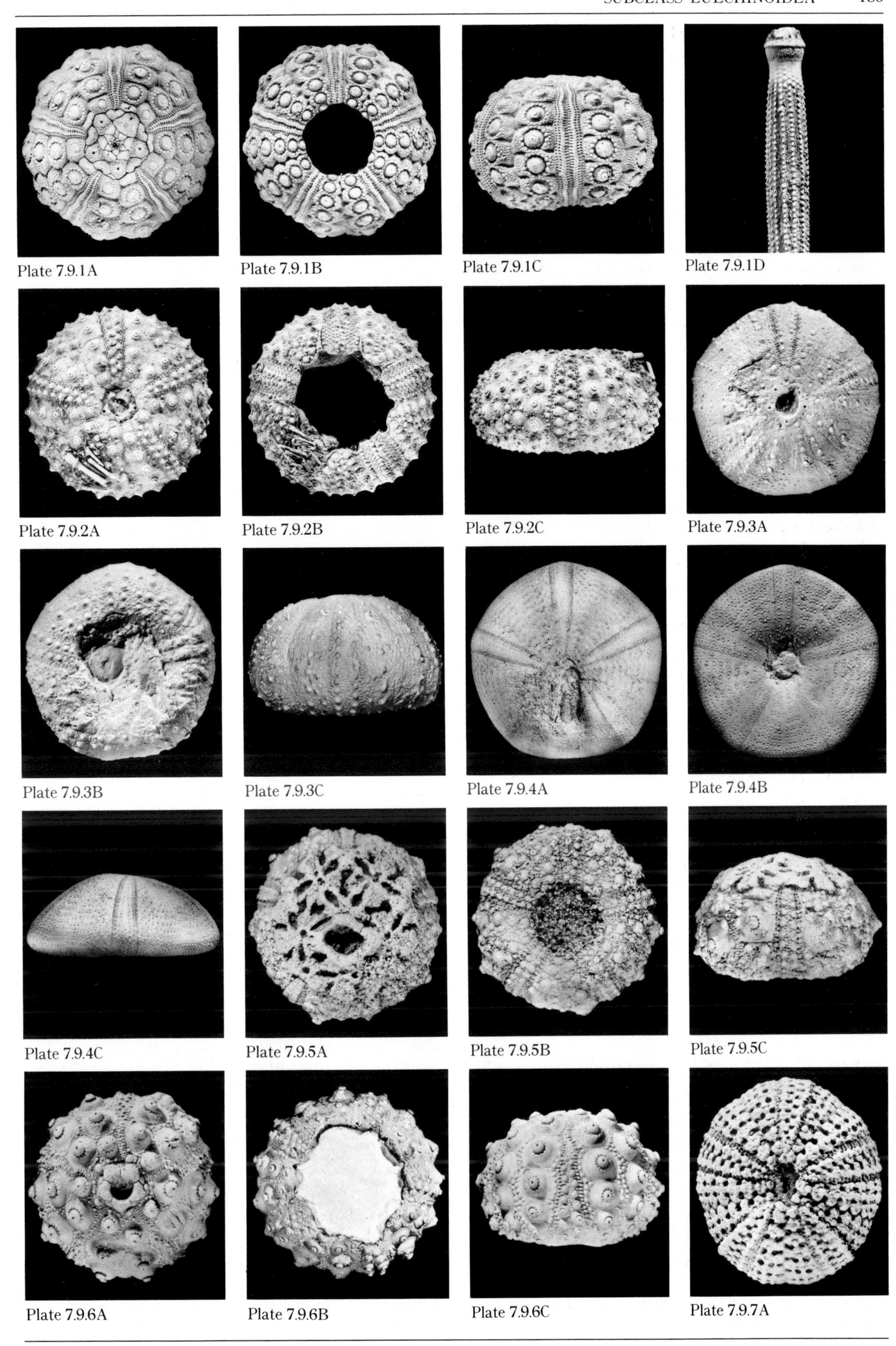

Plate 7.9.1A Plate 7.9.1B Plate 7.9.1C Plate 7.9.1D

Plate 7.9.2A Plate 7.9.2B Plate 7.9.2C Plate 7.9.3A

Plate 7.9.3B Plate 7.9.3C Plate 7.9.4A Plate 7.9.4B

Plate 7.9.4C Plate 7.9.5A Plate 7.9.5B Plate 7.9.5C

Plate 7.9.6A Plate 7.9.6B Plate 7.9.6C Plate 7.9.7A

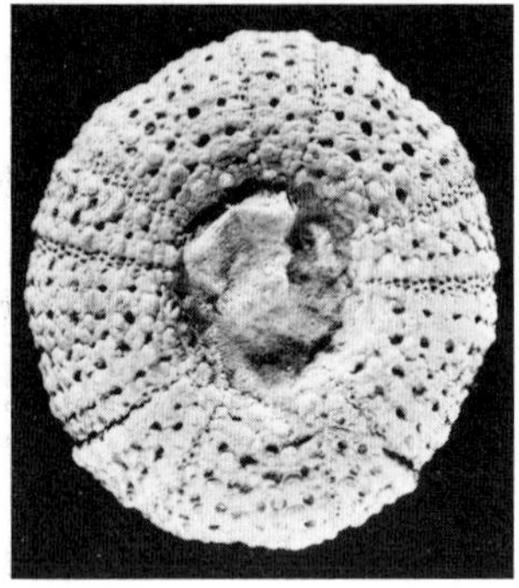

Plate 7.9.7B

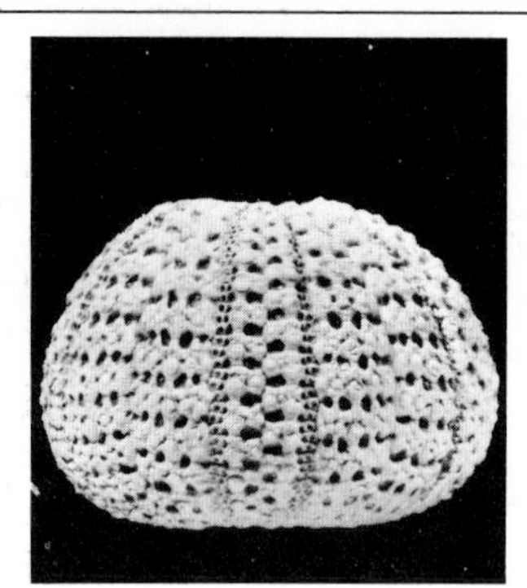

Plate 7.9.7C

Plate 7.9.8A

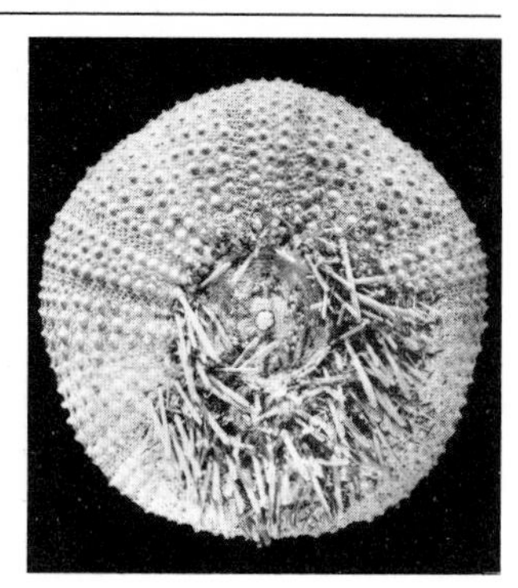

Plate 7.9.8B

horizontal sutures (Fig. 7.9.4). Peristome with gill notches. Lantern camarodont (closed foramen magnum and keeled teeth). Eocene.
Ambipleurus sp.: Eocene, ?Pakistan.

Pl. 7.9.8. *Lytechinus* A. Agassiz, 1863
Test medium, low hemispherical, pentaradially symmetrical. Endocyclic. Apical system monocyclic (Fig. 7.9.3). Ambulacral plates compounded, with primary and secondary tubercles in regular columns, and conspicuous non-tuberculate median space adorally. Interambulacra with regular columns of tubercles and also with conspicuous non-tuberculate median space adorally (Fig. 7.9.4). Peristome with gill notches. Lantern camarodont (closed foramen magnum and keeled teeth).
Pleistocene–Recent. Continental shelf, often on soft bottoms, highly mobile, using its spines for locomotion.
Lytechinus variegatus (Leske): Recent, S. Carolina, USA.

Order Echinoida

Pl. 7.9.9. *Echinus* Linné, 1758
Test large, spherical to subspherical, pentaradially symmetrical. Endocyclic. Apical system dicyclic (Fig. 7.9.3). Ambulacra compound with a primary tubercle on every second or third compound plate. Interambulacra broad, each plate with several imperforate tubercles (Fig. 7.9.4). Peristome with gill notches. Lantern camarodont (closed foramen magnum and keeled teeth).
Pliocene–Recent. Epifaunal, carnivorous, continental shelf.
Echinus esculentus Linné: Recent, England.

Superorder Gnathostomata (Jurassic–Recent)

Order Holectypoida (Jurassic–Recent)

Pl. 7.9.10. *Holectypus* Desor, 1842
Test medium, hemispherical, with flat to concave oral side, secondarily bilaterally symmetrical. Exocyclic, periproct marginal or inframarginal. Apical system with 5 genital plates, number 5 being imperforate (Fig. 7.9.3). Ambulacra non-petaloid, plates mainly simple but compound adorally. Interambulacra broad with scattered small tubercles on the adoral side and larger, coarser tubercles on the oral side (Fig. 7.9.4). Lantern and gill slits present.
L. Jurassic (Pliensbachian)–U. Cretaceous (Senonian).
Holectypus depressa (Leske): M. Jurassic (Bajocian), England.

Pl. 7.9.11. *Conulus* Lambert, 1911
Test medium, flat, on oral side, domed aborally, secondarily symmetrical. Exocyclic, periproct inframarginal. Apical system with 4 adjoining genital plates (ethmophract) (Fig. 7.9.3). Ambulacra non-petaloid with reduced plates (excluded from perradial or adradial sutures). Interambulacra with numerous small tubercles (Fig. 7.9.4). Lantern and gill slits absent.
U. Cretaceous.
Conulus albogalerus Leske: U. Cretaceous, England.

Order Clypeasteroida (Palaeocene–Recent)

Pl. 7.9.12. *Clypeaster* Lamarck, 1801
Test medium to large, ovoid, concave on oral surface, secondarily bilaterally symmetrical. Exocyclic, periproct inframarginal. Apical system with 5 genital pores, plates fused (Fig. 7.9.3). Ambulacra petaloid, consisting of regularly alternating primary plates and demiplates (i.e. touches adradial but not perradial suture). Interambulacra with primordial plates greatly reduced (Fig. 7.9.4). Peristome central, in deep hollow. Test has internal supports.
U. Eocene–Recent. Shallow water, semi-infaunal, detritus feeder.
Clypeaster rosaceus (Linné): Recent, West Indies.

Pl. 7.9.13. *Echinocyamus* Van Phelsum, 1774
Test small, flattened, oval in outline, secondarily bilaterally symmetrical. Exocyclic, periproct on oral side. Apical system with genital plates fused (Fig. 7.9.3). Ambulacra with poorly defined petals, pore pairs usually oblique. Interambulacra terminated adorally with a single plate. Peristome central. Test has internal supports.
?Palaeocene, Eocene–Recent. Temperate to tropical, infaunal in coarse sediments.
Echinocyamus nummuliticus Duncan & Sladen: Eocene, Pakistan.

Pl. 7.9.14. *Laganum* Link, 1807
Test medium, flattened, outline angulated, secondarily bilaterally symmetrical. Exocyclic, periproct on oral side. Apical system fused with groove for hydropores, 5 genital pores (Fig. 7.9.3). Ambulacra petaloid, with food groove adorally. Interambulacra with 5 to 6 coronal plates to column on oral surface: ends adapically in a single large plate. Peristome central. Test has internal supports.
Eocene (Europe), Miocene–Recent (Indo-Pacific). Tropical, infaunal, detritus feeder.
Laganum depressum (Lesson): Recent, Palawan, Philippines.

Pl. 7.9.15. *Mellita* L. Agassiz, 1841
Test medium to large, compressed, thin, secondarily bilaterally symmetrical with narrow, elongate lunules (openings in test). Exocyclic, periproct oral, between posterior lunule and peristome. Apical system slightly anterior, pentagonal, with 4 genital pores (Fig. 7.9.3). Ambulacra petaloid, outer member of pore

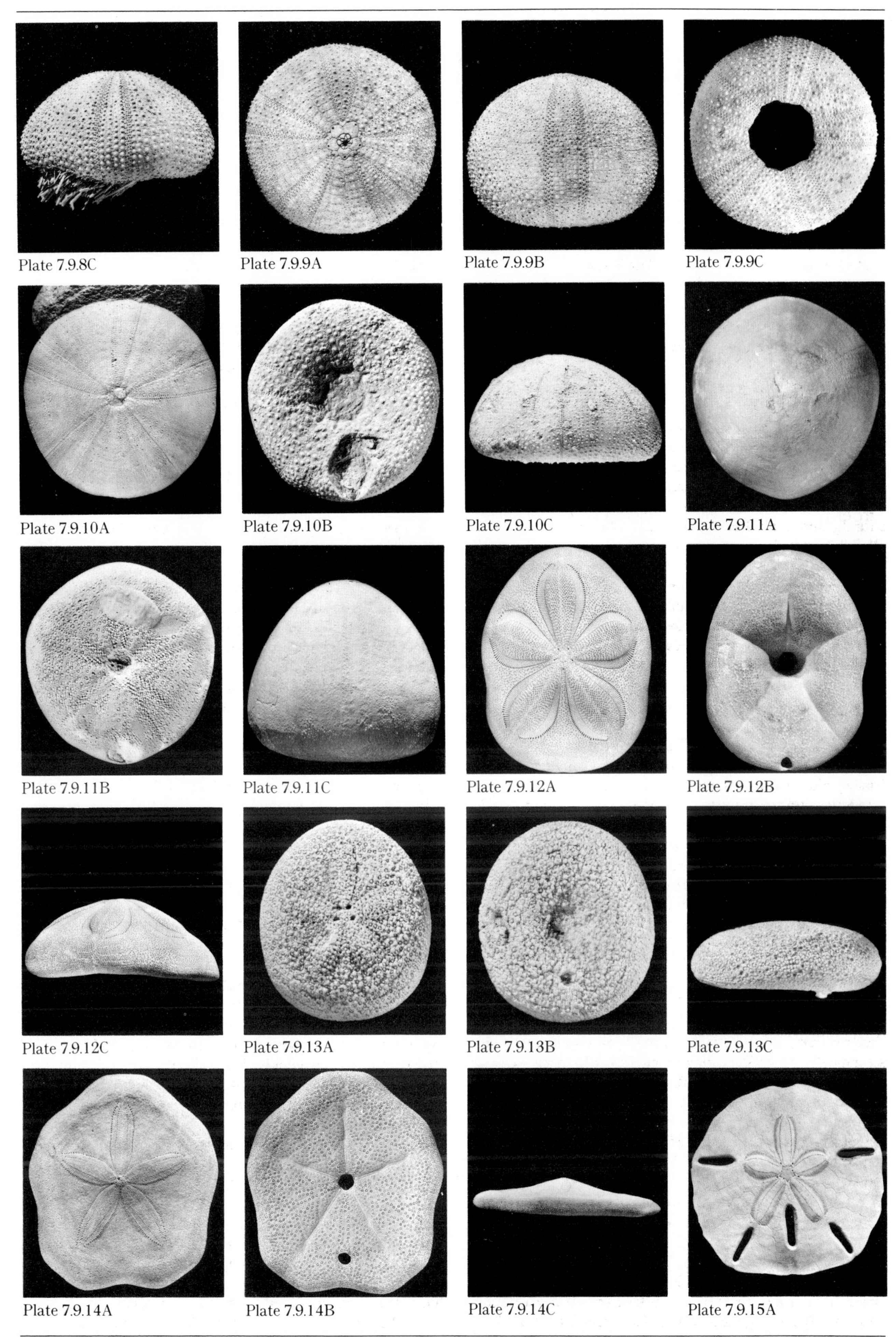

Plate 7.9.8C Plate 7.9.9A Plate 7.9.9B Plate 7.9.9C

Plate 7.9.10A Plate 7.9.10B Plate 7.9.10C Plate 7.9.11A

Plate 7.9.11B Plate 7.9.11C Plate 7.9.12A Plate 7.9.12B

Plate 7.9.12C Plate 7.9.13A Plate 7.9.13B Plate 7.9.13C

Plate 7.9.14A Plate 7.9.14B Plate 7.9.14C Plate 7.9.15A

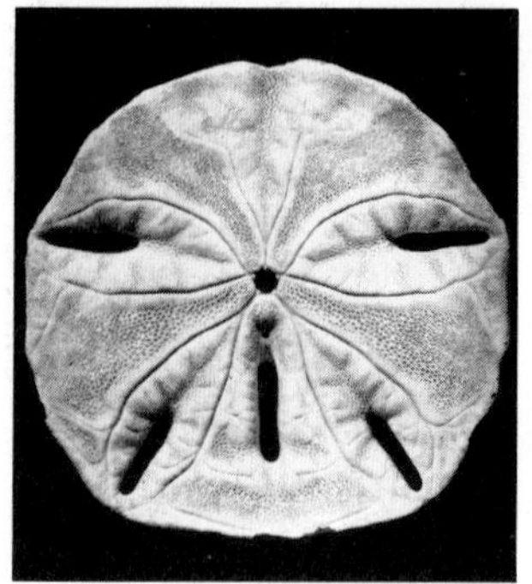

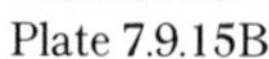

Plate 7.9.15B

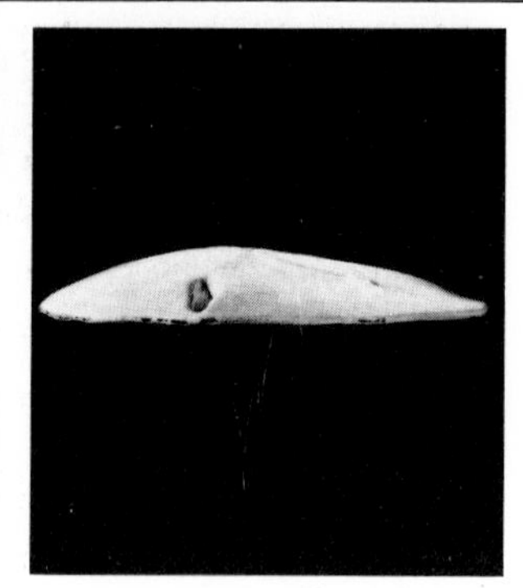

Plate 7.9.15C

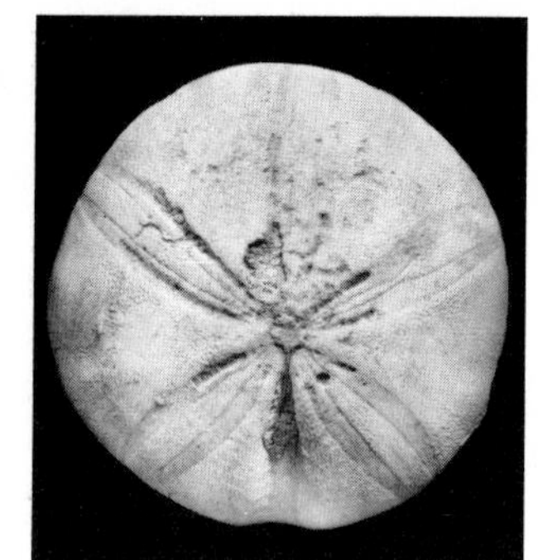

Plate 7.9.16A

Plate 7.9.16B

pair greatly elongated. On oral surface, interambulacra as wide as ambulacra. Peristome slightly anterior with bifurcating food grooves leading to it. Test has internal supports.
Miocene–Recent. Tropical and warm temperate Americas, infaunal, detritus feeder.
Mellita quinquiesperforata Leske: Recent, S. Carolina, USA.

Superorder Atelostomata (Jurassic–Recent)

Order Cassiduloida (Jurassic–Recent)

Pl. 7.9.16. *Clypeus* Leske, 1778
Test medium to large, compressed, secondarily bilaterally symmetrical. Endocyclic, periproct within a circlet of apical plates modified by elongation of posterior oculars and loss of gonopore from genital 5 (Fig. 7.9.3, similar to *Nucleolites*). Ambulacra petaloid, outer pores slit-like, phyllodes present. Interambulacra broad with numerous rows of small tubercles; bourrelets (inflated adoral part) well developed. Peristome anterior.
Jurassic (Bajocian–Kimmeridgian). Probably infaunal deposit feeder.
Clypeus plotii Klein: M. Jurassic (Bajocian), Gloucester, England.

Pl. 7.9.17. *Nucleolites* Lamarck, 1801
Test small to medium, compressed, heart-shaped in outline, secondarily bilaterally symmetrical. Endocyclic, periproct within a circlet of apical plates (Fig. 7.9.3). Ambulacra petaloid, outer pores slit-like, phyllodes narrow. Interambulacra with numerous small tubercles, those on the oral side being better developed, with bourrelets. Peristome anterior.
M. Jurassic (Bajocian)–U. Cretaceous (Cenomanian). Probably infaunal, deposit feeder.
Nucleolites sp.: Jurassic, England.

Pl. 7.9.18. *Echinolampas* Gray, 1825
Test medium to large, ovoid, inflated, secondarily bilaterally symmetrical. Exocyclic, periproct marginal to inframarginal. Apical system monobasal (4 genital plates fused) (Fig. 7.9.3). Ambulacra petaloid, poriferous zones unequal in length, wide interporiferous zones, phyllodes broad. Interambulacra with numerous small tubercles, bourrelets well developed. Buccal pores around peristome.
Eocene–Recent. Infaunal, deposit feeder.
Echinolampas rangi Desmoulins: Recent, locality unknown.

Order Holasteroida (L. Jurassic–Recent)

Pl. 7.9.19. *Holaster* L. Agassiz, 1836
Test medium, heart-shaped, inflated, secondarily bilaterally symmetrical. Exocyclic, periproct on truncate posterior. Apical system elongate, with oculars II and IV meeting in the mid-line, separating genital plates 1 and 4 from 2 and 3. Ambulacra (except III) subpetaloid, pores elongate (Fig. 7.9.3); ambulacrum III non-petaloid, pores small. Interambulacra broad with fine tubercles; interambulacrum 5 inflated to form a plastron. Peristome anterior.
L. Cretaceous (Valanginian)–Eocene.
Holaster subglobosus Leske: U. Cretaceous (Cenomanian), Folkestone, England.

Pl. 7.9.20. *Echinocorys* Leske, 1778
Test medium to large, subconical, inflated, secondarily bilaterally symmetrical. Exocyclic, periproct inframarginal. Apical system elongate, 4 genital plates, oculars II and IV adjacent (Fig. 7.9.3). Ambulacra non-petaloid, pores round or outer pore slightly elongate. Interambulacra broad, with very small tubercles. Peristome anterior.
U. Cretaceous (Turonian)–Palaeocene (Danian). Probably semi-infaunal deposit feeder.
Echinocorys scutata Leske: U. Cretaceous (Senonian), England.

Order Spatangoida (L. Cretaceous (Berriasian)–Recent)

Pl. 7.9.21. *Micraster* L. Agassiz, 1836
Test medium, heart-shaped, secondarily bilaterally symmetrical. Exocyclic, periproct at truncate posterior margin with subanal fasciole. Apical system with 4 genital pores; the 4 genital plates adjoin one another (Fig. 7.9.3). Ambulacra petaloid, with round or elongate conjugate pores. Interambulacra broad, plastron developed in 5. Peristome anterior, arcuate.
U. Cretaceous (Cenomanian)–Palaeocene (Danian). Infaunal (see Nichols 1959).
Micraster coranguinum (Leske): U. Cretaceous, England.

Pl. 7.9.22. *Spatangus* Gray, 1825
Test medium, heart-shaped, secondarily bilaterally symmetrical. Exocyclic, periproct at truncate posterior margin, with subanal fasciole. Apical system ethmolytic (genital plate 2 extends posteriorly between oculars I and II and genital 1 on one side and oculars III, IV and V and genitals 3 and 4 on the other), with four genital pores (Fig. 7.9.3). Anterior ambulacrum with small pores in a single series, other ambulacra petaloid. Interambulacra broad with tubercles of different size on different parts of the test. Plastron present. Peristome arcuate, towards anterior.
Eocene–Recent. Infaunal deposit feeder in continental shelf shell gravels (see Nichols 1959).
Spatangus purpureus Müller: Recent, England.

Plate 7.9.16C
Plate 7.9.17A
Plate 7.9.17B
Plate 7.9.17C
Plate 7.9.18A
Plate 7.9.18B
Plate 7.9.18C
Plate 7.9.19A
Plate 7.9.19B
Plate 7.9.19C
Plate 7.9.20A
Plate 7.9.20B
Plate 7.9.20C
Plate 7.9.21A
Plate 7.9.21B
Plate 7.9.21C
Plate 7.9.22A
Plate 7.9.22B
Plate 7.9.22C
Plate 7.9.23A

Pl. 7.9.23. *Lovenia* Desor, 1847

Test medium, oral to heart-shaped, secondarily bilaterally symmetrical. Exocyclic, periproct at truncate posterior margin with subanal fasciole. Apical system ethmolytic (as in *Spatangus*) (Fig. 7.9.3), with 3 or 4 genital pores, and surrounded by an internal fasciole which also encloses part of the anterior non-petaloid ambulacrum. Other ambulacra petaloid. Some species have recessed primary tubercles on paired ambulacra. Interambulacra with recessed tubercles. Peristome towards anterior.

Eocene–Recent. Infaunal, neritic to bathyal.

Lovenia forbesi Tennison-Woods & Duncan: Eocene, Murray River, Victoria, Australia.

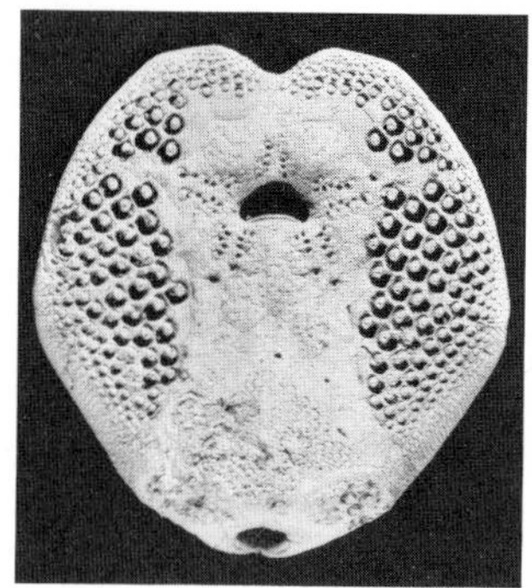

Plate 7.9.23B

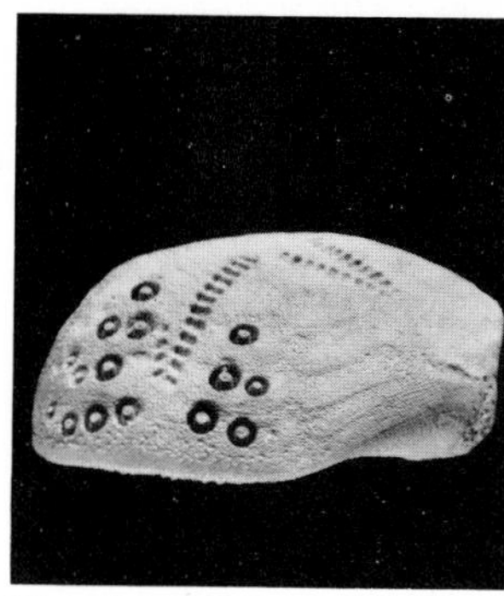

Plate 7.9.23C

CHAPTER 8

Graptolithina

by R. B. Rickards

The terminology used in the following key and generic diagnoses is essentially that used by Bulman (1970) and by Rickards and Palmer (1981) and the classification that of the latter authors. Graptolites have been placed in several different phyla at different times, but in the present century have usually been included with coelenterates, bryozoans or hemichordates. Since the work of Kozlowski (1938, 1949) most palaeontologists have regarded them as hemichordates, an opinion increasingly strengthened in recent decades. The most important similarities include the presence of a black stolon system and zooidal tubes with a closely similar incremental growth ring construction: indeed modern and fossil pterobranchs, and graptolites, are the only two animal groups with such a combination of characters. The main differences lie at the ultrastructural level: the periderm ultrastructure of graptolites hinges on the collagen fibril, that of pterobranchs on an as yet unidentified fibril. In the animal kingdom variations of ultrastructural composition are, however, little known so that it is difficult to know what weight to put upon this particular difference.

Dendroids and rhabdopleuran hemichordates probably had a common ancestor in the M. Cambrian or late L. Cambrian (Rickards 1979) and the former gave rise to the other principal graptolite order, the Graptoloidea, in the late Tremadoc. The dendroids became extinct in the U. Carboniferous and the much more diverse, planktonic graptoloids in the latest L. Devonian or earliest M. Devonian.

The fundamental morphology of graptolites is relatively simple. The colony is built of incremental half-rings dovetailed along either a ventral suture or on ventral and dorsal sutures (the zigzag sutures). Various amounts of cortex are plastered on this fusellar layer, usually on the outside. The cortex is essentially composed of bandage-like wrapping, with collagen fibrils parallel to the length of each bandage, and the bandages themselves are associated with particular thecal apertures. The fusellar layer half-rings have a spongy core of anastomosing collagen fibrils and an outer membrane of more ordered fibrils. Various less studied membranes and electron-dense structures are associated with these two basic components.

The growth increments construct a series, or several series, of tubes called thecae and the whole comprises a graptolite colony which may have a few thecae or tens of thousands of thecae. The rows of thecae may branch and become quite long (almost 1 m). Each branch is termed a stipe; a combination of stipes ($1 \rightarrow n$) is the colony or rhabdosome; and an association of colonies a synrhabdosome. As indicated below, different orders have different kinds of thecae, though relatively few in number, and these are arranged in a distinctive manner and connected to a black stolon system, or its unsclerotized homologue, which runs the length of the colony.

Key

Class Graptolithina While distinctive general form at generic level is usually regarded as sufficient for inclusion in the class Graptolithina (=graptolites), actual proof requires identification of the fusellar incremental growth structure with regular half-rings and a zigzag contact. Such features distinguish them from other phyla and from other hemichordates.

Principal orders

Order Dendroidea (=dendroids). Stipes composed of stolothecae, autothecae and bithecae produced by regular triad divisions of stolon; bithecae, usually alternate, along the length of the stipe; rhabdosomes either sessile, with sicula embedded in holdfast or attached to 'roots', or planktonic with sicula attached to nema or nematophorous apparatus; usually large and of dendroid habit; dichotomous or irregular branching of stipes; stipe connections by anastomosis or dissepiments; autothecae and bithecae open at regular intervals; little autothecal apertural modification and almost no bithecal apertural modification.

Order Graptoloidea Planktonic. Relatively few stipes, only one thecal type (homologous with autothecae), no sclerotized stolons, conspicuous common canal; sicula pendent to apical nema or cauda; stipes pendent to scandent, uni- to quadriserial; may be much thecal, apertural, modification.

Minor orders

Order Tuboidea Sessile encrusting or dendroid rhabdosomes; autothecae and bithecae conspicuous, stolothecae less so, developed from diad divisions of stolon, latter sometimes partially sclerotized; lengths of all preceding variable; autothecal apertures usually regularly spaced, bithecae less so.

Order Camaroidea Encrusting; autothecae with inflated basal camera and tubular collum, indistinct stolothecae, tubular bithecae in some; probably irregular divisions of stolon, diad in places.

Order Crustoidea Encrusting; autothecae with erect distal neck and apertural modifications, bithecae cylindrical, adnate, stolothecae tubular with conspicuous stolons which display triad division.

Order Stolonoidea Sessile or encrusting; only stolothecae and (?) autothecae present, derived from stolons which are of exaggerated development, irregular in form and division.

Order Archaeodendrida Probably autothecae singly or in groups of three, isolate distally; possibly stolothecae, stipes may be biserial; rhabdosomes (?) dendroid habit, sessile; possibly sclerotized stolons.

Order Dithecoidea Biserially arranged autothecae with distally isolated apertures, (?) other thecal types, (?) dendroid habit, sessile.

Order Dendroidea

Pl. 8.1. *Dendrograptus* Hall, 1858
Irregularly branched, robust dendroid habit, 10 to 150 mm; stipes divergent, unconnected after dichotomies; often with robust proximal stem, often with no thecae visible; autothecae denticulate, spined or rarely with varied apertural processes.
?M. Cambrian, U. Cambrian–Carboniferous, entirely benthonic with holdfast or 'root' structure.
Dendrograptus sp.: Silurian, Gaspé Peninsula, Canada.

Pl. 8.2, 3. *Dictyonema* Hall, 1851
Cylindrical to nearly discoidal conical rhabdosome with thecate or non-thecate stem or siculate without stem, 20 to 250 mm; branching dichotomies; most have branches closely spaced, subparallel, connected by variously spaced dissepiments; autothecae denticulate, spined, or with complex and occasionally fused or anastomosing apertural processes; bithecal apertures vary from inconspicuous to swollen.
U. Cambrian–Carboniferous, benthonic with varied holdfasts or complex 'root' structures, or planktonic with nema, vanes ('floats'), or divided nema.
Pl. 8.2. *Dictyonema flabelliforme* (Eichwald): Tremadoc, Shropshire, England. Pl. 8.3. *Dictyonema* sp.: Silurian, USA.

Pl. 8.4. *Callograptus* Hall, 1865
Rhabdosome ?irregular, bulbously conical or flabellate, usually with thick stem, thecae not visible, 30 to 150 mm; branching dichotomous, fairly regularly, stipes subparallel, joined by rare dissepiments and rare anastomosis.
U. Cambrian–Carboniferous, benthonic with holdfasts.
Callograptus hopkinsoni Bulman: Arenig, Pembrokeshire, Wales.

Pl. 8.5. *Desmograptus* Hopkinson, 1875
Rhabdosome usually conical, stipes flexuous with regular anastomosis, rare dissepiments, 20 to 100 mm; autothecae denticulate to isolate.
?Tremadoc, L. Ordovician–Carboniferous, benthonic with holdfasts.
Desmograptus cancellatus (Hopkinson): Caradoc, Pembrokeshire, Wales.

Pl. 8.6. *Aspidograptus* Bulman, 1943
Rhabdosome roughly dendroid, but ?4 initial, curved stipes, 20 to 50 mm, so that branching often appears as 4 clusters; branching irregular, close, with repeated bifurcation; autothecae denticulate.
U. Cambrian–Ordovician, benthonic with holdfasts.
Aspidograptus implicatus (Hopkinson): Arenig, Shropshire, England.

Pl. 8.7. *Anisograptus* Ruedemann, 1937
Rhabdosome triradiate, dichotomous divisions to sixth order, typically horizontal, rarely declined or slightly reclined, 20 to 60 mm; autothecae denticulate, bithecae short, simple, inconspicuous.
Tremadoc, planktonic, sparser, more rigid rhabdosome than any of above dendroids.
Anisograptus flexuosus Bulman: Tremadoc, Hammersborg, Norway.

Pl. 8.8, 9. *Clonograptus* Nicholson, 1873
Bilaterally symmetrical rhabdosome, usually horizontal, produced by dichotomous branching up to ninth order, usually less, each branch pair initially diverging, becoming subparallel; 30 to 70 mm; autothecae either slightly denticulate (*Dichograptus*-like) or strongly isolated and usually with thin periderm; bithecae in earlier species.
Tremadoc–Ordovician (Llanvirn), large, planktonic form with characteristic symmetry and unusually long stipes.
Pl. 8.8. *Clonograptus persistens* Harris & Thomas: Ordovician, Victoria, Australia. Pl. 8.9. *C. trochograptoides* Harris & Thomas: Ordovician, Victoria, Australia.

Pl. 8.10. *Adelograptus* Bulman, 1941
Rhabdosome with lax, usually declined stipes, and divisions up to at least fourth order, although often less, 30 to 150 mm; divisions often appear to be lateral rather than dichotomous; autothecae denticulate, bithecae in stratigraphically earlier species, but always inconspicuous and difficult to discern.
Tremadoc–Ordovician (Arenig), planktonic, more lax rhabdosome than other dendroids.
Adelograptus victoriae (T. S. Hall): Ordovician, Victoria, Australia.

Pl. 8.11. *Ptilograptus* Hall, 1865
Characteristic rhabdosome shape with few main stipes but with lateral branches set alternately along main stipes, giving whole a fern-like aspect; 20 to 120 mm; autothecae denticulate.

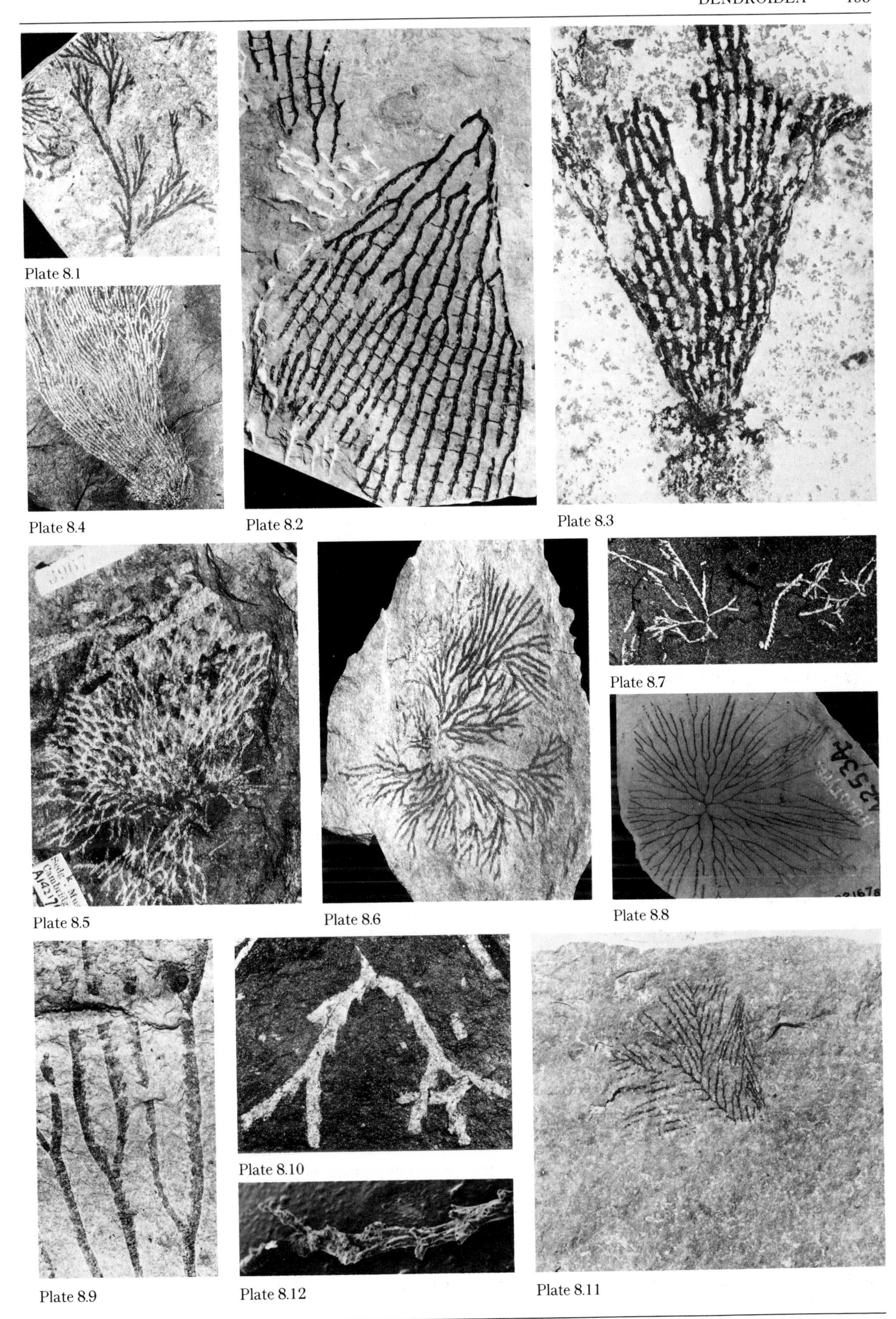

Plate 8.1

Plate 8.4

Plate 8.2

Plate 8.3

Plate 8.5

Plate 8.6

Plate 8.7

Plate 8.8

Plate 8.9

Plate 8.10

Plate 8.12

Plate 8.11

L. Ordovician–U. Silurian, benthonic form with ?stem and holdfast.
Ptilograptus plumosus J. Hall: Arenig, Ordovician, Marathon, Texas, USA.

Pl. 8.12. *Acanthograptus* Spencer, 1878
Rhabdosome dendroid, with stout branches divided irregularly and rarely ?anastomosing, 'spiny' as a result of 'twigs' usually of 2 autothecae and 2 bithecae projecting at more or less regular intervals; 20 to 100 mm. Can be confused only with *Koremagraptus* and *Palaeodictyota*, but shows far less anastomosis, if at all.
L. Ordovician–U. Silurian, benthonic form with holdfasts and, often, a robust, more or less thecate stem.
Acanthograptus musciformis (Wiman): U. Ordovician, Gotland, Sweden.

Order Graptoloidea

Pl. 8.13. *Goniograptus* McCoy, 1876
Rhabdosomes of remarkable symmetry based upon 4 diverging, zigzag main stipes, from the zigs and zags of which are thrown off alternately lateral branches of some length, up to 48 in number, giving colony as a whole a quadrate or subcircular outline; 30 to 300 mm; thecae either more or less denticulate, dichograptid or rather isolate aperturally.
L. Ordovician, more or less horizontally disposed planktonic form.
Goniograptus thureaui (McCoy): Ordovician, Victoria, Australia; 3 species of *Tetragraptus s.l.* on same slab.

Pl. 8.14. *Loganograptus* Hall, 1868
More or less bilaterally symmetrical rhabdosome but with distal ends of stipes sometimes flexuous, 8 to 16 branches, rarely exceeding fourth order, proximal concentrated, progressive dichotomies, often enclosed in proximal web; usually 50 to 300 mm; thecae dichograptid, not usually denticulate, overlapping about one-half.
L. Ordovician, horizontally disposed planktonic form.
Loganograptus logani McCoy: Ordovician, Victoria, Australia.

Pl. 8.15–17. *Tetragraptus* Salter, 1863 *sensu lato*
Rhabdosome bilaterally symmetrical, 4 pendent, horizontal or reclined stipes with short funicle, occasional web or disc in horizontal forms; 10 to 150 mm (larger in horizontal species); thecae dichograptid, occasionally denticulate, often with overlap close to three-quarters; proximal development where known is isograptid, dextral (Cooper and Fortey 1982).
L. Ordovician, pauciramous dichograptoid, planktonic.
Pl. 8.15. *Tetragraptus T. bryonoides* (J. Hall); Pl. 8.16. *fruticosus* (J. Hall); Pl. 8.17. *T. acclinans* Keble; all Ordovician, Victoria, Australia.

Pl. 8.18. *Trochograptus* Holm, 1881
Rhabdosome based upon 4 main stipes from 2 progressive dichotomies to second order, followed by widely spaced unpaired lateral branches of third and fourth orders, the latter quite common; 150 to 500 mm; thecae simple tubular dichograptid with moderate overlap.
L. Ordovician, horizontally disposed planktonic form.
Trochograptus spectabilis (Harris & Thomas): Ordovician, Victoria, Australia.

Pl. 8.19. *Dichograptus* Salter, 1863 *sensu lato*
Rhabdosome with 8 or fewer stipes resulting from progressive dichotomies to third order, first 2 within a few mm of sicula, third order very long or with fourth order dichotomy, rarely more; funicular region sometimes with web; 50 to 400 mm; thecae with considerable overlap, occasionally denticulate or spinose, moderately inclined.
L. Ordovician, horizontally disposed planktonic form.
Orthodichograptus robbinsi Thomas: Ordovician, Victoria, Australia.

Pl. 8.20. *Phyllograptus* Hall, 1858 *sensu lato*
Rhabdosome quadriserial scandent, 4 second-order stipes, derived in 2 quite different ways (therefore di- or polyphyletic) robust, wide, and leaf-like in appearance; nema unknown; thecae simple tubes, sometimes denticulate, curved, elongate, mostly upwardly directed, and with overlap commonly in excess of three-quarters.
L. Ordovician, planktonic forms with some provincial influence.
Phyllograptus sp.: Ordovician, Victoria, Australia; on same slab are pendent *Didymograptus*, *Tetragraptus fruticosus* and *Goniograptus* sp.

Pl. 8.21, 22. *Didymograptus* McCoy, 1851 *sensu lato*
Rhabdosome with 2 pendent, horizontal or reclined stipes, occasionally deflexed, reflexed or declined; 20 to 600 mm; thecae simple tubes, variable overlap, straight or with slight ventral curvature; development usually isograptid, dichograptid in some.
L.–M. Ordovician, planktonic, presumably with pendent, horizontal or reclined dispositions.
Pl. 8.21. *Didymograptus murchisoni* Beck: Llanvirn, Pembrokeshire, Wales. Pl. 8.22. *D. elongatus* Harris & Thomas: Ordovician, Victoria, Australia.

Pl. 8.23. *Dicranograptus* Hall, 1865
Rhabdosome unibiserial, initially scandent biserial, distally 2 uniserial reclined stipes; 10 to 100 mm; development diplograptid; thecae sigmoidally curved, often introverted, commonly with mesial spines; nema minute in early growth stages, or absent entirely.
L.–U. Ordovician, vertically oriented planktonic form, cosmopolitan, but with local abundances.
Dicranograptus sp.: Ordovician, Doladrook, Victoria, Australia.

Pl. 8.24. *Dicellograptus* Hopkinson, 1851
Rhabdosome with 2 uniserial reclined stipes, straight or variably curved, including spirally curved; 20 to 200 mm; development diplograptid; thecae with strong sigmoidal curvature, often introversion, mesial spines, genicular thickening, and prothecal folds.
L.–U. Ordovician, cosmopolitan plankton with local abundances.
Dicellograptus sp.: Ordovician, Doladrook, Victoria, Australia.

Pl. 8.25. *Leptograptus* Lapworth, 1873
Biramous, slender flexuous stipes, reclined, with no secondary stipes, thus distinguished from multiramous genera (e.g. *Nemagraptus*, *Syndyograptus*) each of which has a characteristic multiramous arrangement; 40 to 250 mm; thecae leptograptid, i.e. elongate, low angled, relatively simple, possibly with slight denticulation, and slight ventral geniculation of typical amount.
?L. Ordovician, M.–U. Ordovician, cosmopolitan planktonic form, locally abundant.
Leptograptus flaccidus (J. Hall): Hartfell, Ordovician, Scotland.

Pl. 8.26. *Nemagraptus* Emmons, 1855
Two main stipes S-shaped or reclined, with regular lateral branches off each; sicula, thecae and stipes all of leptograptid type.

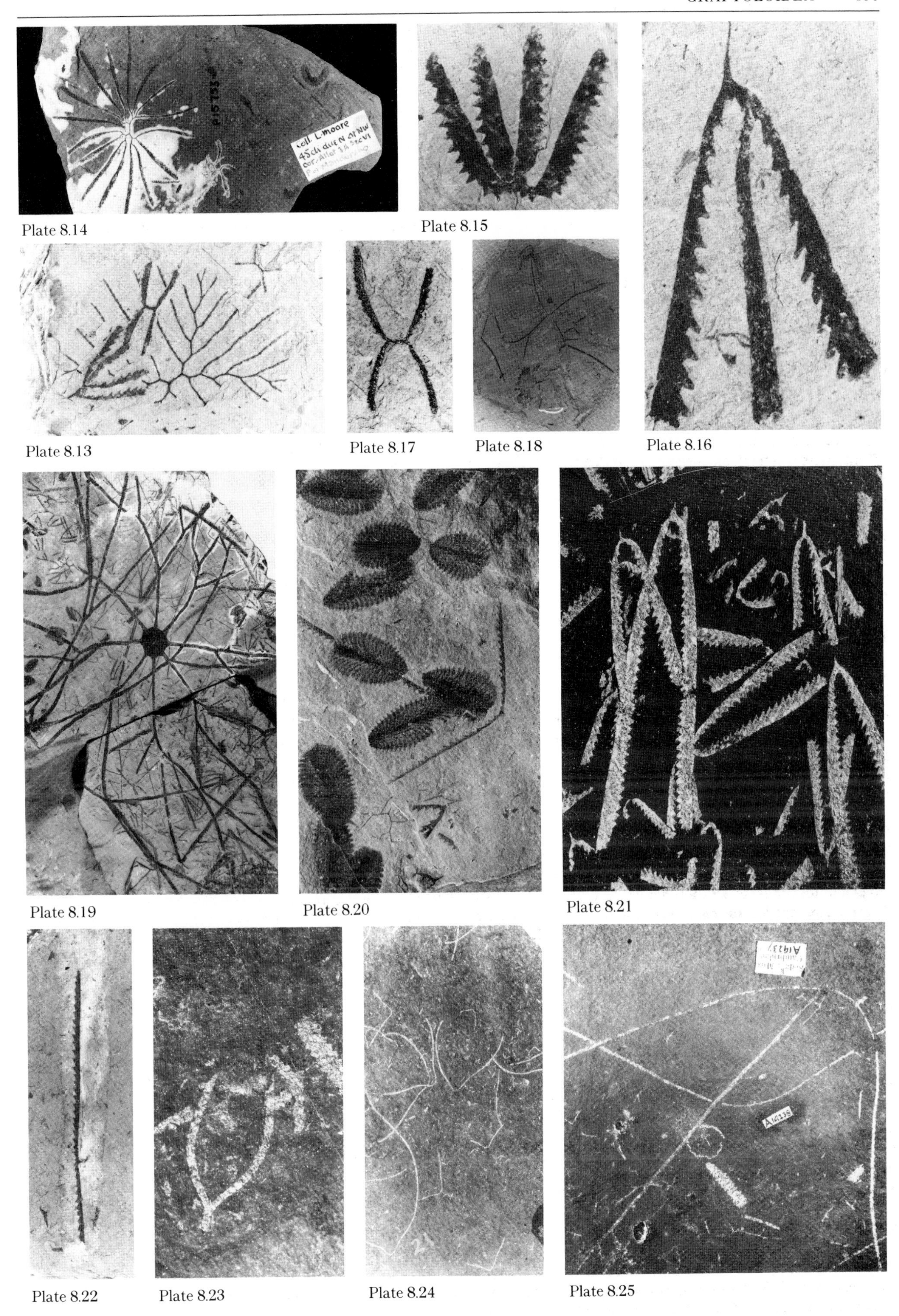

Plate 8.14

Plate 8.15

Plate 8.13

Plate 8.17

Plate 8.18

Plate 8.16

Plate 8.19

Plate 8.20

Plate 8.21

Plate 8.22

Plate 8.23

Plate 8.24

Plate 8.25

M.–U. Ordovician, cosmopolitan genus.
Nemograptus gracilis Hall: Caradoc, Ordovician, Ireland.

Pl. 8.27. *Isograptus* Moberg, 1892
Two reclined, robust stipes, 4 to 40 mm; thecae elongate, high inclination and overlap, especially proximally; development isograptid; first few thecae grow entirely downward; sicula, with or without short nema, usually long and prominent.
L. Ordovician, largely Pacific province genus.
Isograptus caduceus (Salter): Ordovician, Victoria, Australia.

Pl. 8.28, 29. *Glossograptus* Emmons, 1855
Rhabdosome biserial, monopleural, axonophorous, more or less heavily spined; development pericalycal from dicalycal thl[1]; thecae mucronate, basically orthograptid with apertural flange additions; robust nema with vane-like thickenings.
L.–U. Ordovician, vertically oriented plankton, cosmopolitan.
Glossograptus holmi Bulman: Llanvirn, Newfoundland, Canada.

Pl. 8.30. *Diplograptus* McCoy, 1850
Rhabdosome biserial scandent, distally projecting robust nema; thecae strongly sigmoidal (amplexograptid or climacograptid) proximally, gradually changing to almost orthograptid distally.
L. Ordovician–L. Silurian (but polyphyletic groups), vertical plankton.
Diplograptus magnus H. Lapworth: Llandovery, Powys, Wales.

Pl. 8.31. *Amplexograptus* Elles & Wood, 1907
Diplograptid rhabdosomes with uniform, strongly sigmoidal thecae with short supragenicular wall, usually inclined slightly outwards, apertural flanges or thickenings.
L.–U. Ordovician (but polyphyletic groups), vertical plankton.
Amplexograptus coelatus (Lapworth): Caradoc, Ordovician, Dyfed, Wales.

Pl. 8.32. *Climacograptus* Hall, 1865 *sensu lato*
Diplograptid roughly circular rhabdosome with uniform, strongly sigmoidal thecae; apertures more or less slit-like and narrow, supragenicular wall parallel to rhabdosomal axis; flanges and spines present in some; nemal vanes present in some.
L. Ordovician–L. Silurian, vertical plankton.
Climacograptus rectangularis (McCoy): Llandovery, Silurian, Lake District, England.

Pl. 8.33. *Cystograptus* Hundt, 1942; emend Jones & Rickards, 1967
Diplograptid rhabdosome with rectangular cross-section, thecae with ogee curvature, apertures everted; sicula unusually long (10 mm); large, long, nemal vane developed, around which colony may grow.
L. Silurian, vertically oriented, probably vane uppermost, plankton.
Cystograptus vesiculosus (Nicholson): Llandovery, Silurian, Wales.

Pl. 8.34. *Pseudoclimacograptus* Přibyl, 1947
Climacograptus-like but with supragenicular walls convex, or almost straight or concavo-convex; medium septum characteristically zigzag or undulating, especially in the proximal region; apertures deep, narrow, often introverted; and often with genicular flanges or hoods; nema has a distal vane in type species.
L. Ordovician–L. Silurian, vertical plankton, in some pendent to a vane.
Pseudoclimacograptus angulatus sebyensis Jaanusson: Llandeilo, Newfoundland, Canada.

Pl. 8.35. *Orthograptus* Lapworth, 1873
Diplograptid with straight tubular thecae, with or without spines, and variable thecal overlap; basal rhabdosomal spines present in some.
M. Ordovician–L. Silurian (polyphyletic groups), vertical plankton.
Orthograptus amplixucaulis J. Hall: Ashgill, Ordovician, Scotland.

Pl. 8.36. *Glyptograptus* Lapworth, 1873
Diplograptid rhabdosome, thecae with gentle, flowing sigmoidal curvature sometimes lessening in distal parts of the rhabdosome; supragenicular wall leaning outwards, occasionally concavo-convex.
L. Ordovician–L. Silurian (but polyphyletic), vertical plankton.
Glyptograptus persculptus (Salter): Llandovery, Silurian, Wales.

Pl. 8.37, 38. *Petalograptus* Suess, 1851
Diplograptid with leaf-like outline and tabular cross-section, 5 to 50 mm; thecae straight tubes or with ventral curvature and often with slightly everted apertures and considerable overlap.
Pl. 8.37. *Petalograptus altissimus* Elles & Wood: Llandovery, Silurian, France. Pl. 8.38. *P. minor* Elles: Llandovery, Lake District, England (*Pseudoclimacograptus* and *Monograptus* on same slab).

Pl. 8.39–41. *Retiolites* Barrande, 1850
Periderm largely reduced to strongly developed reticulum on well-formed clathria of parietal, pleural, apertural and aboral lists; 10 to 50 mm; nema (= virgula) quickly incorporated in obverse side, with zigzag list on reverse side; rarely a thin membrane on inside of reticulum, covering much of stipes except apertures; characteristic ancora stage of early growth.
L. Silurian, cosmopolitan.
Retiolites geinitzianus (Barrande): Llandovery, Silurian, W. Germany.

Pl. 8.42. *Holoretiolites* Eisenack, 1951
Retiolitid *s.l.* with climacograptid thecae outlined in minimal clathrial elements. 3 to 8 mm; ventral thecal lists; nema short, central, not extending distally, but distal appendix.
U. Silurian.
Holoretiolites mancki Münch: Wenlock, Silurian, Germany.

Pl. 8.43. *Dimorphograptus* Lapworth, 1876
Rhabdosome with uniserial proximal end and biserial distal portion, 5 to 45 mm; thecae orthograptid or glyptograptid, but equally often with a characteristic partial apertural isolation; development with initial bud from sicula directed distally.
L. Silurian, vertically oriented unibiserial plankton. (*Note:* It is this genus which can be used to demonstrate the vertical hydrodynamic orientation of biserial rhabdosomes.)
Dimorphograptus elongatus Lapworth: Llandovery, Silurian, Lake District, England (*Climacograptus* and *Cystograptus* on same slab).

Pl. 8.44. *Rhaphidograptus* Bulman, 1936
Dimorphograptid with climacograptid thecae, initial bud downwardly directed, and uniserial portion sometimes as short as a single theca; 10 to 40 mm.
L. Silurian, often as synrhabdosomes, occasionally with proximal connections in such; probably the most cosmopolitan and common Silurian planktonic element in the type Llandovery region where it outnumbers all other graptolite species added together.
Rhaphidograptus toernquisti Elles & Wood: Llandovery, Silurian, Lake District, England (*Monograptus* (*Coronograptus*) on same slab).

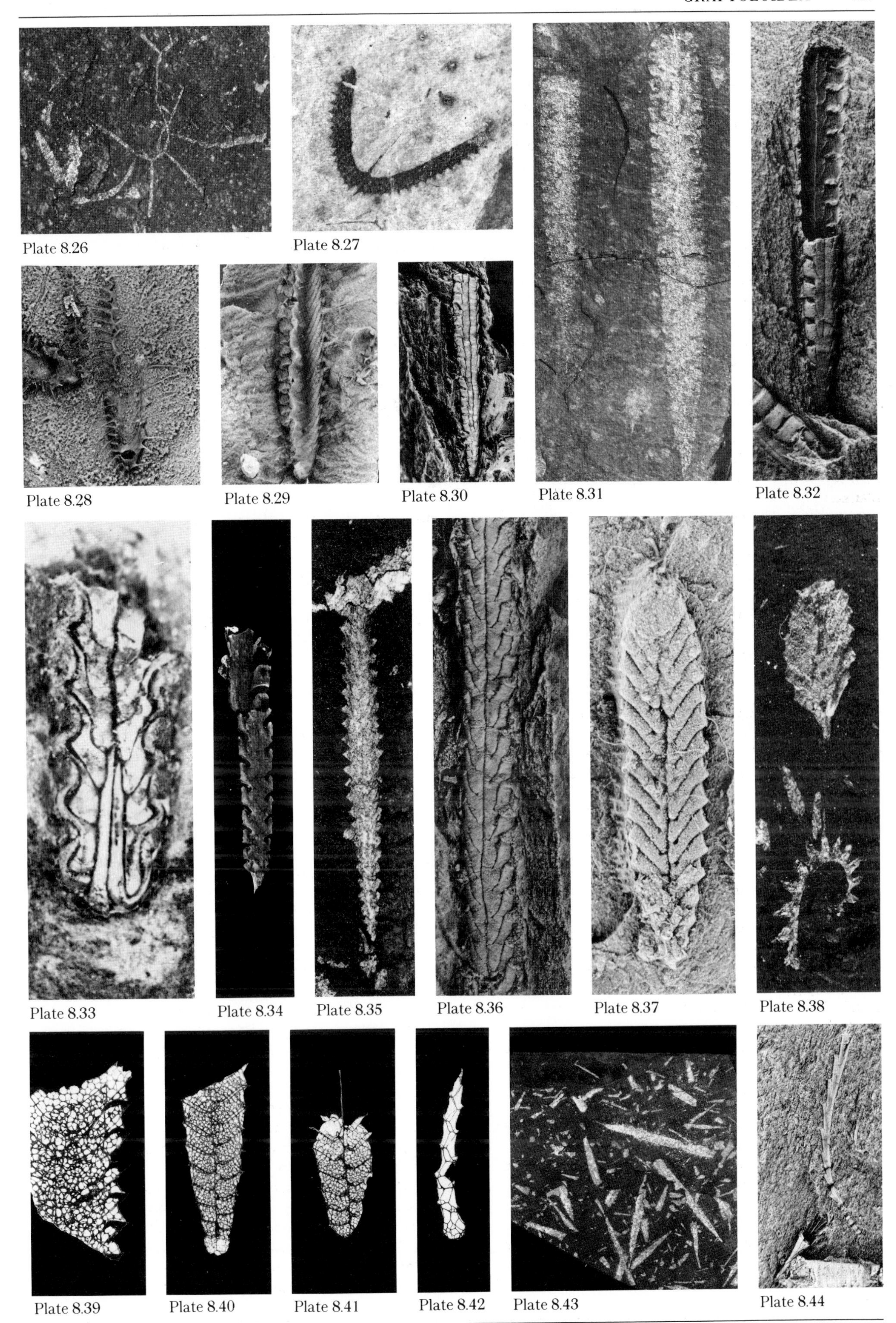

Plate 8.26

Plate 8.27

Plate 8.28

Plate 8.29

Plate 8.30

Plate 8.31

Plate 8.32

Plate 8.33

Plate 8.34

Plate 8.35

Plate 8.36

Plate 8.37

Plate 8.38

Plate 8.39

Plate 8.40

Plate 8.41

Plate 8.42

Plate 8.43

Plate 8.44

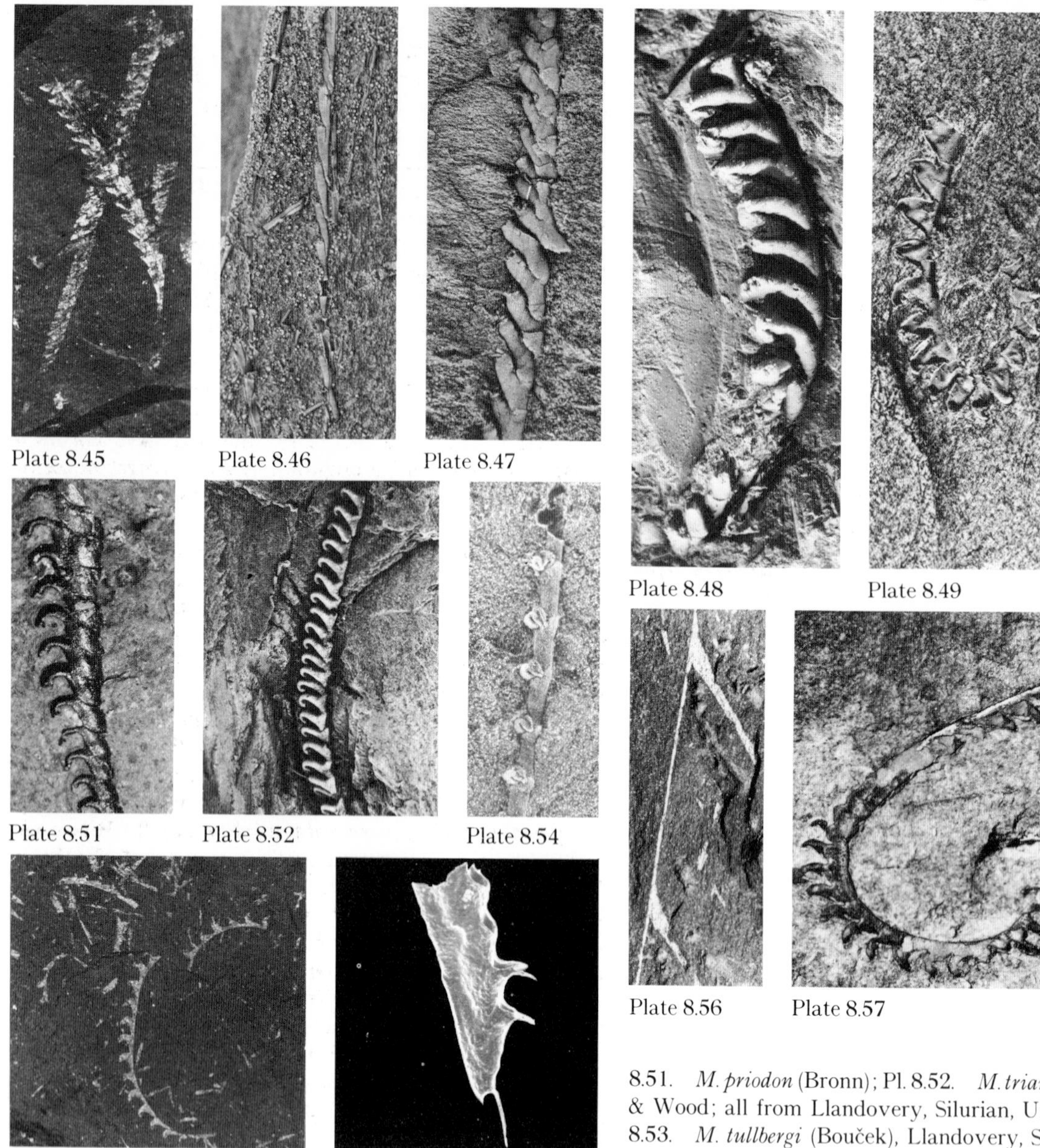

Pl. 8.45. *Akidograptus* Davies, 1919, *sensu lato*
Elongate, thorn-like proximal end, with elongate early thecae, possibly with 1 reduced or missing; sicula long, commonly with divided virgella; thecae approximately orthograptid, but with characteristic aperture horizontal or gently turned inwards; rhabdosome 5 to 30 mm.
L. Silurian, vertically oriented plankton, rarely with vanes.
Akidograptus acuminatus (Nicholson): Llandovery, Silurian, Scotland.

Pl. 8.46–54. *Monograptus* Geinitz, 1852, *sensu lato*
Rhabdosome uniserial, scandent 3 to 750 mm; initial bud upwardly directed; nema incorporated in dorsal stipe wall and distally continuing for a considerable distance beyond thecae; thecae vary from simple overlapping tubes to isolated tubes, and those with variously complex apertural apparatuses.
L. Silurian–uppermost L. Devonian, straight, vertically oriented stipes or variously coiled stipes.
Pl. 8.46. *Monograptus atavus* Jones and *M. revolutus* Kurck (*Dimorphograptus* on same slab); Pl. 8.47. *M. concinnus* Lapworth; Pl. 8.48. *M. convolutus* (Hisinger); Pl. 8.49. *M. fimbriatus* (Nicholson); Pl. 8.50. *M. crenulata sensu* Elles & Wood; Pl. 8.51. *M. priodon* (Bronn); Pl. 8.52. *M. triangulatus major* Elles & Wood; all from Llandovery, Silurian, United Kingdom; Pl. 8.53. *M. tullbergi* (Bouček), Llandovery, Silurian, France; Pl. 8.54. *M. nodifer* Törnquist *s.l.*: Llandovery, Silurian, Oslo, Norway.

Pl. 8.55. *Saetograptus* Přibyl, 1942
Monograptid with lateral apertural lappets or spines of monofusellar tissue on proximal thecae or throughout rhabdosome.
U. Silurian, straight, vertically oriented, cosmopolitan plankton.
Saetograptus varians (Wood): Ludlow, Silurian, Wales.

Pl. 8.56. *Rastrites* Barrande, 1850
Curved monograptid with strong metathecal isolation and varied apertural apparatuses.
L. Silurian, cosmopolitan plankton.
Rastrites maximus Carruthers: Llandovery, Silurian, Lake District, England.

Pl. 8.57. *Cyrtograptus* Carruthers, 1867
Coiled monograptid rhabdosome with often spectacular development of thecal cladia, sometimes of several orders; thecae biform, strongly hooked proximally, less so distally.
U. Silurian (Wenlock), cosmopolitan with presumed horizontal disposition.
Cyrtograptus centrifugus Bouček: Wenlock, Silurian, Lake District, England.

CHAPTER 9

Arthropods

The arthropods are characterized by a number of features: bilateral symmetry, the repetition of similar appendage-bearing somites down the trunk (i.e. serial segmentation, which tends to become reduced in some groups), an exoskeleton which is moulted to allow increase in size and, in most cases, jointed limbs (the latter giving rise to the name 'arthropod'). The exoskeleton is composed of a combination of chitin and proteins, but may be strengthened by mineralization usually with calcium carbonate ($CaCO_3$), but with calcium phosphate ($CaPO_4$) in some fossil groups. In addition, living arthropods at least are united in the possession of a haemocoel, a blood-filled cavity which contains the heart. The haemocoel contributes to the distension of the body during moulting and provides a hydrostatic stiffening in arthropods with a flexible cuticle.

There are three major living groups of arthropods: the crustaceans, chelicerates and uniramians, and one major fossil group – the trilobites. The origin and evolutionary relationships of these groups are uncertain and their taxonomic status is controversial. The three major living groups are clearly distinguished by a number of features, particularly the segmentation of the head, the way in which the limbs of the jaw operate (mandibular mechanisms) and the nature of the embryological development. These differences are so fundamental that a number of zoologists including Manton (1977), based on her work on mandibular mechanisms and locomotion, and Anderson (1973), based on investigations of embryology, have argued that these three arthropod groups evolved from different soft-bodied worm-like ancestors, and they have therefore designated them separate phyla. Phylum status for the Uniramia is widely accepted. The wide diversity of form shown by the Palaeozoic arthropods, however, particularly those of the M. Cambrian Burgess Shale of British Columbia which in some cases combine features of the crustaceans, chelicerates and trilobites (although most are 'non-aligned' – i.e. cannot be assigned to these major groups) leaves room for the possibility of a common origin of these aquatic groups at least (Hessler and Newman 1975; Briggs 1983). For this reason the arthropods are here divided into two phyla – the Uniramia, and the rest of the arthropods (Arthropoda *sensu stricto*). The preservation of unmineralized cuticle depends on exceptional conditions and only the mineralized parts of arthropod exoskeletons are normally fossilized. The major arthropod groups are readily identified, in most cases, on the basis of the major divisions of the dorsal exoskeleton. The distinctions between them were less clear in the Palaeozoic, however, and in some cases evidence of the appendages may be required to allow the affinity of a fossil arthropod to be determined.

PHYLUM ARTHROPODA

9.1 Subphylum unknown – 'non-aligned' arthropods

The number of non-aligned arthropods (those which do not belong to one of the four major groups) is highest in the Cambrian and diminishes through the Palaeozoic. Examples are known, however, at least as young as Devonian. Their recognition usually depends on the evidence of the appendages and they were usually lightly skeletonized which accounts for the occurrence of most of the known examples in exceptionally preserved faunas such as the Cambrian Burgess Shale and the Devonian Hunsrück Slate of W. Germany. In the past there has been a tendency either to force them into the major groups or to group them together in taxa such as the 'Trilobitoidea' and

Plate 9.1.1

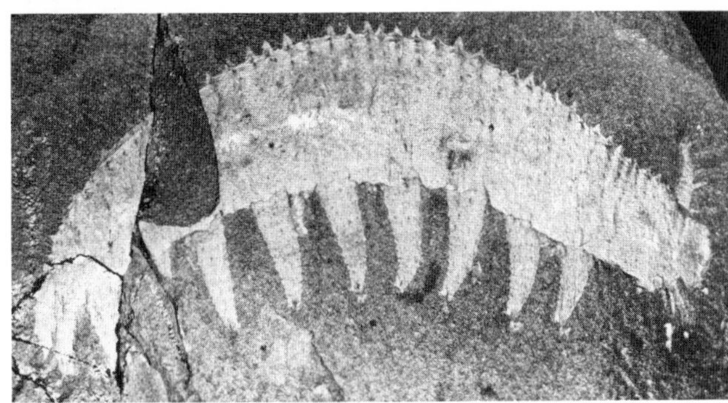

Plate 9.1.2

Plate 9.2.1

Plate 9.2.2

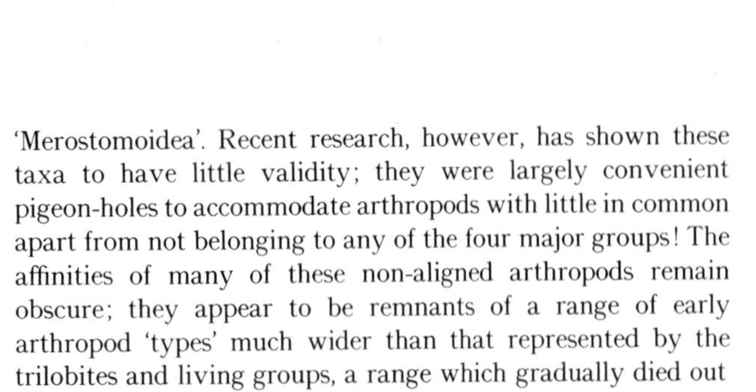

'Merostomoidea'. Recent research, however, has shown these taxa to have little validity; they were largely convenient pigeon-holes to accommodate arthropods with little in common apart from not belonging to any of the four major groups! The affinities of many of these non-aligned arthropods remain obscure; they appear to be remnants of a range of early arthropod 'types' much wider than that represented by the trilobites and living groups, a range which gradually died out during the Upper Palaeozoic. Only a few can be illustrated here.

Pl. 9.1.1. *Marrella* Walcott, 1912
Cephalic shield bearing 2 pairs of large spines; 2 pairs of antennae; large number of trunk somites bearing undifferentiated biramous appendages; maximum length 2 cm.
M. Cambrian; benthic, marine.
Marrella splendens Walcott: M. Cambrian, Burgess Shale, British Columbia.

Pl. 9.1.2. *Aysheaia* Walcott, 1911
Elongate annulated body; 1 pair of lateral anterior appendages; 10 pairs of short, stubby, unbranched trunk limbs; maximum length 6 cm.
M. Cambrian; benthic, marine.
Aysheaia pedunculata Walcott: M. Cambrian, Burgess Shale, British Columbia.

9.2 Subphylum Crustacea (Cambrian–Recent)

The crustaceans are the most varied group of arthropods. They are characterized by the following attributes. The body is usually divided into three sections: head, thorax and abdomen. The head may bear a carapace which in some crustaceans unites it to the thorax to form a cephalothorax. The head bears five pairs of appendages: two pairs of antennae anteriorly, which are usually sensory in function, and a pair of mandibles and two pairs of maxillae posteriorly, which are normally used in feeding. Crustacean appendages are very variable in structure. The larval development of crustaceans involves metamorphosis through a number of stages, usually commencing with the nauplius. The subdivision of the Crustacea into major taxa is based mainly on the nature of the carapace, the divisions (tagmata) of the trunk and the structure of the limbs. For an explanation of morphological terms used in this section refer to

Plate 9.2.3

Tasch (1980: 540–96) or other standard textbooks.

Four crustacean classes have a substantial fossil record: Branchiopoda, Ostracoda (essentially microfossils, and not treated here), Maxillopoda and Malacostraca.

Class Branchiopoda

The members of this class are very variable in morphology. A carapace is usually present, either bivalved or a univalve dorsal shield. The diagnostic features are mainly in the morphology of the limbs, particularly those of the head which are very rarely preserved. The trunk appendages are usually foliaceous, but are absent from the posterior part of the trunk, which ends in a caudal furca. L. Devonian–Recent. The order Conchostraca is the most extensively represented in the fossil record.

Order Conchostraca

Body and appendages enclosed within a bivalved carapace which displays 'growth lines' which reflect successive moults; maximum length 2 cm. L. Devonian–Recent; non-marine, vary from infaunal to planktonic.

Pl. 9.2.1. *Euestheria* Depéret & Mazeran, 1912
The illustration shows a right valve.
Euestheria forbesii Jones: U. Triassic, Cacheuta, Argentina.

Class Maxillopoda

The class is characterized by a thorax of six appendage-bearing somites and an abdomen of four somites lacking limbs which terminates in a telson with furca. A number of maxillopodans have become modified to exploit a parasitic mode of life. U. Silurian–Recent. This class includes four subclasses: Mystacocarida, Copepoda, Branchiura and Cirripedia. Only the Cirripedia has a substantial fossil record.

Subclass Cirripedia

Sessile (after free-swimming naupliar stages), attached by first antenna, body contained within a carapace which may be composed of calcareous plates, thoracic appendages modified as cirri for filter-feeding. U. Silurian–Recent; marine. Only the order Thoracica has a fossil record (apart from some traces attributed to other cirripedes).

Order Thoracica

Carapace usually mineralized with calcium carbonate and making up a capitulum of 6 principal plates and a variable number of additional smaller ones. Plate morphology complex. The carapace tends to disarticulate (except in balanomorphs) so that commonly only isolated plates are found. One group (lepadomorphs) is characterized by a muscular peduncle. U. Silurian–Recent.

Pl. 9.2.2. *Balanus* Da Costa, 1778
Balanomorph showing fused lateral plates; the opercular valves of some of the individuals in the illustrated specimen have been lost. Maximum diameter of individuals *c.* 3 cm.
Balanus concavus Bronn: Pliocene, Suffolk, England.

Class Malacostraca

The class is characterized by a carapace covering the head and part of the trunk, a well-differentiated thorax and abdomen consisting of eight and six (seven in phyllocarids) somites respectively, and a telson. Cambrian–Recent (the malacostracans are the most abundant fossil crustaceans with the exception of the ostracodes). The class includes three subclasses: Phyllocarida, Hoplocarida and Eumalacostraca, of which the Hoplocarida has fewest fossil representatives.

Subclass Phyllocarida

Large bivalved carapace, 7 abdominal somites, telson with caudal furca. Cambrian–Recent; marine, benthic–nektonic. Most of the fossil forms are assigned to the order Archaeostraca.

Order Hymenostraca

Carapace folded; telson bearing 3 pairs of spines. Maximum carapace length *c.* 4 cm; Cambrian–L. Ordovician.

Pl. 9.2.3. *Hymenocaris* Salter, 1853
The illustration shows the carapace, abdomen and telson.
Hymenocaris vermicauda Salter: L. Ordovician, Portmadoc, Gwynedd, Wales.

Order Archaeostraca

Carapace hinged; telson with median process. Carapaces reach

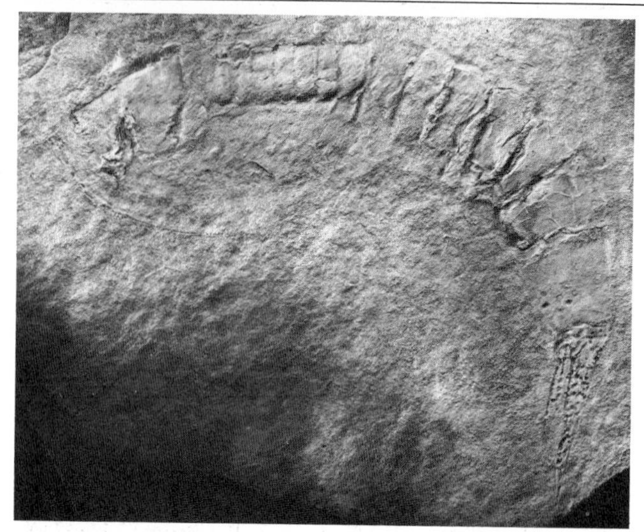

Plate 9.2.4

Plate 9.2.5

Plate 9.2.6

lengths of up to 60 cm. L. Ordovician–U. Triassic.

Pl. 9.2.4. *Ceratiocaris* M'Coy, 1849
The illustration is a left lateral view showing a faint outline of the carapace, the large mandible, the clear distinction between the shorter thoracic and longer abdominal somites, and the telson.
Ceratiocaris papilio Salter *in* Murchison: M. Silurian, Lesmahagow, Strathclyde, Scotland.

Subclass Eumalacostraca

Carapace not bivalved, 6 abdominal somites, simple caudal furca lacking. Devonian–Recent. Most of the Eumalacostraca belong to 2 superorders: Peracarida and Eucarida. (Note: Dimensions exclude appendages.)

Superorder Peracarida

Carapace not fused dorsally with all thoracic somites, females with a seasonal brood pouch formed by flap-like outgrowths from the base of the thoracic limbs. Carboniferous–Recent; mainly marine, but with freshwater and terrestrial representatives.

Order Waterstonellidea

Carapace covering thorax, antenna with scale, large abdomen ending in tail fan. Maximum length *c.* 6 cm. L. Carboniferous; marine to brackish water.

Pl. 9.2.5. *Tealliocaris* Peach, 1908
Tealliocaris woodwardi (Etheridge): L. Carboniferous, Lothian, Scotland.

Superorder Eucarida

Carapace fused dorsally with all thoracic somites.

Order Decapoda

First 3 pairs of thoracic limbs modified for feeding (i.e. maxillipeds), therefore no more than 5 are locomotory (i.e. pereiopods). The first periopod commonly ends in a strong claw (chela).

Infraorder Astacidea

Abdomen well developed, with large pleura. Prominent rostrum. Maximum length *c.* 50 cm. Permotriassic–Recent; marine to freshwater.

Pl. 9.2.6. *Hoploparia* M'Coy, 1849
The illustration is a lateral view of a slightly disarticulated specimen.
Hoploparia longimana (Sowerby): L. Cretaceous, Dorset, England.

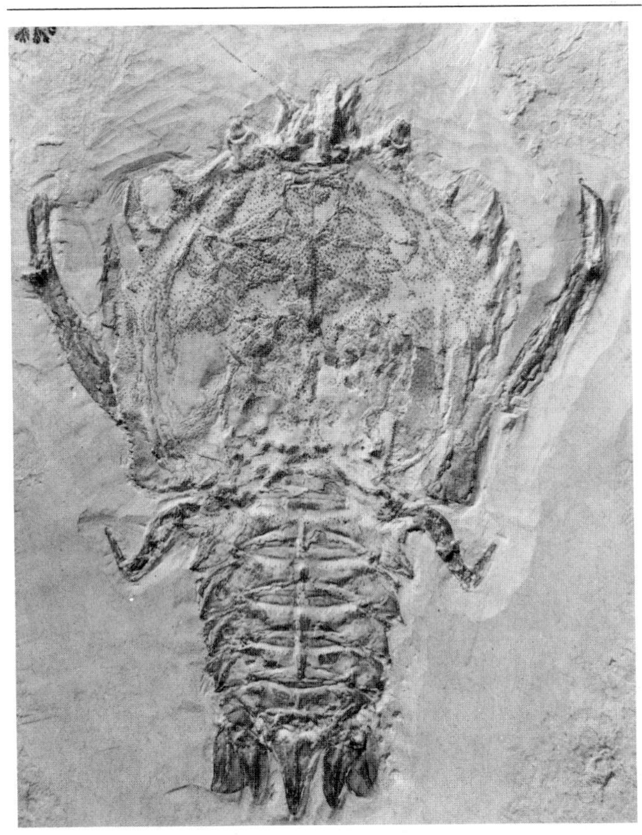

Plate 9.2.7

Infraorder Palinura

Abdomen well developed, rostrum not usually prominent. Maximum length 15 cm. Triassic–Recent; marine.

Pl. 9.2.7. *Eryon* Desmarest, 1817
Eryon arctiformis (von Schlotheim): U. Jurassic, Solenhofen, W. Germany.

Infraorder Brachyura

Short wide carapace, abdomen short, flattened, flexed under sternum and commonly fused. L. Jurassic–Recent; mainly marine, rarely brackish, freshwater, terrestrial.

SUPERFAMILY RANINOIDEA

Elongate carapace, not covering proximal part of abdomen. Maximum length *c.* 20 cm; L. Cretaceous–Recent.

Pl. 9.2.8. *Notopocorystes* M'Coy, 1849
The appendages on the illustrated specimen are incomplete distally.
Notopocorystes broderipi (Mantell): L. Cretaceous, Folkestone, Kent, England.

SUPERFAMILY PORTUNOIDEA

Flat, square or oval carapace, fifth locomotory limb usually modified as a paddle. Maximum width *c.* 20 cm. U. Cretaceous–Recent.

Pl. 9.2.9. *Portunus* Weber, 1795
Portunus lancetidactylus Smirnov: Oligocene, Caucasus, USSR.

Plate 9.2.8

Plate 9.2.9

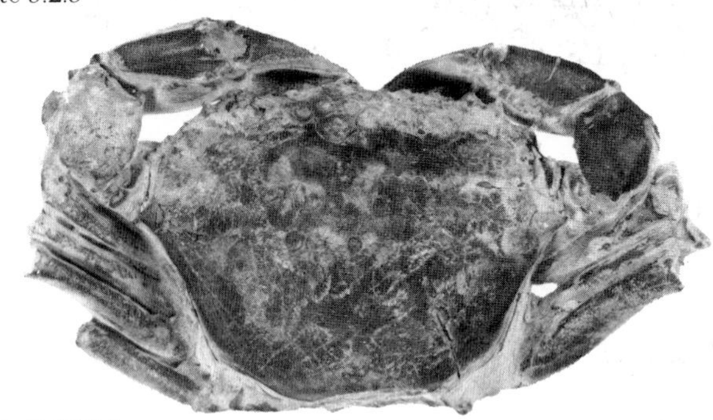

Plate 9.2.10A

Plate 9.2.10B

SUPERFAMILY XANTHOIDEA

Square or oval carapace, anterior margin notched, locomotory limbs ambulatory. Maximum width *c.* 15 cm. U. Cretaceous–Recent.

Pl. 9.2.10. *Archaeogeryon* Colosi, 1924
The illustrations show the dorsal (A) and ventral (B) side of the same specimen.
Archaeogeryon peruvianus (d'Orbigny): Tertiary, Monte Leone, Patagonia, Argentina.

9.3 Subphylum Chelicerata (Ordovician–Recent)

The chelicerates include two major groups, the essentially aquatic merostomes and the mainly terrestrial arachnids. A classification incorporating this division is followed here, as alternative schemes, based on recent investigations, have yet to become widely accepted. The body of chelicerates is divided into two sections, an anterior prosoma (cephalothorax) and a posterior opisthosoma (abdomen). There are normally six prosomal appendages. There are no antennae and the only appendages originating in front of the mouth, the chelicerae, are used in feeding. The prosomal appendages behind the mouth (postoral) are used for both feeding and locomotion. There is no mandible, and the first postoral appendage, which is termed the 'pedipalp' in arachnids, is used for a variety of functions. The appendages of the opisthosoma are either modified as gills, or reduced. The opisthosoma in merostomes usually terminates in a tail spine, the telson. The division of the chelicerates into major taxa is based on the morphology of the prosoma and its appendages, and the nature and number of somites in the opisthosoma. The majority of the living chelicerates, the spiders, scorpions, ticks and mites, belong to the terrestrial arachnids. The only living merostomes are the horseshoe crabs, but the extinct related eurypterids were an important element of Palaeozoic aquatic arthropod faunas. For an explanation of morphological terms used in this section refer to Clarkson (1979: 292–300) or other standard textbooks.

Class Merostomata

The prosomal shield usually bears a median eye and lateral compound eyes. There are six pairs of prosomal appendages, the first (chelicerae) for feeding, the remainder mainly locomotory but with spinose coxae used as jaws. The opisthosomal somites are free or fused, not exceeding eleven in number, the appendages mainly gills. The telson is well developed. Ordovician–Recent. There are two subclasses: Xiphosura and Eurypterida.

Subclass Xiphosura

Prosoma large with a dorsal shield, number of opisthosomal somites variable, telson long and pointed. Silurian–Recent. There are 2 orders: the Palaeozoic Synziphosurida and the Limulida.

Order Limulida

Large prosoma with median and lateral eyes, up to 9 well-developed opisthosomal somites, telson longer than opisthosoma. Maximum length *c.* 60 cm. Devonian–Recent; benthic, marine to brackish-fresh, rarely amphibious.

Pl. 9.3.1. *Belinurus* König, 1820
Anterior opisthosomal somites articulate, pronounced genal spines. Maximum length *c.* 7 cm.
Belinurus baldwini Woodward: U. Carboniferous, Rochdale, Greater Manchester, England.

Pl. 9.3.2. *Mesolimulus* Størmer, 1952
Fused opisthosoma with movable marginal spines, triangular genal angles, clear axial furrows, but no distinct annulation on opisthosoma. Maximum length *c.* 25 cm.
Mesolimulus walchi (Desmarest): U. Jurassic, Solenhofen, W. Germany.

Subclass Eurypterida

Elongate body; prosoma relatively small, last pair of appendages commonly swimming paddles; opisthosoma of 12 articulated somites, usually divided into a preabdomen of 7 and a postabdomen of 5 respectively; telson varies from long spine to flat paddle. Average length 10 to 20 cm, but maximum approaching 2 m. Ordovician–Permian; benthic to nektonic, marine to brackish-fresh, rarely amphibious. There are *c.* 4 orders of eurypterids, only one of which is illustrated here.

Order Pterygotida

Large eyes on margin of prosoma, large toothed chelicerae, 3 pairs of slender walking legs, wide paddle-shaped telson. Maximum length approaching 2 m. Silurian–Devonian; marine, brackish.

Pl. 9.3.3. *Erettopterus* Salter, 1859
Note characteristic preservation of chelicerae, directed posteriorly after moulting with the chelae lying near the anterior margin of the prosoma. The paddle-shaped sixth limb is directed backward, beyond the prosoma.
Erettopterus bilobus (Salter): U. Silurian, Lesmahagow, Strathclyde, Scotland.

Class Arachnida

The body is divided into a prosoma (=cephalothorax), bearing six pairs of appendages, and an opisthosoma (=abdomen) consisting of up to twelve somites. Arachnids are air breathers, respiring with book lungs and/or tracheae. Silurian–Recent. Fossil arachnids are rare, with a few exceptions such as the Oligocene Baltic amber. Representatives of only three of the more important of the *c.* 16 orders are illustrated here.

Order Scorpionida

Cephalothorax with median eyes and 2 to 5 pairs of lateral eyes, large chelate pedipalps; segmented abdomen divided into wide preabdomen, and slender postabdomen, stinging telson. Average length 2 to 12 cm, maximum approaching 1 m. Silurian–Recent; mainly terrestrial (earliest representatives probably amphibious).

Pl. 9.3.4. *Buthiscorpius* Petrunkevitch, 1953
The illustrated specimen shows the division of the body into cephalothorax, preabdomen and postabdomen. The appendages and telson are not evident.
Buthiscorpius buthiformis (Pocock): U. Carboniferous, Rochdale, Greater Manchester, England.

Order Trigonotarbida

Ventral side (coxosternal region) of prosoma with 5 pairs of

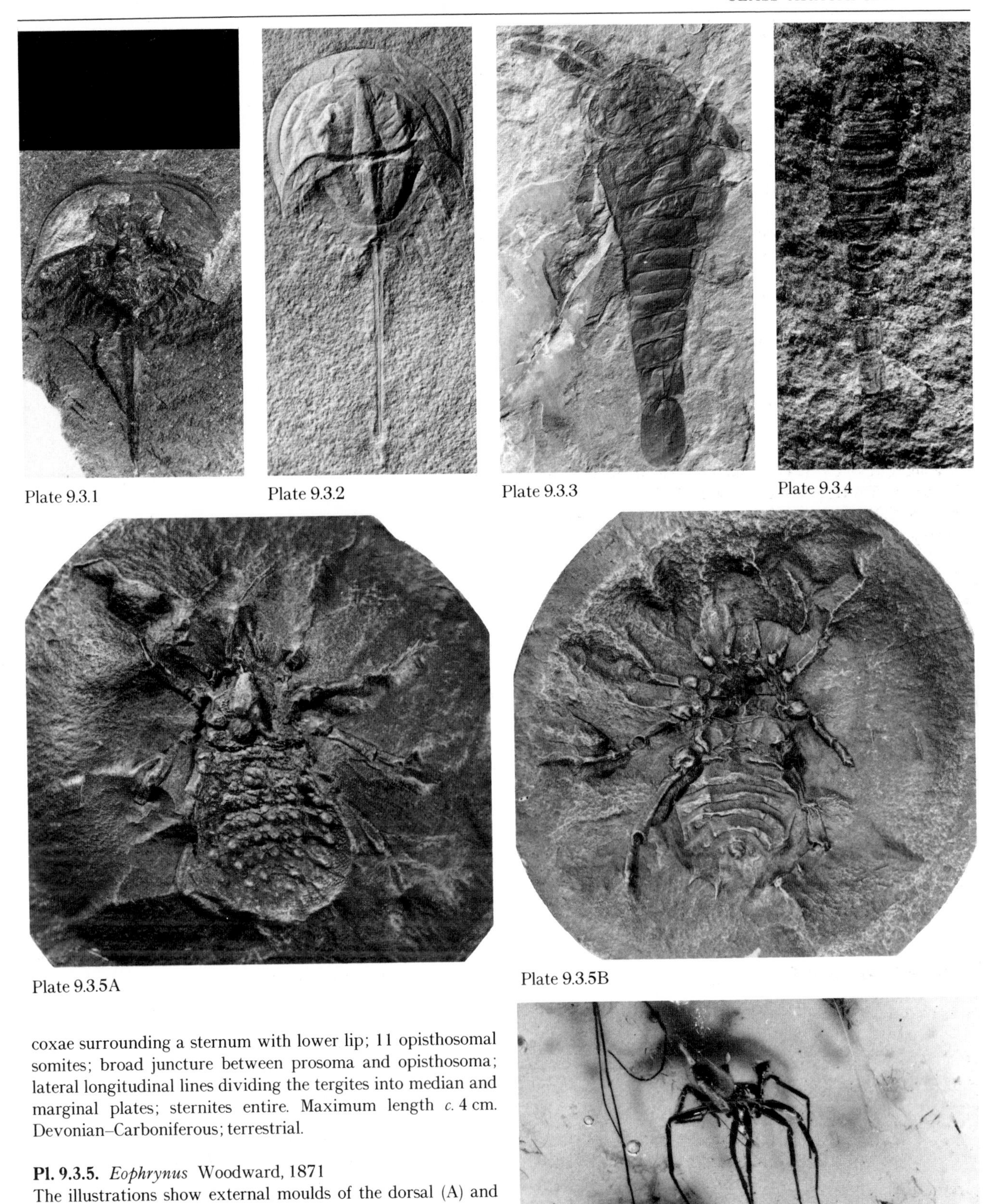

Plate 9.3.1

Plate 9.3.2

Plate 9.3.3

Plate 9.3.4

Plate 9.3.5A

Plate 9.3.5B

Plate 9.3.6

coxae surrounding a sternum with lower lip; 11 opisthosomal somites; broad juncture between prosoma and opisthosoma; lateral longitudinal lines dividing the tergites into median and marginal plates; sternites entire. Maximum length *c.* 4 cm. Devonian–Carboniferous; terrestrial.

Pl. 9.3.5. *Eophrynus* Woodward, 1871
The illustrations show external moulds of the dorsal (A) and ventral (B) sides of the same specimen.
Eophrynus prestvicii (Buckland): U. Carboniferous, Dudley, West Midlands, England.

Order Araneida

Constriction between cephalothorax and abdomen; chelicerae developed as a fang, 5 pairs of coxae surround a sternum with lip, pedipalp similar to other limbs; abdomen with up to 12 somites but may be reduced to 5 or 6 completely fused; spinnerets. Maximum length over 30 cm, excluding limbs. ?Devonian, Carboniferous–Recent; terrestrial, rarely secondarily aquatic.

Pl. 9.3.6. *Oxyopes* Petrunkevitch, 1958
Baltic amber, Oligocene, Kaliningrad, USSR.

Plate 9.4.1

Plate 9.4.4

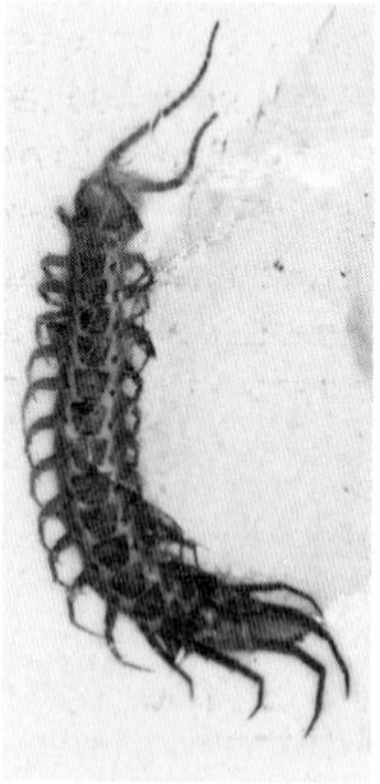

Plate 9.4.2

Plate 9.4.5

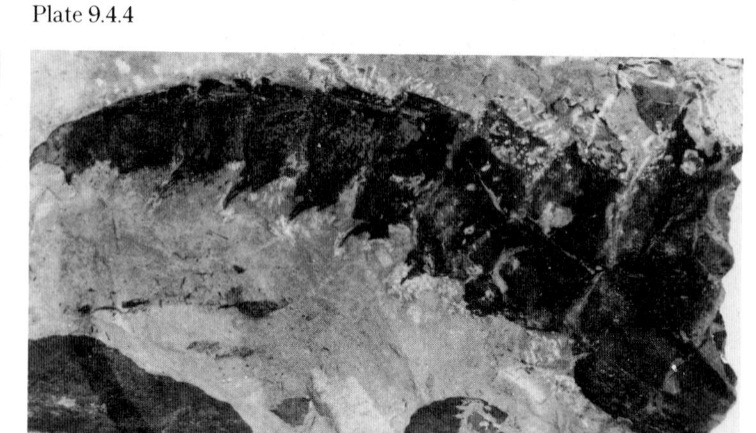

Plate 9.4.3

9.4 Phylum Uniramia (Silurian–Recent)

The uniramians are an essentially terrestrial group respiring with tracheae or directly through the body wall. They lack gills and are characterized by uniramous ('one-branch') limbs. The head bears a single pair of antennae and feeding is achieved by a pair of mandibles and usually by two additional pairs of limbs, the maxillae. The mandible operates as a whole limb (biting with the tip) rather than with the limb base alone (as in crustaceans). There are three major taxa within the Uniramia, the Onychophora, Myriapoda and Hexapoda, distinguished by the divisions of the body into tagmata and the number and nature of the somites.

Superclass Myriapoda

Clear demarcation between head and trunk, the latter in some cases divided into short thorax and multisegmented abdomen. Silurian–Recent; terrestrial. The myriapods are divided into five classes, but only three of these have a significant fossil record.

Class Diplopoda

Trunk somites variable in number and fused into diplosomites, most with two pairs of limbs, cuticle usually mineralized ($CaCO_3$), most species capable of enrolment. Maximum size *c.* 28 cm. Silurian–Recent; most terrestrial, feeding mainly on dead plant matter.

Pl. 9.4.1. *Myriacantherpestes* Burke, 1979
The median section of the incomplete specimen illustrated shows the sternal region and left limbs. The tergites show traces of the large lateral spines.
Myriacantherpestes ferox (Salter): U. Carboniferous, Dudley, West Midlands, England.

Class Chilopoda

Dorsoventrally flattened head, many trunk somites, unfused, each with one pair of limbs, cuticle unmineralized. Maximum size *c.* 30 cm. Cretaceous–Recent; terrestrial, carnivorous.

Pl. 9.4.2. *Scolopendra* Linné, 1758
Oligocene, Baltic amber, Kaliningrad area, USSR.

Class Arthropleurida

Very large, up to 30 trunk somites, one pair of limbs per somite, limbs multisegmented with large lobed plate (rosette plate) at base. Maximum size approaching 2 m. Devonian–U. Carboniferous; terrestrial, herbivorous.

Pl. 9.4.3. *Arthropleura* Jordan and Meyer, 1853
The illustration shows a right limb with basal plates.
Arthropleura armata Jordan and Meyer: U. Carboniferous, Heerlen, Netherlands.

Superclass Hexapoda

Body divided into distinct head, thorax and abdomen; 6 thoracic limbs, abdomen lacking limbs except, in some cases, at distal extremity. Devonian–Recent; terrestrial. Two examples of the predominantly winged class Pterygota are illustrated.

Order Odonata

Dragonflies and damselflies; large eyes, short antennae, 2 pairs of wings, elongate body. Maximum wing span *c.* 18 cm. Triassic–Recent; aquatic larval stage.

Pl. 9.4.4. *Turanophlebia* Pritykina, 1968
U. Jurassic, Solenhofen, Germany.

Order Coleoptera

Beetles; large thorax, anterior of 2 pairs of wings forming well-sclerotized elytra which usually cover the entire abdomen. Maximum length *c.* 15 cm. Permian–Recent; terrestrial, secondarily aquatic. Beetle elytra are used extensively used in Quaternary palaeoecology.

Pl. 9.4.5. *Chrysobotris* Eschscholtz, 1829
L. Cretaceous, Lerida, Spain.

PHYLUM ARTHROPODA

9.5 Subphylum Trilobita

Trilobites are among the earliest macrofossils with hard parts to appear above the base of the Cambrian. They remained an important part of marine faunas until the Carboniferous, becoming extinct in the late Permian. During their long history (Fig. 9.5.1) trilobites diversified into many different marine habitats, and their basic body plan became modified in a host of ways: some became spiny, some blind, while others developed huge eyes. They range in size from comparative giants nearly 1 m long, to minute animals no more than 1 or 2 mm in length. In general terms, trilobites were most diverse in the Cambrian and Ordovician, with a peak (at least as reflected in current family classification) in the U. Cambrian; they were still very abundant in the Ordovician, and at this time reached the acme of their morphological diversification. At the end of this period, many families became extinct, and more again by the end of the Devonian. By the Carboniferous only three families remained, but specimens may still be quite abundant at some localities. The group continued to undergo minor evolutionary bursts right until the end of their history, but in the overall context of a progressive decline in diversity. By the Permian trilobites are distinctly uncommon fossils and, like many other groups, did not survive the end of the period.

Trilobites were exclusively marine, but can be found in almost all kinds of sediment, from deposits that accumulated very near shore to deep-sea shales. Their presumed burrowing and feeding activities can be preserved as the trace fossils *Cruziana* and *Rusophycus* (Whittington 1961). The majority were bottom dwellers, vagrant benthos, and as such their occurrence tends to be related to substrate characteristics and depth. Reefs had their own peculiarly adapted species; these are often rather featureless but with well-developed eyes, or coarsely tuberculate and spiny forms. Deep-sea shales and mudstones have yielded a variety of trilobites with rudimentary eyes, or blind. Such blindness is a secondary characteristic, because the ancestors of these species had normal eyes, and is one of many trilobite features that were capable of appearing independently several times in their history. Most trilobites had good vision. The compound eyes utilized calcite crystals as lenses; each lens had optimal efficiency normal to the lens surface, so it is possible to work out the field of view. Most trilobites had an array of

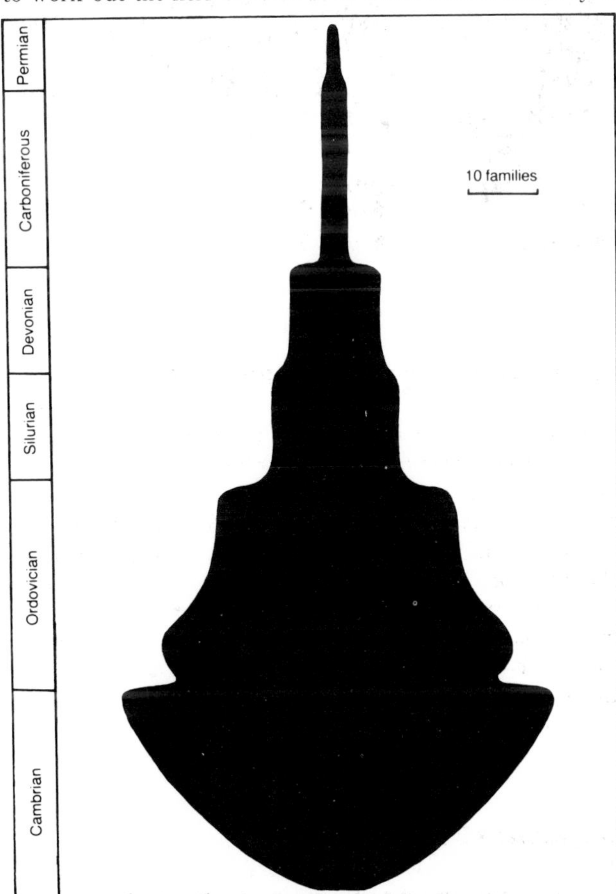

Fig. 9.5.1. Diversity of trilobite families through time.

more or less polygonal lenses (holochroal eyes), which may number several thousand. One group (Phacopina) had fewer, biconvex lenses, of great optical sophistication (schizochroal eyes). Most post-Cambrian trilobites could enrol, much like a wood-louse (pillbug), and they are often found preserved in this way. Enrolment may have offered a certain amount of protection from predators, but trilobites may also have enrolled during times of food scarcity, if they had the capacity to slow down their metabolism. Trilobites grew by moulting, and so one individual could produce many potential fossils during its lifetime. Larval trilobites (protaspides) are known for many species: they are a single shield often less than 1 mm long. Subsequent growth involved the differentiation of cephalon from pygidium, and then the release of the thoracic segments, which are released from the forward end of the pygidium. The adult number of thoracic segments was usually attained at a small size, and thereafter the trilobite continued to grow and change, but without adding further segments. Presumably the protaspis stage was the dispersive phase of the trilobite life cycle, and the tiny trilobites lived as part of the plankton.

The appendages of very few species of trilobites are known, and this is a problem when it comes to attempting to infer details of their life habits. Most living arthropods employ their appendages in a variety of ways, and they are usually specialized for different functions along the length of the animal. Where known, trilobites tend to have appendages which are similar along the length of the body except for a pair of sensory antennae anteriorly. Probably the majority of trilobites lived on or about the sea bottom, feeding off the sediment, or scavenging for organic material. Some may have been predators; this has been suggested for the Cambrian form *Olenoides* which had long, fearsome spines on the bases of the appendages. Some trilobites, with hugely developed eyes and 360° vision, abandoned the sea-floor and became active swimmers. Paradoxically, the same mode of life has been suggested for the diminutive agnostids, which were blind. Some authorities claim to have recognized the different sexes of a single species, but the evidence for this is not compelling in the absence of genitalia. Many trilobites were capable of burrowing, either for protection or in the pursuit of food; some of the species with stalked eyes may have had this mode of life. That trilobites *had* enemies is apparent from those specimens which have sustained damage from attack. It seems likely that early in their history the nautiloids would have been their principal predators, while later trilobites would presumably have been prey to fish also. Whether the spines and knobs adopted by some of the later trilobites were connected with protection from attack is a speculation which cannot be proven.

The wide variety of trilobite skeletal morphology certainly implies a much greater variety of modes of life in detail than we have indicated. Some forms had curious features which cannot be matched on any living arthropod. The trinucleids, for example, with their pitted brim, were evidently specialized for something, but there are many different opinions about what this might have been. The discovery of more species with appendages might help solve such problems.

DIAGNOSIS

Arthropods typically with calcified dorsal exoskeleton displaying trilobation along the long axis of the body and transverse division into cephalon, articulated thorax and pygidium. Appendages known in only a few species but the following arrangement seems to be characteristic: one pair of preoral single-branched (uniramous) antennae and three pairs of two-branched (biramous) postoral cephalic appendages. Further pairs of similar biramous appendages occur along the length of the body.

MORPHOLOGICAL TERMS APPLIED TO TRILOBITES

Most of the commoner terms applied to the trilobite exoskeleton are illustrated in Fig. 9.5.2. Generally, trilobites are found in a fragmentary condition, having separated into pieces along sutures as indicated on the left-hand diagram. The *cranidium* is the mid-part of the cephalon after the free cheeks have separated along the *facial sutures*. Two kinds of facial sutures are shown: *opisthoparian* (left) where the suture runs from the front to the back margin; *proparian* (right) where the suture begins and ends on the front margin. The *gonatoparian* suture (not shown) runs from the front margin into the genal angle. The dorsal exoskeleton is continued on the under (*ventral*) side of the trilobite as a strip of doublure. A labral plate (*hypostoma*) is usually attached to the mid-part of the cephalic doublure, being ventrally correspondent with the glabella. The continuation of the sutures ventrally has assumed some importance in trilobite classification. Three main types are distinguished, here shown (Fig. 9.5.3) with hypostoma attached.

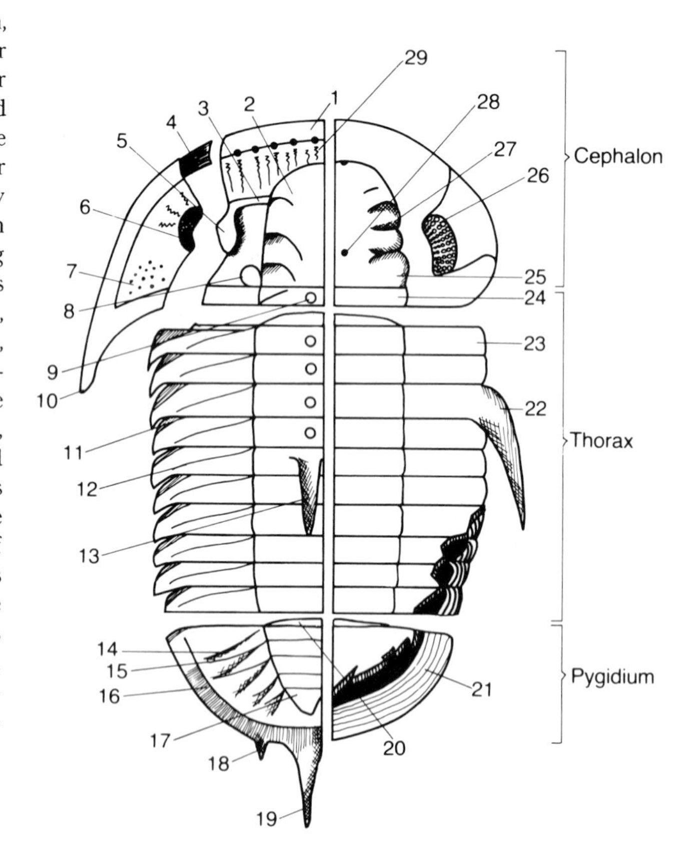

Fig. 9.5.2. Summary of important morphological terms applied to trilobites. (1) Cranidial border; (2) frontal lobe of glabella; (3) eye-ridge; (4) cephalic doublure; (5) palpebral lobe; (6) eye (holochroal), on opisthoparian facial suture; (7) free cheek; (8) baccula; (9) occipital tubercle; (10) genal spine (in this case borne on free cheek, because the facial suture is opisthoparian); (11) articulating facet; (12) pleural furrow (of thoracic segment); (13) axial spine; (14) pleural furrow (of pygidial pleural field); (15) interpleural furrow; (16) pygidial border; (17) terminal piece of pygidial axis; (18) marginal spine; (19) terminal spine; (20) articulating half-ring; (21) pygidial doublure; (22) macropleural segment; (23) pleura; (24) occipital ring; (25) basal glabellar lobe (1L: glabellar lobes are numbered 1L, 2L, 3L, etc. starting with the one adjacent to the occipital ring); (26) proparian suture with schizochroal eye; (27) second lateral glabellar furrow (2S: glabellar furrows are numbered 1S, 2S, 3S, etc. forwards from the posterior end of the glabella); (28) glabellar tubercle; (29) preglabellar field (with caecae).

REMARKS ON TRILOBITE CLASSIFICATION AND IDENTIFICATION

Trilobites display a remarkable diversity of form within their well-defined body-plan and this variety is reflected in the large number of families, currently some 150, which are recognized. Most of these families appear to be valid monophyletic groups, and some can be grouped into seemingly homogeneous superfamilies. There is little detailed agreement, however, concerning the arrangement of these families and superfamilies into suborders and orders. This is principally because the various family-level groups tend to share only those primitive morphological characters characteristic of the majority of trilobites. Thus there is as yet no obvious method of achieving a satisfactory higher classification. Most published higher classifications are essentially based on single characters: the form of the facial sutures or style of enrolment, for instance. The majority of workers consider that a satisfactory scheme is only likely to emerge from consideration of a wider range of characters, including details of ontogenetic development and so on, as well as the morphology of the adult trilobite.

The ordinal and subordinal classification used here is therefore provisional and likely to be subject to considerable modification in the future. Some groups, the order Agnostida, for example, appear to be homogeneous and well defined and their composition is unlikely to be radically altered. Others, particularly the larger suborder Ptychopariina actually embrace a large variety of trilobites (Eldredge 1977) grouped together mainly because they cannot be accommodated in any of the other higher taxa currently distinguished. For all these defects the classification presented is reasonable given present knowledge and it broadly conforms with those used in Clarkson's textbook (1979) and in the relevant volume of the *Treatise on Invertebrate Paleontology* (Moore 1959).

Particular problems arise in trying to frame useful diagnoses by which groups of trilobites may be distinguished. The tendency of the trilobite exoskeleton to dissociate following ecdysis or death, for instance, may produce isolated exoskeletal elements much more difficult to identify than articulated specimens. Further difficulties arise when dealing with juvenile specimens

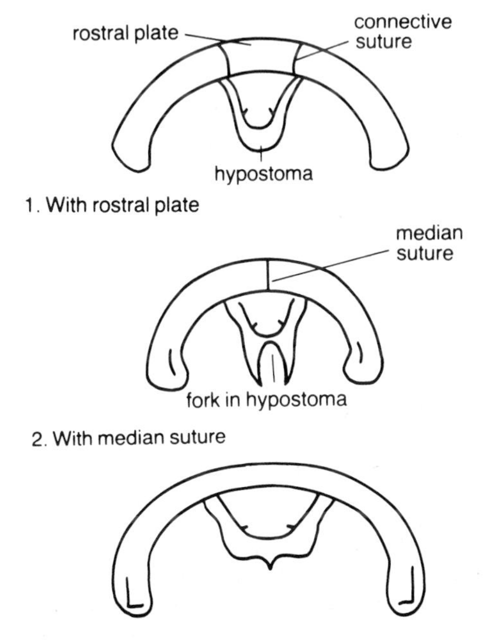

Fig. 9.5.3. Ventral surfaces of trilobite cephala, illustrating various forms of rostral plate and associated sutures.

because their morphology may differ radically from that of adults belonging to the same species. Though complete trilobites are rather rare it is convenient to use complete specimens for illustration: our diagnoses and the key are constructed with this in mind. Identification of fragmentary material using the *Atlas* will inevitably be less successful. We think, however, that a general guide to the identity of fragmentary specimens should be possible simply by means of visual comparison with the illustrations.

Dimensions quoted in the following diagnoses refer to the median length of complete specimens excluding any spines. Such dimensions refer to the maximum size commonly found. In a group of animals which grew continuously, if more slowly, throughout life, absolute maxima cannot be reliably quoted and larger specimens may occur as rarities.

KEY TO ORDERS AND SUBORDERS

The unsatisfactory state of trilobite higher classification has already been mentioned and this problem has inevitably hampered the construction of a key system of identification. Another difficulty arises from the common occurrence of convergent evolution in only distantly related groups of trilobites. The development of blindness or progressive effacement of the exoskeleton, for example, took place independently and at different times in a variety of trilobite stocks. To construct a key to disentangle all such convergent taxa would not only be an almost impossible task, but would necessitate a key many times longer than we have space for here.

In constructing the key only those characters which are relatively easy to observe have been used. For instance, ventral features which may be revealed only after extensive preparation of a specimen have been avoided. Unfortunately, some members of some orders are difficult to distinguish without reference to such characters and may, therefore, not 'key out' well. These points are made not to excuse the deficiencies of our key but to emphasize that it is only a rather rough-and-ready guide, and to caution against its uncritical use.

1. Thorax of 2 or 3 segments .... ORDER Agnostida 2
   Thorax of 4 or more segments 4
2. With eyes, free cheeks or 3 thoracic segments .... SUBORDER Eodiscina
   Otherwise 3
3. Without eyes, pygidium with long, relatively narrow axis showing ring-like segments; cephalic border convex and thick .... SUBORDER Eodiscina
   Without eyes, thorax of 2 segments; pygidial axis with 2 to 3 segments (not ring-like) and often longer terminal piece .... SUBORDER Agnostina
4. Eye-lobes large, crescentic; thorax of many segments (often *c.* 14); pygidium typically small or rudimentary. Glabellar furrows well developed, simple and subparallel .... ORDER Redlichiida 5
   Otherwise 6
5. Opisthoparian .... SUBORDER Redlichiina
   Facial sutures fused and indistinct, eye-lobes fused with glabella .... SUBORDER Olenellina
6. Proparian, glabella expands forwards 7
   Gonatoparian .... SUBORDER Calymenina
   Opisthoparian, or with marginal facial suture 8
7. Schizochroal eyes, sigmoidal 3S .... SUBORDER Phacopina
   Holochroal eyes .... SUBORDER Cheirurina
8. Opisthoparian; glabella with complex structure of fused lobes; pygidium large, often longer than wide, with 3 pairs of furrowed pleurae generally ending in spinose tips. Surface strongly granulose .... ORDER Lichida
   Otherwise 9

9. Opisthoparian. Glabella parallel-sided or tapering forwards, extending to anterior border. Lateral lobes distinct, rounded. Pygidium short, with 2 to 3 segments and 1 or more pairs of marginal spines; largest pair of spines connected to first axial ring by a ridge .... Odontopleurida
   Otherwise 10
10. Opisthoparian. Glabella expanded forwards with concave lateral outline, or barrel-shaped; glabellar furrows splayed so that anterior 2 pairs run obliquely forwards and inwards and posterior pair obliquely backwards and inwards. Thorax not long, typically of 9 segments. Pygidium relatively large, often similar in size to cephalon .... ORDER Corynexochida
   Otherwise 11
11. Opisthoparian. Glabella expanded forwards or hour-glass-shaped, rounded in front. Pygidium large and long, similar in size to cephalon, usually without marginal spines ... 12
   Otherwise 13
12. Anterior sections of facial sutures curve inwards and forwards to cut cephalic margin in front of glabella .... SUBORDER Asaphina
   Anterior sections of facial sutures not curved towards the mid-line .... SUBORDER Illaenina
13. Glabella strongly vaulted, with 4 or fewer pairs of subparallel furrows; anterior 2 pairs often very short, basal pair long and backwardly curved. Pygidium usually large .... ORDER Proetida
   Otherwise 14
14. Facial suture marginal, thorax of many (12 or more) segments; pygidium usually very small ... ORDER Harpina
   Facial suture marginal, thorax of 6 segments; pygidium wide, of many segments .... SUBORDER Trinucleina
   Otherwise 15
15. Facial suture opisthoparian, glabella expands forwards. Thorax of 6 to 8 segments. Pygidium triangular, wide, segmented. Long genal spines. Mostly blind .... SUBORDER Trinucleina
   Facial suture opisthoparian or marginal; glabella tapering forwards or parallel-sided, often not reaching anterior border, typically with 3 pairs of simple furrows running obliquely inwards and back. Eyes often small but may be long or absent. Cephalic border typically present. Thorax generally of about 12 to 13 segments (rarely < 8 or > 20). Pygidium usually short and small, composed of 6 or fewer segments .... SUBORDER Ptychopariina

Note: Ptychopariina represents a stem group for most post-Cambrian trilobites and contains a very large number of varied genera. Besides typical generalized forms (*Asthenopis*, Pl. 9.5.44; *Olenus* Pl. 9.5.36) are specialized forms such as the blind *Shumardia* (Pl. 9.5.26), the proparian *Schmalenseeia* (Pl. 9.5.48) and the large-eyed *Remopleurides* (Pl. 9.5.42).

Order Agnostida

Diminutive trilobites, usually only a few mm long, with cephalon and pygidium similar in outline and size. Thorax of 2 to 3 segments, usually with a broad axis and short, stubby pleurae. Glabellar segmentation highly variable and may be complex, but some Agnostida are almost entirely effaced. Most are blind. Hypostoma specialized. Agnostida apparently lack a protaspis stage in their development. L. Cambrian–Ordovician (Ashgill).

Suborder Agnostina

Blind Agnostida with only 2 thoracic segments. Pygidial axis usually inflated, divided into 3 or fewer segments, one of which usually carries a large tubercle. No half-ring on anterior thoracic segment. L. Cambrian–Ordovician (Ashgill). Division into families is difficult and not used here.

Pl. 9.5.1. *Agnostus* Brongniart, 1822
Agnostid with nearly parallel-sided glabella completely cut across by glabellar furrow. Mid-part of preglabellar field bisected by deep furrow. Long, somewhat conically tipped pygidial axis. Borders moderately wide; pygidial border with pair of short posterolateral spines. Up to 10 mm.
U. Cambrian. Almost worldwide, generally in deep-water sediments.
Agnostus pisiformis (Wahlenberg): U. Cambrian, England.

Pl. 9.5.2. *Condylopyge* Hawle & Corda, 1847
Agnostid with enormously inflated frontal glabellar lobe. Pygidial axis strongly furrowed, tapers at first and then expands again at round posterior lobe. Broad borders. Can be large for an agnostid, up to 15 mm.
Upper L.–M. Cambrian. Europe, maritime Canada, in off-shelf sediments.
Condylopyge rex (Barrande): M. Cambrian, Bohemia, Czechoslovakia.

Pl. 9.5.3. *Glyptagnostus* Whitehouse, 1936
Agnostid with entire dorsal surface dominated by a mosaic-like pattern of furrows which do not extend on to the narrow borders. Pygidium with tiny border spines. Up to 10 mm.
Lower U. Cambrian. Almost world-wide, various facies.
Glyptagnostus reticulatus (Angelin): U. Cambrian, England.

Pl. 9.5.4. *Phalagnostus* Howell, 1935
Agnostid in which effacement is advanced to the extent that few details of cephalic or pygidial axes are visible. Cephalon an almost featureless shield. Pygidium retains prominent, convex rim of greater than usual width; spines lacking. Up to 10 mm.
M. Cambrian, Europe, Siberia and eastern N. America, especially in fine clastic sediments.
Phalagnostus cf. *nudus* (Beyrich): M. Cambrian, Bohemia, Czechoslovakia.

Pl. 9.5.5. *Arthrorhachis* Hawle & Corda, 1847
Agnostid with broad pygidial and cephalic borders. Glabella broadly rounded in front, and carrying a tubercle, but without deep furrows. Pygidial axis relatively short, median tubercle especially prominent on second axial ring. Up to 10 mm. Photographs show 2 cephala and 2 pygidia preserved in silica and dissolved from a limestone matrix.
Ordovician (Tremadoc–Ashgill). World-wide, various facies.
Arthrorhachis elspethi (Cooper): Llandeilo, Virginia, USA.

Suborder Eodiscina

Agnostida with 2 to 3 thoracic segments; some retain eyes. Glabella usually simple, narrow and tapering. Pygidial axis likewise long and narrow, extending close to margin, and generally distinctly segmented into more than 3 axial rings. Border furrows often very deep. L.–M. Cambrian.

FAMILY EODISCIDAE
Eodiscina lacking eyes and facial sutures. L.–M. Cambrian.

Pl. 9.5.6. *Eodiscus* Walcott, 1884
Eodiscid with narrow glabella surrounded by very deep axial furrows; preglabellar field split by very deep furrow. Strong

Plate 9.5.1

Plate 9.5.2

Plate 9.5.3

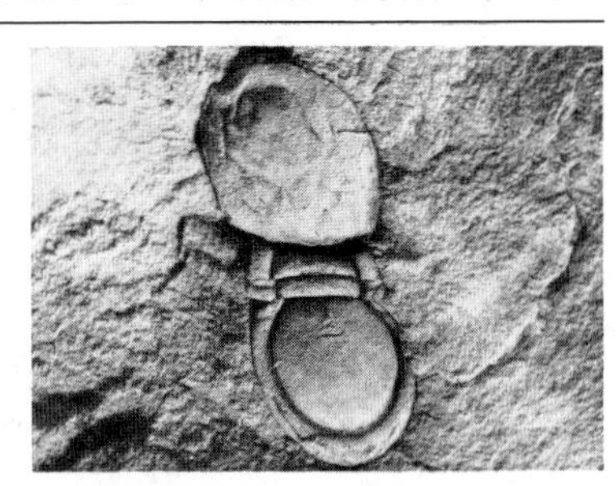
Plate 9.5.4

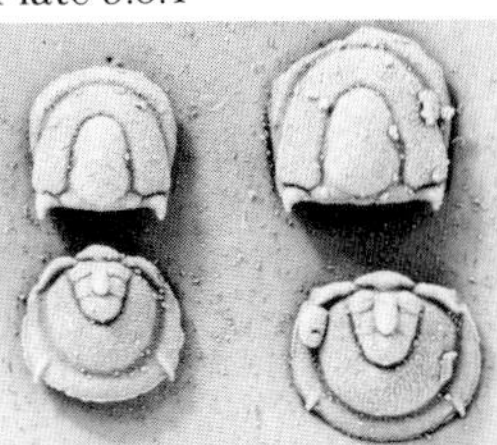
Plate 9.5.5

Plate 9.5.6

Plate 9.5.7

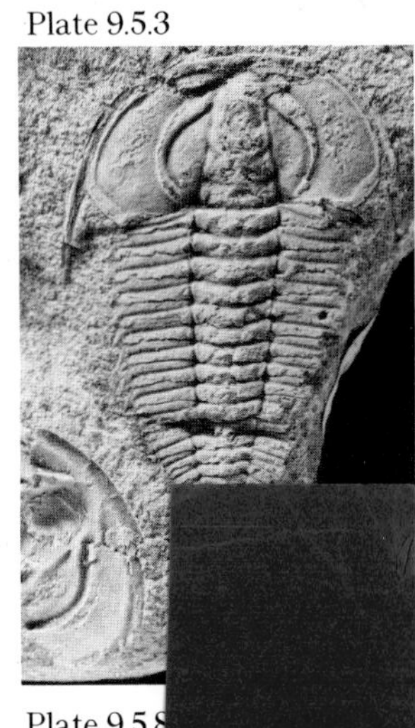
Plate 9.5.8

Plate 9.5.9

occipital spine. Genal areas inflated. Three thoracic segments. Pygidium semicircular, with narrow axis having 7 or more rings. Up to 10 mm.
M. Cambrian. Europe, eastern N. America, in fine clastic sediments deposited in shelf-edge environments.
Eodiscus punctatus (Salter): M. Cambrian, Wales.

FAMILY PAGETIIDAE
Eodiscina with eyes, and proparian facial sutures defining small free cheeks. L.–M. Cambrian.

Pl. 9.5.7. *Pagetia* Walcott, 1916
Pagetiid with border bearing an array of small, radially disposed furrows. Glabella narrow, with shallow furrows; preglabellar field not strongly divided by a furrow, but with a depression in front of glabella. Thorax of 2 segments. Long, narrow pygidial axis carries a posterior spine (not visible on specimen photographed); pygidial border narrow. Up to 15 mm.
L.–M. Cambrian, N. America, Asia, Australia, in fine clastic sediments from shelf-edge environments.
Pagetia bootes Walcott: M. Cambrian, British Columbia, Canada.

Order Redlichiida

Primitive trilobites with numerous thoracic segments with spinose tips, and generally a tiny pygidium consisting of one or a very few segments. Glabella typically well segmented and long, tapering or expanding forwards. Genal spines usually continued from a narrow, tubular cephalic border. Eyes typically cresc[illegible] by elongate, inflated palpebral ridges whic[illegible]ward part of glabella. L.–M. Cambrian. The [illegible]y readily divided into the two suborders recog[illegible]mber of families are distinguished within these[illegible]e do not attempt to differentiate them here.

Sub[illegible]na

Redl[illegible]oparian facial sutures. Early forms tend to h[illegible]onical glabella with glabellar furrows exte[illegible]rds; later forms often with glabella expa[illegible] inflated frontal lobe. L.–M. Cambrian.

Pl. [illegible][illegible]ossman, 1902
Re[illegible]obes very long, extending backwards to the [illegible]l ring. Genal spines set quite far forward, so t[illegible]order curves forwards to the genal spine. An[illegible]cial sutures strongly divergent in front of eye[illegible]racic segment carries a median spine, the base of which is shown on the illustrated example. Small pygidium formed of more than 1 segment. Up to 10 cm.
L. Cambrian. Middle East, Siberia, China, Australia, in shallow water sediments formed near the equator of the time.
Redlichia idonea Whitehouse: L. Cambrian, central Australia.

Pl. 9.5.9. *Paradoxides* Brongniart, 1822
Large Redlichiina, reaching almost 0.5 m, and with more than 15 thoracic segments. Glabella expands forwards to broadly rounded front. Glabellar furrows usually well defined and may

unite across mid-part of glabella. Free cheeks broad, with wide, sickle-like genal spines. Pygidium a small, spade-shaped plate, with indications of several segments on the axis; may be spinose.
M. Cambrian. Eastern N. America, S. America, Europe, N. Africa and Turkey, in fine clastic sediments deposited off shore.
Paradoxides gracilis (Boeck): M. Cambrian, Bohemia, Czechoslovakia.

Pl. 9.5.10. *Xystridura* Whitehouse, 1936
Redlichiina with glabella parallel-sided at first, expanded into broad frontal lobe, and with 3 pairs of short but distinct lateral glabellar furrows. Flattened cephalic border extended into relatively short genal spines. Thirteen thoracic segments with short pleural points. Pygidium relatively large for a redlichiid, with 2 pairs of marginal spines. Up to 10 cm.
M. Cambrian. Australia, in shallow-water sediments.
Xystridura saint-smithi (Chapman): M. Cambrian, Queensland, Australia.

Pl. 9.5.11. *Hamatolenus* Hupé, 1953
Redlichiina with glabella gently tapering to rounded front. Prominent eye-ridges run almost crosswise; in detail they continue as a band around the front of the glabella (part of this band can be seen on the right-hand side of the illustrated specimen). Cephalic border rather wide. Genal spines long and not in the 'advanced' position seen on *Redlichia*. Up to 25 cm.
L. Cambrian. Wales, Morocco, Spain, Israel, in fine clastic sediments.
Hamatolenus douglasi Bassett, Owens & Rushton: L. Cambrian, N. Wales.

Suborder Olenellina Resser, 1938

Redlichiida in which the facial sutures have become fused and non-functional. Typically, the glabella has rather deep lateral furrows, and the frontal glabellar lobe is an almost circular boss. L. Cambrian.

Pl. 9.5.12. *Paedumias* Walcott, 1910
Olenellina with thorax tapering back into a long pointed spine. The third thoracic segment is macropleural – about twice the width of the others and with long, spinose prolongations. Eyes of moderate length. Cephalon surrounded by a very narrow, tubular border. Up to 5 cm.
L. Cambrian. N. America, Greenland, Scotland, Siberia, in shallower-water sediments.
Paedumias cf. *yorkense* Resser & Howell: L. Cambrian, British Columbia, Canada.

Order Corynexochida

Typically middle-sized trilobites with large pygidium; thorax spinose, with 7 to 10 segments (full range for group 2 to 12 segments). Typical glabellar form is notably elongate, with the sides of the glabella often concave. Where developed, glabellar furrows have a splayed arrangement, the hind pair pointing sharply backwards, the anterior 3 pairs becoming progressively directed forwards. Some forms have pit-like glabellar furrows. The hypostoma is fused with the rostral plate. Eyes usually quite large and gently arcuate. Pygidial form variable; many species evolve pygidia which have a superficial resemblance to Ordovician and younger forms; some are spinose. Cambrian. Several families of corynexochids are currently recognized, but some are difficult to define and they are not used here.

Pl. 9.5.13. *Kootenia* Walcott, 1888
Corynexochid with glabellar furrows subdued; eyes of moderate size, placed at about mid-length of glabella. Thorax with 7 segments. Pygidium with well-defined border carrying several pairs of prominent spines; pygidial pleural fields furrowed. Up to 10 cm.
Cambrian. World-wide, in various facies.
Kootenia dawsoni Walcott: M. Cambrian, British Columbia, Canada.

Pl. 9.5.14. *Olenoides* Meek, 1877
Corynexochid with broad glabella carrying 3 pairs of glabella furrows; eyes rather small for the group. Thorax with 7 segments. Pygidium large, with slender marginal spines, and incomplete border compared with *Kootenia*. Pygidium shows both pleural and interpleural furrows, very similar in form to the thoracic segments. Up to 15 cm.
M. Cambrian. The Americas and Asia, in various facies.
Olenoides serratus Rominger: M. Cambrian, British Columbia, Canada.

Pl. 9.5.15. *Ogygopsis* Walcott, 1889
Corynexochid with broadly oval exoskeleton lacking pygidial spines. Long glabella, without obvious furrows. Facial sutures diverge slightly in front of eyes. Thorax of 8 segments. Pygidium longer than cephalon, composed of numerous segments which are clearly expressed on the pleural fields. Narrow, convex pygidial border. Up to 10 cm. This trilobite closely resembles the later asaphids, but a close relationship is unlikely.
M. Cambrian, N. America, in fine clastic sediments and impure limestones.
Ogygopsis klotzi (Rominger): M. Cambrian, British Columbia, Canada.

Pl. 9.5.16, 17. *Oryctocephalus* Walcott, 1886
Corynexochid with glabellar furrows reduced to deep pits. Eyes very large, extending back on a level with the occipital furrow. Very long genal spines. Thorax of 7 segments with long, spinose tips. Large pygidium with deep pleural furrows that slope progressively backwards; several pairs of marginal spines of which 1 pair (see Pl. 9.5.17) is generally greatly extended backwards. Up to 5 cm.
M. Cambrian. Widespread, in fine clastic sediments and impure limestones.
Oryctocephalus reynoldsi Reed: M. Cambrian, British Columbia, Canada.

Pl. 9.5.18. *Albertella* Walcott, 1908
Corynexochid with elongate exoskeleton, and relatively broad axis compared with pleural areas. Glabella with deep furrows and wide occipital ring. Eyes very large and close to glabella. Of the 7 thoracic segments, the third and/or fourth has extended pleural spines. Pygidium narrow, with a single pair of long marginal spines; axis with 4 to 7 rings. Up to 8 cm.
M. Cambrian. N. America, in fine clastic sediments and impure limestones.
Albertella bosworthi Walcott: M. Cambrian, British Columbia, Canada.

Pl. 9.5.19. *Stephenaspis* Rasetti, 1951
Corynexochid somewhat resembling *Albertella*, but generally broader. Glabella closely approaches a narrow cranidial rim; glabellar furrows deep. Nine thoracic segments with progressively longer spines backwards. Large pygidium with straight lateral margins which continue into rather delicate, slightly inward-curved spines. Broad pygidial border. Up to 10 cm.

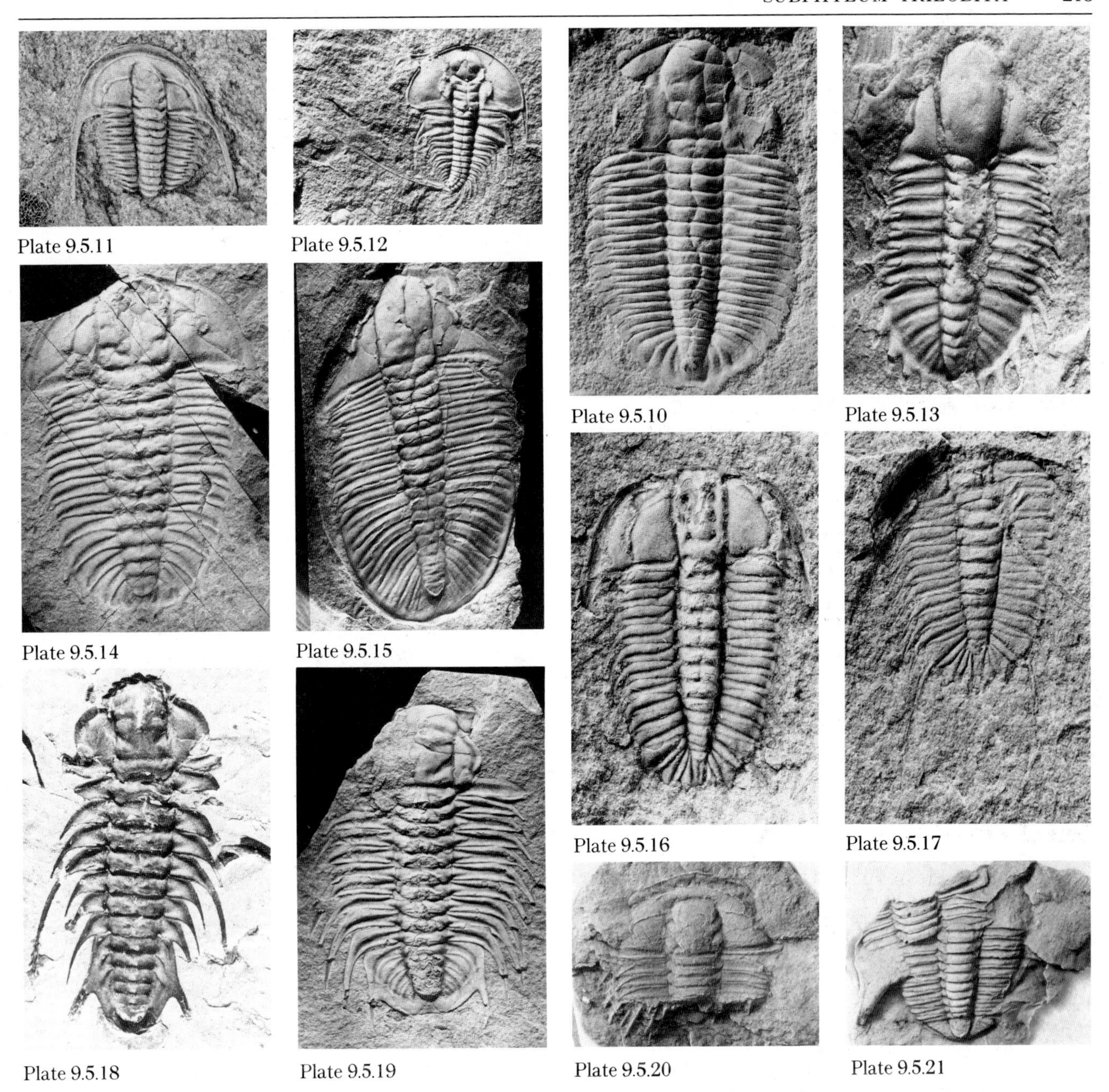

Plate 9.5.11 Plate 9.5.12 Plate 9.5.10 Plate 9.5.13

Plate 9.5.14 Plate 9.5.15 Plate 9.5.16 Plate 9.5.17

Plate 9.5.18 Plate 9.5.19 Plate 9.5.20 Plate 9.5.21

M. Cambrian. Canada, in deeper water sediments.
Stephenaspis bispinosa Rasetti: M. Cambrian, British Columbia, Canada.

Order Ptychopariida

A very large and heterogeneous group of trilobites, posing many problems for classification. Specialized offshoots from the group produce peculiar trilobites which are hard to frame in a general diagnosis. The typical ptychoparioid has opisthoparian facial sutures and a gently tapering glabella, broadly rounded in front, with 3 pairs of rather narrow glabellar furrows which are parallel to one another rather than splayed in a corynexochoid pattern. A rostral plate was probably present primitively – but some of the subgroups are typified by modifications to the ventral sutures. Most ptychoparioids have 8 or more thoracic segments with simple diagonal pleural furrows, but some groups have 6, 5 or exceptionally 4 segments. Pygidia vary enormously: the typical ptychoparioid has a small pygidium with a border in the Cambrian, and a large pygidium with or without a border in the Ordovician and later. Border spines are sporadically developed. L. Cambrian–Devonian (Frasnian).

Suborder Ptychopariina

Primitive ptychoparioids, for the most part with the typical tapering glabellar form and 3 pairs of glabellar furrows. Opisthoparian facial sutures usual (a few become proparian, others blind and hence sutures become marginal), with eyes medially placed not far from glabella. Anterior sections of facial sutures are usually slightly divergent to convergent; posterior sections moderately to highly divergent. Blade-like genal spines are usual. The thorax is generally long, relative to the length of the pygidium. L. Cambrian–Ordovician (Ashgill). Because this large and varied group of trilobites is difficult to classify we only employ superfamilies here.

SUPERFAMILY PTYCHOPARIACEA

Generalized Ptychopariina with 12 to 21 thoracic segments and a small pygidium. Usually gently sloping preglabellar field, narrow cephalic rim. Axial width narrow compared with that of genal and pleural areas. L. Cambrian–Ordovician (Tremadoc).

Pl. 9.5.20, 21. *Proteuloma* Sdzuy, 1958
Ptychopariacean with broad glabella bearing 2 pairs of deep glabellar furrows. Small eyes far out across cheeks. Cephalon covered with fine granules. Border furrow carries sparse, deep pits. Thorax of 14 segments. Pygidium broadly triangular with a very narrow border; obtusely rounded pygidial axis extends almost to border. Up to 10 cm.
Ordovician (Tremadoc). England, Wales, Germany, in fine clastic sediments.
Proteuloma cf. *geinitzi* (Barrande): Tremadoc, Wales.

Pl. 9.5.22. *Elrathia* Walcott, 1924
Ptychopariacean with perfect oval exoskeleton, pygidium accounting for about one-fifth the total length. Moderately wide preglabellar field; flat cephalic rim (partly broken in illustrated specimen). Eyes quite close to glabella; posterior sections of facial sutures strongly divergent. Thirteen thoracic segments with deep pleural furrows. Such furrows weak on pygidium which has a distinct flattened border. Up to 3 cm.
M. Cambrian. USA, in fine clastic sediments and carbonates.
Elrathia kingii (Meek): M. Cambrian, western USA.

Pl. 9.5.23. *Mexicella* Lochman, 1948
Ptychopariacean with egg-shaped outline, tapering backwards. Cranidium unusually effaced for a ptychopariacean, with glabella not defined by deep furrows. Preglabellar field long; cephalic border not sharply defined; eyes far out, relatively small. Genal spines lacking on the species illustrated. Twenty-one thoracic segments, thorax tapers back to a tiny smooth pygidium. Up to 4 cm.
M. Cambrian. N. America, in platform carbonates.
Mexicella stator (Walcott): M. Cambrian, British Columbia.

SUPERFAMILY CONOCORYPHACEA
These are secondarily blind Ptychopariina. They are mostly small to medium-sized trilobites with numerous segments and diminutive pygidium – but some of the later forms, such as *Shumardia*, have few thoracic segments and large pygidia. The Conocoryphacea is undoubtedly a polyphyletic group: the forms included within the superfamily were derived from several different groups of ptychoparioids. L. Cambrian–Ordovician (Ashgill).

Pl. 9.5.24. *Bailiella* Matthew, 1885
Apart from being blind this is a typical ptychoparioid. Small eye-ridges remain, running across fixed cheeks near front of glabella. Facial sutures are near lateral margins of cephalon – the specimen illustrated has lost its spinose free cheeks. Strongly developed cranidial border, widening medially, and short preglabellar field. Thorax of 16 segments. Small, wide pygidium with convex axis extending almost to margin. About 3 cm.
M. Cambrian. Eastern N. America, Scandinavia, Wales, N. Africa, Asia, in fine offshore clastic sediments.
Bailiella lyellii (Hicks): M. Cambrian, Wales.

Pl. 9.5.25. *Hartshillina* Lake, 1940
Highly effaced conocoryphacean. Cephalon very wide, lacking genal spines. Only posterior part of glabella is visible as axial furrows which converge forwards. Posterior border furrow deep; anterior cranidial border lacking. Eight or 9 segments; thoracic axis broad (posterior segments have median spines). Small pygidium with very blunt axis, no border, unfurrowed pleural fields. Surface covered with minute granules. About 2 cm.
M. Cambrian, England and Wales, in fine offshore clastic sediments.
Hartshillina spinata (Illing): M. Cambrian, N. Wales.

Pl. 9.5.26. *Shumardia* Billings, 1862
Small conocoryphacean, less than 0.5 cm long. Glabella with conspicuous lateral lobes at front; long occipital ring. Thorax with 5 to 7 segments, the fourth conspicuously macropleural. Pygidium transverse to elongate, relatively large, axis having at least 3 rings. *Shumardia* is a good example of a secondarily specialized, miniature trilobite. It may have been adapted for a shallow burrowing mode of life. It is probably not closely related to the other conocoryphaceans illustrated here.
Uppermost Cambrian–Ordovician (Ashgill). World-wide, in various facies.
Shumardia salopiensis (Callaway): Tremadoc, England.

SUPERFAMILY DAMESELLACEA
Ptychopariina with tapering glabella, usually somewhat truncate at the front, and with preglabellar field short or absent. Characteristic pygidia have marginal spines, often several pairs of varying lengths.
M.–U. Cambrian, especially in Asia.

Pl. 9.5.27. *Drepanura* Bergeron, 1899
Pygidium only illustrated here. Damesellacea with glabella tapering rapidly with 3 pairs of short lateral furrows; rather small eyes forwardly placed. Thirteen thoracic segments with spinose projections. Pygidium with short axis. Seven to 9 pairs of marginal spines of which the first pair is greatly lengthened. Pygidia of this type were long known to Chinese alchemists.
Upper M.–Lower U. Cambrian, E. Asia and W. Europe, in platform carbonates. (ANGEL WINGS.)
Drepanura premesnili (Bergeron): Cambrian, China.

SUPERFAMILY DIKELOCEPHALACEA
A varied group of ptychoparioids, often with large pygidia and tapering or subrectangular glabellae. Glabellar furrows may pass completely across glabella. Preglabellar field is usually both long and wide, and genal areas generally extended and flat. The typical pygidium has a broad, unfurrowed border, with wide doublure beneath. Thirteen or fewer thoracic segments. U. Cambrian.

Pl. 9.5.28, 29. *Dikelocephalus* Owen, 1852
Large Dikelocephalacea; glabella with first glabellar furrow passing completely across; weak second furrow. Highly curved palpebral lobes close to glabella; strap-like postocular cheeks. Anterior border of cranidium not defined. Broad, flat preglabellar field. Broad free cheeks with rather short genal spines. Wide, fan-like pygidium with few axial rings and backward-curving pleural furrows; short spines at lateral edges. Up to 20 cm.
U. Cambrian. N. America, in shallow-water sandstones.
Dikelocephalus sp.: U. Cambrian, Minnesota, USA.

Pl. 9.5.30, 31. *Pterocephalia* Roemer, 1852
Dikelocephalacean with tapering glabella, with 4 pairs of glabellar furrows, the anterior 2 pairs very short. Broad, dished preglabellar field. Facial sutures curve outward at first in front of eyes, then converge again near the margin. Eyes smaller than *Dikelocephalus* and further from glabella. Large pygidium with axis with many axial rings, and 6 or 7 pairs of distinct pleural ribs. Up to 8 cm.
U. Cambrian. N. America, in platform carbonates.
Pterocephalia sanctisabae Roemer: U. Cambrian, Texas, USA.

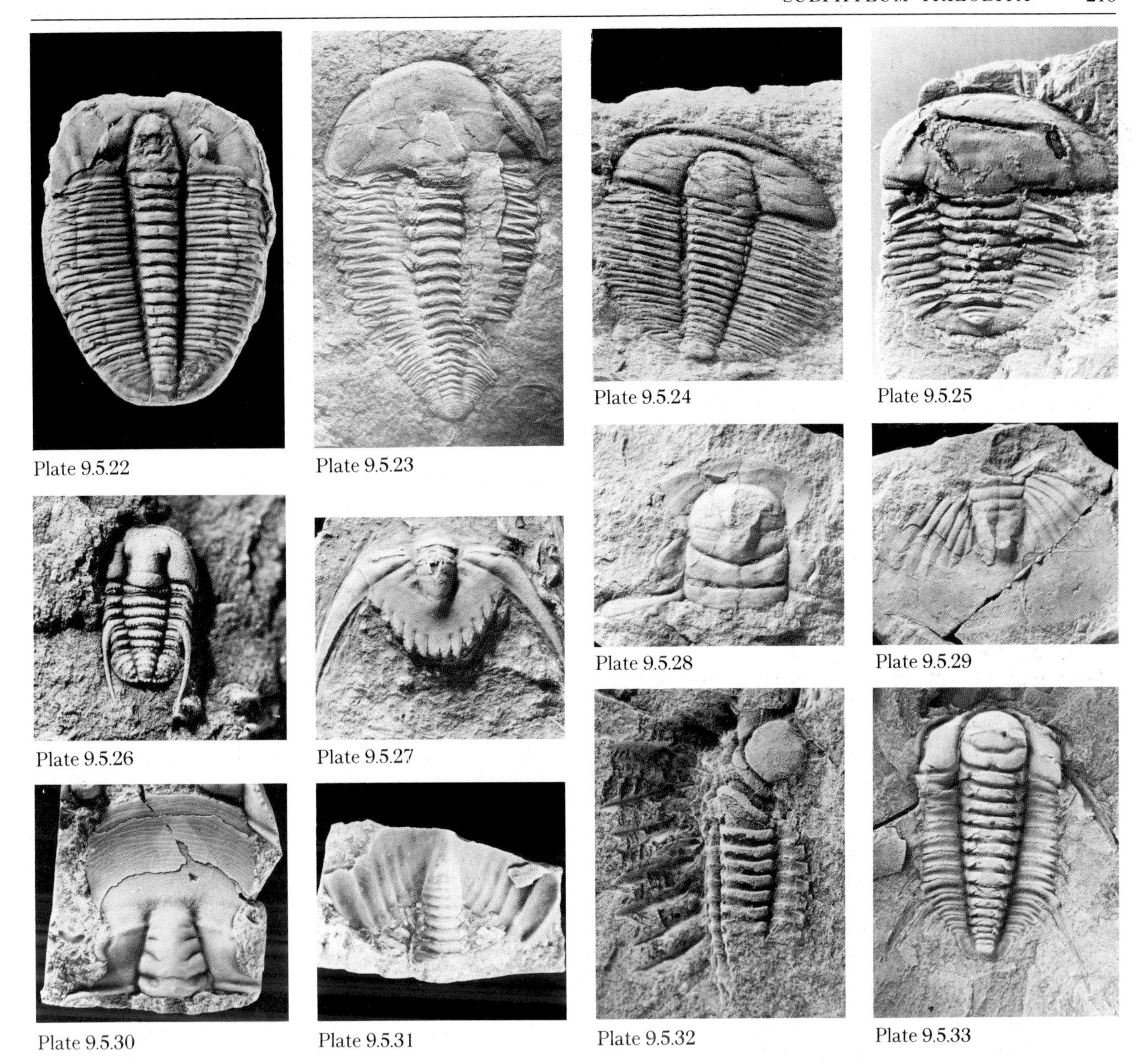

Plate 9.5.22 Plate 9.5.23 Plate 9.5.24 Plate 9.5.25 Plate 9.5.26 Plate 9.5.27 Plate 9.5.28 Plate 9.5.29 Plate 9.5.30 Plate 9.5.31 Plate 9.5.32 Plate 9.5.33

SUPERFAMILY KOMASPIDACEA

Convex and narrow Ptychopariina, with prominent axis and relatively narrow pleural areas. Glabella typically flat-fronted. Eyes usually very large, often extending to more than half cephalic length. Pygidium small, with few segments. The Cambrian and Ordovician members of the superfamily probably had separate origins. U. Cambrian–Ordovician (Ashgill).

Pl. 9.5.32. *Carolinites* Kobayashi, 1940

Komaspidacean with glabella expanded forwards, very convex, especially over occipital ring. Anterior border narrow and upward-arched. Eyes (not preserved on specimen shown) enormous, running along whole side of head. Thorax with 10 segments, very narrow pleurae with stubby tips. Small pygidium, tapering to parallel-sided. Up to 3 cm.

L.–M. Ordovician. Almost world-wide (not S. Europe and Africa), in all facies.

Carolinites sibiricus Chugaeva: Llanvirn, W. Ireland.

Pl. 9.5.33. *Irvingella* Ulrich & Resser, 1924

Komaspidacean with glabella having 1 deep glabellar furrow passing right across. Curved palpebral lobes defined by deep furrows. Eyes very large; long genal spines (one shown on right of photograph). Thorax with 11 or 12 segments, the posterior ones spinose (eighth macropleural on illustrated species). Pygidium semicircular, small, with unfurrowed pleural fields. Up to 3 cm.

U. Cambrian. World-wide, in various facies.

Irvingella nuneatonensis (Sharman): U. Cambrian, England.

SUPERFAMILY NORWOODIACEA

Superfamily includes proparian Ptychopariina. Most species are small, with eyes sited in an anterior position. Some acquire as many as 42 thoracic segments; others have short thoraces and larger pygidia. U. Cambrian, ? L. Ordovician.

Pl. 9.5.34, 35. *Holcacephalus* Resser, 1938

Norwoodiacean with narrow, slightly tapering glabella, somewhat truncate in front. Small eyes, with prominent almost transverse eye-ridges. Broad preglabellar field. Cephalic border prominent. Short, outward-directed genal spines. Prominent occipital spine. Eight narrow thoracic segments. Moderate-sized pygidium with 2 or 3 axial rings, and furrowed pleural fields. About 10 mm.

U. Cambrian. N. America, in platform carbonates.

Holcacephalus sp.: U. Cambrian, Quebec, Canada.

SUPERFAMILY OLENACEA

Ptychopariina with very varied dorsal exoskeletons with regard to glabellar shape, size of pygidium and number of thoracic segments. All except the most primitive *Olenus* species have the free cheeks yoked together by fusion of the rostral plate to the genal doublure. The cephalic doublure is always a thin strip medially. The hypostoma was not attached to the doublure. Exoskeleton thin, and usually caecate. Olenids have the eyes in various positions and they may be large or minute; none are blind. U. Cambrian–Ordovician (Ashgill). Most olenaceans lived in relatively deep-water habitats.

Pl. 9.5.36. *Olenus* Dalman, 1827
Olenacean with subrectangular, often slightly tapering glabella, with 3 pairs of lateral glabellar furrows. Preglabellar field present; eyes medially placed; postocular sutures straight, defining sharply triangular cheeks. Genal spines present. Thorax of 13 to 15 segments, spinose, with rather flat pleurae and narrow facets. Pygidium small, often with little marginal spines. About 3 cm.
U. Cambrian. Widespread.
Olenus micrurus Salter: U. Cambrian, N. Wales.

Pl. 9.5.37. *Parabolina* Salter, 1849
Olenacean with slightly longer glabella than *Olenus* and short preglabellar field. Eyes small and anteriorly positioned. Twelve thoracic segments are prolonged into long spinose tips. Large pygidium differing little in pleural structure from preceding segments; long and prominent marginal spines. Up to 12 cm.
U. Cambrian. Europe, S. America, eastern N. America, Kazakhstan.
Parabolina spinulosa (Wahlenberg): U. Cambrian, Wales.

Pl. 9.5.38. *Peltura* Milne Edwards, 1840
Olenacean with oval exoskeleton having broad axial regions compared with *Olenus* or *Parabolina*. Subsquare glabella, slightly tapering forwards, and closely encroaching on narrow cranidial border. Small eyes, in an anterior position; postocular sutures slightly convex outward. No genal spines. Thorax of 12 segments. Small transverse pygidium with a blunt axis, few segments and sometimes with marginal spines. Up to 4 cm.
U. Cambrian. Europe, eastern N. America. Where it occurs, it does so in great abundance.
Peltura scarabaeoides (Wahlenberg): U. Cambrian, N. Wales.

Pl. 9.5.39. *Triarthrus* Green, 1832
Often small olenid with 12 to 16 segments and usually lacking genal spines. Semicircular cephalon with prominent borders. Glabella has 2 pairs of deep, subparallel glabellar furrows which curve gently backwards. Small eyes are usually placed close to the glabella opposite the more anterior of these glabella furrows. Thorax tapers posteriorly to small, triangular pygidium, with up to 5 segments, and furrowed pleurae. About 3 cm. This is one of the few trilobites with appendages preserved. Our photograph shows a pair of antennae, and on the right-hand side some of the walking limbs.
Ordovician. World-wide.
Triarthrus eatoni (Hall): Llandeilo, New York, USA.

SUPERFAMILY PTYCHASPIDACEA

Convex Ptychopariina with pygidium somewhat smaller than the cephalon. Two or 3 pairs of glabellar furrows, posterior pair often transglabellar; typically the glabella is convex and has a truncate front. Stout genal spines are characteristic. Thorax of 12 segments, or fewer. Pygidium usually with distinctly furrowed pleural fields. A granulose surface sculpture is typical. This superfamily is probably more closely allied to the Dikelocephalacea than current classification will allow. U. Cambrian, of platformal sediments in N. America and Asia.

Pl. 9.5.40. *Prosaukia* Ulrich & Resser, 1933
Photograph shows slab with typical cranidium and numerous free cheeks. Glabella quadrate, with 2 deep pairs of glabellar furrows. Narrow preglabellar field, and distinct anterior border. Large palpebral lobes, far back. Lateral border furrow on free cheek stops short of genal spine. Pygidium large, with median flattening. Up to 10 cm.
U. Cambrian, N. America, NE. Asia.
Prosaukia cf. *misa* (Hall): U. Cambrian, Wisconsin, USA.

SUPERFAMILY REMOPLEURIDACEA

Opisthoparian, large-eyed Ptychopariina, with ventral median suture, and typically with spinose pygidia. Two or 3 pairs of slit-like glabellar furrows are usual, often isolated within the glabella. The glabella itself usually shows a bulge in width just in front of the occipital ring, and in later forms this bulge expands to fill the area between the palpebral lobes. Pygidial spines are pointed-tipped; there may be 1 pair to many (usually 3 or 4). A few early forms have entire pygidial margins. U. Cambrian–Ordovician (Ashgill). World-wide.

Pl. 9.5.41. *Amphitryon* Hawle & Corda, 1847
Remopleuridacean with glabella broad and virtually circular in front of the occipital ring, with 3 pairs of furrows; palpebral lobes extend along entire length of glabella. Broad cranidial border extending into wide genal spines. Thorax of 11 segments with wide pleurae for a remopleurid, extended into spines. Pygidium with 2 pairs of spines. Free cheeks not shown on illustrated specimen. Up to 8 cm.
U. Ordovician (Ashgill). Sweden, Czechoslovakia, Great Britain, in various facies.
Amphitryon radians (Barrande): Ashgill, Bohemia, Czechoslovakia.

Pl. 9.5.42. *Remopleurides* Portlock, 1843
Glabella with circular form like *Amphitryon*, with 2 pairs of glabellar furrows usually weakly shown on exterior surface. Free cheeks with narrow genal spines (not shown on specimen illustrated). Thorax of 11 segments, with very broad axis and short pleurae. One segment macropleural on species illustrated. Pygidium very small, usually with 1 axial ring and a bilobed terminal piece, and 2 short pairs of marginal spines. Up to 5 cm.
L.–U. Ordovician. Cosmopolitan, in various facies. Probably an actively swimming trilobite.
Remopleurides sp.: Caradoc, Scotland.

Pl. 9.5.43. *Bohemilla* Barrande, 1872
Bizarre remopleuridacean modified for pelagic life, at one time excluded from the trilobites. Three pairs of glabellar furrows, the first pair hooked. Huge eyes far forward; genal spines curve out almost sideways in very advanced position; thorax of 5 (more?) segments, with pleurae almost entirely reduced. Pygidium unknown. Up to 3 cm.
L.–U. Ordovician. Czechoslovakia, Great Britain, in fine offshore clastic sediments.
Bohemilla stupenda Barrande: Caradoc, Bohemia, Czechoslovakia.

SUPERFAMILY SOLENOPLEURACEA

A heterogeneous group of somewhat generalized Ptychopariina with generally small pygidia with narrow borders. Glabella usually domed, with a broadly arcuate frontal outline. Degree

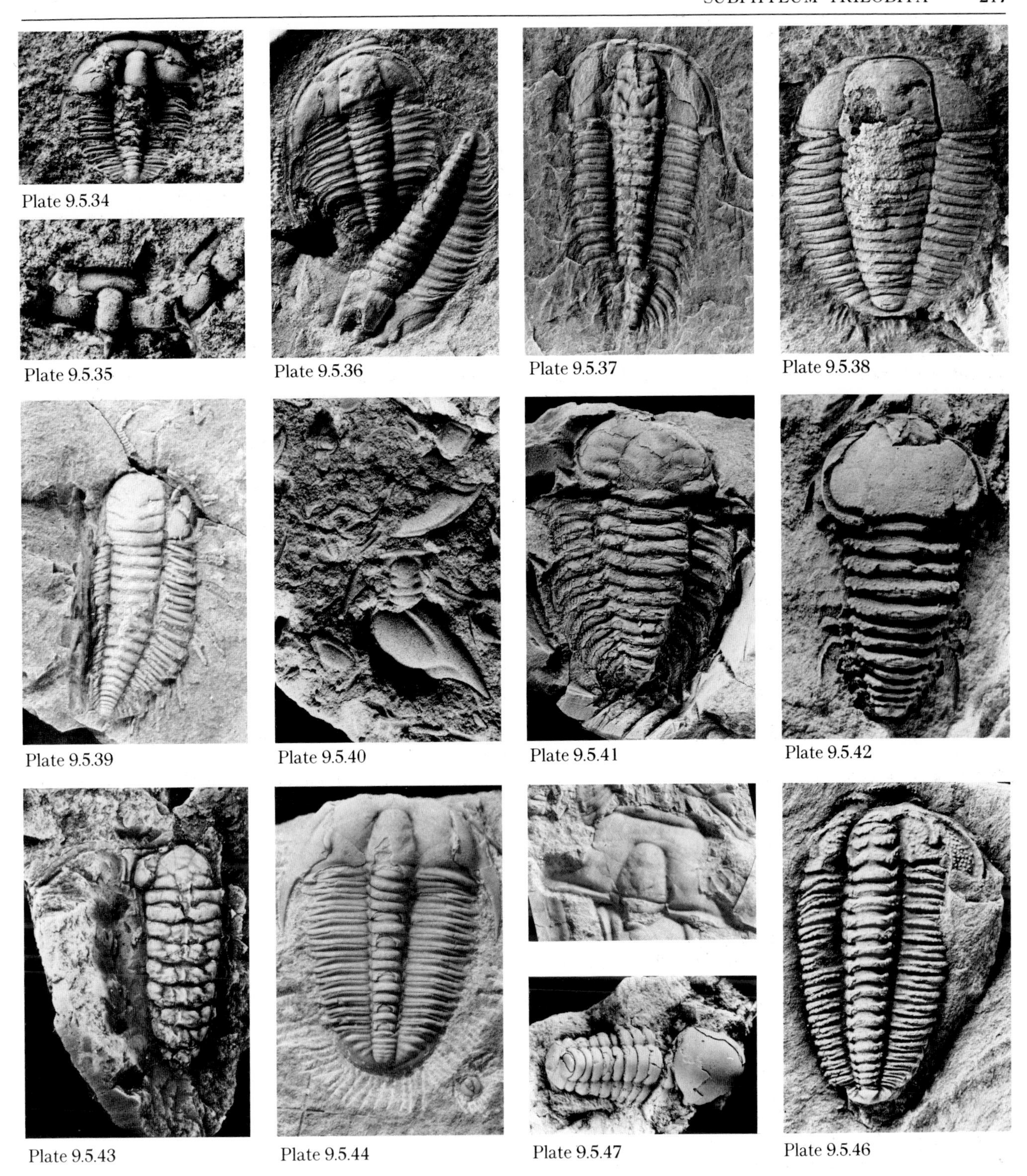

Plate 9.5.34

Plate 9.5.35

Plate 9.5.36

Plate 9.5.37

Plate 9.5.38

Plate 9.5.39

Plate 9.5.40

Plate 9.5.41

Plate 9.5.42

Plate 9.5.43

Plate 9.5.44

Plate 9.5.47

Plate 9.5.46

of effacement variable. Characteristically, the group has a dorsal sculpture of tubercles or granules; some are smooth. M. Cambrian–L. Ordovician.

Pl. 9.5.44, 45. *Asthenopsis* Whitehouse, 1939
Solenopleuracean with broadly ovate exoskeleton. Glabella tapers forwards, and carries 3 pairs of glabellar furrows which show as broad depressions. Eyes quite close to posterior border furrows. Well-defined, broad border which continues into broad genal spines. Fourteen thoracic segments with tiny spinose tips. Pygidium with 5 axial rings, 3 pleural ribs, and distinct, flat border. Up to 4 cm.
M. Cambrian. Australia, in platform carbonates.
Asthenopsis laevior Whitehouse: M. Cambrian, Australia.

Pl. 9.5.46. *Sao* Barrande, 1846
Solenopleuracean with elongate exoskeleton covered in coarse tubercles. Glabella with glabellar lobes elevated into crest-like structures. Thorax with 17 segments. Pygidium very small, with only 2 segments. Up to 5 cm. There are spines on the thorax which are not preserved on the illustrated specimen.
M. Cambrian. Europe, in fine clastic sediments.
Sao hirsuta Barrande: M. Cambrian, Bohemia, Czechoslovakia.

Pl. 9.5.47. *Stenopilus* Raymond, 1924
Cranidium virtually featureless; small palpebral lobes in anterior position. Thorax of 10 segments loosely held together, with convex axis; downsloping pleurae with blunt tips. Small pygidium with knob-like axis, border more or less vertical. Up

to 3 cm. Classification of this trilobite in this superfamily is problematic. On Pl. 9.5.47, the head is to the right.
U. Cambrian. USA, ?Siberia, in platform carbonates, especially among stromatolites.
Stenopilus pronus Raymond: U. Cambrian, Oklahoma, USA.

SUPERFAMILY BURLINGIACEA

A small group (2 genera) of aberrant Ptychopariina with perfectly oval, rigid dorsal shields which may have lacked articulation. Strongly proparian. Pleural areas progressively backward-deflexed posteriorly. M.–U. Cambrian.

Pl. 9.5.48. *Schmalenseeia* Moberg, 1903
Minute (<3 mm) burlingiacean with a narrow axis. Glabella tapering, with well-marked furrows and a small circular frontal lobe. Border flat, with a median ridge. Seven thoracic segments with flat pleurae. Pygidium hardly differentiated from thorax, with 6 or 7 axial rings. Median tubercles on thoracic and pygidial axis.
U. Cambrian. Scandinavia, England, Newfoundland, in fine offshore clastic sediments.
Schmalenseeia amphionura Moberg: U. Cambrian, Newfoundland.

SUPERFAMILY MARJUMIACEA

A polyphyletic assemblage of advanced Ptychopariina. Thoracic segments with falcate tips, 14 or fewer in number. The anterior border on the cranidium is usually prominent and convex. Eyes of moderate size usually close to the glabella, and not in a forward position. Pygidium of moderate to large size, well differentiated in structure from thorax, sometimes with spinose margin. Upper M.–U. Cambrian.

Pl. 9.5.49. *Modocia* Walcott, 1924
Oval dorsal exoskeleton a few cm long. Glabella tapering; glabellar furrows hardly defined. Preglabellar field of moderate width. Thorax of 13 to 14 segments; on illustrated species the ninth bears a median spine. Pygidium transversely elliptical, with 3 axial rings, and without a distinct border. Up to 3 cm.
Upper M.–U. Cambrian. N. America, Europe, in fine clastic sediments and carbonates.
Modocia anglica Rushton: U. Cambrian, England.

Suborder Asaphina

Ptychopariida with cephalon and pygidium equal in size, or nearly so; thorax with 6 to 9 segments. A high degree of cephalic effacement is common and glabellar furrows are often not visible. Pygidial and cephalic doublure often wide. In most of the group the free cheeks are separated by a median suture on the ventral side; in some the cheeks have become fused as a single piece. On the dorsal surface the anterior sections of the facial sutures often curve adaxially at the border to meet in front of the glabella. U. Cambrian–Ordovician (Ashgill). Divided into a number of large families, which are distinctive enough to be diagnosed below.

FAMILY ASAPHIDAE

Asaphina with 8 thoracic segments. Ventral median suture present. Usually moderate to large semicircular eyes placed close to glabella. Effacement of glabellar furrows is usual; many forms also lose the occipital furrow. Large pygidia are semicircular to triangular, with broad doublure, formed of numerous segments, which may or may not show on the axis and/or pleural fields. A forked hypostoma is developed in many asaphids, and is almost confined to this group. U. Cambrian–Ordovician (Ashgill). Includes large species, commonly exceeding 15 cm in length.

Pl. 9.5.50. *Asaphus* Brongniart, 1822
Asaphid with broadly triangular cephalon with rounded genal angles. Glabella with distinct occipital ring, and expanded frontal lobe. No lateral borders on free cheeks. Broad articulating facets on thorax. Pygidium without a border; long axis shows clear segmentation, but this is weakly reflected on the pleural fields. Up to 8 cm.
Ordovician (Arenig–Llandeilo), Baltic, especially in carbonates.
Asaphus expansus (Wahlenberg): Llanvirn, Sweden.

Pl. 9.5.51. *Ogygiocarella* Harrington & Leanza, 1957
Asaphid with a perfect, broad oval exoskeleton, with pygidium larger than cephalon. Glabella with slight constriction at about one-third its length; glabellar furrows visible. Genal spines present. Thorax with very narrow axis, and short, articulating facets. Pygidium with numerous segments expressed both on axis and pleural fields, furrows extending near margin. Up to 18 cm.
Ordovician (Arenig–Llandeilo). Europe, S. America, in fine clastic sediments.
Ogygiocarella angustissima (Salter): Llandeilo, England.

Pl. 9.5.52. *Basilicus* Salter, 1849
Very large (can exceed 30 cm) asaphid, elongate-oval, with long pygidium exceeding the cephalon in length. Hypostoma deeply forked. Glabella largely effaced posteriorly, not showing occipital ring. Cephalon surrounded by flattened border which extends into genal spine. Pygidium likewise with flattened border. Prominent pygidial ribs do not extend on to border. Photograph is of an external mould.
Ordovician (Llanvirn–Llandeilo). Great Britain, ?China, N. America, especially in carbonates and coarse clastic sediments.
Basilicus tyrannus (Murchison): Llandeilo, Wales.

Pl. 9.5.53. *Isotelus* DeKay, 1824
Very effaced asaphid, with both cephalon and pygidium with triangular outline, and equal in size. Genal spines lacking. Glabella hardly visible; short, triangular postocular fixed cheeks. Rather poorly defined border present on both cephalon and pygidium. Specimens of 15 cm not unusual.
Ordovician (Llandeilo–Ashgill). N. America, Siberia, Greenland, Europe, China, in shallow-water sediments, especially limestones.
Isotelus gigas Dekay: Llandeilo, New York, USA.

Pl. 9.5.54. *Asaphellus* Callaway, 1877
Asaphid with relatively small eyes. Preocular facial sutures not highly divergent; postocular sutures curve backwards sharply at their ends. Glabella effaced. Cephalic and pygidial border present. Specimen figured shows doublure: on thorax doublure is penetrated by small holes (panderian openings). Pygidium with pleural fields hardly showing segmentation. Up to 10 cm.
Ordovician (Tremadoc). England, Wales, S. America, China, in fine clastic sediments and carbonates.
Asaphellus homfrayi (Salter): Tremadoc, Welsh borderland.

FAMILY DIKELOKEPHALINIDAE

Asaphina with short, tapering glabella; depressed areas adjacent to base of glabella. Broad, flat preglabellar field, proportionately wider than in Asaphidae. More or less fan-shaped pygidium with 1 or 2 pairs of marginal spines. Ordovician (Tremadoc–Llandeilo).

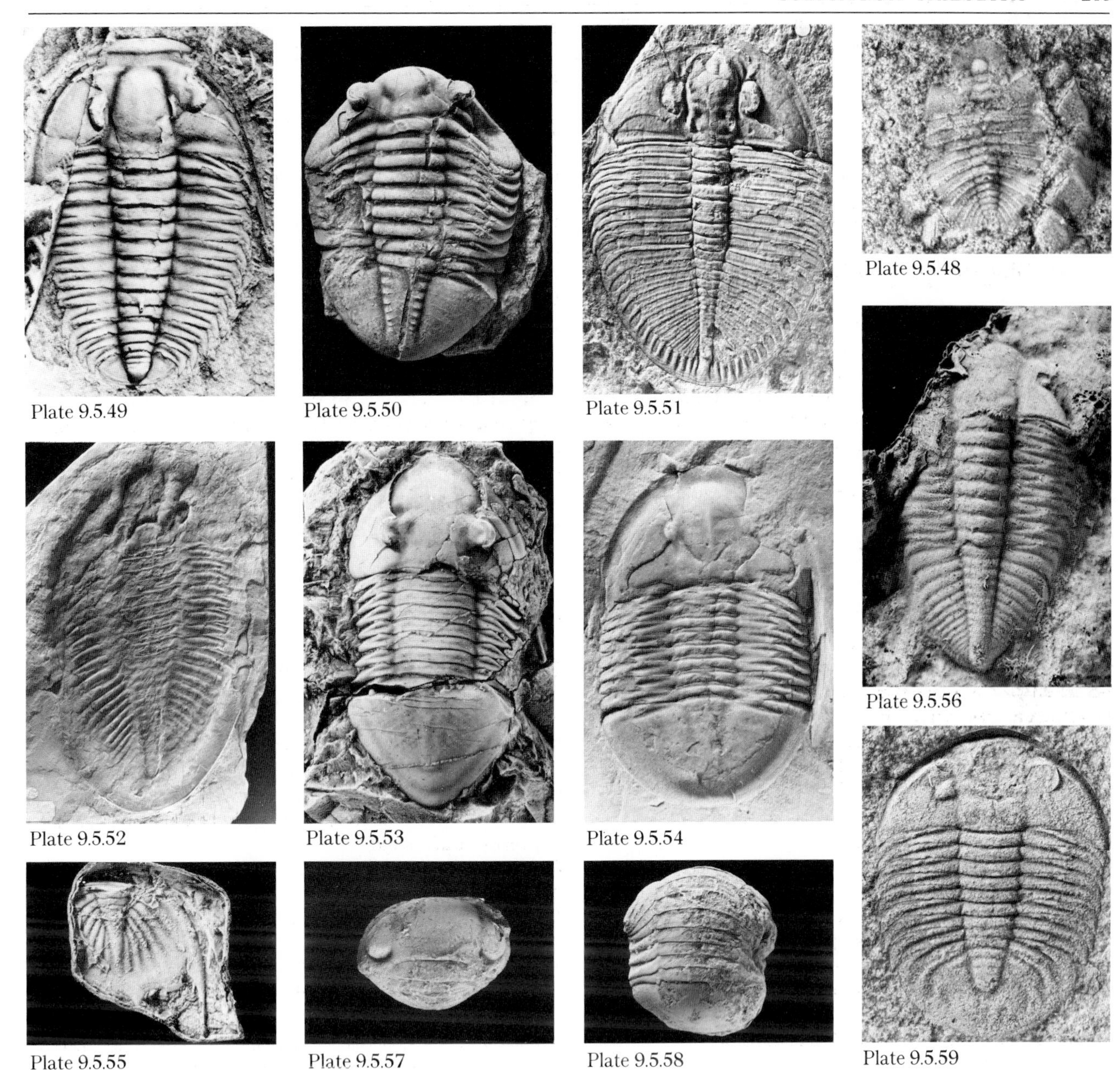

Plate 9.5.48

Plate 9.5.49

Plate 9.5.50

Plate 9.5.51

Plate 9.5.52

Plate 9.5.53

Plate 9.5.54

Plate 9.5.56

Plate 9.5.55

Plate 9.5.57

Plate 9.5.58

Plate 9.5.59

Pl. 9.5.55. *Hungioides* Kobayashi, 1936
Pygidium only shown here. Cranidium with tapering glabella which comes to a point anteriorly. Eyes large, far back. Large pygidium with progressively backward-sloping ribs, wide border, and 2 pairs of marginal spines, the first pair long. Length of whole trilobite probably exceeded 10 cm.
Ordovician (Arenig–Llanvirn). Czechoslovakia, Germany, China, Australia, S. America, in shallow-water sediments.
Hungioides acutinasus Fortey and Shergold: Arenig, central Australia.

SUPERFAMILY CYCLOPYGACEA
Medium to large Asaphina, with 5 to 9 thoracic segments. Glabella expands forwards to entire cranidial width in front of palpebral lobes. Eyes greatly enlarged in some forms. Primitively with median suture as in asaphids, but many later forms have united cheeks. Glabella usually without incised glabellar furrows. Pygidia with or without marginal spines. Hypostoma not forked. Ordovician.

FAMILY TAIHUNGSHANIIDAE
Cyclopygacea with 8 thoracic segments, retaining median sutures. Pygidium with pair (rarely 2 pairs) of marginal spines, and may show many segments. Ordovician.

Pl. 9.5.56. *Taihungshania* Sun, 1931
Taihungshaniid with well-defined glabella, eyes in anterior position. Thoracic segments with spinose tips. Large, long pygidium, having narrow axis with many axial rings, and at least 10 pleural ribs, and long pair of lateral spines off first segment. Length up to 10 cm.
Ordovician (Tremadoc–Llanvirn). France, China, in fine clastic sediments.
Taihungshania miqueli (Thoral): Arenig, France.

FAMILY NILEIDAE
Cyclopygacea with 7 to 8 thoracic segments; all except earliest have cheeks united by a wide band of doublure. Glabella with prominent median tubercle. Eyes small to large, but never globular. Pygidium semicircular, often with a rather short axis, or totally effaced. Ranges through Ordovician.

Pl. 9.5.57, 58. *Nileus* Dalman, 1827
Short, wide cephalon with broad axial region, but glabella

hardly defined. Very large eyes. Narrow free cheeks lacking genal spines. Thoracic segments with strong, adaxial articulation. When enrolled, cephalon fits exactly against pygidium. Wide pygidium is virtually featureless, but may have ill-defined short axis and border. Up to 8 cm.
Ordovician (Tremadoc–Caradoc). Almost world-wide, mainly in carbonates.
Nileus armadillo Dalman: Llanvirn, Sweden.

Pl. 9.5.59. *Homalopteon* Salter, 1866
Nileid with relatively small, anteriorly placed eyes and short genal spines. Glabella quite well defined at base; postocular cheeks wide. Semicircular pygidium with short axis. Two pairs of rather deep pygidial pleural furrows which curve backwards distally. Up to 8 cm.
Ordovician (Llanvirn–Llandeilo). Great Britain.
Homalopteon radians (M'Coy): Llandeilo, England.

FAMILY CYCLOPYGIDAE

Cyclopygacea with hypertrophied, globular eyes, taking up virtually all the free cheek. No genal spines. Thorax short. Glabella later becomes almost featureless. Except earliest forms, free cheeks united as in Nileidae. Pygidium usually semicircular, with a border. Throughout Ordovician, cosmopolitan. Family modified for active swimming life habits and commonest in deeper water sediments.

Pl. 9.5.60. *Degamella* Marek, 1961
Cyclopygid with long, ovate almost featureless cranidium. Thorax with rapidly tapering axis and only 6 segments. Pygidium with axis tapering to a point, and rather ill-defined, flattened border. Eyes not shown on the specimen figured. Usually 9 cm or less.
Ordovician (Arenig–Ashgill). World-wide, in various facies.
Degamella princeps (Barrande): Llandeilo, Bohemia, Czechoslovakia.

Pl. 9.5.61, 62. *Pricyclopyge* Richter & Richter, 1954
Cyclopygid with almost round to forward expanding cranidium (on the figured specimen the eyes are crushed over part of it). Six thoracic segments; third segment carries a pair of odd depressions (on internal mould) on the axis; sixth segment may be macropleural. Pygidium triangular, with relatively long axis, furrowed pleural fields and distinct border. Up to 5 cm.
Ordovician (Arenig–Llandeilo). S. Europe, Turkey, in various facies.
Pricyclopyge prisca (Barrande): Llanvirn, Bohemia, Czechoslovakia.

SUPERFAMILY CERATOPYGACEA

Asaphina having narrow marginal cephalic rim and short genal spines which are not flattened (may be absent). Glabella long, with occipital ring and pre-occipital median tubercle. Pygidium with 1 or 2 pairs of marginal spines (a few forms without), which are clearly extensions of the pygidial pleurae. Upper M. Cambrian–Ordovician (Tremadoc). These remarks apply to the family Ceratopygidae.

Pl. 9.5.63. *Proceratopyge* Wallerius, 1895
Ceratopygid with glabella tapering gently forwards. Eyes of moderate size and with strong eye ridges. Thorax of 9 segments with spinose tips. Pygidium with distinct border and 1 pair of long marginal spines. Pleural field furrowed. Up to 3 cm.
M.–U. Cambrian. Europe, Asia, Australia, in fine clastic sediments and platform carbonates.
Proceratopyge sp.: U. Cambrian, England.

Pl. 9.5.64, 65. *Dichelepyge* Harrington & Leanza, 1952
Specimens illustrated are distorted cranidium and pygidia, and typical of the preservation of ceratopygids in shales. *Dichelepyge* has deep glabellar furrows, small eyes and somewhat concave preglabellar field. Pygidium with 2 pairs of lateral marginal spines and broad doublure. Up to 3 cm.
Ordovician (Tremadoc). S. America, Wales, Kazakhstan, USSR, in fine clastic sediments.
Dichelepyge bicornis (Lisogor): Tremadoc, N. Wales.

Suborder Illaenina

Commonly effaced Ptychopariida with opisthoparian facial sutures. Anterior sections of facial sutures distinctly divergent anteriorly. Glabella expanding forwards, lateral glabellar furrows often faint or absent; 4 or fewer pairs of glabellar muscle scars. Thorax of 8 to 10 segments. Pygidium rounded posteriorly, usually with short axis. Ordovician (Arenig)–Devonian (Frasnian). 'Smoothed out' illaenines are often found in great numbers in Lower Palaeozoic reefs.

FAMILY ILLAENIDAE

Effaced Illaenina with glabella indistinct anteriorly and lacking lateral furrows. Pygidium wide, usually short in dorsal view and weakly convex in relation to cephalon. Ordovician (Arenig)–Silurian (Wenlock).

Pl. 9.5.66, 67. *Illaenus* Dalman, 1827
Illaenid with cephalic axial furrows almost parallel or converging forwards posteriorly. Thorax of 10 segments. Pygidial axis short, wide anteriorly and narrowing rapidly back. Up to 5 cm.
Ordovician (Arenig–Ashgill). Cosmopolitan, especially in limestones.
Illaenus cf. *sarsi* Jaanusson: Llanvirn, Sweden.

Pl. 9.5.68. *Stenopareia* Holm, 1886
Illaenid with small eyes. Cephalic axial furrows only distinct posteriorly where they converge forwards. Thorax of 9 segments. (Specimen illustrated has anterior part of thorax 'telescoped' beneath cephalon.) Pygidium with very short axis. Up to 12 cm.
Ordovician (Llandeilo)–Silurian (Wenlock). N. America, Europe, Asia, in shallow-water sediments, especially carbonates.
Stenopareia balclatchiensis (Reed): Caradoc, Scotland.

FAMILY SCUTELLUIDAE

Illaenina with glabella widening markedly forwards in its anterior quarter, sometimes with lateral furrows. Eye typically large, backwardly placed. Pygidium of similar size to cephalon, typically with short axis and radially disposed ribs, but both may be effaced on dorsal surface. Ordovician (Arenig)–Devonian (Frasnian). Effaced genera here included in this family most obviously differ from illaenids in their lesser convexity, much wider thoracic axis which does not have the inner halves of the pleurae horizontal, and larger pygidium. Some authors, however, would assign such forms to the Illaenidae.

Pl. 9.5.69. *Bumastus* Murchison, 1839
Effaced scutelluid with cephalic axial furrows initially converging forwards then expanding in front of prominent lateral muscle impression; median tubercle of glabella placed opposite posterior end of eye. Thorax of 10 segments, axis about 70% of total width. External surface of pygidium lacking furrows. Up to 15 cm.
Silurian (Wenlock). USA and England, especially in carbonates.
Bumastus barriensis Murchison: Wenlock, England.

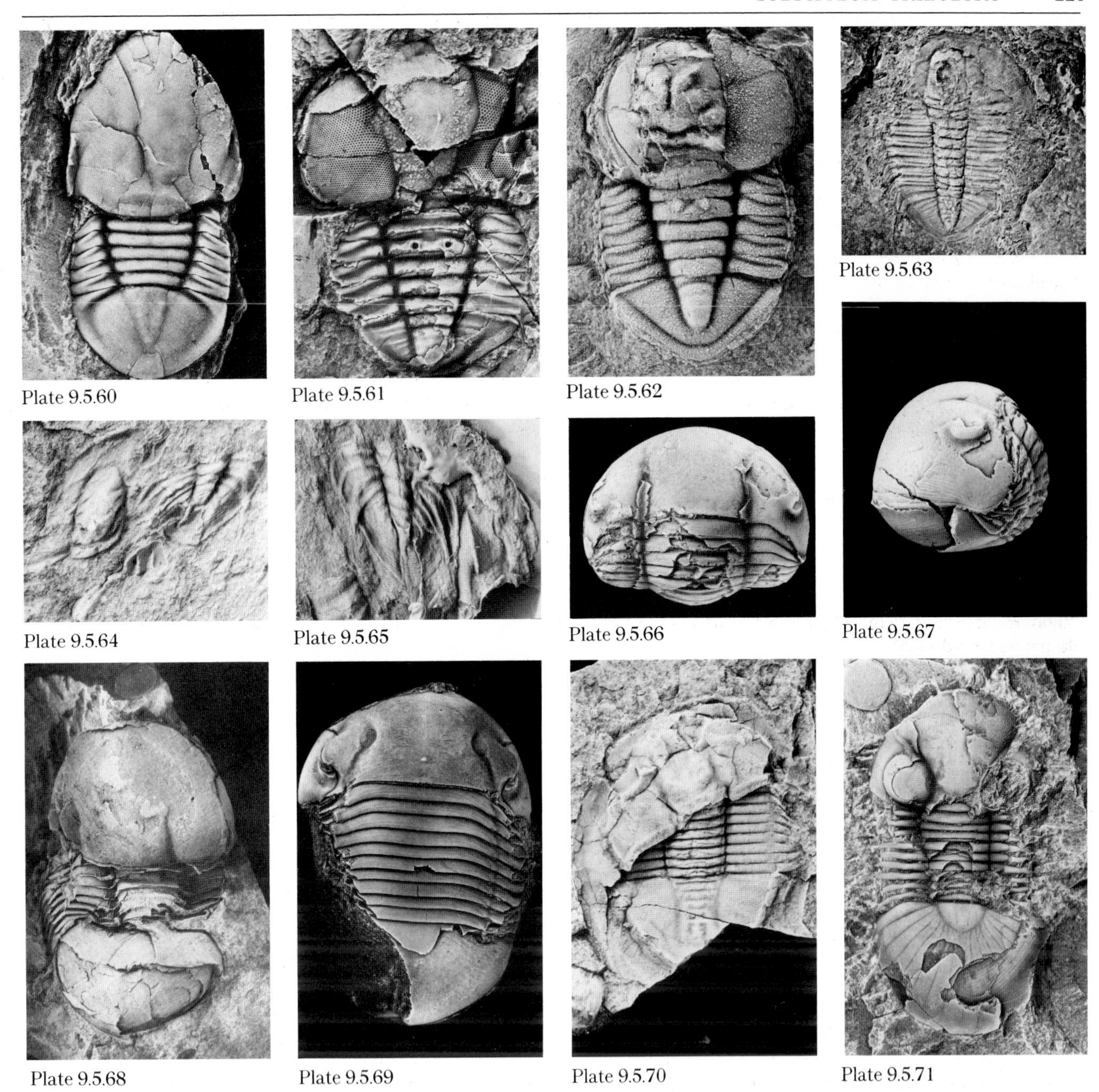

Plate 9.5.60 Plate 9.5.61 Plate 9.5.62 Plate 9.5.63

Plate 9.5.64 Plate 9.5.65 Plate 9.5.66 Plate 9.5.67

Plate 9.5.68 Plate 9.5.69 Plate 9.5.70 Plate 9.5.71

Pl. 9.5.70. *Protostygina* Prantl & Přibyl, 1948
Scutelluid of low convexity, with 4 or fewer pairs of faint glabellar furrows. Eyes small, placed midway out on cheek. Long, broad-based genal spine. Thorax of 9 segments, axis about 25% of total width. Pygidium with relatively long segmented axis, broad concave border and very faint radial ribs. Up to 7 cm.
Ordovician (Llanvirn). Czechoslovakia, in fine clastic sediments.
Protostygina bohemica (Barrande): Llanvirn, Czechoslovakia.

Pl. 9.5.71. *Paralejurus* Hawle & Corda, 1847
Scutelluid with vaulted exoskeleton, cephalon shorter than pygidium. Narrow, concave anterior cephalic border. Glabellar muscle impressions only clear on internal mould; 1 large pair posteriorly with a smaller pair in front. Thorax of 10 segments (1 segment broken off the illustrated specimen), axis at least 35% of the total width. Pygidium with short axis and radial ribs defined by narrow furrows. Up to 12 cm.
Devonian (Siegenian–Eifelian). Europe and N. Africa, especially in limestones.
Paralejurus cf. *brongniarti* (Barrande): L. Devonian (Pragian), Czechoslovakia.

Suborder Trinucleina

Ptychopariida with opisthoparian or marginal facial sutures, generally blind. Glabella typically, expanding forwards; 3 or fewer pairs of glabellar furrows. Thorax usually of 5 to 8 segments. Pygidium wide, generally triangular in outline, with narrow axis extending to posterior margin and border strongly declined. Ordovician (Tremadoc)–Silurian (Ludlow).

FAMILY OROMETOPIDAE

Trinucleina with straight-sided glabella lacking obvious furrows, preoccipital part extending backwards to form a spine (this spine broken from figured specimen). Broad preglabellar field and narrow cephalic border present. Opisthoparian, bearing eyes. Thorax of 7 to 8 segments. Pygidium short, with 6 or fewer axial rings and only 1 pair of pleural furrows.

Pl. 9.5.72. *Orometopus* Brøgger, 1896
Characters of family, no other genera are assigned. Up to 6 mm.
Ordovician (Tremadoc). Europe and S. America, in fine clastic sediments.
Orometopus cf. *praenuntius* (Salter): Tremadoc, N. Wales.

FAMILY TRINUCLEIDAE
Trinucleina with bilaminar (two-layered) fringe pierced by many opposed pits. Facial suture marginal, separating upper from lower lamella. Mostly blind. Thorax of 6 segments. Ordovician (Arenig–Ashgill). Trinucleids are of particular stratigraphic importance in zoning Ordovician strata.

Pl. 9.5.73. *Trinucleus* Murchison, 1839
Trinucleid with flat fringe showing prominent radial alignment of similarly sized pits; on upper lamella these set into radial grooves with strong ridges between. Glabella with prominent frontal lobe and 3 pairs of short, lateral glabellar furrows. Up to 3 cm.
Ordovician (Llanvirn–Llandeilo, L. Caradoc?). England and Wales, USSR?, generally in fine clastic sediments.
Trinucleus fimbriatus Murchison: Llandeilo, Wales.

Pl. 9.5.74. *Protolloydolithus* Williams, 1948
Trinucleid with fringe having 2 outer arcs of larger pits separated by prominent concentric ridge; pits inwards of these smaller and may be irregularly arranged. Only the basal glabellar furrow is prominent. Up to 3 cm.
Ordovician (Llanvirn–L. Llandeilo). England and Wales, in fine clastic sediments.
Protolloydolithus salax Rushton & Hughes: Llanvirn, England.

Pl. 9.5.75. *Bergamia* Whittard, 1955
Fringe narrow, with steeply sloping inner part. Pits set in radial grooves with intervening ridges present on both lamellae. Glabella like *Trinucleus*. Up to 2 cm.
Ordovician (Arenig–Llandeilo). England and Wales, USSR, generally in fine clastic sediments.
Bergamia artemis Rushton & Hughes: Llanvirn, England.

FAMILY DIONIDIDAE
Trinucleina with bilaminar fringe pierced by many opposed pits; these largest peripherally and irregularly arranged. Facial suture marginal, separating upper and lower lamellae. Blind. Glabella expanding slightly anteriorly, with prominent lateral lobes. A pair of prominent ridges runs inwards across each cheek from a point near base of genal spine. Thorax of 6 segments, the most anterior longer than the others. Ordovician (Arenig–Ashgill).

Pl. 9.5.76. *Dionide* Barrande, 1847
Dionidid with glabella widening only slightly anteriorly and bearing a median tubercle. Fringe broad. Axial rings of thorax and pygidium have anterolateral corners isolated by weak furrow. Up to 4 cm.
Ordovician (Arenig–Ashgill). USA, Europe, E. Asia, in clastic sediments.
Dionide formosa (Barrande): Llanvirn, Portugal.

FAMILY RAPHIOPHORIDAE
Trinucleina with forwardly expanding glabella often extending in front of general cephalic outline; preglabellar field absent, border absent or narrow. Facial sutures marginal or opisthoparian but running close to margin. Blind. Thorax typically of 5 to 7 segments, most anterior segments usually longer than the others. Ordovician (Arenig)–Silurian (Ludlow).

Pl. 9.5.77. *Cnemidopyge* Whittard, 1955
Raphiophorid with convex glabella extending somewhat in front of cephalic margin. Glabella produced anteriorly into a long spine which is circular in cross-section. Genal spines longer than thorax and pygidium together. Thorax of 6 segments, all of similar length. Pygidium long, with many axial rings and pairs of pleural furrows. Up to 4 cm.
Ordovician (Llandeilo). England and Wales, usually in fine clastic sediments.
Cnemidopyge nuda (Murchison): Llandeilo, Wales.

Pl. 9.5.78. *Raphiophorus* Angelin, 1854
Raphiophorid with triangular cephalon. Glabella spear-shaped, highly convex, projecting well in front of cephalic margin. Glabella produced anteriorly into a long spine (missing from illustrated specimen) which is circular in cross-section. Genal spines longer than thorax and pygidium together. Thorax of 5 segments, anterior segment elongated. Pygidium short and very wide, with 3 or fewer axial rings. Up to 6 mm.
Ordovician (Caradoc)–Silurian (Ludlow). USA, Europe, N. Africa, China, Australia, most facies except platform carbonates.
Raphiophorus parvulus Forbes: Ludlow?, England.

Suborder Harpina

Ptychopariida with genal spines or long, flat genal prolongations. Facial suture marginal or opisthoparian, but with anterior and posterior sections running close together. Glabella narrowing forwards with 1 to 3 pairs of furrows, posterior pair isolating triangular basal lobes. Preglabellar field broad, sloping down to flat or upwardly concave border. Eyes may be present, but commonly reduced to prominent tubercles; strong eye-ridges present. Thorax with 12 or (frequently) more segments. Pygidium short and usually much wider than long. U. Cambrian–Devonian (Frasnian).

FAMILY HARPEDIDAE
Harpina with eyes reduced to tubercles, each bearing 2 lenses. Facial suture marginal. Semicircular depressed areas present adjacent to posterior part of glabella. Prominent bilaminar fringe developed pierced by irregularly distributed opposed pits; fringe often extending backwards almost as far as the pygidium. Thorax of 12 to 29 segments. Pygidium very short and wide, with few segments (pygidium missing from figured specimen). Ordovician (Tremadoc)–Devonian (Frasnian).

Pl. 9.5.79. *Paraharpes* Whittington, 1950
Cephalon oval in outline. Glabella convex, bounded posterolaterally by large depressed areas. Fringe flat, with larger pits marginally and close to cheeks (specimen figured is a mould, so that pits appear as 'tubercles'). Thorax of 23 to 25 segments. Up to 4 cm.
Ordovician (Caradoc?–Ashgill). USA?, England and Scotland, in shelf sediments.
Paraharpes hornei (Reed): Ashgill, Scotland.

Suborder uncertain

FAMILY ISOCOLIDAE
Frequently blind, opisthoparian trilobites with facial suture running close to cephalic margin. Cephalon convex, with large, forwardly expanding or barrel-shaped glabella bearing 3 or fewer pairs of furrows. Thorax of 6 to 7 segments. Pygidium wide and short, axis not reaching posterior margin and bearing

Plate 9.5.72

Plate 9.5.73

Plate 9.5.74

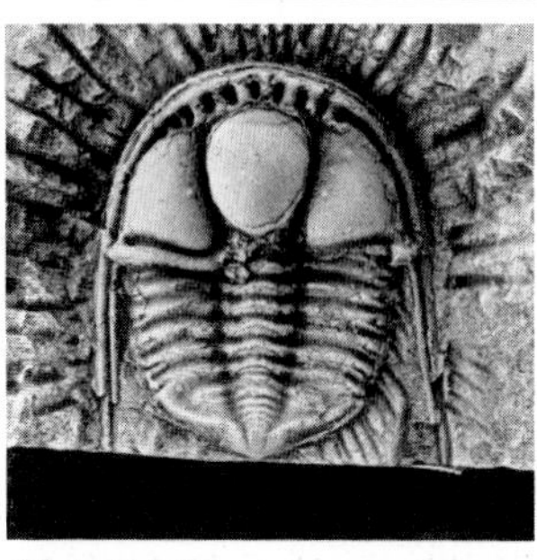

Plate 9.5.75

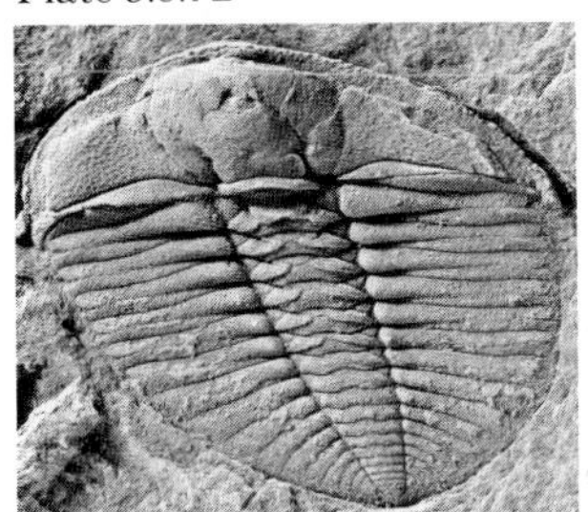

Plate 9.5.76

Plate 9.5.77

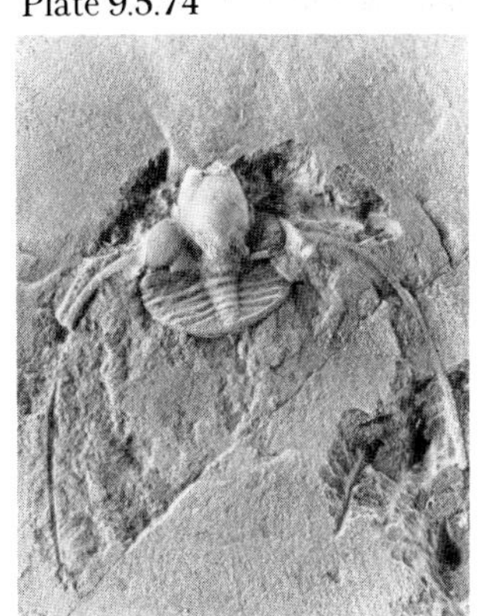

Plate 9.5.78

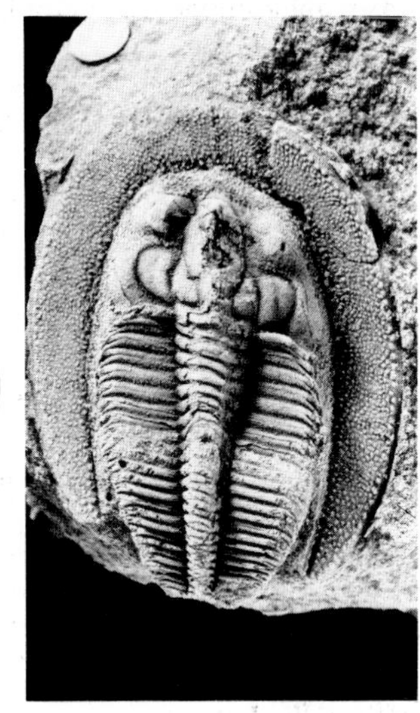

Plate 9.5.79

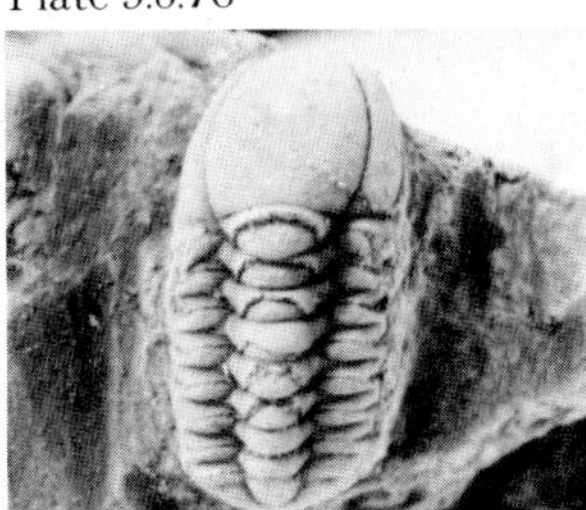

Plate 9.5.80

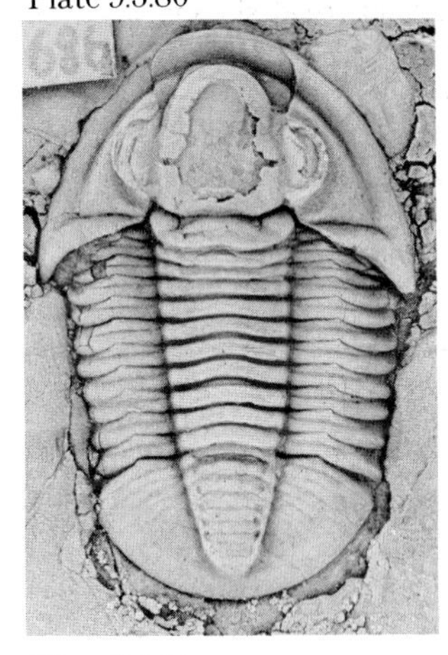

Plate 9.5.81

Plate 9.5.82

up to 3 rings. Ordovician (Arenig?, Llanvirn–Ashgill)–Silurian? (L. Llandovery).

Pl. 9.5.80. *Cyphoniscus* Salter, 1853
Isocolid with smooth, barrel-shaped glabella which dominates cephalon. No genal spines. Thorax of 6 segments. Pygidium without ring furrows on axis and only 1 pair of pleural furrows. Up to 2 cm, often smaller.
Ordovician (Ashgill). Europe, USSR. Like other isocolids, characteristic of 'reef' limestones.
Cyphoniscus socialis Salter: Ashgill, Eire.

Order Proetida

Typically small opisthoparian trilobites, usually with glabella narrowing forwards. 1S longest and deepest, backwardly curved; 2S, 3S and 4S progressively shorter and fainter. Thorax typically with 8 to 10 segments (range 6 to 22). Pygidium often without spines, with distinct pleural furrows. Ordovician (Tremadoc)–Permian (Tartarian). The order Proetida was recently separated from the Ptychopariida. Protaspis growth stages of this group are closely similar.

FAMILY PROETIDAE

Proetida with glabella tapering forwards or parallel-sided; frontal lobe may be expanded in U. Palaeozoic genera; 1 to 4 pairs of glabellar furrows. Eye generally placed close to glabella. Thorax usually of 10 segments, rarely 8 or 9. Pygidium with 3 to 33 axial rings and 3 to 14 pairs of pleural ribs. Ordovician (Arenig)–Permian (Tartarian).

Pl. 9.5.81. *Proetus* Steininger, 1831
Proetid with preglabellar field absent or very short; glabellar furrows weakly impressed. Pygidium subsemicircular in outline, with 6 to 12 axial rings and 4 to 6 pairs of pleural ribs. Up to 3 cm.
Ordovician (Ashgill)–Carboniferous (Silesian). Cosmopolitan, in shelf sediments.
Proetus concinnus (Dalman): Wenlock, England.

Pl. 9.5.82. *Cyphoproetus* Kegel, 1928
Proetid with preglabellar field short or absent. 1S deep, 1L prominent; median occipital tubercle often forwardly placed. Lateral cephalic margin often incurved at base of genal spine. Thorax of 9 to 10 segments. Pygidium without border; 5 to 8 axial rings and 3 to 6 pairs of pleural ribs. Up to 2 cm.
Ordovician (Caradoc)–Silurian (Ludlow). Europe, in shelf sediments.
Cyphoproetus depressus (Barrande): Wenlock, England.

Pl. 9.5.83. *Cummingella* Reed, 1942
Proetid with fiddle-shaped glabella; lateral furrows variably incised. Eye very large, placed close to glabella. Short genal spine. Thorax of 9 segments. Pygidium with 7 to 18 axial rings and 5 to 8 pairs of pleural ribs. Up to 3 cm.
Carboniferous (Dinantian–Silesian). Europe and Asia, especially in 'reef' limestones.
Cummingella sp.: Dinantian, S. Wales.

Pl. 9.5.84. *Decoroproetus* Přibyl, 1946
Proetid with broad preglabellar field. Glabellar furrows weak or absent. Thorax of 10 segments (the 2 anterior segments have been 'telescoped' beneath the cephalon in the illustrated specimen, but their tips are visible on the left-hand side). Pygidium with 5 to 10 axial rings and 4 to 6 pairs of pleural ribs; pleural furrows deepen and curve more strongly back close to margin. Up to 2 cm.
Ordovician (Llandeilo)–Devonian (Eifelian). N. America, Europe, N. Africa, Asia, especially in offshore clastic sediments and dark limestones.
Decoroproetus wigwig Thomas: Wenlock, Welsh borderland.

Pl 9.5.85, 86. *Ditomopyge* Newell, 1931
Proetid with forwardly expanding glabella; prominent 1L and preoccipital lobe. Thorax of 9 segments. Pygidium with border; 8 to 18 axial rings and 7 to 12 pairs of pleural ribs. Up to 3 cm.
Carboniferous (Silesian)–Permian (Tartarian). Cosmopolitan (except S. America and Africa), in shallow-water sediments.
Ditomopyge decurtata (Gheyselinck): L. Permian (Wolfcampian), Kansas, USA.

Pl. 9.5.87. *Nipponaspis* Koizumi, 1972
Proetid with fiddle-shaped glabella, wider posteriorly than anteriorly. Eye large and crescentic. Genal spine present. Thorax of 9 segments. Pygidium without border (the illustrated specimen is a mould and what could be misinterpreted as a border is actually the doublure); 10 to 11 axial rings defined by shallow ring furrows; 7 to 8 pairs of pleural ribs. Up to 3 cm.
Carboniferous (Silesian)–Permian (Kazanian). Ellesmere Island, Canada, Spain and Japan, in shallow-water sediments.
Nipponaspis leonensis (Romano): Silesian, NW. Spain.

Pl. 9.5.88, 89. *Timoraspis* Hahn & Hahn, 1967
Proetid with forwardly expanding glabella; deep 1S, 1L and preoccipital lobe coalesced. Thorax of 9 segments. Pygidium without border; 13 to 14 faint axial rings and 10 pairs of externally very weakly defined ribs. Up to 3 cm.
Permian (Artenskian–Kazanian). Sicily and Timor, in 'reef' limestones.
Timoraspis breviceps (Gheyselinck): Kazanian, Timor.

FAMILY BRACHYMETOPIDAE
Proetida with preglabellar field. Glabella narrowing forwards with 3 or fewer pairs of furrows; 1L usually isolate. Anterior sections of facial sutures divergent, often strongly so. Thorax of 8 to 10 segments. Pygidial axis with 6? to 14 rings; pleural ribs flattened or with posterior bands elevated above anterior. Silurian (Llandovery)–Permian (Tartarian).

Pl. 9.5.90. *Warburgella* Reed, 1931
Brachymetopid with short preglabellar field. Occipital lobes well developed; 1S deep. Pygidium with 5 to 7 pairs of flat-topped ribs. Up to 2 cm.
Silurian (Llandovery)–Devonian (Siegenian). Cosmopolitan, especially in calcareous facies.
Warburgella stokesii (Murchison): Wenlock, England.

Pl. 9.5.91. *Prantlia* Přibyl, 1946
Brachymetopid with long preglabellar field. Glabellar furrows indistinct. Pygidium with 7 to 10 axial rings and 5 to 6 pairs of flat-topped tibs. Up to 1.5 cm.
Silurian (Wenlock and Ludlow). Europe, Australia, ?Japan, especially in fine clastic sediments.
Prantlia grindrodi Owens: Wenlock, England.

FAMILY BATHYURIDAE
Proetida with glabella parallel-sided or expanded frontally; 3 or fewer pairs of faint furrows. Eyes large, generally far back and close to glabella. Thorax of 9 to 10 segments. Pygidium with up to 6 segments, no border furrow. Ordovician (Tremadoc–Caradoc).

Pl. 9.5.92, 93. *Punka* Fortey, 1979
Bathyurid with well-defined vaulted glabella. Preglabellar field short or absent; cephalic border wide, flattened or concave. Pygidium wider than long, flattened; axis with 4 or fewer rings; 3 to 4 pairs of pleural ribs. Up to 4 cm.
Ordovician (Arenig–Llandeilo). N. America, Greenland, Spitsbergen, in platform carbonates.
Punka flabelliformis Fortey: Arenig, Newfoundland.

FAMILY DIMEROPYGIDAE
Proetida with ovate glabella bearing 3 or fewer pairs of short, shallow lateral furrows. Preglabellar field steeply sloping, often with median furrow. Thorax of few segments (8 in *Dimeropyge*). Pygidium short and wide, with 3 to 6 segments; axis often with median depression.
Ordovician (Arenig–Ashgill).

Pl. 9.5.94, 95. *Ischyrotoma* Raymond, 1925
Dimeropygid with cephalic axial furrows only slightly bowed-out; 2 pairs of faint glabellar furrows. Preglabellar field short or absent. No genal spine. Thorax of 8 segments. Pygidium with 4 to 6 segments. Up to 1 cm.
Ordovician (Arenig–Llandeilo). N. America, W. Ireland, especially in platform carbonates.
Ischyrotoma anataphra Fortey: Arenig, Newfoundland.

FAMILY AULACOPLEURIDAE
Proetida with glabella tapering forwards or parallel-sided. Three or fewer pairs of glabellar furrows, 1S deep, 1L isolated; 2S and 3S weak or absent. Preglabellar field present. Thorax of 6 to 22 segments. Pygidium usually short, with 2 to 13 axial rings and 1 to 7 pairs of pleural ribs.
Ordovician (Tremadoc)–Permian (Tartarian).

Pl. 9.5.96. *Otarion* Zenker, 1833
Aulacopleurid with elongate 1L. Eye small, placed opposite outer end of 1S. Preglabellar field convex. Thorax of 13 to 22 segments. Pygidium with 5 to 8 axial rings; pleural areas much wider than axis anteriorly, with 3 to 7 pairs of ribs. Up to 5 cm.
Ordovician (Tremadoc)–Devonian (Frasnian). N. America, Greenland, Europe, Asia, in all facies.
Otarion diffractum Zenker: Ludlow, Czechoslovakia.

Pl. 9.5.97. *Namuropyge* Richter & Richter, 1939
Aulacopleurid with fused facial sutures; eyes stalked and apparently lacking lenses. Two rows of spines present on cephalic margin. Thorax of 7 segments. Pygidium with marginal spines and 9 to 13 axial rings; posterior pleural bands much elevated above anterior. Up to 1 cm.
Carboniferous (Viséan). Europe, in carbonates (especially 'reefs').
Namuropyge acanthina (Coignou): Viséan, England.

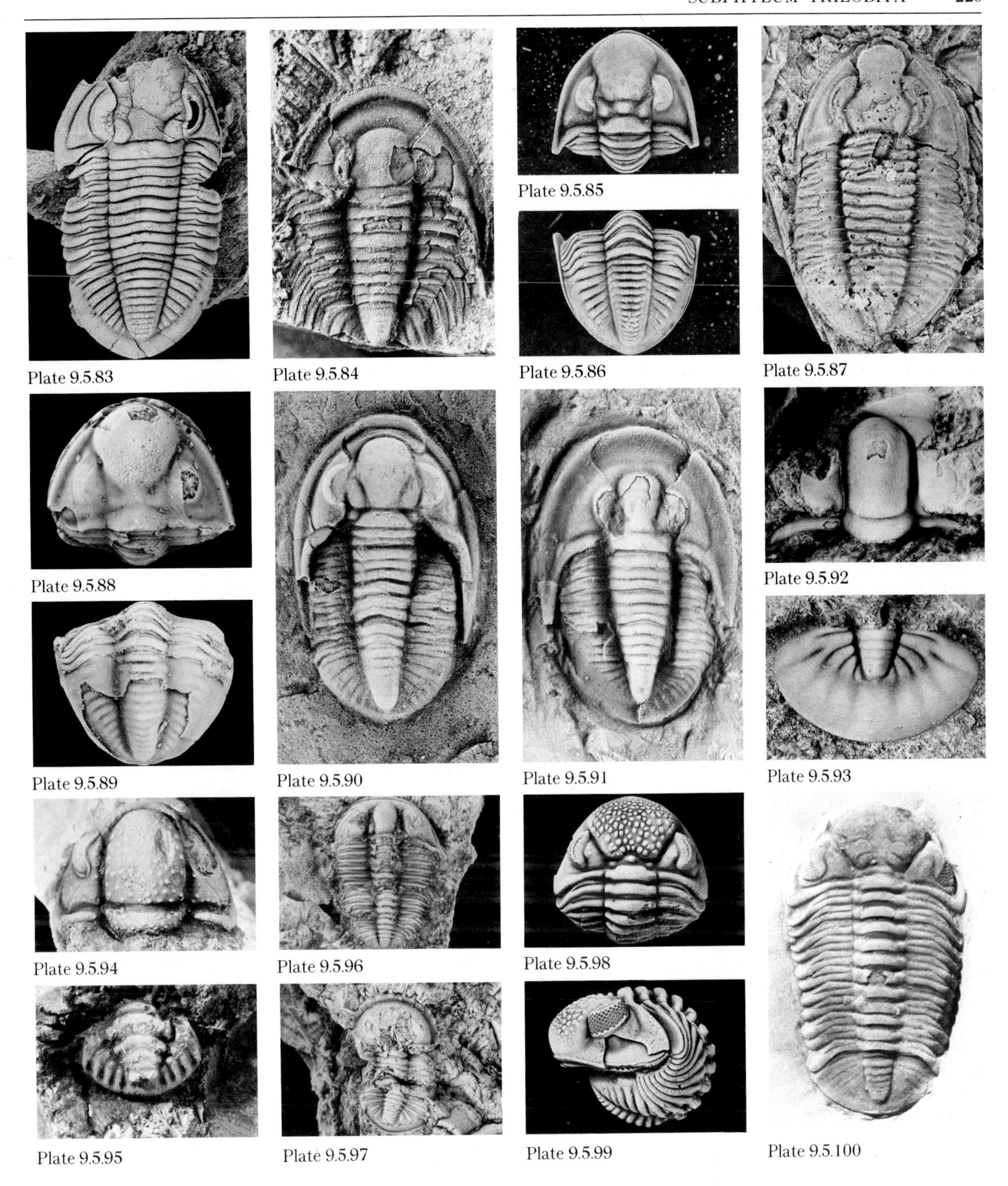

Plate 9.5.83 Plate 9.5.84 Plate 9.5.85 Plate 9.5.86 Plate 9.5.87 Plate 9.5.88 Plate 9.5.89 Plate 9.5.90 Plate 9.5.91 Plate 9.5.92 Plate 9.5.93 Plate 9.5.94 Plate 9.5.96 Plate 9.5.98 Plate 9.5.95 Plate 9.5.97 Plate 9.5.99 Plate 9.5.100

Order Phacopida

Variable group of typically proparian or gonatoparian trilobites; preglabellar field absent or very short; 4 or fewer pairs of glabellar furrows. Thorax of 8 to 19 segments. Pygidium smaller than cephalon. Ordovician (Tremadoc)–Devonian (Famennian).

Suborder Phacopina

Phacopina with schizochroal eyes and proparian sutures, though latter may be fused; glabella expanding forwards. Thorax of 11 segments. Ordovician (Arenig)–Devonian (Famennian).

FAMILY PHACOPIDAE

Phacopina with generally convex exoskeleton. Glabella widening strongly forwards; 2S and 3S weak, 3S strongly flexed; 1S extends across glabella. No genal spines. Thoracic pleurae with rounded tips. Pygidium rather small and rounded, margin entire. Ordovician (Ashgill)–Devonian (Famennian).

Pl. 9.5.98, 99. *Phacops* Emmrich, 1839 □
Phacopid with inflated glabella, generally flattened on top and with prominent basal lobes. Conspicuous tuberculation partly obscures 2S and 3S. Axial furrows indistinct in front of eyes. Pygidium with 9 to 11 rings and 8 or fewer pleurae. Up to 6 cm.

Devonian (Siegenian–Famennian). USA, Europe, N. Africa, in fine clastic sediments and limestones.
Phacops rana africanus Burton & Eldridge: Givetian, Morocco.

Pl. 9.5.100. *Ananaspis* Campbell, 1967
Phacopid with rather weakly inflated glabella and weak basal lobes. No strong sculpture, 2S and 3S distinct. Axial furrows deep in front of eyes. Pygidium with 6 to 10 rings and 8 or fewer pairs of pleural ribs. Up to 2 cm.
Silurian (Llandovery–'Pridoli'), ?L. Devonian. USA, Europe, Australia, especially in calcareous facies.
Ananaspis stokesii (Milne Edwards): Wenlock, England.

FAMILY DALMANITIDAE

Phacopina with generally flattened exoskeleton. Three pairs of deep glabellar furrows; intervening lobes of similar length. Long genal spines. Thoracic pleurae with spinose tips. Pygidium large, often with 1 or more marginal spines. Ordovician (Arenig?)–Devonian (Frasnian).

Pl. 9.5.101. *Dalmanites* Barrande, 1852
Dalmanitid with broad, flat, anterior cephalic border. Pygidium long, pointed or with a median spine posteriorly; 11 to 16 axial rings and 4 to 7 pairs of deeply furrowed pleurae. Up to 10 cm.
Silurian (Llandovery)–Devonian (Givetian). N. America, Europe, USSR, ?Australia, in shelf sediments.
Dalmanites myops König: Wenlock, England.

FAMILY PTERYGOMETOPIDAE

Phacopina with convex exoskeleton. Three pairs of lateral glabellar furrows increasing in length anteriorly. Pygidium similar in length to cephalon, without posterior spine. Ordovician (Arenig–Ashgill).

Pl. 9.5.102. *Achatella* Delo, 1935
Pterygometopid with cephalic axial furrows curved evenly outwards; 3L larger than 1L and 2L. Pygidium with 9 to 15 axial rings and 8 to 13 pairs of distinct, only weakly furrowed, ribs. Up to 4 cm.
Ordovician (Llandeilo–Ashgill). N. America and Scotland, in shelf sediments.
Achatella retardata (Reed): Ashgill, Scotland.

Suborder Cheirurina

Phacopida typically with proparian sutures. Glabella usually expanding forwards or barrel-shaped. Eyes holochroal, often small. Exoskeleton often tuberculate and with fine pitting on cheeks. Pygidium often highly modified with distinct ribs and spinose margin. Ordovician (Tremadoc)–Devonian (Givetian).

FAMILY CHEIRURIDAE

Cheirurina with 3 to 4 pairs of lateral glabellar furrows, 1S longest, most distinct and most curved; or with single basal furrow, continuous across glabella and containing nodular basal lobes. Thorax of 9 to 12 segments with spinose tips. Pygidium with 1 to 4 axial rings and pairs of pleural spines. Ordovician (Tremadoc)–Devonian (Givetian).

Pl. 9.5.103. *Ktenoura* Lane, 1971
Cheirurid with forwardly expanding glabella. Three pairs of glabellar furrows; 1S isolating triangular 1L, 2S and 3S extend about one-third the way across glabella. Eye placed opposite 2L and 3L. Thorax of 11 segments with furrowed pleurae (the distinctive pattern of furrowing seen is characteristic of many cheirurids). Pygidium with 3 axial rings and 3 pairs of backwardly directed spines. Up to 3 cm.
Silurian (Llandovery–Ludlow). England and Czechoslovakia, in shelf sediments, especially calcareous facies.
Ktenoura retrospinosa Lane: Wenlock, England.

Pl. 9.5.104. *Sphaerexochus* Beyrich, 1845
Cheirurid with highly inflated glabella dominating cephalon. 1S deep and strongly curved, 2S and 3S weak. Cheeks small and vertical (missing from figured specimen), eye set close to glabella. Thorax of 10 segments with unfurrowed pleurae. Pygidium with 3 pairs of short lobate spines. Up to 4 cm.
Ordovician (Llanvirn)–Silurian (Ludlow). Cosmopolitan, in shelf sediments.
Sphaerexochus mirus Beyrich: Wenlock, England.

Pl. 9.5.105. *Sphaerocoryphe* Angelin, 1854
Cheirurid with glabella greatly inflated in front of single transverse furrow, 1L nodular. Cheek small, with long genal spine. Thorax of 9 segments with spinose tips. Pygidium with 4 axial rings and 2 to 3 pairs of marginal spines; anterior part resembles a thoracic segment. Up to 2 cm.
Ordovician (Llanvirn–Ashgill). USA, Europe, USSR, in shelf sediments.
Sphaerocoryphe robustus Walcott: Caradoc, New York, USA.

FAMILY ENCRINURIDAE

Cheirurina with parallel-sided or forwardly expanding glabella; 3 pairs of short glabellar furrows, often reduced to deep pits. Thorax of 10 to 12 segments. Pygidium with 16 or fewer pairs of ribs and a larger number of axial rings. Ordovician (Arenig)–Devonian (basal Gedinnian).

Pl. 9.5.106, 107. *Encrinurus* Emmrich, 1844
Encrinurid with forwardly widening glabella; glabella furrows somewhat obscured by coarse tuberculation. Eyes often stalked, placed opposite 2L or 3L. Pygidium roughly triangular, with 5 or more pairs of pleural ribs. Up to 8 cm.
Ordovician (Ashgill)–basal Devonian. Cosmopolitan, in shelf sediments.
Encrinurus variolaris (Brongniart): Wenlock, England.

Pl. 9.5.108, 109. *Lyrapyge* Fortey, 1980
Glabella widening forwards, incorporating anterior border; 3 pairs of transverse furrows. Prominent eye-ridge runs forward to outer end of forked 3S. Pygidium wide, with 8 to 9 axial rings. Four pairs of stout pygidial pleural ribs; these converge back and continue into upturned marginal spines. Up to 3 cm.
Ordovician (Arenig). Spitsbergen and USSR, in shelf limestones.
Lyrapyge ebriosus Fortey: Arenig, Spitsbergen.

FAMILY STAUROCEPHALIDAE

Cheirurina with frontal glabellar lobe spherical; 3 pairs of glabellar furrows. No preglabellar field or anterior border. Proparian. Thorax of 10 to 12 segments. Pygidium small, with 3 to 4 axial rings and 3 pairs of spines. Ordovician (Caradoc)–Silurian (Ludlow).

Pl. 9.5.110. *Staurocephalus* Barrande, 1846
Staurocephalid with short 1S and 2S on parallel-sided posterior part of glabella; 3S extends across glabella, frontal lobe greatly inflated and overhanging anterior margin. Short fixigenal spine. Thorax of 10 segments. Pygidial spines slender. Up to 1.5 cm.
Ordovician (Caradoc)–Silurian (Ludlow). USA, Europe, USSR, Australia, shelf carbonates and fine clastic sediments.
Staurocephalus susanae Thomas: Wenlock, England.

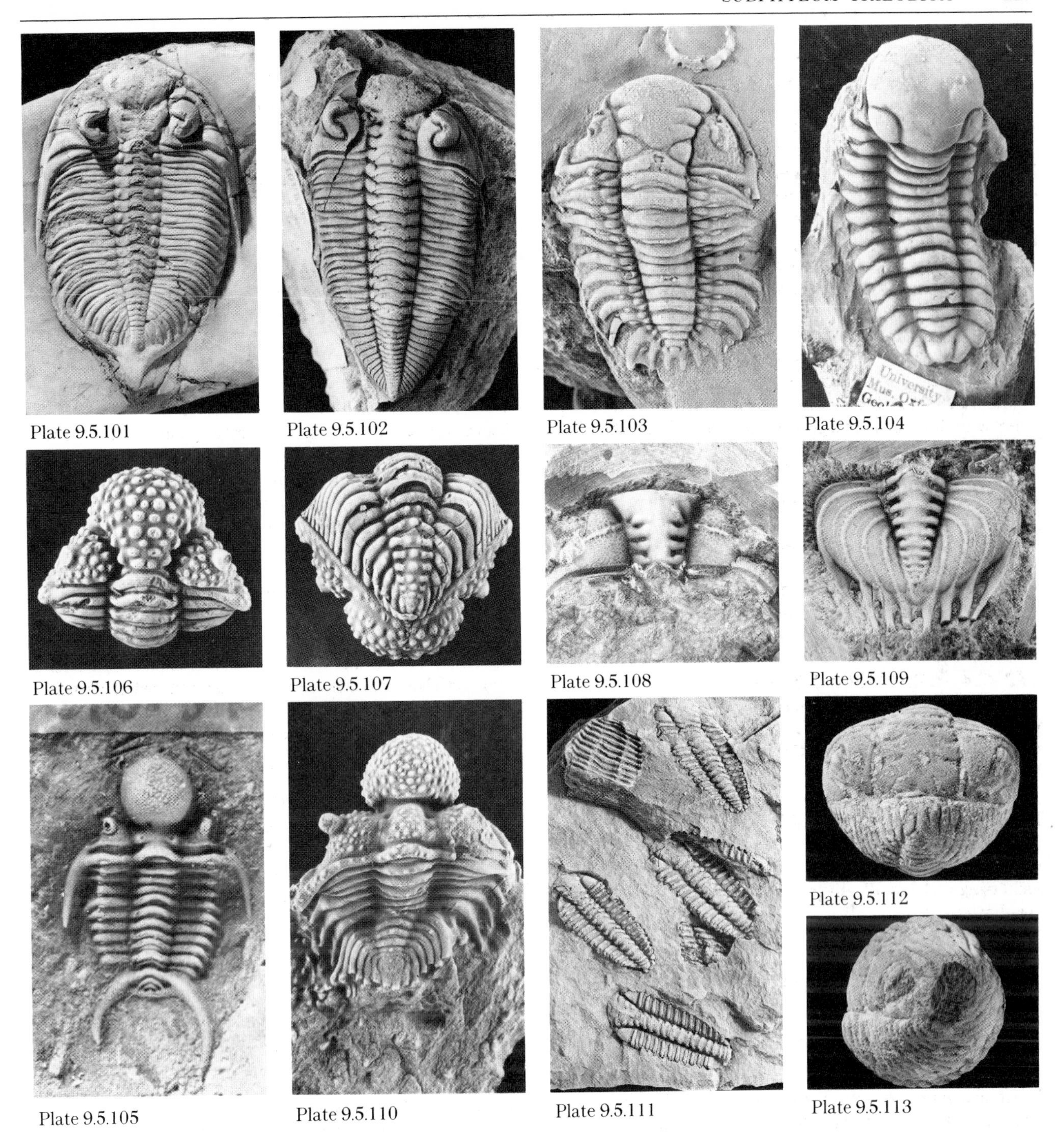

Plate 9.5.101 Plate 9.5.102 Plate 9.5.103 Plate 9.5.104

Plate 9.5.106 Plate 9.5.107 Plate 9.5.108 Plate 9.5.109

Plate 9.5.105 Plate 9.5.110 Plate 9.5.111 Plate 9.5.112 Plate 9.5.113

FAMILY PLIOMERIDAE

Cheirurina typically with proparian suture. Glabella usually expanding forwards or parallel-sided, with 2 to 3 pairs of furrows. No preglabellar field. Thorax of 11 to 19 segments. Pygidium with 2 to 6 axial rings and equal number of pleural ribs. Ordovician (Arenig–Ashgill).

Pl. 9.5.111. *Placoparia* Hawle & Corda, 1847

Pliomerid with opisthoparian suture; glabella straight-sided, slightly expanding forwards. 3S reaches axial furrow at anterior corner of glabella; 1S and 2S transverse. Thorax of 11 to 12 segments, posterior band of each pleura inflated. Pygidium with 4 axial rings and 4 pairs of inflated ribs ending in blunt spines. Up to 4 cm.

Ordovician (Arenig–Caradoc). Europe and N. Africa, in fine clastic sediments. Illustration is of a slab with several articulated specimens.

Placoparia zippei (Boeck): Llanvirn/Llandeilo, Portugal.

Pl. 9.5.112, 113. *Pliomera* Angelin, 1852

Pliomerid with gonatoparian facial suture. 3S placed in front of anterolateral corner of glabella; frontal lobe indented at midline. No eye-ridges, eyes placed about half-way along cephalon. Thorax of 12 to 18 segments. Pygidium with 4 to 5 rings; pleural ribs ending in blunt points, most posterior ribs completely enclose the small axial terminal piece. Up to 10 cm.

Ordovician (Llanvirn–Caradoc). Europe, S. America, mainly in shelf limestones.

Pliomera fischeri (Eichwald): Llanvirn, Russian platform. Illustration shows two views of enrolled specimen.

Suborder Calymenina

Phacopina with forwardly narrowing glabella. Typically gonatoparian; eyes holochroal, often small. Thorax of 11 to 13 segments with rounded tips. Pygidium semicircular or triangular in outline, without spinose margin. Ordovician (Tremadoc)–Devonian (Frasnian).

FAMILY CALYMENIDAE

Calymenina with 2 to 4 pairs of glabellar furrows, glabellar lobes often rounded. Cephalic borders convex and well defined. Pygidial axis extends close to posterior margin, with 5 to 8 rings; pleural fields usually steeply sloping and distinctly furrowed. Ordovician (Arenig)–Devonian (Eifelian).

Pl. 9.5.114. *Calymene* Brongniart, 1822
Calymenid with bell-shaped glabella. 2L protrudes across axial furrow and is met by a 'buttress' on the fixed cheek. Thorax with 12 (rare) or 13 segments. Pygidium rather wide. Up to 10 cm.
Silurian (Llandovery)–Devonian (Eifelian). Cosmopolitan, in shelf sediments.
Calymene puellaris Reed: Ludlow, Gotland.

Pl. 9.5.115. *Flexicalymene* Shirley, 1936
Glabella tapering evenly forwards with no 'buttressing' of lobes. Thorax of 12 or 13 segments. Pygidium distinctly triangular in outline. Up to 10 cm.
Ordovician (Llandeilo)–Silurian (Wenlock). N. America and Europe, in shelf sediments.
Flexicalymene senaria (Conrad): Caradoc, Quebec.

FAMILY HOMALONOTIDAE

Calymenina with 4 or fewer pairs of weakly defined glabellar furrows. Cephalic borders indistinct or absent, especially anteriorly. Thoracic axis often wide. Ordovician (Tremadoc)–Devonian (Frasnian).

Pl. 9.5.116. *Plaesiacomia* Hawle & Corda, 1847
Homalonotid with subcircular, convex cephalon. No anterior or lateral border. Glabella tapering rapidly forwards, with weakly impressed furrows. Eye anteriorly placed. Pygidial axis with 5 or fewer rings; border furrow deep, border flexed strongly down. Up to 2 cm.
Ordovician (Arenig–Caradoc). Europe, Middle East, in shallow-water clastic sediments.
Plaesiacomia vacuvertis Thomas: Llanvirn, Saudia Arabia.

Pl. 9.5.117. *Trimerus* Green, 1832
Homalonotid with subtriangular cephalon more than half as long as wide. Frontal area broad, with small portion of rostral plate dorsal. Axis wide, trilobation indistinct. Pygidium triangular, pointed behind, with distinct segmentation. Up to 20 cm.
Silurian (Llandovery)–Devonian (Givetian, ?Frasnian). Cosmopolitan in shallow-water sediments.
Trimerus johannis Salter: Wenlock, Wales.

Order Lichida

Typically densely granulated, opisthoparian, isopygous trilobites. Glabella large, extending to anterior border. Glabella with complex lobation. Pygidium often longer than wide with 3 pairs of furrowed pleurae, typically ending in spinose tips. Ordovician (Tremadoc)–Devonian (Famennian).

FAMILY LICHIDAE

Lichida with anterior sections of facial sutures converging forwards. Thorax of 10 to 11 segments and respectively 4 or 3 pairs of pygidial pleural ribs. Ordovician (Arenig)–Devonian (Famennian). Lichids are of distinctive appearance and include some of the largest trilobites, up to 70 cm in length.

Pl. 9.5.118. *Hemiarges* Gürich, 1901
Median part of glabella bounded by 2 pairs of partly fused lobes, occipital lobe fused with 1L. Genal spine stout and broad-based. Pygidial axis connected with border by a narrow ridge, posterior bands of first and second pygidial pleurae inflated. Margin generally with 3 or more pairs of spines. Up to 3 cm.
Ordovician (Llandeilo)–Silurian (Ludlow). USA, Arctic, Europe, in shelf sediments.
Hemiarges scutalis (Salter): Wenlock, England.

Pl. 9.5.119, 120. *Platylichas* Gürich, 1901
Median part of glabella bounded by a single pair of large lobes, occipital lobes well developed. Pygidial axis extending about half length of pygidium. Three pairs of furrowed pygidial pleurae ending in free points. Up to 6 cm.
Ordovician (Llanvirn)–Silurian (Wenlock, Ludlow?). USA and Europe, in shelf sediments.
Platylichas grayi (Fletcher): Wenlock, England.

Pl. 9.5.121. *Ceratarges* Gürich, 1901
Median part of glabella bounded by 2 pairs of fused lobes, occipital lobe fused with 1L. Genal spine long, slender and forwardly placed. Further long spines arise from glabella and pygidium. Up to 6 cm.
Devonian (Gedinnian–Eifelian, Famennian?). USA, Europe, Australia, in shelf sediments. One of the most bizarre of trilobites.
Ceratarges armata Goldfuss: Eifelian, Eifel region.

Order Odontopleurida

Typically spinose and densely sculptured trilobites with cephalon larger than pygidium. Glabella extends to anterior cephalic margin or almost so, tapering forwards from occipital ring or parallel-sided. Eye-ridges run from anterior end of glabella to palpebral lobe. Opisthoparian facial sutures, often placed on sutural ridges. Distinct notch in margin of free cheek adjacent to point where anterior section of facial suture cuts cephalic margin. Thorax of 8 to 10 segments; tips of each bear 2 to 3 pairs of spines (anterior pair or pairs may be downwardly directed and difficult to see). Pygidium short, with 2 to 3 axial rings. One or more pairs of pygidial border spines, largest pair connected to the first axial ring by prominent ridge. Upper M. Cambrian–Devonian (Givetian).

FAMILY ODONTOPLEURIDAE

Odontopleurida with anterior sections of facial sutures parallel or converging in front of eyes. Ordovician (Arenig)–Devonian (Givetian).

Pl. 9.5.122. *Odontopleura* Emmrich, 1839
Odontopleurid with relatively large and elevated 1L and 2L, 3L absent or minute. Occipital ring elongated, with weak occipital lobes and a pair of slender occipital spines. Palpebral lobe placed opposite the anterior end of 1L, half-way out across cheek. Anterior sections of facial suture converge forwards. Free cheek with slender, laterally directed marginal spines. Thorax of 9 segments with both anterior and posterior pleural spines slender and outwardly directed. Pygidium three times as wide

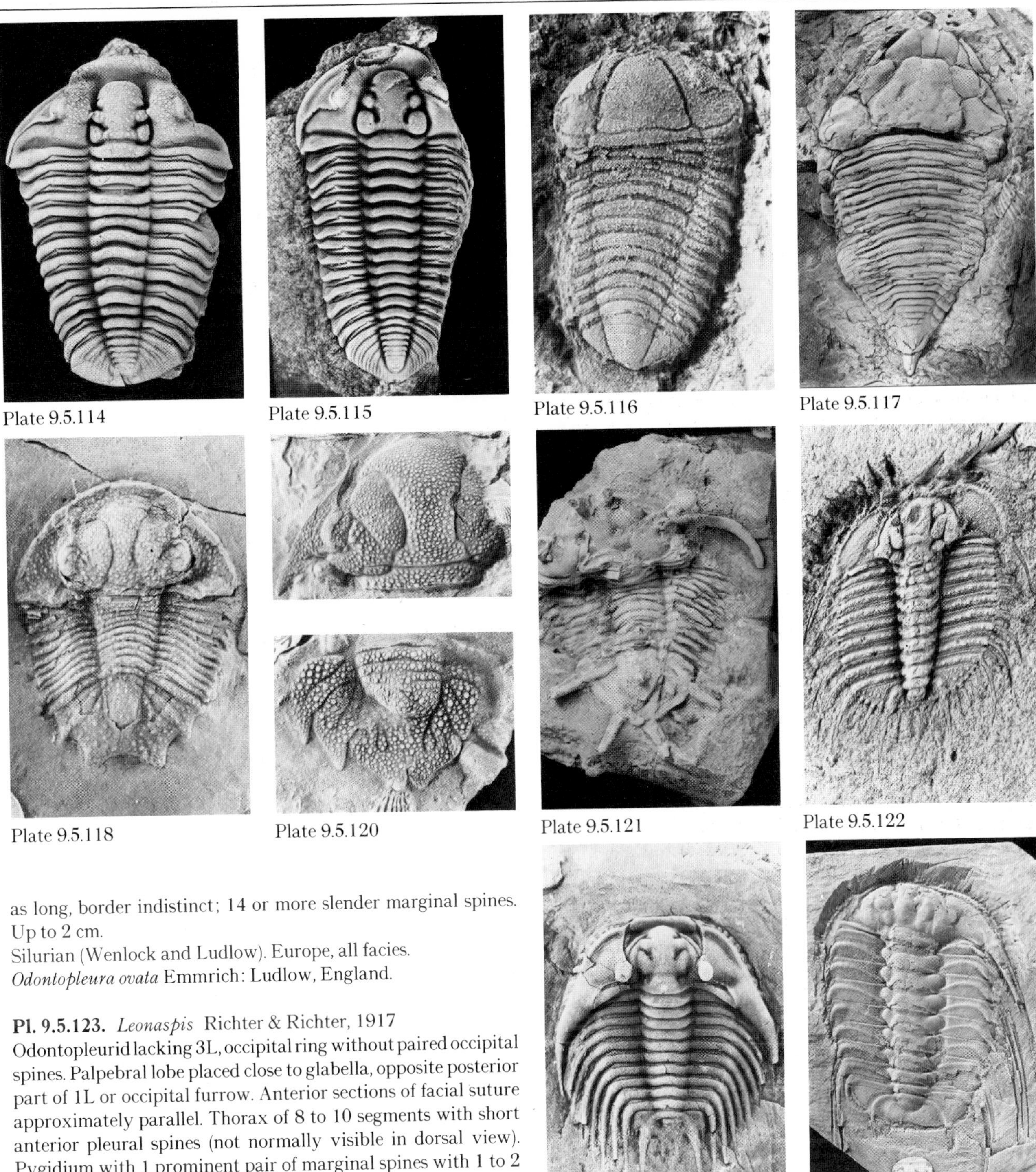

Plate 9.5.114 Plate 9.5.115 Plate 9.5.116 Plate 9.5.117

Plate 9.5.118 Plate 9.5.120 Plate 9.5.121 Plate 9.5.122

Plate 9.5.123 Plate 9.5.124

as long, border indistinct; 14 or more slender marginal spines. Up to 2 cm.
Silurian (Wenlock and Ludlow). Europe, all facies.
Odontopleura ovata Emmrich: Ludlow, England.

Pl. 9.5.123. *Leonaspis* Richter & Richter, 1917
Odontopleurid lacking 3L, occipital ring without paired occipital spines. Palpebral lobe placed close to glabella, opposite posterior part of 1L or occipital furrow. Anterior sections of facial suture approximately parallel. Thorax of 8 to 10 segments with short anterior pleural spines (not normally visible in dorsal view). Pygidium with 1 prominent pair of marginal spines with 1 to 2 further pairs between them and others outside. Up to 2 cm.
Silurian (Llandovery)–Devonian (Eifelian). Europe, N. and S. America, Asia, Australia, in shelf sediments.
Leonaspis deflexa (Lake): Wenlock, England.

Pl. 9.5.124. *Selenopeltis* Hawle & Corda, 1847
Odontopleurid with roughly rectangular cephalon. Three pairs of lateral glabellar lobes, 1L divided longitudinally by a faint furrow. Eye centrally placed on cheek. Thorax of 9 segments, anterior pleural spine short and curved. Pygidium with single pair of marginal spines. Up to 5 cm.
Ordovician (Arenig–Ashgill). Europe, N. Africa, Middle East, in fine clastic sediments.
Selenopeltis inermis inermis (Beyrich): Llandeilo/Caradoc, Welsh borders.

Selected list of references

Owing to the large number of references entailed, only the more important are given here.

CHAPTER 1. INTRODUCTION

Clarkson, E. N. K., 1979. *Invertebrate Palaeontology & Evolution.* Allen & Unwin, London.

Stoll, N. R. *et al.*, 1964. *International Code of Zoological Nomenclature. Adopted by the XV International Congress of Zoology.* London.

Tasch, P., 1973. *Paleobiology of the Invertebrates. Data retrieved from the fossil record.* Wiley, New York.

CHAPTER 2. PORIFERA

Berquist, P. R., 1978. *Sponges.* University of California Press, Berkeley and Los Angeles, 268 pp.

De Laubenfels, M. W., 1955. Porifera, *in* Moore, R. C. (Ed.) *Treatise on Invertebrate Paleontology*, Part E, E21–E112. Geological Society of America and University of Kansas Press, Lawrence, Kansas.

Finks, R. M., 1970. The evolution and ecological history of sponges during Paleozoic times, *Symposium of the Zoological Society of London*, **25**, 3–22.

Hartman, W. D. and Goreau, T. F., 1972. Ceratoporella (Porifera: Sclerospongiae) and the chaetetid 'corals', *Trans. Conn. Acad. Arts. Sci.*, **44**, 133–8.

Hartman, W. D., Wendt, J. W. and Wiedenmayer, F., 1980. Living and fossil sponges (notes for a short course), *Sedimenta* VIII. The University of Miami, 274 pp.

Lecompte, M., 1956. Stromatoporoidea, *in* Moore, R. C. (Ed.) *Treatise on Invertebrate Paleontology*, Part F, pp. 107–44. Geological Society of America and University of Kansas Press, Lawrence, Kansas.

Stearn, C. W., 1972. The relationship of the stromatoporoids to the sclerosponges, *Lethaia*, **5**, 369–88.

Stearn, C. W., 1975. The stromatoporoid animal, *Lethaia*, **8**, 89–100.

Stearn, C. W., 1980. Classification of the Palaeozoic stromatoporoids, *J. Paleont.*, **54**, 881–902.

CHAPTER 3. CNIDARIA

Alloiteau, J., 1952. Anthozoaires II. Madréporaires post-paléozoïques, *in* J. Piveteau (Ed.) *Traité de paléontologie. Tome premier. Les stades inférieurs d'organisation du règne animal. Introduction. Généralités. Protistes. Spongiaires. Coelentérés. Bryozoaires*, pp. 539–684, pls. 1–10. Masson, Paris.

Alloiteau, J., 1957. *Contribution à la systématique des madréporaires fossiles*, 2 vols. Centre National de la Recherche Scientifique, Paris.

Beauvais, L., 1980. Sur la taxinomie des madréporaires mésozoïques, *Acta palaeont. polon.*, **25**, 345–60.

Beauvais, M., 1982. *Révision systématique de madréporaires des couches de Gosau (Crétace supérieur, Autriche)*, 5 vols. Travaux du laboratoire de Paléontologie des Invertébrés, Université Pierre et Marie Curie.

Chevalier, J.-P., 1962. Recherches sur les madréporaires et les formations récifales miocènes de la Méditerranée occidentale, *Mém. géol. Soc. Fr.* (NS), **40** (93), 1–562, pls. 1–26.

Chevalier, J.-P., 1971. Les scléractiniaires de la Mélanésie française, Nouvelle-Calédonie, Iles Chesterfield, Iles Loyauté, Nouvelles Hébrides), première partie, *in Expédition française sur les récifs coralliens de la Nouvelle-Calédonie*, Vol. 5, pp. 1–307 and pls. 1–38. Êditions de la Fondation Singer-Polignac, Paris.

Cuif, J.-P., 1968. Étude ontogénique de quelques madréporaires Caryophyllidae [sic] actuels et fossiles. *Mém. Mus. natl. Hist. nat.* (C), **16** (3), 101–56, pls. 1–7.

Cuif, J.-P., 1972–76. Recherches sur les madréporaires du Trias. I. Famille Stylophyllidae (1972), *Bull. Mus. natl. Hist. nat.* (3) *Sciences de la Terre*, **17** (97), 213–91. II. Astraeoida. Révision des genres *Montlivaltia* et *Thecosmilia*. Étude de quelques types structuraux du Trias de Turquie (1974), ibid., **40** (275), 293–400. III. Étude des structures pennulaires chez les madréporaires triasiques (1975), ibid., **44** (310), 46–127. IV. Formes cerio-méandroïdes et thamastérioïdes du Trias des Alpes et du Taurus sud-anatolien (1976), ibid., **53** (381), 69–195.

Cuif, J.-P., 1980. Microstructure *versus* morphology in the skeleton of Triassic scleractinian corals, *Acta palaeont. polon.*, **25**, 361–74.

Hill, D., 1981. Rugosa and Tabulata, *in* Teichert, C. (Ed.) *Treatise on Invertebrate Paleontology*, F, suppl. 1, xl + 762 pp. Geological Society of America and University of Kansas Press, Lawrence, Kansas.

Oliver, W. A., Jr, 1980. The relationship of the scleractinian corals to the rugose corals, *Paleobiology*, **6**, 146–60.

Russo, A., 1979. Studio monografio sui coralli dell' Eocene di Possagno Treviso, Italia), *Mem. Acad. naz. Sci. Lett. Art, Modena*, **6** (2), 1–87, pls. 1–15.

Scrutton, C. T., 1979. Early fossil cnidarians, *in* House, M. R. (Ed.) *The Origin of Major Invertebrate Groups*, pp. 161–207. Academic Press, London and New York.

Vaughan, T. W. and Wells, J. W., 1943. Revision of the suborders, families, and genera of the Scleractinia, *Spec. Pap. geol. Soc. Amer.*, **44**, xv + 363 pp., pls. 1–51.

Wells, J. W., 1956. Scleractinia, *in* R. C. Moore (Ed.) *Treatise on Invertebrate Palaeontology. Part F. Coelenterata*, pp. F328–F444. Geological Society of America and University of Kansas Press, Lawrence, Kansas.

CHAPTER 4. BRYOZOA

Boardman, R. S. *et al.*, 1983. Bryozoa, Vol. 1, Part G (2nd edn), *in* Robison, R. A. (Ed.) *Treatise on Invertebrate Paleontology*, Geological Society of America and University of Kansas Press, Lawrence, Kansas.

Ryland, J. S., 1970. *Bryozoans*. Hutchinson, London.

CHAPTER 5. BRACHIOPODA

Doescher, R. A. 1981. Living and fossil brachiopod genera 1775–1979, *Smithson. Contr. Paleobiol.*, **42**, 1–238.

McKerrow, W. S. (Ed.) 1978. *The Ecology of Fossils*. Duckworth, London.

Rowell, A. J., 1982. The monophyletic origin of the Brachiopoda. *Lethaia*, **15**, 299–307.

Rudwick, M. J. S., 1970. *Living and Fossil Brachiopods*. Hutchinson, London.

Williams, A. *et al.*, 1965. Brachiopoda, *Treatise on Invertebrate Paleontology*, Part H. Geological Society of America and University of Kansas Press, Lawrence, Kansas.

Wright, A. D. 1979. Brachiopod radiation. *Systematics Ass. Spec. Vol.*, **12**, 235–52.

CHAPTER 6. MOLLUSCA

6.2. Amphineura

Smith, A. G. 1960. Amphineura, *in* Moore, R. C. (Ed.) *Treatise on Invertebrate Paleontology*, Part I, Mollusca 1, pp. 141–76. Geological Society of America and University of Kansas Press, Lawrence, Kansas.

6.4, 6.5. Bivalvia, Rostroconchia

Boss, K. 1982. Mollusca: Bivalvia, *in* Parker, S. P. (Ed.) *Synopsis and Classification of Living Organisms*, Vol. 1, pp. 1103–63. McGraw-Hill, New York.

Carter, J. G., 1980. Environmental and biological controls of bivalve shell mineralogy and microstructure (Ch. 2, pp. 69–113), and Guide to bivalve shell microstructures (Appendix 2, Part B, pp. 645–73), *in* Rhoads, D. C. and Lutz, R. A. (Eds.) *Skeletal Growth of Aquatic Organisms*. Plenum Publishing Corporation, New York.

Moore, R. C. (Ed.) 1969, 1971. *Treatise on Invertebrate Paleontology*, Part N, Mollusca 6 (Bivalvia), Vols. 1, 2 (1969) and 3 (1971). Geological Society of America and University of Kansas Press, Lawrence, Kansas.

Morton, B., 1982. The functional morphology of *Parilimya fragilis* (Bivalvia: Parilimyidae nov. fam.) with a discussion on the origin and evolution of the carnivorous septibranchs and a reclassification of the Anomalodesmata, *Trans. zool. Soc. Lond.*, **36**, 153–216.

Pojeta, J. Jr, 1971. Review of Ordovician pelecypods. *Prof. Pap. U.S. Geol. Surv.*, **695**, 46 pp. 20 pl.

Pojeta, J. Jr. and Runnegar, B. 1976. The paleontology of Rostroconch molluscs and the early history of the phylum Mollusca, *Prof. Pap. U.S. Geol. Surv.*, **968**, 88 pp., 54 pls.

Taylor, J. D., Kennedy, W. J. and Hall, A. 1969, 1973. The shell structure and mineralogy of the Bivalvia. Introduction. Nuculacea–Trigonacea [*sic*], *Bull. Brit. Mus. (Nat. Hist). Zoology*, suppl. 3, 125 pp. 29 pls. (1969); II. Lucinacea–Clavagellacea, Conclusions, *Bull. Brit. Mus. (Nat. Hist.) Zoology*, **22**, 9, 255–94, 15 pls. (1973). London.

Yonge, Sr M. and Thompson, T. E. (Eds.) 1978. Evolutionary systematics of bivalve molluscs, *Phil. Trans. R. Soc. Lond.*, **B284**, 199–436. London.

6.6. Gastropoda

Knight, J. B., Cox, L. R., Keen, A. M., Smith, A. G., Batten, R. L., Yochelson, E. L., Ludbrook, N. H., Robertson, R., Yonge, C. M. and Moore, R. C., 1960. Mollusca 1, *in* Moore, R. C. (Ed.) *Treatise on Invertebrate Paleontology*, Part I, Mollusca 1. Geological Society of America and University of Kansas Press, Lawrence, Kansas, 351 pp.

Peel, J. S. (in press). Class Gastropoda, *in* Boardman, R. S., Cheetham, A. H. and Rowell, A. J. (Eds.) *Invertebrate Paleontology*. Blackwell.

Wenz, W., 1938–44. Gastropoda. Allgemeiner Teil und Prosobranchia, *in* Schindewolf, O. H. (Ed.) *Handbüch der Paläozologie*, Band 6, Gebrüder Borntraeger, 1639 pp.

Zilch, A., 1959–60. Gastropoda Teil 2 Euthyneura, *in* Schindewolf, O. H. (Ed.) *Handbüch der Paläozoologie*, Band 6, Gebrüder Borntraeger, 834 pp.

6.7. Cephalopoda

Arkell, W. J. *et al.*, 1957. *Treatise on Invertebrate Paleontology*, Part I, Mollusca 4, Cephalopoda, Ammonoidea. Geological Society of America and University of Kansas Press, Lawrence, Kansas, xxii + 490 pp.

Cousteau, J.-Y. and Diolé, P. 1975. *Octopus and Squid: the soft intelligence*. Cassell, London, 304 pp.

Denton, E. J., 1974. On the buoyancy and on the lives of modern and fossil cephalopods. *Proc. Roy. Soc., Lond.*, **B185**, 273–99.

Donovan, D. T., 1964. Cephalopod phylogeny and classification. *Biol. Rev.* (Cambridge), **39**, 259–87.

Dzik, J., 1984. Phylogeny of the Nautiloides. *Palaeontol. Polon.*, No. 45. 219 pp., 47 pls.

Flower, R. H., 1964. Saltations in nautiloid coiling. *Evolution*, **9**, 244–60.

Flower, R. H. and Gordon, M., 1959. More Mississippian belemnites, *J. Paleontol.*, **33**, 809–42.

Holland, C. H., 1979. Early cephalopods, *in* House, M. R. (Ed.) *The Origin of Major Invertebrate Groups*, Ch. 13, pp. 367–78. Academic Press, London and New York, x + 515 pp.

House, M. R., 1970. On the origin of the clymenid ammonoids, *Palaeontology*, **13**, 664–76.

House, M. R. and Senior, J. R. (Eds.) 1981. *The Ammonoidea*. Academic Press, London and New York, xiv + 593 pp.

Jeletzky, J. A., 1964. Comparative morphology, phylogeny, and classification of fossil Coleoidea, *University of Kansas Palaeontol. Contr., Mollusca*, Article 7, 162 pp.

Kennedy, W. J. and Cobban, W. A., 1976. Aspects of ammonite biology, biogeography and biostratigraphy. *Spec. Pap. Palaeontol.*, No. 17, v + 94 pp.

Lane, F. W., 1959. *Kingdom of the Octopus; the life history of the Cephalopoda*. Jarrolds, London, 287 pp.

Lehmann, U., 1981. *The Ammonoids: their life and their world* (trans. J. Lettan). Cambridge University Press, 246 pp.

Lippov, N. P. and Drushchitz, V. V., 1958. *Osnovy Paleontologii, Mollyuski-Golovonogie II*. Moscow, 188 pp.

Mikaylova, I. A., 1983. Sistema i filogeniya melovyk ammonoidey. *Akad. Nauk. S.S.S.R.*, Moscow, 279 pp.

Naef, A. 1922. *Die fossilen tintenfische*. G. Fischer, Jena, v + 322 pp.

Pivetau, J. (Ed.) 1952. *Traité de Paleontologie*, Vol. 2. Masson et Cie, Paris, 790 pp.

Ruzhencev, V. E. (Ed.) 1962a. *Osnovy Paleontologii, Mollyuski-Golovonogie I*. Moscow, 425 pp.

Ruzhencev, V. E., 1962b. Printsipy sistematiki, sistema i filogeniya ammonoidei. *Trudy Paleontol. Inst., Acad. Nauk. S.S.S.R.*, **83**, 332 pp.

Saunders, W. B., 1981. The species of living *Nautilus* and their distribution. *The Veliger* (California Malacological Society), **24**, 8–16.

Teichert, C. 1967. *Major Features of Cephalopod Evolution*. University of Kansas, Department of Geology, Special Publ., No. 2, pp. 162–210.

Teichert, C., *et al.*, 1964. *Treatise on Invertebrate Paleontology*, Part K, Mollusca 3, Cephalopoda, General features, Endoceratoidea, Actinoceratoidea, Nautiloidea, Bactritoidea. Geological Society of America and University of Kansas Press, Lawrence, Kansas, xxviii + 519 pp.

Thomel, G., 1980. *Ammonites*. Editions Serre, Paris, 229 pp.

Yochelson, E. L., 1977. Agmata, a proposed extinct phylum of early Cambrian age, *J. Paleontol.*, **51**, 437–54.

Yochelson, E. L., Flower, R. H. and Webers, G. F., 1963. The bearing of the new late Cambrian monoplacophoran genus *Knightconus* upon the origin of the Cephalopoda, *Lethaia*, **6**, 275–310.

CHAPTER 7. ECHINODERMATA

7.1–7.8. Carpoids to Holothuroidea

Bell, B. M., 1976. A study of North American Edrioasteroidea (Echinodermata) *Mem. N.Y. St. Mus. Sci. Serv.*, **21**, 447 pp.

Bockelie, J. F., 1981. The Middle Ordovician of the Oslo Region, Norway, 30. The eocrinoid genera *Cryptocrinites, Rhipidocystis* and *Bockia*, *Norsk Geol. Tidssk.*, **61**, 123–47.

Breimer, A. and Macurda, D. B., 1972. The phylogeny of the fissiculate blastoids. *Verhandel. Konink, Nederl, Akad. Wetensch. Naturk.*, **26**, 390 pp.

Breimer, A. and Ubaghs, G., 1974. A critical comment on the classification of the pelmatozoan echinoderms. *Proc. K. Nederl. Akad. Wetensch.*, **B77**, 398–417.

Jefferies, R. P. S., 1979. The origin of chordates – a methodological essay, *in* House, M. R. (Ed.) *The Origin of Major Invertebrate Groups. Systematics Ass. Spec. Vol.* No. 12, pp. 443–77. Academic Press, London.

Jefferies, R. P. S., 1981. Fossil evidence on the origin of the chordates and echinoderms. *Atti Convegni Lincei*, **49**, 487–561.

Kesling, R. V., 1967. Cystoids, *in* Moore, R. C. (Ed.) *Treatise on Invertebrate Paleontology*, Part S, Echinodermata 1. Geological Society of America and University of Kansas Press, Lawrence, Kansas.

Parsley, R. L. and Mintz, L. W., 1975. North American Paracrinoidea: (Ordovician: Paracrinozoa: new Echinodermata), *Bull. Amer. Paleont.*, **68**, 1–115.

Paul, C. R. C., 1971. Revision of the *Holocystites* fauna (Diploporita) of N. America, *Fieldiana, Geol.*, **24**, 1–166.

Paul, C. R. C., 1972. Morphology and function of exothecal pore-structures in cystoids, *Palaeontology*, **15**, 1–28.

Paul, C. R. C., 1973. *British Ordovician Cystoids*. Palaeontographical Society (Monogr.) 64 pp.

Paul, C. R. C. and Smith, A. B. 1984. The early diversification and phylogeny of Echinodermata, *Biol. Rev.*, **59** (4).

Philip, G. M., 1979. Carpoids – echinoderms or chordates? *Biol. Rev.*, **54**, 439–71.

Sprinkle, J. 1973. Morphology and evolution of blastozoan echinoderms, *Mus. Comp. Zool., Harvard Univ. Spec. Publ.*, 283 pp.

Ubaghs, G., 1967. Eocrinoidea, *in* Moore, R. C. (Ed.), *Treatise on Invertebrate Paleontology*, Part S, Echinodermata 1(1) Geological Society of America and University of Kansas Press, Lawrence, Kansas.

Ubaghs, G. and Caster, K. 1967. Homolozoa, *in* Moore, R. C. (Ed.) *Treatise on Invertebrate Paleontology*, Part S, Echinodermata 1. Geological Society of America and University of Kansas Press, Lawrence, Kansas.

Ubaghs, G. *et al.*, 1978. Crinoidea, *in* Moore, R. C., Teichert, C. (Eds.) *Treatise on Invertebrate Paleontology*, Part T, Echinodermata 2. Geological Society of America and University of Kansas Press, Lawrence, Kansas.

7.9. Echinoidea

Durham, J. W., Fell, H. B., Fischer, A. G., Kier, P. M., Melville, R. V., Pawson, D. L. and Wagner, C. D., 1966. Echinoids, *in* Moore, R. C. (Ed.), *Treatise on Invertebrate Paleontology*, Part V, Echinodermata 3, Vols. 1 and 2, pp. U211–U640.

Kier, P. M. 1974. Evolutionary trends and their functional significance in the post-Palaeozoic echinoids, *Mem. Paleont. Soc.*, **5**, 1–95.

Kier, P. M. and Grant, R. E., 1965. Echinoid distribution and habits, Key Largs Coral Reef Reserve, Florida, *Smithson. Misc. Coll.*, **149** (6), 1–69.

Mortensen, T. H., 1928–52. *A Monograph of the Echinoidea*, 5 vols. Reitzel, Copenhagen and Oxford University Press.

Nichols, D., 1959. Mode of life and taxonomy in irregular sea urchins in function and taxonomic importance, *Publ. Syst. Assoc.*, **3**, 61–80.

Smith, A. B., 1981. Implications of lantern morphology for the phylogeny of post-Palaeozoic echinoids, *Palaeontology*, **24**, 779–801.

CHAPTER 8. GRAPTOLITHINA

Bulman, O. M. B., 1970. Graptolithina, *in* Teichert, C. (Ed.) *Treatise on Invertebrate Paleontology* (2nd edn), Part V, pp. i–xxxii, 1–163. Geological Society of America and University of Kansas Press, Lawrence, Kansas.

Cooper, R. A. and Fortey, R. A., 1982. The Ordovician graptolites of Spitsbergen, *Bull. Brit. Mus. (Nat. Hist.)*, **36** (3), 157–302.

Rickards, R. B., 1979. Early evolution of graptolites and related groups, *in* House, M. R. (Ed.) *The Origin of Major Invertebrate Groups. Syst. Ass. Spec. Vol.* No. 12, pp. 435–441. Academic Press, London.

Rickards, R. B. and Palmer, D. C., 1981. Graptolites II, *in* Baldwin, S. *et al. Educational Palaeontological Reproductions.*

CHAPTER 9. ARTHROPODS

9.1–9.4. Phylum Arthropoda, Subphyla: unknown; Crustacea; Chelicerata; Phylum Uniramia

Anderson, D. T., 1973. *Embryology and Phylogeny in Annelids and Arthropods.* Pergamon Press, Oxford.

Briggs, D. E. G., 1983. Affinities and early evolution of the Crustacea: the evidence of the Cambrian fossils, *in* Schram, F. R. (Ed.) *Crustacean Phylogeny*, A. A. Balkema, Rotterdam.

Clarkson, E. N. K., 1979. *Invertebrate Palaeontology and Evolution.* Allen and Unwin, London.

Hessler, R. R. and Newman, W. A., 1975. A trilobitomorph origin for the Crustacea, *Fossils and Strata*, **4**, 437–59.

Manton, S. M., 1977. *The Arthropoda, Habits, Functional Morphology and Evolution.* Clarendon Press, Oxford.

Tasch, P., 1980. *Paleobiology of the Invertebrates. Data retrieval from the fossil record* (2nd edn). Wiley, New York.

9.5 Phylum Arthropoda, Subphylum Trilobita

Clarkson, E. N. K., 1979. *Invertebrate Palaeontology and Evolution.* Allen & Unwin, London, x + 323 pp.

Eldredge, N., 1977. Trilobites and evolutionary patterns, *in* Hallam, A. (Ed.) *Patterns of Evolution*, Ch. 9, pp. 305–32. Elsevier, Amsterdam.

Moore, R. C. (Ed.) 1959. *Treatise on Invertebrate Paleontology*, Part O, Arthropoda 1. Geological Society of America and University of Kansas Press, Lawrence, Kansas, xix + 560 pp., 415 figs.

Whittington, H. B., 1961. A natural history of trilobites, *Natural History*, **70**, 8–17.

Taxonomic index